Formal Approaches to Computing and Information Technology

Also in this series:

On the Refinement Calculus
C. Morgan and T. Vickers (eds.)
ISBN 3-540-19809-1

Systems, Models and Measures
A. Kaposi and M. Myers
ISBN 3-540-19753-2

Proof in VDM: A Practitioner's Guide

by

Juan C. Bicarregui
John S. Fitzgerald
Peter A. Lindsay
Richard Moore
Brian Ritchie

Springer-Verlag
London Berlin Heidelberg New York
Paris Tokyo Hong Kong
Barcelona Budapest

Juan C. Bicarregui and Brian Ritchie, Informatics Department
Rutherford Appleton Laboratory, Chiton, Didcot, Oxfordshire
OX11 0QX, UK

John S. Fitzgerald, Dependable Computing Systems Centre,
20 Windsor Terrace, The University,
Newcastle upon Tyne NE1 7RU, UK

Peter A. Lindsay, Software Verification Research Centre,
Department of Computer Science, University of Queensland, St Lucia,
Queensland 4072, Australia

Richard Moore, Department of Computer Science, The University
Manchester M13 9PL, UK

Series Editor

Steve A. Schuman, BSc, DEA, CEng
Department of Mathematical and Computing Sciences
University of Surrey, Guildford, Surrey GU2 5XH, UK

ISBN 3-540-19813-X Springer-Verlag Berlin Heidelberg New York
ISBN 0-387-19813-X Springer-Verlag New York Berlin Heidelberg

British Library Cataloguing in Publication Data
A catalogue record for this book is available from the British Library

Library of Congress in Publication Data
A catalog record for this book is available from the Library of Congress

Apart from any fair dealing for the purposes of research or private study, or criticism or review, as permitted under the Copyright, Designs and Patents Act 1988, this publication may only be reproduced, stored or transmitted, in any form or by any means, with the prior permission in writing of the publishers, or in the case of reprographic reproduction in accordance with the terms of licences issued by the Copyright Licensing Agency. Enquiries concerning reproduction outside those terms should be sent to the publishers.

© Springer-Verlag London Limited 1994
Printed in Great Britain

The use of registered names, trademarks etc. in this publication does not imply, even in the absence of a specific statement, that such names are exempt from the relevant laws and regulations and therefore free for general use.

The publisher makes no representation, express or implied, with regard to the accuracy of the information contained in this book and cannot accept any legal responsibility or liability for any errors or omissions that may be made.

Typesetting: Camera ready by author
Printed and bound by Antony Rowe Ltd, Chippenham, Wiltshire
34/3830-543210 Printed on acid-free paper

Foreword

Formal specifications were first used in the description of programming languages because of the central role that languages and their compilers play in causing a machine to perform the computations required by a programmer. In a relatively short time, specification notations have found their place in industry and are used for the description of a wide variety of software and hardware systems. A formal method – like VDM – must offer a mathematically-based specification language. On this language rests the other key element of the formal method: the ability to reason about a specification. Proofs can be employed in reasoning about the potential behaviour of a system and in the process of showing that the design satisfies the specification.

The existence of a formal specification is a prerequisite for the use of proofs; but this prerequisite is not in itself sufficient. Both proofs and programs are large formal texts. Would-be proofs may therefore contain errors in the same way as code. During the difficult but inevitable process of revising specifications and developments, ensuring consistency is a major challenge. It is therefore evident that another requirement – for the successful use of proof techniques in the development of systems from formal descriptions – is the availability of software tools which support the manipulation of large bodies of formulae and help the user in the design of the proofs themselves.

Unfortunately, experience indicates that even the simultaneous presence of formal descriptions and tools to support the construction of proofs will not be enough to ensure that they are instantly accepted. Learning from the previous technology transfer difficulties, it is clear that it is necessary to modify the way people think about systems and to teach them a whole new approach if they are to reason successfully about their specifications and designs. It is a key contribution of this book that it takes seriously the challenge of teaching practitioners how to construct their own proofs.

In 1977, Ole-Johan Dahl wrote a paper with the prescient title of 'Can Program Proving Be Made Practical?'. His argument was basically that, if each program proof is to be started on a blank sheet of paper, the process will never become viable. It is necessary that collections of useful results or theories about data types are documented and made available to potential users of proof tools. The system – *mural* – which the authors of this book built, placed considerable emphasis on the development of theories. Some organisations which have built their own theorem provers have realised that the 'theory base' which has been developed with the tools is a more valuable asset than the theorem prover itself. Readers of this book should be grateful that the authors are prepared to expose and make available the theories which they have developed for the most important parts of VDM-SL.

The *mural* system put great emphasis on the design of a user interface which would make it easier for people to employ a computer in the development of proofs. It is difficult, within the limitations of a textbook, to explain the process by which proofs are constructed. The authors of this book have been successful in conveying how one should tackle the task of designing the proof of a theorem. Any reader who conscientiously works through this text should be in an admirable position to move on from the stage of using formal specifications solely as a description of a system and be prepared to use formal reasoning as a support both for ascertaining properties of a specification and for using proofs in the development process.

Manchester Cliff Jones
September 1993

Preface

Recent advances in computing technology have led to an increasing willingness on the part of engineers and innovators to entrust critical operations to computing systems, both for reasons of safety and for increased efficiency over older technologies. This has posed a challenge to the computing community to develop ways of engineering computer systems so that they meet the stringent requirements placed upon them. There have been many responses to this challenge, among them the exploitation of formal methods.

Formal methods involve the construction of a mathematical model or theory of the required behaviour of a product in the early stages of its development. Such modelling is widely employed in more "traditional" engineering disciplines to assist with analysing the behaviour of complex systems: an aeronautical engineer, for example, uses a mathematical model of lift and thrust on an aircraft wing to help determine its optimum design. In a similar way, a mathematical model, in the form of a *formal specification*, can be used to describe the essential behaviour of a computing system at an abstract level.

A major benefit of this approach over less mathematical techniques is the degree of rigour which can be brought to arguments about the behaviour of the system described by the model. A formal specification can be shown to be consistent using mathematical proofs. The same techniques can be used to help increase confidence that the specification captures informally-stated requirements. Design decisions can be checked for fidelity to the specification as development progresses. In a number of formalisms (e.g. VDM [Jon90], RAISE [RSL92], refinement calculus [Mor90]) this is done as a staged process of *refinement* or *reification* in which increasingly concrete designs and implementations are shown to preserve the behaviour described in more abstract specifications.

Other benefits arise from the fact that the initial specification is abstract as well as formal. The essential functionality of the desired system can be described more concisely than would be possible if implementation detail were included. As a result, the most important properties, such as safety, can be reasoned about at a stage of the development when they are easier to understand and when any errors are less costly to rectify than is the case if they are uncovered in later stages of design or in testing. In this way formal methods can be seen as one way of increasing the degree of confidence that a computer system will exhibit both required and predictable behaviour.

Much research has gone into improving the accessibility and practical applicability of formal methods. Effort has been put into the standardisation of specification languages such as that of VDM (VDM-SL [BSI92]) and Z [BN92]. In addition, new languages have been and are being developed. Some of these attempt to combine the ideas of formal specification with those of other design methods, for instance object-oriented design (e.g. RSL [RSL92], Object Z [DKRS91]). Others attempt to incorporate the expressive power required to specify such non-static properties of a system as concurrency (e.g. VVSL [Mid90], CCS [Rob89], CSP [Hoa85]), real-time constraints and fault-tolerance (e.g. [Ost92], [Vyt92]). Another important area of work has been tool support for formal methods (e.g. the tools reports in [WL93]).

Numerous books and courses deal with these aspects of formal methods, but comparatively few offer help to the practitioner or student wishing to gain the full benefit of rigorous or formal proof in the areas mentioned above. Texts which do cover proof tend to present only sketch proofs, and give little indication of the process by which a proof can be constructed. One of the authors of this book (RM) recently received a letter reflecting this view:

"There is an example of an adequacy proof on page . . . of . . . However, I am unsure how to make use of it and I find it difficult to follow. I have not created any proofs previously and do not know how to set about the process."

The process of creating proofs is the main subject of this book. The emphasis is on proof as an integral part of the system developer's toolkit, rather than as an onerous duty to be performed in order to exhibit conformance to some set of mathematical criteria in the form of proof obligations. It is demonstrated how proof can be used to improve understanding of a specification or a design step, how it can uncover errors, and how it can also be used to show that the specified system exhibits the required properties. An important lesson is that understanding why an attempted proof has failed is often more valuable than knowing the details of a successful proof.

It should be stressed at the outset that this is not a book about VDM *per se*. Rather it is about proving properties of formal specifications in general, with VDM used simply as a vehicle to illustrate techniques which can just as easily be applied to other specification languages. The book will therefore be of interest to potential practitioners of formal methods who are seeking to overcome the "prover's block" exhibited by the correspondent mentioned above. It will also interest those scientists working on proof support systems for formal methods, as well as those developing proof theories for other specification languages. The tutorial nature of the text, including the exercises and substantial case study, is intended to make it suitable for industrial and university-level courses. Some familiarity with writing and understanding specifications in at least one formal specification language is assumed. However, the first part of Chapter 1 gives a brief summary of VDM for those readers whose experience lies elsewhere. The remainder of Chapter 1 provides an overview of the logical framework on which the material of the rest of the book is based.

Like other formal specification languages, VDM-SL provides an underlying logic and a collection of primitive types (e.g. numbers, truth values) and type constructors (e.g. sets, lists) out of which specifications are built. Proofs about a particular specification will therefore involve, at least in part, reasoning about these built-in primitives, the properties of which are defined via a collection of axioms. Part I (Chapters 2 to 9) gives axioms and definitions for the basic VDM logic, data types and type constructors, and discusses how such axiomatisations can be designed, as well as problems which might be encountered. It also shows how theories of useful results about these constructs can be built up by proof. These chapters introduce important proof strategies, such as induction, case distinction, and the technique of structuring proofs by using subsidiary lemmas. They also demonstrate the use of informal argument as a tool, both for determining whether a particular result is provable and for determining the outline structure of a more rigorous or formal proof. These points are illustrated with the help of detailed worked examples, with explanations of the key stages in the production of a proof and of the arguments used to determine the best strategy for its construction.

Having developed a collection of useful results about the primitive constructs of the specification language, the next stage is to use these in proving properties of a specification or a refinement step. This is the subject of Part II (Chapters 10 to 13). Chapter 10 shows how to construct a theory from a specification, including the axioms describing the essential properties of the specification and the proof obligations representing properties that the specification must possess if it is to be considered sound. Chapter 11 extends these ideas to reasoning about refinements. The techniques discussed so far are illustrated in Chapter 12, which contains a substantial case study of an air-traffic control subsystem, including an abstract specification and two levels of refinement. The case study also shows how validation conditions can be used to discover errors in a specification and to help to demonstrate that a specification actually exhibits the required safety properties.

Part I gives an axiomatisation of the most commonly used parts of the VDM-SL language [Daw91]. However, some constructs (e.g. function types) have been omitted because their inclusion renders the treatment of more familiar constructs less intuitive, or because their own formal axiomatisation is complex. These constructs, and other advanced topics, are discussed in Chapter 13.

The size of the VDM-SL language prevents full coverage of all its constructs, and a few have been omitted for lack of space, but these (e.g. many well-known arithmetic operators) are sufficiently similar to the constructs treated in the text that the reader should have little difficulty arriving at a reasonable axiomatisation using the techniques described. Chapter 13 also discusses issues relating to the logical approach taken in the other chapters, for example limitations of the logical frame and the axiomatisations chosen.

The final part of the book, Part III, contains a collection of useful theorems for those readers wishing to apply the techniques learned to their own examples.

It is worth stressing that the techniques discussed throughout the book can be applied equally to proofs done by hand and to proofs constructed using a computer. Indeed, the logical framework and proof style presented here have been shown to be suited to machine support [JJLM91].

Each chapter in the main text ends with exercises aimed at reinforcing the lessons taught there. In the case study of Chapter 12, the exercises are an integral part of the study itself, and are presented at appropriate points throughout the chapter. In addition, Part III contains numerous derived results which can be used as practice material. Chapter 13 can be considered additional reading for those wishing a deeper understanding of some of the more esoteric issues arising in connection with the axiomatisation of a specification language.

Further material, including answers to exercises, is available as a separate volume. Entitled "Proof in VDM: Readers' Notes", this can be obtained by anonymous file transfer protocol (ftp) or in hardcopy. The ftp version can be obtained from the University of Manchester (ftp.cs.man.ac.uk) in the directory /pub/Proof-in-VDM. The files are stored as compressed PostScript. Copies are also available by post from the following addresses. A small fee will be charged to cover printing and postage.

Dept. of Computing Science, The University of Newcastle upon Tyne, Newcastle upon Tyne NE1 7RU, United Kingdom

Informatics Department, Rutherford Appleton Laboratory, Chilton, Didcot, Oxon OX11 0QX, United Kingdom

Software Verification Research Centre, University of Queensland, St Lucia, Queensland 4072, Australia

This book represents a significant collaborative effort by a geographically diverse group of authors, all of whom have contributed to the material presented throughout the book. Readers wishing to make further enquiries are, however, invited to contact the authors on the following basis: RM and JSF for the basic axiomatisation and proof techniques presented in Chapters 2 to 9 and 14; JCB and BR for theories of specifications and reifications discussed in Chapters 10 and 11; PAL for the logical framework outlined in

Section 1.3; RM and PAL for the case study of Chapter 12; RM, BR and JSF for the material presented in Chapter 13.

Acknowledgements

The authors owe a considerable debt of gratitude to Cliff Jones for his thoughtful advice and support both in the production of this volume and in the research which underlies it.

We are very grateful to Peter Gorm Larsen of the Institute of Applied Computer Science (IFAD), Denmark for his valuable review comments. Technical discussions with Peter have helped us identify many of the issues relating to the extension of our work to the full VDM-SL language (Chapter 13): we wish him well in taking this work further in his doctoral research. In a similar vein, we are grateful to our colleagues in the development of the mural system, during the design of which many of the ideas described here were originally formulated. Thanks also to Ian Hayes for discussions concerning early drafts of the air-traffic control case study, and to Ralph Nelson, Senior Tower Controller at Brisbane Airport, for advice on terminology.

This book has been some two years in the making. Our thanks therefore to Linda Schofield and the staff at Springer-Verlag for their patience and support, and to the anonymous referees for their telling and constructive comments.

The authors gratefully acknowledge the technical assistance of the Department of Computing Science at Newcastle University in the maintenance of the book's source text. Typesetting was done using a version of the LAT$_E$X system set up by David Carlisle of Manchester University, with mathematical and index macros by Mario Wolczko and Brian Ritchie.

JSF would like to thank colleagues in the Computing Science Department at the University of Newcastle upon Tyne for valuable discussions and technical support; RM thanks the Department of Computer Science, University of Manchester for financial support; BR and JCB would like to thank colleagues at the SERC Rutherford Appleton Laboratory; and PAL would like to thank colleagues in the Department of Computer Science and the Software Verification Research Centre at The University of Queensland.

September 1993

Juan C. Bicarregui
John S. Fitzgerald
Peter A. Lindsay
Richard Moore
Brian Ritchie

Contents

1 Introduction 1
  1.1 Background 1
  1.2 How proofs arise in practice: an introductory example ... 2
  1.3 A logical framework for proofs 9
  1.4 Summary 19

I A Logical Basis for Proof in VDM

2 Propositional LPF 23
  2.1 Introduction 23
  2.2 Basic axiomatisation 24
  2.3 Derived rules; reasoning by cases; reasoning using contradiction 25
  2.4 Using definitions: conjunction 28
  2.5 Implication; definedness; further defined constructs .. 32
  2.6 Summary 36
  2.7 Exercises 36

3 Predicate LPF with Equality 39
  3.1 Predicates 39
  3.2 Types in predicates 40
  3.3 Predicate calculus for LPF: proof strategies for quantifiers 41
  3.4 Reasoning about equality: substitution and chains of equality 51
  3.5 Extensions to typed predicate LPF with equality 56
  3.6 Summary 58
  3.7 Exercises 58

4 Basic Type Constructors 61
  4.1 Introduction 61
  4.2 Union types 61
  4.3 Cartesian product types 63
  4.4 Optional types 66

4.5 Subtypes	67
4.6 A note on composite types	68
4.7 Summary	69
4.8 Exercises	69
5 Numbers	**71**
5.1 Introduction	71
5.2 Axiomatising the natural numbers	72
5.3 Axiomatisation of addition and proof by induction	75
5.4 More on proof by induction	79
5.5 Using direct definitions	81
5.6 Summary	84
5.7 Exercises	84
6 Finite Sets	**85**
6.1 Introduction	85
6.2 Generators for sets; set membership; set induction	85
6.3 Proof using set induction	87
6.4 Quantification over sets	90
6.5 Subsets; set equality; cardinality	92
6.6 Other set constructors	96
6.7 Set comprehension	99
6.8 Reasoning about set comprehension	102
6.9 Summary	104
6.10 Exercises	104
7 Finite Maps	**107**
7.1 Introduction	107
7.2 Basic axiomatisation	108
7.3 Axiomatisation using generators	109
7.4 Extraction and abstraction of lemmas	115
7.5 Using subsidiary definitions	119
7.6 Polymorphic subtypes and associated induction rules	122
7.7 Map comprehension	126
7.8 Summary	129
7.9 Exercises	129
8 Finite Sequences	**133**
8.1 Introduction	133
8.2 Basic axiomatisation	133
8.3 Destructors	136
8.4 Equality between lists	136
8.5 Operators on lists	136
8.6 An alternative generator set	145
8.7 Summary	147
8.8 Exercises	147

9 Booleans ... 149
9.1 Introduction ... 149
9.2 Basic axiomatisation ... 149
9.3 Formation rules for boolean-valued operators ... 151
9.4 An example of a well-formedness proof obligation ... 154
9.5 Summary ... 158
9.6 Exercises ... 158

II Proof in Practice

10 Proofs From Specifications ... 161
10.1 Introduction ... 161
10.2 Type definitions ... 162
10.3 The state ... 166
10.4 Functions and values ... 167
10.5 Operations ... 175
10.6 Validation proofs ... 177
10.7 Summary ... 178
10.8 Exercises ... 178

11 Verifying Reifications ... 181
11.1 Introduction ... 181
11.2 Data reification ... 182
11.3 Operation modelling ... 184
11.4 An example reification proof ... 186
11.5 Implementing functions ... 189
11.6 Implementation bias and unreachable states ... 190
11.7 Summary ... 191
11.8 Exercises ... 192

12 A Case Study in Air-Traffic Control ... 193
12.1 Introduction ... 193
12.2 The air-traffic control system ... 194
12.3 Formalisation of the state model ... 197
12.4 Top-level operations ... 211
12.5 First refinement step ... 221
12.6 Second refinement step ... 240
12.7 Concluding remarks ... 241

13 Advanced Topics ... 245
13.1 Introduction ... 245
13.2 Functions as a data type ... 246
13.3 Comparing elements of disjoint types ... 247
13.4 Recursive type definitions ... 248
13.5 Enumerated sets, maps and sequences ... 252

13.6 Patterns 254
13.7 Other expressions 256
13.8 Other types 263

III Directory of Theorems

14 Directory of Theorems 267
   14.1 Propositonal LPF 267
   14.2 Predicate LPF with equality 273
   14.3 Basic type constructors 281
   14.4 Natural numbers 284
   14.5 Finite sets 287
   14.6 Finite maps 302
   14.7 Finite sequences 314
   14.8 Booleans 319
   14.9 Specifications 321
   14.10 Reifications 326
   14.11 Case study I: abstract specification 327
   14.12 Case study II: refinement 333

Bibliography 343

Index 347

Index of Symbols 351

Index of Rules 353

Chapter 1

Introduction

1.1 Background

This book is about formal techniques for the specification and development of computing systems. In particular, it addresses the role of proof as an aid in building specifications, checking them and developing working systems from them. As a vehicle for this, the specification and development techniques of VDM (the Vienna Development Method) are used. Prior familiarity with VDM is not essential to an understanding of this text, but a good working knowledge of the method can be gained from [Jon90], [AI91] or [WH93].

VDM is a collection of techniques for the rigorous or formal development of computing systems. It chiefly consists of:

A specification language: The language VDM-SL is used to present specifications in a model-oriented style. A specification consists of a data model, defining an abstraction of the main data types with which the proposed system is concerned, together with a set of operations which express the required behaviour of the system in an abstract manner. A *state* type is usually defined as part of the data model, as an abstraction of the internal state of the system, although many applications do not in fact require a state. Each operation is defined as a relation between input and output values of various defined types. When a state model is used, an operation may also change the state of the system as a side-effect.

Data reification techniques: The data model defined in a specification is an abstraction of the data types which will appear in the final implementation, and might be quite different in form and structure. Data reification techniques allow the specification to be progressively rewritten in terms of data models which more and more closely approximate the data types of the implementation. As implementation detail is introduced, each successively more concrete specification can be shown to exhibit the behaviour defined by the more abstract specifications.

Operation decomposition techniques: In an abstract specification operations are specified as mathematical relations, but in the final computing system they are implemented as programs. Operation decomposition techniques allow the staged introduction of programming constructs (loops, conditionals, and so on) into operation definitions. VDM-SL has a repertoire of predefined operation combinators for giving imperative-style operation specifications.

This book concentrates on the specification and data reification techniques of VDM.

As motivation, Section 1.2 takes a simple example of a VDM development and illustrates the kind of reasoning involved in validating its correctness. Section 1.3 describes a framework for conducting this reasoning.

1.2 How proofs arise in practice: an introductory example

In this section, a simple specification is built and a small refinement step illustrated. This highlights the need to reason about a specification as it is being written and developed, exemplifying the kinds of facts one might wish to prove in the process.

1.2.1 Requirements

Here is an extract from a hypothetical informal requirements document sent by a client to a specifier:

> I am building a formally-developed debugger for a block-structured programming language. As part of this, I need a symbol table which records the names and values of all the variables in the program at any point. I need operations to:
>
> 1. enter a block, stacking the outer block's variables;
> 2. leave a block, forgetting about its variables;
> 3. find the value of any variable accessible from the current block;
> 4. ...
>
> A variable is in scope in all the blocks contained within the block where it is defined, except where it is redefined locally.

The client has asked for other operations (e.g. to add and modify variables) but these are not considered in this brief introduction.

1.2.2 Specification

The specifier reads the requirements and notices that the client has been good enough to state what operations are required. The next step is to come up with a suitable model of the symbol table. One approach is to treat the table as a stack of frames, a frame being a mapping from variables to values.

In VDM, models are built using primitive types and type constructors. There are, for example, primitive types modelling the natural numbers and Boolean values (respectively $\mathbb{N}$ and $\mathbb{B}$), and type constructors modelling Cartesian product types ($\_ \times \_$), disjoint union types ($\_ \mid \_$), finite sets ($\_$-set), finite maps ($\_ \xrightarrow{m} \_$) and finite sequences ($\_^*$).

In the symbol table example, the type of frames can be modelled as a class of maps:

$$Frame = Var \xrightarrow{m} Val$$

1.2 How proofs arise in practice: an introductory example

where *Var* and *Val* are types for variables and values respectively. The details of their definitions are not relevant here.

The state of the symbol table can be modelled as a sequence of frames, most recent frame first. Initially (before the first block of the program is entered), the symbol table is empty:

state *Symbol_Table* of
    fstack : *Frame**
init *mk-Symbol_Table(fs)* $\triangleq$ *fs* = [ ]
end

The primitive types and type constructors of VDM-SL have associated operators which may be applied to values of the relevant types. For example, sequences have many predefined operators, among them:

the empty sequence	[ ]	sequence enumeration	$[a, b, c, ...]$
sequence concatenation	_ ⁀ _	length of a sequence	len _
head of a sequence	hd _	elements of a sequence	elems _
tail of a sequence	tl _	indices of a sequence	inds _

Since a sequence has been chosen to model the symbol table, these operators can be applied to it, allowing the specifier to describe the head, tail, elements, and so on, of the symbol table.

In addition to the primitive types, type constructors and their associated operators, VDM supports logical assertions composed from terms using the operators. For example:

> **Assertion 1.1** If *fs* is a non-empty symbol table, then the result of popping the most recent frame off *fs* is again a symbol table:
>
> $$(fs: Frame^* \land fs \neq [\,]) \Rightarrow (tl\,fs): Frame^*$$

The ability to make assertions about elements of the defined types and state space allows the operations to be specified implicitly. An operation can be specified in VDM-SL by defining its input and output variables, together with their types; the access (read-only, read/write) it has to the so-called *external* state variables; its *precondition*, which describes those inputs and states for which the operation's behaviour is defined; and its *postcondition*, which describes the relationship between inputs and outputs and the effect on the state.

For example, the operation for entering a block can be specified thus:

Enter_Block (*frame*: *Var* $\xrightarrow{m}$ *Val*)
ext wr *fstack* : *Frame**
pre true
post *fstack* = [*frame*] ⁀ $\overleftarrow{fstack}$

where the input variable *frame* represents the frame corresponding to the block being entered. This operation updates the symbol table by pushing the new frame onto the stack. In the postcondition, the variable $\overline{fstack}$ denotes the value of the state variable when *Enter_Block* is invoked and *fstack* stands for its value when the operation returns.

The implicit specification style of VDM allows the specifier to give just enough information to describe the effects of an operation, without being over-prescriptive.

The operation for leaving a block can be specified as follows:

Leave_Block ()
  ext wr *fstack* : *Frame**
  pre *fstack* ≠ [ ]
  post *fstack* = tl $\overline{fstack}$

The behaviour of the *Leave_Block* operation is not defined when the symbol table is empty.

What would the client, who knows little about formal specification, make of the specifier's work so far? This specification is unlikely to be helpful if it is offered simply as a piece of text without some supporting argument that it is meaningful, self-consistent, and does indeed describe the required system behaviour. In short, the specifier needs a semantics for the specification language which supports reasoning about the behaviour it describes. This is provided, in part, by the mathematical properties of the building blocks of the specification: the primitive types, type constructors, operators on constructed types, and so on. Using these, it is possible to make some assertions about the putative symbol table specification and to discuss their validity.

VDM provides a number of proof obligations which, when discharged, show the mathematical self-consistency of a specification. For example, an argument should be given to say why the postcondition of *Leave_Block* is meaningful, since the tl_ operator is defined only on non-empty sequences. Such a proof obligation is called a *well-formedness obligation*. For the *Leave_Block* operation, the precondition gives a sufficient condition for the postcondition to be well-formed, since it ensures that *fstack* is non-empty when the operation is invoked.

Another kind of proof obligation is to show that operation specifications are *satisfiable*. For the *Enter_Block* operation, this proof obligation can be formulated as follows:

Obligation 1.2: Given any input *frame*: $Var \xrightarrow{m} Val$ and state $\overline{fstack}$: *Frame** satisfying the precondition of *Enter_Block*, there is a state *fstack*: *Frame** such that the postcondition of *Enter_Block* is satisfied.

An informal proof of this obligation might go as follows:

The type of the input is	*frame*: $Var \xrightarrow{m} Val$,
so by definition of *Frame*	*frame*: *Frame*,
and by properties of sequences	[*frame*]: *Frame**.
Next, it is given that	$\overline{fstack}$: *Frame**,
so by properties of sequences	[*frame*] $\frown \overline{fstack}$: *Frame**.

1.2 How proofs arise in practice: an introductory example

Let *fstack* be this new value: $\mathit{fstack} = [\mathit{frame}] \curvearrowright \overline{\mathit{fstack}}$.

By substitution of equals   *fstack*: *Frame**,
so *fstack* is a state (as required)
and the postcondition holds   post-*Enter_Block*.

It remains to specify the operation for looking up the value of a variable. The visible variables are those of the current block and all those of containing blocks whose names have not been redefined in the current block. The specifier decides to write a function *curr_vars* which takes a symbol table and extracts from it the collection of all currently visible variables and their values:

$\mathit{curr\_vars} : \mathit{Frame}^* \to (\mathit{Var} \xrightarrow{m} \mathit{Val})$

The specifier leaves the body of the function undefined temporarily in order to finish off the specification of the look-up operation:

Lookup (*v*: *Var*) *r*: *Val*
ext rd *fstack* : *Frame**
pre $v \in$ dom *curr_vars*(*fstack*)
post $r = (\mathit{curr\_vars}(\mathit{fstack}))(v)$

The function *curr_vars* is *auxiliary*: it is defined purely for convenience in writing the specification; it is not an operation requiring implementation. A first attempt to define the function might result in something like:

$\mathit{curr\_vars} : \mathit{Frame}^* \to (\mathit{Var} \xrightarrow{m} \mathit{Val})$
$\mathit{curr\_vars}(\mathit{fs}) \;\;\triangleq\;\;$ if *fs* = [ ] then $\{\mapsto\}$ else (hd *fs*) $\dagger$ *curr_vars*(tl *fs*)

where $\{\mapsto\}$ is the empty map and $\dagger$ is the map override symbol. However, as the reader may have noticed, the specification of *curr_vars* given above does not define the desired function because the arguments of the map override are the wrong way round. This means that, where frames have variables in common, the more recent values get overwritten by the older values, which is not what the client intended. The function body is well-formed and agrees with its signature, so this error would not be spotted by a type-checker. In fact, the error in *curr_vars* is not even one of internal consistency in the specification: the *Lookup* operation is satisfiable, so discharging the satisfiability proof obligation will not help in spotting the fault.

Such faults can easily arise in formal specification as the result of a misunderstanding of the requirements, or of oversights in the definition. One way to overcome such problems and improve confidence in a specification is to posit *validation conjectures* (or *validation conditions*), which are statements of properties which the system is expected to possess, then to show that these are logical consequences of the specification. For the example above, one such validation conjecture might be:

Validation 1.3: Suppose that, after initialisation, *Enter_Block*($\{x \mapsto v_1\}$) is applied, followed immediately by *Enter_Block*($\{x \mapsto v_2\}$); then the result of *Lookup*(*x*) should be v_2.

By considering the effect the operations have on the state, this could be stated more

formally as:
$$(curr\_vars([\{x \mapsto v_2\}, \{x \mapsto v_1\}]))(x) = v_2$$

Unfolding the definition of *curr_vars*, it becomes clear that Validation 1.3 cannot be proved:

Let s_2 stand for and let s_1 stand for	$[\{x \mapsto v_2\}, \{x \mapsto v_1\}]$ $[\{x \mapsto v_1\}]$.
Then $curr\_vars(s_2)$ is	$\{x \mapsto v_2\} \dagger curr\_vars(s_1)$.
Now, $curr\_vars(s_1)$ is and $curr\_vars([\,])$ is so by properties of maps, $curr\_vars(s_1)$ equals	$\{x \mapsto v_1\} \dagger curr\_vars([\,])$, $\{\mapsto\}$, $\{x \mapsto v_1\}$.
Thus $curr\_vars(s_2)$ equals which simplifies to again, by properties of maps.	$\{x \mapsto v_2\} \dagger \{x \mapsto v_1\}$ $\{x \mapsto v_1\}$,
Finally, $(curr\_vars(s_2))(x)$ is which equals contrary to expectations!	$\{x \mapsto v_1\}(x)$, v_1,

This example illustrates that proof is a tool not only for showing internal consistency of specifications but also for validating them against their requirements. Obviously it is still possible to miss some "bugs" in a specification, since one may not suggest all the correct validation theorems. Even extensive proof can only serve to increase confidence that a specification conforms to its requirements. It is, in general, impossible to show perfect conformance at this boundary between the formal and informal.

In the symbol table example, the specifier corrects the definition of *curr_vars* to read:

$curr\_vars : Frame^* \rightarrow (Var \xrightarrow{m} Val)$
$curr\_vars(fs) \triangleq$ if $fs = [\,]$ then $\{\mapsto\}$ else $curr\_vars(tl\,fs) \dagger (hd\,fs)$

With this new definition, it is possible to prove the validation conjecture above.

1.2.3 Data reification

The specification given above provides an abstract model of the system exhibiting the required external behaviour, but it pays no attention to the efficiency of operations. For instance, a direct implementation of the specification of the *Lookup* operation would be particularly inefficient since the *curr_vars* function recursively traverses the whole of the sequence of frames in order to build a map of the visible variables and their values. Some improvement in efficiency could be made by algorithm refinement. For example, the succession of recursive calls could be stopped as soon as the required maplet is found (namely, as soon as a frame is encountered which has the variable in its domain).

Algorithm refinement on its own, however, might still not deliver the required efficiency.

1.2 How proofs arise in practice: an introductory example

If it is known that *Lookup* is to be used very frequently, it might be better to choose a new data model which brings to the fore the information it requires. The process of going from an abstract data model to a more concrete one is known as *data reification*. One possible reification of the data model given above would be to model the state as a map from variables to stacks of values, where the head of each sequence is the current value associated with that variable and its tail comprises the values that have been overridden in the present context. With this model *Lookup* could be considerably more efficient, though *Enter_Block* and *Leave_Block* become more awkward as a consequence.

The specifier might define the new, more concrete state as follows:

state *Symbol_Table_2* of
    vmap : $Var \xrightarrow{m} Val^*$
inv *mk-Symbol_Table_2*(*vmap*) $\triangleq$ [ ] $\notin$ rng *vmap*
end

The invariant indicates that variables that are out of scope are modelled by omission from the map.

With the new data model, the *Lookup* operation could be re-specified in what appears to be a more efficient way as:

Lookup (*v*: *Var*) *r*: *Val*
    ext rd *vmap* : $Var \xrightarrow{m} Val^*$
    pre *v* ∈ dom *vmap*
    post *r* = hd *vmap*(*v*)

This operation has the same "signature" (that is, parameter and results types) as its abstract counterpart, but does it describe the same behaviour? More generally, what is required in order to show that an operation on the new, concrete state is a faithful representation of the abstract operation? The requirement is that it should exhibit behaviour that is *at least as good as* that of its abstract counterpart, that is, the concrete specification should exhibit all the properties of the abstract one. Thus, it is possible to develop a system by stepwise refinements and be assured that the development preserves top-level properties.

The key to dividing the justification of the system as a whole into a separate treatment for each operation lies in establishing a correspondence between the two state spaces. Then it is sufficient to show that each operation separately respects this correspondence.

One way to establish such a correspondence is to provide a *retrieve function* which maps elements of the concrete data model back to elements of the abstract data model. Given this, it is possible to compare the abstract and concrete versions of each operation individually and define conditions under which the concrete operation's behaviour is at least as good as its abstract counterpart's. The requirements are twofold. First, the domain of termination of the concrete operation must be at least as wide as that of the abstract one: that is, the concrete precondition must be weaker. Second, any non-determinacy in the concrete operation must be contained within the non-determinacy of the abstract operation: that is, the concrete postcondition must be stronger. These criteria are made precise and formalised in Chapter 11. The process of developing more concrete versions of operations is called *operation modelling*.

For the symbol table example, the retrieve function must construct a sequence of maps from the map of variables to sequences:

$retrieve : (Var \xrightarrow{m} Val^*) \rightarrow (Var \xrightarrow{m} Val)^*$
$retrieve(m) \triangleq \ldots$

But how is it to do this? On attempting to define the retrieve function one finds that there is insufficient information in the concrete state to reconstruct the abstract state. For example, the concrete state $\{x_1 \mapsto [v_1], x_2 \mapsto [v_2], x_3 \mapsto [v_3, v_4]\}$ could have arisen from the initial state either by applying $Enter\_Block(\{x_1 \mapsto v_1, x_3 \mapsto v_4\})$ followed by $Enter\_Block(\{x_2 \mapsto v_2, x_3 \mapsto v_3\})$, or by applying $Enter\_Block(\{x_2 \mapsto v_2, x_3 \mapsto v_4\})$ followed by $Enter\_Block(\{x_1 \mapsto v_1, x_3 \mapsto v_3\})$. In the first case the corresponding abstract state is $[\{x_2 \mapsto v_2, x_3 \mapsto v_3\}, \{x_1 \mapsto v_1, x_3 \mapsto v_4\}]$ whereas in the second case it is $[\{x_1 \mapsto v_1, x_3 \mapsto v_3\}, \{x_2 \mapsto v_2, x_3 \mapsto v_4\}]$.

The problem arises since two different abstract states are being modelled by the same concrete state. On further consideration, the specifier realises that when new variable bindings are formed by *Enter_Block* the information as to which variables have just been bound is thrown away. This will cause a problem for *Leave_Block*: how can it be known which variable bindings should be released? Thus it is impossible to ensure that the concrete operations faithfully reproduce the behaviour of their abstract counterparts, and so the choice of concrete data model is inadequate. In this example, the problem was revealed when trying to construct the retrieve function. Other chances to catch errors occur when discharging the proof obligations associated with reifications (see Chapter 12 for an example).

1.2.4 Onwards ...

The example above should begin to give the reader a feel for the kind of reasoning that is involved in software development using VDM. Verification and validation techniques such as those discussed above reveal errors in specifications and refinements and expose oversights which might otherwise remain undiscovered until much later in the development process. Attempting proofs is a good way to increase one's understanding of the system being modelled.

Informal proofs of the kind employed in traditional mathematics texts is heavily reliant on human intuition: steps in the argument are omitted which the reader is expected to fill in mentally or simply accept as valid. A *formal proof*, on the other hand, is one in which every step is justified by some formal rule of inference. Such proofs can be seen simply as exercises in symbol manipulation: checking the correctness of the steps in the proof is reduced to pattern matching against established inference rules. This can be done mechanically without any understanding of what the individual steps mean. Machine-assisted construction and checking of proofs reduces the possibility of errors occurring in proofs significantly beyond what can be achieved using pencil and paper.

The purpose of this book is to introduce the reader to techniques for building formal proofs. In doing so, a great many questions must be settled first. For example, what does it mean to appeal to one of the facts stated earlier "by substitution of equals"? What are the permitted inferences? How does one appeal to definitions in the specification? The first step in answering these questions is to define a logical framework within which they can be posed. This is done in Section 1.3.

Once a logical framework is established, it is possible to embark on the task of codifying and expressing useful properties of the specification language's components: its logic, primitive types, type constructors and their associated operators. This is dealt with in Chapters 2 to 9. In Chapters 10 and 11 the focus returns to specifications and refinements, with a clearer idea of how theorems are to be formally expressed and proved. The lessons of these chapters are then brought to bear on a realistic problem, the specification and development of an air-traffic control subsystem, in Chapter 12.

1.3 A logical framework for proofs

1.3.1 Introduction

In order to reason formally about specifications and refinements, three things are required: a *formal language* in which assertions can be formulated; an *interpretation* of the meaning of the expressions and statements of the formal language; and a set of *axioms* and *inference rules* describing inferences which are valid for the given interpretation. These three components are explained in turn below.

For a specification language like VDM-SL, the formal language consists of a collection of symbols together with ways of combining them to form expressions and statements. Some of these symbols form part of the basic specification language (e.g. $+$, $\wedge$, $\mathbb{Z}$), others describe the types, functions etc. defined in a particular specification. Symbols are used to represent values (e.g. [ ], 3), value constructors (e.g. $\_\frown\_$), predicates (e.g. $\_=\_$), types (e.g. $\mathbb{N}$), type constructors (e.g. $\_^*$), and so on. Statements built from the symbols above include $[\,]\frown[3] = [3]\frown[\,]$ and $[3] : \mathbb{N}^*$.

The interpretation of the symbols and expressions of a VDM specification can be found in any standard text book on VDM. As examples, the symbol [ ] represents the empty sequence, and $\_\frown\_$ represents sequence concatenation; the expression $\mathbb{N}^*$ represents the type of sequences of natural numbers, and [3] represents the singleton sequence whose only member is the number 3; the statement [ ] : $\mathbb{N}$ represents the (false) assertion that the empty sequence is a natural number; and so on.

An *inference rule* is a rule which says how statements can be inferred from other statements. An example inference rule is "If we assert a statement of the form $P \Rightarrow Q$ and we also assert the statement P, then we can also assert the statement Q". This rule is in fact a schema for a whole class of inference rules, because the symbols P and Q can be instantiated to any statement. The exact form of inference rules used in this book is explained below. An inference rule is *valid* if it is consistent with the interpretation given to the statements of the formal language: that is, if all its hypotheses are true then its conclusion is also true. In this book, an *axiom* is an inference rule whose validity is taken to be self-evident.

Given a formal language, an axiom set and some rules of inference, one can set about deriving theorems and new inference rules. If the axioms and rules of inference are valid in the interpretation attached to the statements of the formal language, then any statements which can be inferred from them must also be valid. Thus inference is reduced to an exercise in symbol manipulation, and the correctness of reasoning can be checked purely mechanically, independent of the particular interpretations given to the symbols. This is the main principle on which formal reasoning is based.

The process of showing how the validity of one statement is derived from others by applying rules of inference is called *proof*, and the inference rule which summarizes the outcome of the proof is called a *derived rule*. A *theory* is a collection of symbols, axioms and derived rules which are related together in some way: the examples discussed above, for instance, form part of a theory of sequences of natural numbers.

The following section informally describes the *logical framework* used to present the logic in subsequent chapters. Readers interested in a more detailed, formal description of the logical framework are referred to [JJLM91]. Note that a number of example rules are presented in this section for illustration only and are not necessarily themselves applicable to VDM. The rules for VDM are introduced in subsequent chapters.

1.3.2 Constants and expressions

The basic building blocks of proofs, inference rules and logical statements are *expressions*. Three kinds of symbol are used in expressions:

- *variables*, which vary over values, e.g. vs, x, v_1, v_2;

- *constants*, which correspond to value and type constructors, e.g. [ ], [_], _⁀_, 0, N, _*, _∧_; and

- *binders*, which correspond to constructors which introduce (and bind) new variables, e.g. ∀, ∃, set comprehension.

A constant takes a fixed number of arguments, known as its *arity*. For example, the constant [ ] takes no arguments, and the constant _⁀_ takes two arguments.

Expressions are built from these components. An expression is either:

- a variable symbol;

- a constant symbol together with the appropriate number of arguments, themselves expressions, e.g. [0], hd([vs]⁀fs); or

- a binder symbol with a variable (the variable it *binds*) and an expression representing the *universe* over which the variable ranges, together with the *body* of the binding (itself an expression), e.g. $\forall n: N \cdot \text{hd}([n]\frown ns) = n$.

The *scope* of the bound variable is limited to the body of the binding. Variables not in the scope of a binder are called *free variables*. Expressions are considered equivalent up to renaming of bound variables (α-equivalence): for example, the expression $\forall x: N \cdot x \times x \geq x$ is to all intents and purposes the same as the expression $\forall y: N \cdot y \times y \geq y$.

A special notation for subtypes directly supports reasoning about data types with invariants. For example, the following type expression represents the type of all natural numbers greater than three:

$$\ll x: N \mid x > 3 \gg$$

Subtypes are discussed in Section 4.5.

This book is very liberal regarding concrete syntax for the logic. Constants are presented in prefix, postfix, or infix forms as seems most readable. Parentheses are often omitted for commutative/associative operators such as _∧_ and _+_. The operator precedence and association of [Daw91] is used throughout.

1.3.3 Hilbert-style inference

Inference rules and metavariables

The description of rules and proofs begins with a basic Hilbert-style system[1]. A (Hilbert-style) *inference rule* consists of a list of *hypotheses* above a horizontal line and a *conclusion* below it. The rule states that the conclusion holds whenever the hypotheses hold. Thus, in a theory of natural numbers, the following rule asserts that if 3 is a natural number then $3 + 1$ is also a natural number:

$$\frac{3:\mathsf{N}}{(3+1):\mathsf{N}}$$

Some rules have no hypotheses, for example the rule asserting that 0 is a natural number:

$$\frac{}{0:\mathsf{N}}$$

The two rules above refer to specific constants (0, 3, _ + _, 1, _: _, N), but clearly the first rule would still be valid with any natural number in place of the 3. Instead of writing such a rule for every number, symbols, called *metavariables*, are used to represent arbitrary expressions. For example, the following rule, in which n is a metavariable, states that if an arbitrary expression n represents a natural number then so does the expression $n + 1$:

$$\frac{n:\mathsf{N}}{(n+1):\mathsf{N}}$$

When rules are used to justify steps in proofs, their metavariables are *instantiated* (i.e. replaced by expressions). Note that each occurrence of the same metavariable must receive the same instantiation. Thus for example, the first rule given above is an instance of the more general rule, obtained by instantiating n with the constant 3.

In the logical framework of this book, metavariables can also take arguments, in much the same way as functions can take arguments. Consider the following rule, which describes the substitution of equal values in an expression:

$$\frac{a = b;\ P(a)}{P(b)}$$

The metavariable $P(\_)$ can be instantiated by any expression having a "placeholder" for a subexpression. For example, $P(\_)$ could be instantiated by $\forall x:\mathsf{N} \cdot \_ = x \vee x > \_$, in which case $P(0)$ would then stand for that expression with 0 in the place of the placeholder: $\forall x:\mathsf{N} \cdot 0 = x \vee x > 0$.

In the rule above, a and b are also metavariables. Thus the rule could be instantiated to justify a step of reasoning such as "if $2 = 1 + 1$ and *is-even*(2) then *is-even*$(1 + 1)$". The appropriate instantiation replaces a by 2, b by $1 + 1$, and $P(\_)$ by *is-even*$(\_)$.

Note that, in general, metavariables can have any number of placeholders. Thus $P(a, b)$ instantiates to $2 + 1$ upon instantiating a by 1, b by 2, and $P(\_a, \_b)$ by $\_b + \_a$, where $\_i$ stands for placeholder i. Under the same instantiation, $P(a, a)$ becomes $1 + 1$. When building instantiations, bound variables may need to be renamed in order to avoid capture

---

[1]The reader is referred to Section 2.4 of [End72] for more information on Hilbert-style inference systems.

of free variables. For example, when instantiating $P(\_)$ by $\exists x: \mathbf{N} \cdot 2 \times x \neq \_$ and a by $x+x$, the expression $P(a)$ becomes (something α-equivalent to) $\exists y: \mathbf{N} \cdot 2 \times y \neq x+x$.

Before moving on to consider the use of rules in proofs, a few syntactic points need to be made. Each rule may have more than one hypothesis, in which case the hypotheses are separated by semicolons or appear on separate lines. A rule also has a name, which is used when referring to it in proofs. This appears in a box to the left of the rule, and is generally mnemonic, following the informal conventions outlined in Section 1.3.7. Rules which are axioms are marked on the right with the letters "Ax". The following examples illustrate these points:

$$\boxed{\text{modus ponens}} \;\; \frac{P;\; P \Rightarrow Q}{Q} \qquad\qquad \boxed{\text{0-form}} \;\; \frac{}{0:\mathbf{N}} \;\; \text{Ax}$$

Proofs

A *(formal) proof* is an argument that some conclusion can be inferred from a number of assumptions. For example, suppose one wants to prove that, given some sequence of natural numbers ns, concatenating the sequence $[0]$ with it produces a sequence of natural numbers. That is, from the assumption $ns : \mathbf{N}^*$ infer that $[0] \frown ns : \mathbf{N}^*$. In the proof notation used here, the (incomplete) proof is written:

> from $ns: \mathbf{N}^*$
>
> ...
>
> infer $[0] \frown ns : \mathbf{N}^*$ ⟨?? justify ??⟩

The keyword from identifies a line recording assumptions, while the keyword infer identifies a line containing a conclusion. The marker "⟨?? justify ??⟩" indicates that the justification of some assertion has not yet been worked out. The marker "..." indicates where some lines may have to be inserted when constructing such a justification.

In completing this example proof, the following rules concerning the theory of sequences of numbers are used:

$$\boxed{\text{0-form}} \;\; \frac{}{0:\mathbf{N}} \qquad \boxed{\text{singl-form}} \;\; \frac{a:A}{[a]:A^*} \qquad \boxed{\frown\text{-form}} \;\; \frac{s_1:A^*;\; s_2:A^*}{(s_1 \frown s_2):A^*}$$

The rule '0-form' has no hypotheses, allowing the fact that 0 is a natural number to be asserted anywhere. Applying it in the current proof gives a line containing its conclusion as the assertion, justified by appealing to the rule:

> from $ns: \mathbf{N}^*$
> 1 $0:\mathbf{N}$ 0-form
>
> ...
>
> infer $[0] \frown ns : \mathbf{N}^*$ ⟨?? justify ??⟩

The new line contains a reference number (1), an expression representing the assertion that the line purports to establish ($0:\mathbf{N}$), and a *justification* indicating which inference rule has been applied to justify the assertion ('0-form').

1.3 A logical framework for proofs

The rule 'singl-form' contains two metavariables, a and A. If a is instantiated to 0 and A to N, the following instance of the rule results:

$$\frac{0:\mathsf{N}}{[0]:\mathsf{N}^*}$$

Its hypothesis matches Line 1 in the proof, so the rule can be applied, allowing the inference that $[0]:\mathsf{N}^*$. The new line is justified by the name of the applied rule and a numerical reference to the line on which the assertion matching its hypothesis occurs:

```
         from ns: N*
         1    0 : N                          0-form
         2    [0]: N*                        singl-form (1)
              ...
              infer ([0] ⌢ ns): N*           ⟨?? justify ??⟩
```

The proof is completed by applying '⌢-form', instantiating s_1 by [0], s_2 by ns and A by N to yield the following instance of the rule:

$$\frac{[0]:\mathsf{N};\ ns:\mathsf{N}^*}{([0]\mathbin{\frown} ns):\mathsf{N}^*}$$

The completed proof is:

```
         from ns: N*
         1    0 : N                          0-form
         2    [0]: N*                        singl-form (1)
              infer ([0] ⌢ ns): N*           ⌢-form (2, h1)
```

Lines are numbered sequentially between from and infer keywords. Assumptions are referred to by their position in the from line: "h1" for the first assumption, "h2" for the second and so on.

The proof can be seen as either an exercise in symbol manipulation or an argument about sequences of natural numbers. For this proof, the argument can be read as follows:

> "Suppose ns represents a sequence of numbers (Assumption h1). Using rule '0-form' it can be asserted that 0 is a number (Line 1). Using rule 'singl-form' it follows from Line 1 that [0] is a sequence of numbers (Line 2). Finally, using rule '⌢-form' it follows from Line 2 and Assumption h1 that $[0] \mathbin{\frown} ns$ is a sequence of numbers."

Derived rules

The proof has established a new logical statement, $[0] \mathbin{\frown} ns : \mathsf{N}^*$, contingent on the assumption that $ns:\mathsf{N}^*$. This can be stated formally as a new rule:

$$\boxed{[0]\text{-}{\frown}\text{-form}}\ \frac{ns:\mathsf{N}^*}{([0]\mathbin{\frown} ns):\mathsf{N}^*}$$

A rule extracted from a proof as above is said to be *derived* from the rules used in its proof. Derived rules can be used in other proofs as required. A point to be noted is that the derived rule itself has *ns* as a metavariable. Any metavariables which appear in the statement of the rule being proved must not be instantiated during the course of the proof: instantiation of metavariables only takes place for the rules used in justifications in the proof.

In this book, derived rules are sometimes also called *lemmas* or *theorems*.

Valid proofs

A proof is *valid* precisely when:

- Justifications refer only to preceding lines.
- For each justification, there is an instance of the inference rule such that the hypotheses (of the instance) correspond to the assertions on the lines to which it refers and the conclusion corresponds to the assertion on the line being justified.
- At each step, the instantiation is valid in the syntactic context of the proof. Roughly, all symbols must be "in scope" where the proof is being constructed, or be metavariables of the rule being derived.

A rule is regarded as *proved* when it has a valid proof with justifications referring only to axioms and already proved rules.

1.3.4 Natural Deduction style

So far, a proof has been viewed as a sequence of justified assertions. While straightforward, this view is limiting. In order to give proofs a structure which more closely resembles that of a natural argument, the idea of local scoping of assumptions is introduced. This comes from Gentzen's system of *Natural Deduction* [Pra65, GLT89]. Consider, for example, the following well-known inference rules:

Deduction Rule: "To prove $P \Rightarrow Q$ (that is, P implies Q), assume P then prove Q."

Case Distinction Rule: "If $A \vee B$ (that is, A or B) is known, then in order to prove C it suffices to prove C assuming A and also to prove C assuming B."

In each of these rules, there is a reference to a *subproof* showing that some fact can be derived from some local assumption (Q from P, C from A, and C from B). The local assumption holds only in the subproof.

In order to capture this kind of inference rule, the logical framework incorporates the symbol "⊢" (called a *turnstile*) to indicate derivation via a subproof. The statement

$P, Q \vdash R$

1.3 A logical framework for proofs

is called a *sequent*[2]. Its meaning is that the expression R is derivable from the local assumptions P and Q in a subproof. Expressions to the left of the turnstile are called *local assumptions* or *local hypotheses*; the expression to the right is called the *local conclusion*. Local assumptions are separated by commas.

Using this notation, the Deduction and Case Distinction Rules are written as follows:

$$\boxed{\text{deduction}} \; \frac{P \vdash Q}{P \Rightarrow Q} \qquad\qquad \boxed{\text{cases}} \; \frac{A \vee B; \; A \vdash C; \; B \vdash C}{C}$$

In order to use these rules, the syntax for proofs is extended to accommodate subproofs. For example, consider the following rule:

$$\frac{P \Rightarrow Q; \; Q \Rightarrow R}{P \Rightarrow R}$$

Its proof contains a step which is justified by appealing to the deduction rule, the sequent hypothesis of which generates the subproof labelled '1':

```
     from P ⇒ Q; Q ⇒ R
   1    from P
   1.1      Q                    modus ponens (1.h1, h1)
         infer R                 modus ponens (1.1, h2)
     infer P ⇒ R                 deduction (1)
```

Subproofs are numbered in the same way as lines. Within a subproof, which may itself contain subproofs, the from and infer keywords indicate the local assumptions and local conclusion, and line numbering is nested and sequential. Local assumptions are referred to in justifications by their position in the from line, prefixed by the number of the subproof. Thus "1.h1" refers to the first assumption of Subproof 1. Recall that "h1" refers to the first assumption of the whole proof.

For this proof, the argument can be read as follows:

> "Suppose P implies Q (Assumption h1) and Q in turn implies R (Assumption h2). Assume that P holds (Assumption 1.h1). By 'modus ponens', it follows that Q must hold (Line 1.1) and hence, again by 'modus ponens', that R also holds.
>
> Finally, since R has been shown to follow from P (Subproof 1), then by the 'deduction' rule it follows that P implies R."

The notions of subproof and the notational conventions employed will become familiar to the reader through many examples in subsequent chapters.

---

[2]The turnstile used here is specific to the logical framework of this book, and is subtly different from the turnstile often used in Hilbert-style or Sequent Calculus systems. In particular, unlike conventional Hilbert-style systems, it does not involve separate scoping of variables on the two sides of the ⊢ (see Section 1.3.5).

Justification by sequent hypotheses

As indicated above, some rules have sequent hypotheses which represent inferences which can be used in the rule's proof. Consider, for example, the rule:

$$\boxed{\text{one case}} \quad \frac{P \vee Q; \; P \vdash R}{R \vee Q}$$

the proof of which is:

from $P \vee Q; \; P \vdash R$
1   from P
1.1 R sequent h2 (1.h1)
      infer $R \vee Q$ left case (1.1)
2   from Q
      infer $R \vee Q$ right case (2.h1)
infer $R \vee Q$ cases (h1, 1, 2)

The sequent hypothesis is used at Line 1.1 to infer R (its local conclusion) from P (its local assumption). The proof also relies on the following two inference rules:

$$\boxed{\text{left case}} \; \frac{P}{P \vee Q} \qquad \boxed{\text{right case}} \; \frac{Q}{P \vee Q}$$

1.3.5 Natural Deduction with local scoping of variables

Sequents provide local scoping of assumptions within formal proofs. The Edinburgh Logical Framework (ELF) [HHP87] extends Gentzen's Sequent Calculus so that sequents can introduce and bind new variables. The logical framework of this book combines the ELF idea with Natural Deduction, to allow local scoping of *variables* as well as assumptions within proofs. Consider for example the following inference rule:

Generalisation Rule: "To prove $\forall x{:}X \cdot P(x)$ (i.e. for all x of type X, $P(x)$ holds), it suffices to introduce a new variable a to stand for an arbitrary value of type X and, assuming $a{:}X$, prove that $P(a)$ holds."

Nothing should be assumed about a other than the fact that it stands for a value of type X. The Generalisation Rule is written:

$$\boxed{\text{generalisation}} \; \frac{a{:}X \vdash_a P(a)}{\forall x{:}X \cdot P(x)}$$

The subscript a on the turnstile indicates that the *sequent variable a* is "bound" throughout the sequent in the same way that variables are bound by quantifiers like $\forall$ and $\exists$. Sequents are considered equivalent up to renaming of their sequent variables, so that $a{:}X \vdash_a P(a)$ is indistinguishable from $b{:}X \vdash_b P(b)$. This means that, when a sequent hypothesis with sequent variables is applied in a proof (see previous section), the sequent variable(s) may be renamed to match existing variables in the proof. This is illustrated in Section 3.3.1.

1.3 A logical framework for proofs

When the 'generalisation' rule is used to justify a step in a proof, use of a is restricted to the subproof corresponding to the sequent hypothesis[3]. To see how such a rule is used in proofs, consider a proof of the following rule:

$$\frac{\forall u: A \cdot \forall v: B \cdot P(u,v)}{\forall v: B \cdot \forall u: A \cdot P(u,v)}$$

In order to establish the conclusion of the rule using 'generalisation', it is first necessary to introduce a subproof with a new local variable, b say, and local assumption $b:B$, as follows:

    from $\forall u: A \cdot \forall v: B \cdot P(u,v)$
1   from $b:B$
        ...
    infer $\forall u: A \cdot P(u,b)$ ⟨?? justify ??⟩
    infer $\forall v: B \cdot \forall u: A \cdot P(u,v)$ generalisation (1)

The local conclusion of Subproof 1 follows from another application of 'generalisation':

    from $\forall u: A \cdot \forall v: B \cdot P(u,v)$
1   from $b:B$
1.1   from $a:A$
        ...
       infer $P(a,b)$ ⟨?? justify ??⟩
    infer $\forall u: A \cdot P(u,b)$ generalisation (1.1)
    infer $\forall v: B \cdot \forall u: A \cdot P(u,v)$ generalisation (1)

Finally, the proof can be completed by two applications of the following rule for specialisation:

$$\boxed{\text{specialisation}} \quad \frac{t:X; \ \forall y: X \cdot P(y)}{P(t)}$$

The completed proof is:

from $\forall u: A \cdot \forall v: B \cdot P(u,v)$
1   from $b:B$
1.1   from $a:A$
1.1.1 $\forall v: B \cdot P(a,v)$ specialisation (1.1.h1, h1)
       infer $P(a,b)$ specialisation (1.h1, 1.1.1)
    infer $\forall u: A \cdot P(u,b)$ generalisation (1.1)
infer $\forall v: B \cdot \forall u: A \cdot P(u,v)$ generalisation (1)

For this proof, the argument can be read as follows:

---

[3] If a rule with a sequent hypothesis is applied in a proof at a line where the sequent's local variable is already in use, the local variable must be renamed to avoid a clash.

"Suppose $\forall u\colon A \cdot \forall v\colon B \cdot P(u,v)$ (Assumption h1). Let b be an arbitrary element of B (Assumption 1.h1). Now let a be an arbitrary element of A (Assumption 1.1.h1). It follows from the main assumption by specialisation that $\forall v\colon B \cdot P(a,v)$ holds (Line 1.1). Hence, in turn, it follows by specialisation that $P(a,b)$ holds.

But since a stands for an arbitrary element of A, it follows (back in Subproof 1) that $\forall u\colon A \cdot P(u,b)$. Finally, since b is arbitrary, it follows (back in the main proof) that $\forall v\colon B \cdot \forall u\colon A \cdot P(u,v)$."

1.3.6 Definitions

Sometimes a constant can be defined directly in terms of other expressions. For example, the logical operator "and" can be defined in terms of "not" ($\neg$) and "or" ($\vee$) as follows:

$$e_1 \wedge e_2 \stackrel{\text{def}}{=} \neg(\neg e_1 \vee \neg e_2)$$

where e_1 and e_2 are formal parameters standing for arbitrary expressions.

This definition introduces a new symbol ($\wedge$) which can be considered to be a syntactic shorthand for the expression that defines it. Thus $e_1 \wedge e_2$ always has the same value as $\neg(\neg e_1 \vee \neg e_2)$ and any expression or subexpression matching one side can be replaced in a proof by the corresponding expression matching the other side. Replacing an expression matching the right hand side by one matching the left is called *folding*. The converse process is called *unfolding*. These terms appear within proofs as justifications. Consider, for example, the following proof fragment:

$$\vdots$$
5	$\neg((A \wedge B) \vee \neg C)$	
6	$\neg(\neg(\neg A \vee \neg B) \vee \neg C)$	unfolding (5)
7	$(\neg A \vee \neg B) \wedge C$	folding (6)

$$\vdots$$

Here, Line 6 results from Line 5 by unfolding the subexpression $A \wedge B$, and Line 7 results from Line 6 by folding the whole expression.

Rules can be derived about the defined construct which can then be used to reason directly about the defined symbol without using its definition. For example:

$$\frac{e_1 \wedge e_2}{e_1} \qquad \frac{e_1 \wedge e_2}{e_2} \qquad \frac{e_1;\ e_2}{e_1 \wedge e_2}$$

Recursive definitions are also allowed. These are discussed in Section 8.5.

1.3.7 Rule naming conventions

Throughout this book some informal mnemonic naming conventions have been followed in order to make rules easier to remember.

Rule names generally consist of up to three components, separated by dashes. The first component lists the various symbols acted on, also separated by dashes. The main symbol being acted on appears first, followed by any subsidiary symbols in turn. The second component indicates the type of the rule, for example "introduction", "elimination", "formation". The third (optional) component gives any subsidiary information about the way the manipulation is being done (e.g. "left", "right") or about separate cases of related rules (e.g. = or ≠). The convention should become clearer by considering the following examples. Note, however, that these conventions are not always followed.

"Zero Formation":

$$\boxed{\text{0-form}}\ \frac{}{0:\mathbb{N}}\ \textbf{Ax}$$

The "0" in this rule name indicates that this is a rule about 0, the "form" that it is a *formation* rule, that is that it gives typing information about its subject. The letters "**Ax**" indicate that it is an axiom.

Other kinds of rule are: *definition* (defn) rules, which give (a case of) a definition of their subject; *introduction* (I) and *elimination* (E) rules, which say respectively how a symbol can be introduced and eliminated; *commutativity* (comm) and *associativity* (ass) rules, which say that a binary operator is commutative or associative; *induction* (indn) rules, for certain data types; *satisfiability* (sat) rules, which state that a given operation is satisfiable.

"Or Introduction Right":

$$\boxed{\vee\text{-I-right}}\ \frac{e_1}{e_1 \vee e_2}\ \textbf{Ax}$$

In this rule the symbol $\vee$ (for 'or') is being introduced, that is it appears in the conclusion of the rule but not in the hypotheses. The new item e_2 is introduced to the right of the 'or'.

"Membership of Intersection Elimination Left":

$$\boxed{\in\text{-}\cap\text{-E-left}}\ \frac{a:A;\ s_1:A\text{-set};\ s_2:A\text{-set};\ a \in s_1 \cap s_2}{a \in s_2}$$

This rule is primarily about membership of intersection, hence the first two components of the name $\in$ and $\cap$. It is an elimination rule because the intersection is in the hypotheses and not the conclusion. Furthermore, it is a "left-hand" rule because the argument to the left of the intersection has been eliminated.

Some rules appear without names at all. Such rules are not part of the axiomatisation as a whole; indeed they may not even be valid. They are presented simply for the purpose of discussion and do not appear in the directory of theorems (Chapter 14).

1.4 Summary

At this point, it is worth reviewing the main points of the chapter:

- A VDM-SL specification is model-oriented. It defines types to model the inputs, outputs and internal state of a system. Value constructors and logical operators allow the definition of states, invariants, auxiliary functions and state-modifying operations. These provide a basis for reasoning about specifications and refinements.

- Opportunities for proof arise in a number of contexts in the formal specification and design of computing systems:
    - discharging *proof obligations* relating to internal consistency and satisfiability of a specification;
    - discharging proof obligations relating to the correctness of design decisions in the reification process; and
    - showing the truth of *validation conjectures*, which state expected properties of the specification.

  Performing such proofs increases confidence that a specification or reification step is correct.

- Failure to complete a proof can be just as valuable as success: it indicates changes which can improve a specification or design.

- A general framework for logic has been described which provides the basis for the reasoning system for VDM defined in later chapters. A fully formal, detailed description of the logical framework is given in [JJLM91].

- A *formal language*, *axioms* and *rules of inference* provide a basis for proof of results, including obligations and conjectures.

- Axioms, theorems, lemmas and derived results are all written as *inference rules*, and called *rules* for short. Axioms are distinguished by the letters **Ax**. Rules are really rule schemas, with *metavariables* capturing genericity. Rules may have sequent hypotheses representing local scoping of assumptions and variables.

- *Proofs* are block-structured, reflecting the structure of the rules applied. Blocks within a proof are called *subproofs*. Subproofs can have local assumptions and local variables.

- Each step in a proof involves one of the following:
    - instantiation and application of a rule;
    - application of a sequent hypothesis; or
    - folding or unfolding a definition.

Subsequent chapters give definitions and rules for reasoning about VDM specification and refinement. They demonstrate a wide range of techniques for constructing proofs, and show how to reason about specifications and reifications.

Part I

A Logical Basis for Proof in VDM

Chapter 2

Propositional LPF

2.1 Introduction

In general, a proof is a reasoned argument that some assertion (the conclusion of the proof) is true under the assumption that certain other assertions (the hypotheses of the proof) are themselves true. Each step of the argument is itself an assertion and represents a valid deduction from preceding assertions in the sense that there should be some law which justifies the step in the mathematical inference system being used to support the reasoning. The basic logic of assertions, propositional logic, is the subject of this chapter.

One point worth noting before beginning is that, whilst the so-called "classical logic" is probably the most familiar form of propositional logic, it is by no means the only form. Indeed, VDM is based on a generalisation of classical logic called the *Logic of Partial Functions* (LPF; see [BCJ84]; [Jon90]; [Che86]), and it is this generalisation which is discussed here. The proof techniques illustrated are, however, equally applicable to other forms of propositional logic. Moreover, since LPF is a generalisation of classical logic, all the inference rules which are valid in LPF are also valid in classical logic (though the converse is not true).

The main aim of this chapter is to introduce in as simple a setting as possible the basic ideas and general proof techniques which are needed in the following chapters. The starting point is the definition of a basic set of axioms for propositional LPF. This is followed by a discussion of a very common proof technique, reasoning by cases, and several worked examples are presented. These examples are also used to illustrate both how one can try to convince oneself before starting a proof that a particular inference rule is provable and how informal reasoning can suggest a structure for the formal proof. Proof by contradiction is also discussed. The next section deals with extending a theory by adding definitions, and shows how definitions are used to justify steps in a proof. The example proofs in this section show how one can determine potentially useful proof strategies by considering the form of the available inference rules. The final section introduces the notions of undefinedness and implication, and discusses the differences between LPF and classical logic which these engender. The use of sequent hypotheses in proofs is explained with the help of the examples.

2.2 Basic axiomatisation

The idea behind giving an axiomatisation of a theory is to define a set of symbols representing the concepts one wishes to reason about in the theory, together with a set of inference rules defining their most basic properties. This set of inference rules, the axioms of the theory, are taken to be true without proof. Other inference rules proved in the theory (derived rules) are consequences of these basic axioms.

Propositional LPF can be described in terms of three basic logical symbols[1], a constant 'true' representing truth and the logical constructors '$\neg$' representing negation (not) and '$\vee$' representing disjunction (or). Their fundamental properties are defined via a series of axioms expressing the introduction and elimination rules for the simplest combinations of them.

The easiest of these symbols to deal with is the constant 'true'. Its properties are defined by a single rule 'true-I' which states that 'true' is true under no assumptions:

$$\boxed{\text{true-I}} \; \frac{}{\text{true}} \; \text{Ax}$$

Three axioms are required to define the basic properties of disjunction. The two introduction rules '$\vee$-I-right' and '$\vee$-I-left' state respectively that the assertion $e_1 \vee e_2$ is true if the assertion e_1 is true or if the assertion e_2 is true:

$$\boxed{\vee\text{-I-right}} \; \frac{e_1}{e_1 \vee e_2} \; \text{Ax} \qquad \boxed{\vee\text{-I-left}} \; \frac{e_2}{e_1 \vee e_2} \; \text{Ax}$$

The elimination rule '$\vee$-E' is somewhat less intuitive and is the first example of a rule with sequent hypotheses. It has the form:

$$\boxed{\vee\text{-E}} \; \frac{e_1 \vee e_2; \; e_1 \vdash e; \; e_2 \vdash e}{e} \; \text{Ax}$$

The first hypothesis of the rule asserts that $e_1 \vee e_2$ is true, and there are only two ways that this is possible, namely for either e_1 or e_2 to be true separately. The sequent hypotheses can thus be considered as representing these two possible cases, with the rule being interpreted as stating that if $e_1 \vee e_2$ is true and if it is possible to prove some assertion e first by assuming that e_1 is true and second by assuming that e_2 is true then the assertion e is true. This rule thus represents (one form of) reasoning by cases, examples of which are given in the next section (Section 2.3). That section also shows how using a rule which has sequent hypotheses to justify a step in a proof leads to subproofs, with the hypotheses of the sequent becoming the local hypotheses of the subproof and the conclusion of the sequent its local goal.

Returning to the axiomatisation of propositional LPF, a further three axioms are needed to describe the basic properties of negation. These are:

$$\boxed{\neg\neg\text{-I}} \; \frac{e}{\neg\neg e} \; \text{Ax} \qquad \boxed{\neg\neg\text{-E}} \; \frac{\neg\neg e}{e} \; \text{Ax} \qquad \boxed{\text{contradiction}} \; \frac{e_1; \; \neg e_1}{e_2} \; \text{Ax}$$

The first two ('$\neg\neg$-I' and '$\neg\neg$-E') are easy to understand and effectively amount to

---
[1] Axiomatisations based on other combinations of "primitive" symbols are possible.

saying that double negation of some assertion e has the same value as the assertion e itself. Again, the third axiom is perhaps not quite so intuitive, as its hypotheses state that both some assertion e_1 and its negation $\neg e_1$ are true. At first sight it seems that this rule could therefore never be used as an assertion cannot be both true and false at the same time. In practice, however, the rule is often used in proofs employing reasoning by cases when one of the cases under consideration cannot actually be realised. This is illustrated in the next section (Section 2.3).

Three more axioms are needed to complete the definition of propositional LPF, dealing with the simplest possible assertions built from combinations of negation and disjunction. The introduction axiom '$\neg$-$\vee$-I' can best be thought of as stating that if each of the assertions e_1 and e_2 is false then the assertion $e_1 \vee e_2$ is also false. The elimination rules '$\neg$-$\vee$-E-left' and '$\neg$-$\vee$-E-right' state the converse of this, namely that if the assertion $e_1 \vee e_2$ is known to be false then each of the assertions e_1 and e_2 must be false:

$$\boxed{\neg\text{-}\vee\text{-I}} \; \frac{\neg e_1; \; \neg e_2}{\neg(e_1 \vee e_2)} \; \mathbf{Ax}$$

$$\boxed{\neg\text{-}\vee\text{-E-left}} \; \frac{\neg(e_1 \vee e_2)}{\neg e_2} \; \mathbf{Ax} \qquad \boxed{\neg\text{-}\vee\text{-E-right}} \; \frac{\neg(e_1 \vee e_2)}{\neg e_1} \; \mathbf{Ax}$$

2.3 Derived rules; reasoning by cases; reasoning using contradiction

Whilst it would be perfectly possible to attempt to prove everything using just the basic axioms, in practice this would lead to very long and intractable proofs. Rather it is better to extend the reasoning power by stating and proving new rules embodying more powerful valid inferences. These rules can be used in turn to prove rules which are more powerful still, and a library of useful derived rules can be built up in this way. In essence, therefore, a derived rule acts as a shorthand for its proof: any step in a proof which is justified by appeal to a derived rule could instead be justified by multiple steps corresponding to all the steps in the proof of that derived rule.

When constructing derived rules it is useful to keep in mind two general principles. First, the rule should be stated in as general a form as possible. To put this another way, it is not worth stating a derived rule which represents an instance of some more general derived rule. Second, derived rules will ordinarily represent commonly used inference steps and not inference steps which are specific to one particular proof and which are not likely to be used elsewhere (though it is worth relaxing this second criterion if a particular proof threatens to become excessively long and cumbersome).

The next point to consider is how to avoid wasting time trying to prove a rule which is unprovable, or, to put it another way, how to decide whether or not a particular rule is provable simply by considering its statement (that is without attempting a formal proof). A good way of doing this is to reason informally about the rule, by using one's intuitive ideas of what the assertions comprising its hypotheses and conclusion mean to consider the circumstances under which they are (separately) true. This is best illustrated by an example.

Suppose one wishes to construct a rule stating that disjunction is commutative, that is that the arguments of a disjunction are interchangeable. The obvious form for such a rule is:

$$\boxed{\vee\text{-comm}}\ \frac{e_1 \vee e_2}{e_2 \vee e_1}$$

Informally, this rule amounts to the statement that the assertion $e_2 \vee e_1$ is true if the assertion $e_1 \vee e_2$ is true. Considering first the hypothesis of the rule, this can only be true in two cases, namely if the assertion e_1 is true or if the assertion e_2 is true. In each of these cases, the assertion $e_2 \vee e_1$ is true, so the rule is provable.

The other advantage of such informal argument is that its structure generally mirrors that of the corresponding formal proof. In this particular example, the facts that the informal argument employed reasoning by cases and that a disjunction is amongst the hypotheses suggest that the rule '$\vee$-E' is likely to be useful. Applying this to justify the conclusion of the proof yields two subproofs corresponding not only to the two sequent hypotheses of the '$\vee$-E' rule but also to the two cases considered in the informal argument, these cases being represented by the local hypotheses of the subproofs:

```
        from e₁ ∨ e₂
    1       from e₁
                ...
                infer e₂ ∨ e₁              ⟨?? justify ??⟩
    2       from e₂
                ...
                infer e₂ ∨ e₁              ⟨?? justify ??⟩
        infer e₂ ∨ e₁                      ∨-E (h1, 1, 2)
```

Each subproof is now easy to complete, being respectively simple instances of the rules '$\vee$-I-left' and '$\vee$-I-right'. The completed proof is thus:

```
        from e₁ ∨ e₂
    1       from e₁
                infer e₂ ∨ e₁              ∨-I-left (1.h1)
    2       from e₂
                infer e₂ ∨ e₁              ∨-I-right (2.h1)
        infer e₂ ∨ e₁                      ∨-E (h1, 1, 2)
```

Another simple example is the rule '$\vee$-E-left-$\neg$':

$$\boxed{\vee\text{-E-left-}\neg}\ \frac{e_1 \vee e_2;\ \neg e_1}{e_2}$$

Again, one would start by reasoning informally about this rule.

As in the previous example, the hypothesis $e_1 \vee e_2$ leads to the conclusion that either e_1 or e_2 must be true. Here, however, extra information, namely that e_1 is false, is provided by the second hypothesis. This means that the first of these two cases is ruled out, which

2.3 Derived rules; reasoning by cases; reasoning using contradiction

in turn means that e_2 must be true. This shows that the rule should indeed be provable.

Turning now to the formal proof, the facts that there is a disjunction amongst the hypotheses and that the informal argument proceeded by considering cases again indicate that the rule '∨-E' is likely to be useful, application of which yields two subproofs in exactly the same way as seen in the previous example:

```
from e₁ ∨ e₂; ¬e₁
1    from e₁
         ...
     infer e₂                    ⟨?? justify ??⟩
2    from e₂
         ...
     infer e₂                    ⟨?? justify ??⟩
infer e₂                         ∨-E (h1, 1, 2)
```

The second subproof here is actually trivially true as its local hypothesis is the same as its goal (it effectively amounts to proving that e_2 is true on the assumption that e_2 is true!). Such subproofs are not shown in proofs in this book. Rather, the fact that a step in a proof is justified by appeal to a trivially true subproof is recorded by referring to the symbol 'triv' instead of some line number in the justification.

The first subproof has a hypothesis which contradicts the second hypothesis of the overall proof and corresponds to the case that was ruled out as impossible in the informal argument. In the formal proof this subproof is justified by appeal to the rule 'contradiction'. Note how this is used to justify the required conclusion in this "illegal" case. The completed proof is therefore:

```
from e₁ ∨ e₂; ¬e₁
1    from e₁
     infer e₂                    contradiction (1.h1, h2)
infer e₂                         ∨-E (h1, 1, triv)
```

Clearly, an entirely analogous proof of the related rule '∨-E-right-¬'

$$\boxed{\text{∨-E-right-¬}} \; \frac{e_1 \vee e_2; \; \neg e_2}{e_1}$$

could be constructed, except that in that case the first subproof would follow trivially by assumption and the second would be proved by contradiction. A much simpler proof can be produced, however, which makes use of the derived rule for the commutativity of disjunction ('∨-comm'). The point to note here is that the rule '∨-E-right-¬' can be transformed into the rule '∨-E-left-¬' by first commuting the disjunction in its first hypothesis and then swapping e_1 and e_2 throughout. The proof which results from this insight shows how the judicious use of derived rules can save work:

```
from e₁ ∨ e₂; ¬e₂
1    e₂ ∨ e₁                              ∨-comm (h1)
infer e₁                                  ∨-E-left-¬ (1, h2)
```

Of course, one could just as easily have chosen to prove the rule '∨-E-right-¬' first, afterwards proving the rule '∨-E-left-¬' from that by using the commutativity of disjunction.

2.4 Using definitions: conjunction

Although any propositional assertion could in principle be expressed in terms of the three logical symbols introduced so far (truth, negation and disjunction), assertions written in this way not only become long-winded and unwieldy very rapidly but also fail to express one's intuitive understanding in anything like a natural way. For example, the notion that two assertions e_1 and e_2 are both true would have to be expressed by saying that the disjunction of the negation of e_1 and the negation of e_2 is false, that is as the assertion $\neg(\neg e_1 \vee \neg e_2)$. This notion of conjunction (∧, or and) does not add anything fundamentally new to the theory of propositional LPF, however, as it can be expressed in terms of the existing notions of disjunction and negation as shown above. It is therefore inappropriate to extend the theory by adding axioms to describe the properties of conjunction as these should all be deducible from the properties of negation and disjunction. Rather one makes a syntactic definition:

$$e_1 \wedge e_2 \stackrel{\text{def}}{=} \neg(\neg e_1 \vee \neg e_2)$$

This effectively defines the pattern $e_1 \wedge e_2$ as a shorthand for the expression on the right-hand side of the defining equation.

The standard introduction and elimination rules for conjunction

$$\boxed{\wedge\text{-I}} \; \frac{e_1; \; e_2}{e_1 \wedge e_2} \qquad \boxed{\wedge\text{-E-right}} \; \frac{e_1 \wedge e_2}{e_1} \qquad \boxed{\wedge\text{-E-left}} \; \frac{e_1 \wedge e_2}{e_2}$$

are provable from the above definition and the rules for negation and disjunction. Their proofs are simple, but illustrate how definitions are used to justify steps in a proof.

Consider first the statements of these three rules. The introduction rule '∧-I' asserts that if e_1 and e_2 are both true then $e_1 \wedge e_2$ is true, and the elimination rules '∧-E-right' and '∧-E-left' express respectively that if $e_1 \wedge e_2$ is true then e_1 is true and e_2 is true. These properties exactly match one's intuitive understanding of conjunction. Indeed, the whole idea of stating such rules for a defined construct is that they should encapsulate the way one naturally reasons about that construct. This means, however, that the technique of planning the formal proof by using informal natural reasoning does not work for rules such as these which represent the most basic properties of defined symbols. Some different approach is therefore needed here.

At this stage, no derived inference rules mentioning conjunction are available to help with the proofs of the introduction and elimination rules. The only thing that is known

2.4 Using definitions: conjunction

about conjunction is its definition in terms of negation and disjunction. The only way the proofs can proceed, therefore, is by making use of this definition to rewrite the assertions containing a conjunction. This introduces two new forms of justification, folding and unfolding of definitions.

Consider first the elimination rule '$\wedge$-E-right'. The first step in the proof is to unfold the definition of the conjunction in its hypothesis. This yields a new line in the proof justified by unfolding:

$$
\begin{array}{ll}
\text{from } e_1 \wedge e_2 & \\
1 \quad \neg(\neg e_1 \vee \neg e_2) & \text{unfolding (h1)} \\
\quad \ldots & \\
\text{infer } e_1 & \langle ??\text{ justify }??\rangle
\end{array}
$$

This has reduced the task to proving that e_1 is true if the assertion $\neg(\neg e_1 \vee \neg e_2)$ is true, which still probably defies one's intuition. However, the problem is now stated only in terms of negation and disjunction, so it is clear that the only possible way to proceed is to use rules relating to these. The question is, how does one choose which rule might be the most useful to apply?

In fact, there are various considerations which can help with the selection of useful rules at some point in a proof. The first step is to look at the current *knowns* and *goals* of the proof. The knowns are all the assertions in a proof which could be used to match against the hypotheses of any rule being applied. Typically this comprises all accessible hypotheses in the proof (including local hypotheses of containing subproofs) and anything that has been proved from these by steps of forward reasoning. In the current proof, therefore, the knowns are the assertions $e_1 \wedge e_2$ and $\neg(\neg e_1 \vee \neg e_2)$. The goals, on the other hand, represents those lines of the proof which have not yet been justified. These therefore represent those assertions which could be used to match the conclusion of the rule being applied. The only goal in the current proof is the assertion e_1.

Next, consideration of steps already carried out in a proof can help to filter the set of "useful" knowns. For instance, it was argued above that the only possible way of deducing anything from the first of the knowns was by unfolding the definition of conjunction. Since this has already been done to generate Line 1 of the proof above, there is nothing further to be gained by considering it. It can therefore be discarded from the set of knowns, leaving $\neg(\neg e_1 \vee \neg e_2)$ as the only useful known.

The next step in the procedure is to try to find those rules from the set of all available rules which could be applied to these knowns and goals. It must be remembered, however, that rules can be applied either forwards to knowns or backwards to goals, so that a particular rule might be applicable in one direction but not in the other. The aim is thus to arrive at a list of rules together with the direction(s) in which each can be applied.

Additional assistance with this process can be gained by looking at the structure of the available knowns and goals. First, the only available known is a larger expression than the only goal. Moreover, it contains references to two variables e_1 and e_2 whereas the goal only refers to the single variable e_1. This suggests that one should think either of applying rules to the known to generate some smaller assertion, preferably independent of e_2, or rules to the goal to try to generate something closer in form to the known. Because the goal is a single variable, however, it is not easy to get a good hint of what rule would be most useful if applied backwards, so the choice reduces to selecting a rule to apply forwards to the known.

At this stage of the development of the theory, the rules 'true-I', '∨-I-right', '∨-I-left', '∨-E', '¬¬-I', '¬¬-E', 'contradiction', '¬-∨-I', '¬-∨-E-left', '¬-∨-E-right', '∨-comm', '∨-E-left-¬' and '∨-E-right-¬' are available. The rules '∨-E', '¬¬-E' and '∨-comm' can be rejected immediately as they do not have a hypothesis which matches the known. Also, those rules with more hypotheses than the number of available knowns are unlikely to be useful, so all rules in the list with more than one hypothesis can be ignored. This reduces the selection of potentially useful rules to 'true-I', '∨-I-right', '∨-I-left', '¬¬-I', '¬-∨-E-left' and '¬-∨-E-right'. Pretty clearly, the first of these is unlikely to help as the goal does not mention the constant 'true'. Further, the next three rules in the list can also be removed according to the criterion that the fact that the goal is smaller than the known suggests applying a rule which generates some assertion which is smaller than the known. The choice is thus between '¬-∨-E-left' and '¬-∨-E-right'. Finally, the fact that the goal is independent of e_2 points towards the rule '¬-∨-E-right' being the correct choice. It is worth pointing out here that a different heuristic which states that the most useful rule is likely to be the one which matches the complex expression most closely (in the sense of having the most common structure) would have led to the same choice of rule.

Applying this rule to the proof leads to:

$$\begin{array}{ll}
\text{from } e_1 \wedge e_2 & \\
1 \quad \neg(\neg e_1 \vee \neg e_2) & \text{unfolding (h1)} \\
2 \quad \neg\neg e_1 & \text{¬-∨-E-right (1)} \\
\quad \ldots & \\
\text{infer } e_1 & \langle\text{?? justify ??}\rangle
\end{array}$$

which is easy to complete – the goal can be inferred directly from the new known (Line 2) by using the rule '¬¬-E'. The finished proof is thus:

$$\begin{array}{ll}
\text{from } e_1 \wedge e_2 & \\
1 \quad \neg(\neg e_1 \vee \neg e_2) & \text{unfolding (h1)} \\
2 \quad \neg\neg e_1 & \text{¬-∨-E-right (1)} \\
\text{infer } e_1 & \text{¬¬-E (2)}
\end{array}$$

The proof of the other elimination rule '∧-E-left' is entirely analogous.

Turning now to the proof of the introduction rule '∧-I', although two rules about conjunction are now available (the elimination rules), they are not going to be any help with this proof as they have the conjunction as their hypothesis and not as their conclusion. Again, therefore, the only possible starting step is to use the definition of conjunction. In this case, this is applied backwards to the overall conclusion, which means that the conclusion is justified by folding the definition from its expanded form as shown:

2.4 Using definitions: conjunction

from e_1; e_2
...
1    $\neg(\neg e_1 \vee \neg e_2)$ $\langle$?? justify ??$\rangle$
infer $e_1 \wedge e_2$ folding (1)

The selection of potentially useful rules then proceeds as described above, except that in this case the atomicity of the knowns suggests working backwards from the goal (Line 1). Of the rules available, only '∨-E', '¬¬-E', 'contradiction', '¬-∨-E-left', '¬-∨-E-right', '¬-∨-I', '∨-E-left-¬', '∨-E-right-¬', '∧-E-left' and '∧-E-right' have a conclusion which matches the assertion on Line 1 (note how the rules '∧-E-left' and '∧-E-right' have become available for use as derived rules). Again, consideration of the relative complexity of the knowns and the goal, in this case that the knowns are all simpler than the goal, leads one to reject rules which have hypotheses which are more complicated than their conclusion. This reduces the choice to either 'contradiction' or '¬-∨-I'. As a general rule, 'contradiction' is normally only useful in subproofs of proofs employing reasoning by cases when the case represented by the subproof corresponds to some impossible situation. Since the current proof is not of this form, this points to using '¬-∨-I' as the next step in the proof. Again, this could have been deduced from the facts that its conclusion matches the goal most closely and that its hypotheses are simpler than its conclusion. This leads to:

from e_1; e_2
...
1    $\neg\neg e_1$ $\langle$?? justify ??$\rangle$
2    $\neg\neg e_2$ $\langle$?? justify ??$\rangle$
3    $\neg(\neg e_1 \vee \neg e_2)$ ¬-∨-I (1, 2)
infer $e_1 \wedge e_2$ folding (3)

Again, the proof is now easy to complete as Lines 1 and 2 follow directly from the first and second hypothesis respectively using the rule '¬¬-I'. The completed proof is thus:

from e_1; e_2
1    $\neg\neg e_1$ ¬¬-I (h1)
2    $\neg\neg e_2$ ¬¬-I (h2)
3    $\neg(\neg e_1 \vee \neg e_2)$ ¬-∨-I (1, 2)
infer $e_1 \wedge e_2$ folding (3)

Now that these basic introduction and elimination properties have been proved, most future proofs involving conjunction will be constructed using intuition and informal argument, as illustrated above for proofs about negation and disjunction, and will not need to make use of the definition of conjunction (see Section 2.3). As an example of this, the rule '∧-comm' stating that conjunction is commutative:

$$\boxed{\wedge\text{-comm}} \;\; \frac{e_1 \wedge e_2}{e_2 \wedge e_1}$$

submits to the informal argument technique as follows: its hypothesis asserts that $e_1 \wedge e_2$ is true, which is only possible if both e_1 and e_2 are true, which in turn means that $e_2 \wedge e_1$ must be true. The corresponding formal proof follows in the obvious way by using the introduction and elimination rules '$\wedge$-I', '$\wedge$-E-right' and '$\wedge$-E-left'.

There are still a few occasions when the direct use of the definition is necessary, however, one example being in the proofs of two of the so-called deMorgan's laws. These rules deal with the distribution of negation over conjunction, and have the form:

$$\boxed{\neg\text{-}\wedge\text{-I-deM}} \;\; \frac{\neg e_1 \vee \neg e_2}{\neg(e_1 \wedge e_2)} \qquad \boxed{\neg\text{-}\wedge\text{-E-deM}} \;\; \frac{\neg(e_1 \wedge e_2)}{\neg e_1 \vee \neg e_2}$$

The definition of conjunction must be used because the introduction and elimination rules '$\wedge$-E-left', '$\wedge$-E-right' and '$\wedge$-I' for conjunction given above do not incorporate any means of reasoning about the negation of conjunction. To put this another way, none of those rules have a hypothesis or a conclusion of the form $\neg(e_1 \wedge e_2)$, which means that none of them can be used to reason about the expression of that form appearing in the deMorgan's laws. Furthermore, of the other inference rules available, only those with a single metavariable in the appropriate position (hypotheses or conclusion) offer any chance of dealing with this expression, but, as indicated earlier in this section, these are unlikely to be of any help because they always generate an expression more complex than the one they are applied to. This points to the use of the definition as the only possible way forward.

In fact, after applying the definition the proofs of the deMorgan's laws are straightforward. For example, that of '$\neg$-$\wedge$-E-deM' is:

```
from ¬(e₁ ∧ e₂)
1      ¬¬(¬e₁ ∨ ¬e₂)           unfolding (h1)
infer ¬e₁ ∨ ¬e₂                 ¬¬-E (1)
```

The proof of '$\neg$-$\wedge$-I-deM' and the deMorgan's laws '$\neg$-$\vee$-I-deM' and '$\neg$-$\vee$-E-deM', which can be found in Chapter 14, are left as exercises for the reader.

2.5 Implication; definedness; further defined constructs

Other notions commonly used when reasoning about propositions are falsehood, implication, and equivalence, which are denoted respectively by the symbols 'false', '$\Rightarrow$' (implies), and '$\Leftrightarrow$' (is equivalent to, also called if and only if). These can be added to the theory as defined constructs like conjunction (see Section 2.4 above). Their definitions are:

$$\text{false} \stackrel{\text{def}}{=} \neg\text{true}$$

2.5 Implication; definedness; further defined constructs

$$e_1 \Rightarrow e_2 \overset{\text{def}}{=} \neg e_1 \vee e_2$$

$$e_1 \Leftrightarrow e_2 \overset{\text{def}}{=} (e_1 \Rightarrow e_2) \wedge (e_2 \Rightarrow e_1)$$

Again, one can derive introduction and elimination rules for these using the definitions and existing rules describing the properties of the symbols used in the definitions. Thus, for example, the introduction rules '$\Rightarrow$-I-left-vac' and '$\Rightarrow$-I-right-vac' for implication follow directly by expanding the definition of the implication in their conclusion and applying the rules '$\vee$-I-left' and '$\vee$-I-right' respectively. Similarly, the elimination rules '$\Rightarrow$-E-left' (sometimes called *modus ponens*) and '$\Rightarrow$-E-right' follow from the derived rules '$\vee$-E-left-$\neg$' and '$\vee$-E-right-$\neg$'.

$$\boxed{\Rightarrow\text{-I-left-vac}} \; \frac{e_2}{e_1 \Rightarrow e_2} \qquad \boxed{\Rightarrow\text{-I-right-vac}} \; \frac{\neg e_1}{e_1 \Rightarrow e_2}$$

$$\boxed{\Rightarrow\text{-E-left}} \; \frac{e_1 \Rightarrow e_2; \; e_1}{e_2} \qquad \boxed{\Rightarrow\text{-E-right}} \; \frac{e_1 \Rightarrow e_2; \; \neg e_2}{\neg e_1}$$

One point worth noting here is that, although equivalence is defined in terms of implication and conjunction, which are themselves defined constructs, its introduction and elimination rules are best proved in terms of the derived rules for conjunction and implication and not by expanding their definitions. Of course, expanding the definitions would yield a valid proof, but this would be much longer and much more complicated than that constructed by reasoning directly in terms of the derived rules.

Differences between classical logic and LPF begin to show up when one goes on to consider other derived rules involving implication. For instance, rules such as the so-called "law of the excluded middle", often written in one of the following forms

$$\frac{}{e \Rightarrow e} \qquad \qquad \frac{}{e \vee \neg e}$$

are valid in classical logic but not in LPF. This is because classical logic deals only with assertions which are everywhere either true or false (as embodied clearly in the second form of the above rule) whereas LPF supports reasoning about assertions which may be undefined. For example, the assertion $x = 0 \vee x/x = 1$ is a perfectly valid assertion about some number x in LPF even though the right-hand clause of the disjunction is undefined when x is zero. Note, however, that the assertion as a whole is well-defined for all numbers x – the left-hand clause of the disjunction is true where the right-hand clause is undefined, which means that the overall assertion is also true at that point.

This distinction is formalised in LPF by introducing a new defined constant 'δ' (delta) into the theory of propositional LPF. This is defined via:

$$\delta e \overset{\text{def}}{=} e \vee \neg e$$

and the assertion δe can thus be interpreted as a statement that the assertion e is either true or false (alternatively, that e is defined). Classical logic can then be considered as that subset of LPF which deals only with assertions e for which δe is true[2]. This subset

---

[2]Note how this corresponds to taking the second form of the law of the excluded middle given above

is treated more fully in the chapter on booleans (Chapter 9).

Another well-known technique from classical logic which is not valid in LPF is that of using the so-called "deduction theorem" to prove that an assertion in the form of an implication holds:

$$\frac{e_1 \vdash e_2}{e_1 \Rightarrow e_2}$$

Here, the sequent hypothesis can be interpreted informally as a statement that e_2 is true if e_1 is true. On the other hand, the implication in the conclusion of the rule, treated informally as the disjunction of $\neg e_1$ and e_2 as suggested by its definition, is true only if e_1 is false or if e_2 is true. This does not follow from the interpretation of the hypothesis, so the rule is not valid in LPF.

In classical logic, however, additional information from the law of the excluded middle is available, in particular that e_1 must be either true or false. Considering these two cases, when e_1 is true the sequent hypothesis means that e_2 must also be true so the implication is true too; on the other hand, when e_1 is false the implication is immediately true. Thus the rule is valid in classical logic.

The above argument suggests that one can generate a version of the deduction theorem which is valid in LPF simply by adding an extra "definedness" hypothesis δe_1 to the classical logic rule to ensure that the assertion e_1 is well-defined. That hypothesis informally amounts to a statement that e_1 must be either true or false, corresponding to the additional information needed to complete the argument above. This leads to the rule '$\Rightarrow$-I':

$$\boxed{\Rightarrow\text{-I}}\ \frac{\delta e_1;\ e_1 \vdash e_2}{e_1 \Rightarrow e_2}$$

In fact, this process of adding definedness hypotheses to classical logic rules to construct versions valid in LPF is a general technique, and the proofs of these rules rely on derived properties of delta. The fact that delta is simply a specialisation of disjunction to the case where one disjunct is the negation of the other means that the introduction and elimination rules 'δ-I', 'δ-I-$\neg$' and 'δ-E' for delta are direct analogues of the introduction and elimination rules '$\vee$-I-left', '$\vee$-I-right' and '$\vee$-E' for disjunction:

$$\boxed{\delta\text{-I}}\ \frac{e}{\delta e} \qquad \boxed{\delta\text{-I-}\neg}\ \frac{\neg e}{\delta e} \qquad \boxed{\delta\text{-E}}\ \frac{\delta e_1;\ e_1 \vdash e_2;\ \neg e_1 \vdash e_2}{e_2}$$

The last of these rules, 'δ-E', offers a second means of reasoning by cases, in the special case where one case is the negation of the other. It is particularly useful in conjunction with rules such as 'δ-=-I' from the theory of equality (see Section 3.4) and 'δ-$\in$' from the theory of sets (see Section 6.3) which allow one to deduce that a particular assertion is everywhere defined. An example of its use in such situations is presented in Section 3.5.2.

As an illustration of its use in the proofs of rules with definedness hypotheses, consider the rule '$\Rightarrow$-I' discussed above. Applying 'δ-E' as the first step of the proof, as suggested by the informal argument where the two possible cases for the value of e_1 were considered, leads to:

---

as an axiom of classical logic.

2.5 Implication; definedness; further defined constructs

```
from δe₁; e₁ ⊢ e₂
1    from e₁
         ...
     infer e₁ ⇒ e₂                     ⟨?? justify ??⟩
2    from ¬e₁
         ...
     infer e₁ ⇒ e₂                     ⟨?? justify ??⟩
infer e₁ ⇒ e₂                          δ-E (h1, 1, 2)
```

The second subproof is easy to complete using the '⇒-I-right-vac' rule. The first subproof is more interesting as it illustrates the last basic form of justification, justification by sequent hypothesis. As explained above, the sequent hypothesis amounts to an assertion that e_2 is true on the assumption that e_1 is true, and this assumption is exactly the local hypothesis of Subproof 1. Line 1.1 of the completed proof shown below is thus justified by applying the sequent hypothesis to the local hypothesis of Subproof 1. The proof is completed using the rule '⇒-I-left-vac':

```
from δe₁; e₁ ⊢ e₂
1      from e₁
1.1        e₂                          sequent h2 (1.h1)
       infer e₁ ⇒ e₂                   ⇒-I-left-vac (1.1)
2      from ¬e₁
       infer e₁ ⇒ e₂                   ⇒-I-right-vac (2.h1)
infer e₁ ⇒ e₂                          δ-E (h1, 1, 2)
```

As a final point in this chapter, it is worth considering another informal technique which can sometimes be used to demonstrate very quickly that a particular rule is not valid. The basis of this is the fact that a rule cannot be valid if some instance of the rule can be shown to be invalid. Considering the (classical logic version of the) deduction theorem as an example, if e_2 is instantiated to e_1 the sequent hypothesis becomes $e_1 \vdash e_1$, which is trivially true by the properties of sequents (since it would correspond to having to prove that e_1 is true on the assumption that e_1 is true). At the same time, the conclusion of the rule becomes the implication $e_1 \Rightarrow e_1$, so this particular instance of the rule effectively amounts to the rule

$$\frac{}{e_1 \Rightarrow e_1}$$

which is just an instance of the first version of the law of the excluded middle given above. This particular instantiation of the deduction theorem would therefore enable one to prove some assertion which is not necessarily true (because the assertion is undefined when e_1 is undefined). This means that the instantiated rule is not valid, which in turn means that the deduction theorem is not valid.

An extension of this technique is to consider particular values for the metavariables in a rule. In this way, for example, if both e_1 and e_2 are taken to be undefined in the rule

$$\frac{}{e_1 \Rightarrow (e_2 \Rightarrow e_1)}$$

then the conclusion of the rule is undefined (because implication is undefined if both its arguments are undefined). The rule is therefore not valid in LPF.

In fact this example illustrates a general principle that must be strictly adhered to whenever stating rules in LPF, namely that the conclusion of a rule can only be undefined if at least one of the hypotheses is either undefined or false at the same time. This consideration is particularly important where the rule has no hypotheses or where its hypotheses are all typing assertions (see Chapter 3): since the hypotheses of such rules can never be either false or undefined their conclusions must always be well-defined. Examples of rules where all hypotheses are typing assertions occur in later chapters.

2.6 Summary

This chapter has dealt with the following topics:

- Basic techniques of proof construction: application of rules, using sequent assumptions, and application of definitions.
- Using informal reasoning to determine whether a rule is provable and as a template for a formal proof.
- Using instantiation of metavariables as a way of seeing that a rule is not valid.
- Extending the level of reasoning by introducing derived rules.
- Some heuristics for selecting appropriate rules when constructing proofs.
- Reasoning by cases using '∨-E' and 'δ-E'.
- Reasoning by contradiction to rule out impossible cases in case distinctions.
- Using symmetry to simplify proofs of pairs of similar rules.
- Undefinedness in LPF.

2.7 Exercises

1. Using informal reasoning

Use informal reasoning techniques to determine which of the following rules are provable and to construct proofs of those that are.

(a)
$$\frac{e_1 \Rightarrow e_2;\ e_2 \vdash e_3}{e_1 \Rightarrow e_3}$$

(b)
$$\frac{e_1 \Rightarrow e_2;\ e_2 \Rightarrow e_3}{e_1 \Rightarrow e_3}$$

2.7 Exercises

(c)
$$\frac{e_2 \Rightarrow e_3;\ e_1 \vdash e_2}{e_1 \Rightarrow e_3}$$

(d)
$$\frac{e_1 \Rightarrow e_3}{e_1 \Rightarrow (e_2 \Rightarrow e_3)}$$

(e)
$$\frac{}{e \Leftrightarrow \neg\neg e}$$

2. Associativity of disjunction

The fact that disjunction is associative is expressed via the two rules:

$$\boxed{\vee\text{-ass-left}}\ \frac{(e_1 \vee e_2) \vee e_3}{e_1 \vee (e_2 \vee e_3)} \qquad \boxed{\vee\text{-ass-right}}\ \frac{e_1 \vee (e_2 \vee e_3)}{(e_1 \vee e_2) \vee e_3}$$

Use the rule '$\vee$-E' to prove the first of these. Prove the second *without* using '$\vee$-E'.

3. Contraposition of implication; reasoning about equivalence

Prove the rule

$$\boxed{\Rightarrow\text{-contrp}}\ \frac{e_1 \Rightarrow e_2}{\neg e_2 \Rightarrow \neg e_1}$$

which allows the arguments of an implication to be interchanged if they are negated. Use it to show that if two expressions are equivalent then so are their negations:

$$\boxed{\Leftrightarrow\text{-}\neg\text{-I}}\ \frac{e_1 \Leftrightarrow e_2}{\neg e_1 \Leftrightarrow \neg e_2}$$

4. Reasoning about definedness

One of the distinguishing features of LPF is that an expression can be well-defined when some sub-expression is undefined. For example, a disjunction is true if one disjunct is true, even if the other is undefined, as embodied in the following rule:

$$\boxed{\delta\text{-}\vee\text{-inherit-sqt}}\ \frac{\delta e_1;\ \neg e_1 \vdash \delta e_2}{\delta(e_1 \vee e_2)}$$

Note that this requires one argument of the disjunction to be defined, but only requires the second to be similarly defined if the first happens to be false.

Prove this rule. State and prove a similar rule dealing with the definedness of conjunction. Note that a rule stating that a disjunction is defined if both its disjuncts are defined:

$$\boxed{\delta\text{-}\vee\text{-inherit}}\ \frac{\delta e_1;\ \delta e_2}{\delta(e_1 \vee e_2)}$$

follows directly from the more general rule as the sequent hypothesis is discharged by the assumption that its local goal is true. The proof is:

from $\delta e_1;\ \delta e_2$
infer $\delta(e_1 \vee e_2)$ δ-$\vee$-inherit-sqt (h1, h2)

Chapter 3

Predicate LPF with Equality

3.1 Predicates

Chapter 2 introduced a calculus for reasoning about logical propositions. In this chapter, the calculus is extended to allow logical statements about arbitrary values drawn from a type. The limitations of propositional logic are apparent from a simple example. Consider the following argument, concerning the availability of a value for a variable identifier in a symbol table (like that introduced in Chapter 1):

1 The identifier "v" is in scope.
2 Any identifier in scope has a value.
3 Therefore the identifier "v" has a value.

This cannot be formulated (finitely) in propositional logic because it makes use of a general assertion about variables (Assertion 2). This assertion stands for a whole class of propositions, one for each possible variable:

If identifier "a" is in scope then it has a value.
If identifier "b" is in scope then it has a value.
...
"If identifier "$zzz5$" is in scope then it has a value.
...

Where there is an infinite class of possible values from which to choose, it is impossible, let alone intractable, to write down all the necessary propositions. It is for this purpose that *predicates* are introduced into the logic. A predicate describes some property of an arbitrary value. For example, the predicate

$in\text{-}scope(x)$

describes the property of being in scope. Predicates may also define relationships between values. For example, in a theory of numbers, the predicate

$is\text{-}factor\text{-}of(x, y)$

states that x is a factor of y. This allows one to write rules capturing properties of whole classes of values, e.g.

$$\frac{\textit{in-scope}(x)}{\textit{has-value}(x)}$$

A predicate consists of a (mnemonic) name and a number of place holders or *free variables* denoting the objects related by the property. A predicate with one free variable is termed *unary*; one with n free variables is *n-ary*. More elaborate predicates can be built from simpler ones by means of the propositional connectives introduced already. For example:

$\textit{prime}(x) \wedge \textit{even}(x)$

is a unary predicate to be satisfied by values which are both prime and even.

Instantiating the free variables of a predicate with actual values yields a proposition which may be true (e.g. *prime*(2)), false (e.g. *even*(7)) or undefined (e.g. *even*([ ])). In VDM, predicates can be partial: they may not denote a logical value (true or false) if their free variables are instantiated by values outside their domain of definition. In the example above, evenness is a property of numbers, not of sequences, so the predicate *even*(_) applied to the empty sequence (*even*([ ])) is meaningless.

The rest of this chapter describes the calculus for reasoning about predicates, enriching the propositional calculus already introduced. Section 3.2 introduces the type membership assertion as a way of describing the domain of definition of a predicate. Section 3.3 follows a similar pattern to Chapter 2 in that basic constructs such as the existential quantifier '∃' are introduced first and their essential properties described via axioms. The universal quantifier '∀' is defined in terms of constructs already given. Along the way, strategies for proofs of assertions involving ∃ and ∀ are discussed.

In Section 3.4 the calculus is extended with a predicate denoting equality between values. Rules governing the use of equality in proofs are given and illustrated in an example proof, which shows the "chain of equality" style of reasoning.

Finally, Section 3.5 shows how the predicate quantifiers and equality can be used in the definition of new kinds of expression, including conditionals and choice.

3.2 Types in predicates

In LPF, a predicate might be meaningless for some instantiations of its free variables. The reason for this is related to the use of LPF in VDM specifications. In VDM, the view is taken that specifications should not prescribe or limit system behaviour outside the domain of definition of the functions and operations in the specification: error behaviour should be explicitly specified. Improperly-applied predicates are therefore not ascribed a logical value at all.

Since predicates can be partial, it is important that axioms in the theory of a specification record the domain of definition of a predicate. For example, a precondition should be placed on the use of *even* to indicate that its argument must be a natural number:

$$\frac{x \text{ is a natural number}}{\delta(\textit{even}(x))}$$

The type judgement form "_ : _" is used to record membership of a type. In effect, for

3.3 Predicate calculus for LPF: proof strategies for quantifiers

any type A, there is a predicate "$x: A$" denoting membership of the type. For the natural numbers example, the rule above is written:

$$\frac{x: \mathbf{N}}{\delta(even(x))}$$

A variable, expression or value which is known to be of a certain type is said to be *denoting*.

The next section is devoted to building the calculus necessary to allow reasoning about whole classes of values using predicates. The simple typing assertion and notion of type introduced so far is sufficient for this. Later chapters cover properties of the special VDM types (union types, finite sets etc.).

3.3 Predicate calculus for LPF: proof strategies for quantifiers

It is often necessary to make assertions using predicates "for all" or "for some" values of a free variable. For example:

$\exists x: \mathbf{N} \cdot is\text{-}prime(x) \wedge even(x)$
"There is some prime number which is also even."

$\forall x: \mathbf{N} \cdot \exists y: \mathbf{N} \cdot is\text{-}prime(y) \wedge is\text{-}factor\text{-}of(y, x)$
"Every natural number has a prime factor."

The calculus of predicate LPF is mostly concerned with the symbols $\exists$ and $\forall$ called the *existential* and *universal quantifiers* respectively. Each quantifier *binds* a free variable in the predicate which forms its main body, giving the variable a type.

The following sections discuss how to conduct proofs about assertions involving $\exists$ and $\forall$. In each case, the axioms and definitions necessary to define the quantifier's basic properties are first introduced. In producing these definitions, it is worth bearing in mind the similarity between $\exists$ and $\vee$, and $\forall$ and $\wedge$. For example, the assertion that there is an even prime number could be thought of as the disjunction of all the possibilities:

$(is\text{-}prime(0) \wedge even(0)) \vee (is\text{-}prime(1) \wedge even(1)) \vee (is\text{-}prime(2) \wedge even(2)) \vee \ldots$

3.3.1 Existential quantification

The axiomatisation of propositional LPF (Chapter 2) begins with disjunction, giving introduction and elimination axioms. In predicate LPF, the axiomatisation begins with the existential quantifier '$\exists$', its properties given by axioms. The introduction axioms for propositional disjunction state that, if one half of a disjunction is true, the whole disjunction is true. For $\exists$, the introduction axiom should state that, if a predicate P is known to be true at some value a of some type A, then one may conclude that there does indeed exist a value of type A such that P holds, for its existence has been demonstrated. The axiom is

3 Predicate LPF with Equality

$$\boxed{\exists\text{-I}} \quad \frac{a:A;\ P(a)}{\exists x:A\cdot P(x)} \quad \text{Ax}$$

This rule is often used in backwards reasoning: to show that a value exists satisfying a predicate, one may produce a *witness* value and show that the witness satisfies the predicate.

Recall the elimination axiom for disjunction ('∨-E'), the basis of case distinction. The axiom for eliminating existential quantification is analogous: if a value satisfying the predicate P is known, and if, for any value satisfying P, it is possible to prove some assertion e, then one can conclude e:

$$\boxed{\exists\text{-E}} \quad \frac{\exists x:A\cdot P(x) \quad y:A,\ P(y) \vdash_y e}{e} \quad \text{Ax}$$

As indicated in Section 1.3.5, if the sequent variable y occurs as a free variable in the expression instantiating e, the sequent variable should be renamed prior to instantiation of the rule.

The other axioms for propositional disjunction describe interaction with negation. Again the similarity with $\exists$ holds. If one can show for an arbitrary x that $P(x)$ is false, then there cannot be an x for which $P(x)$ is true. This is captured by the axiom:

$$\boxed{\neg\text{-}\exists\text{-I}} \quad \frac{x:A \vdash_x \neg P(x)}{\neg(\exists y:A\cdot P(y))} \quad \text{Ax}$$

If there does not exist a y such that $P(y)$ holds, then given any a, $P(a)$ is false:

$$\boxed{\neg\text{-}\exists\text{-E}} \quad \frac{a:A;\ \neg(\exists x:A\cdot P(x))}{\neg P(a)} \quad \text{Ax}$$

Given these axioms, it is possible to start proving useful derived properties of $\exists$, describing the quantifier's interaction with the other features of LPF introduced so far, including the propositional connectives. First consider substitution of the body of a quantified expression by a weaker predicate. If one knows that $\exists y:A\cdot P(y)$, and that Q holds wherever P holds, then one certainly expects $\exists y:A\cdot Q(y)$:

$$\boxed{\exists\text{-subs}} \quad \frac{\exists y:A\cdot P(y) \quad x:A,\ P(x) \vdash_x Q(x)}{\exists y:A\cdot Q(y)}$$

Attempting the proof of '∃-subs' is instructive, chiefly because of the possibility of following a "blind alley". Consider the construction of the proof step by step. Begin as usual by writing the hypotheses and conclusion:

from $\exists y:A\cdot P(y);\ x:A,\ P(x) \vdash_x Q(x)$

...

infer $\exists y:A\cdot Q(y)$ ⟨?? justify ??⟩

One possible strategy discussed in Chapter 2 is to examine the structure of the conclusion and reason backwards to simplify the goal. Taking this approach, the conclusion should

3.3 Predicate calculus for LPF: proof strategies for quantifiers

be justified by '∃-I', which requires introduction of a witness value. Updating the proof yields the following:

from $\exists y: A \cdot P(y);\ x: A,\ P(x) \vdash_{\overline{x}} Q(x)$

...
1 $a: A$ ⟨?? justify ??⟩
2 $Q(a)$ ⟨?? justify ??⟩
infer $\exists y: A \cdot Q(y)$ ∃-I (1, 2)

Now one has to find the witness value a. The reader may by now feel this is leading up a "blind alley", since the hypotheses give little clue to how it should be constructed. Perhaps forwards reasoning from the hypotheses will help. The only available rule for this is '∃-E', yielding the following:

from $\exists y: A \cdot P(y);\ x: A,\ P(x) \vdash_{\overline{x}} Q(x)$
1 from $z: A;\ P(z)$
   ...
   infer ???   ⟨?? justify ??⟩
2 ???   ∃-E (h1, 1)
   ...
3 $a: A$ ⟨?? justify ??⟩
4 $Q(a)$ ⟨?? justify ??⟩
infer $\exists y: A \cdot Q(y)$ ∃-I (3, 4)

One can apply the sequent hypothesis within Subproof 1 by renaming the sequent variable x to be the z introduced in the subproof:

from $\exists y: A \cdot P(y);\ x: A,\ P(x) \vdash_{\overline{x}} Q(x)$
1   from $z: A;\ P(z)$
1.1 $Q(z)$ sequent h2 (1.h1, 1.h2)
         infer ???   ⟨?? justify ??⟩
2   ???   ∃-E (h1, 1)
     ...
3    $a: A$ ⟨?? justify ??⟩
4    $Q(a)$ ⟨?? justify ??⟩
infer $\exists y: A \cdot Q(y)$ ∃-I (3, 4)

This is sufficient to conclude $\exists y: A \cdot Q(y)$ in Subproof 1, and therefore on Line 2:

from $\exists y\colon A \cdot P(y);\ x\colon A,\ P(x) \vdash_{\overline{x}} Q(x)$
1   from $z\colon A;\ P(z)$
1.1 $Q(z)$ sequent h2 (1.h1, 1.h2)
        infer $\exists y\colon A \cdot Q(y)$ $\exists$-I (1.h1, 1.1)
2   $\exists y\colon A \cdot Q(y)$ $\exists$-E (h1, 1)
    ...
3   $a\colon A$ ⟨?? justify ??⟩
4   $Q(a)$ ⟨?? justify ??⟩
infer $\exists y\colon A \cdot Q(y)$ $\exists$-I (3, 4)

Now Line 2 asserts the conclusion of the whole proof. So it appears that the proof can be concluded by '$\exists$-E', without the use of the lines constructed by the initial attempt at backward reasoning (3 and 4):

from $\exists y\colon A \cdot P(y);\ x\colon A,\ P(x) \vdash_{\overline{x}} Q(x)$
1   from $z\colon A;\ P(z)$
1.1 $Q(z)$ sequent h2 (1.h1 1.h2)
        infer $\exists y\colon A \cdot Q(y)$ $\exists$-I (1.h1, 1.1)
infer $\exists y\colon A \cdot Q(y)$ $\exists$-E (h1, 1)

Thus the conclusion follows by '$\exists$-E' and not by '$\exists$-I', as at first suggested by examining the conclusion. This is a good point at which to recall that all the proof strategies discussed in this volume are merely heuristic. In fact this combination of '$\exists$-E' and '$\exists$-I', where '$\exists$-I' is placed within the '$\exists$-E' subproof, is very common in proofs about the existential quantifier. It can be used to prove many other useful results about $\exists$ and the propositional connectives (shown in the Directory: Chapter 14). For example, the result

$$\boxed{\exists\text{-}\Rightarrow\text{-subs}}\ \frac{\exists x\colon A \cdot P(x) \quad x\colon A \vdash_{\overline{x}} (P(x) \Rightarrow Q(x))}{\exists x\colon A \cdot Q(x)}$$

can be proved using exactly the same strategy:

from $\exists x\colon A \cdot P(x);\ x\colon A \vdash_{\overline{x}} (P(x) \Rightarrow Q(x))$
1   from $y\colon A;\ P(y)$
1.1 $P(y) \Rightarrow Q(y)$ sequent h2 (1.h1)
1.2 $Q(y)$ $\Rightarrow$-E-left (1.1, 1.h2)
        infer $\exists x\colon A \cdot Q(x)$ $\exists$-I (1.h1, 1.2)
infer $\exists x\colon A \cdot Q(x)$ $\exists$-E (h1, 1)

3.3.2 Universal quantification

As with propositional logic, one could derive results and conduct proofs using only $\exists$ and the propositional connectives, but that would lead to intractable proofs and would

3.3 Predicate calculus for LPF: proof strategies for quantifiers

not reflect intuition about predicates. Just as propositional logic was extended by definitions of $\wedge$ and other connectives, so predicate logic can be extended by adding universal quantification. The $\forall$ quantifier is defined in terms of $\neg$ and $\exists$. A predicate P holds everywhere over a type A if there does not exist a value at which it does not hold:

$$\forall x: A \cdot P(x) \stackrel{\text{def}}{=} \neg \exists x: A \cdot \neg P(x)$$

This definition allows proofs of assertions involving $\forall$ to be reduced to proofs involving the existential rules introduced already. For example, the introduction and elimination rules for $\forall$ follow from the axioms for $\neg \exists$ given above. Consider the '$\forall$-I' rule, which is analogous to '$\wedge$-I'. If $P(y)$ can be shown to hold for an arbitrary y, the universal quantification holds:

$$\boxed{\forall\text{-I}} \quad \frac{y: A \vdash_y P(y)}{\forall x: A \cdot P(x)}$$

The proof of this rule begins by using the definition of $\forall$ to modify the goal:

    from $y: A \vdash_y P(y)$
        ...
    1    $\neg \exists x: A \cdot \neg P(x)$ ⟨?? justify ??⟩
    infer $\forall x: A \cdot P(x)$ folding (1)

Now the rules of $\exists$ and propositional logic can be applied. Working backwards from the goal, '$\neg$-$\exists$-I' can be applied, opening a subproof:

    from $y: A \vdash_y P(y)$
    1   from $z: A$
            ...
        infer $\neg(\neg P(z))$ ⟨?? justify ??⟩
    2    $\neg \exists x: A \cdot \neg P(x)$ $\neg$-$\exists$-I (1)
    infer $\forall x: A \cdot P(x)$ folding (2)

The proof is easily completed by appealing to the hypothesis and '$\neg\neg$-I':

    from $y: A \vdash_y P(y)$
    1   from $z: A$
    1.1 $P(z)$ sequent h1 (1.h1)
        infer $\neg(\neg P(z))$ $\neg\neg$-I (1.1)
    2    $\neg \exists x: A \cdot \neg P(x)$ $\neg$-$\exists$-I (1)
    infer $\forall x: A \cdot P(x)$ folding (2)

The elimination rule for $\forall$ is, not surprisingly, related to the elimination rule for $\neg \exists$. If $P(x)$ holds for any x in the type A, then it certainly holds for a particular value a of that type:

$$\boxed{\forall\text{-E}} \quad \frac{a\colon A;\ \forall x\colon A \cdot P(x)}{P(a)}$$

The proof of this rule again exploits the definition of $\forall$. The $\forall$ hypothesis is replaced by its definition in terms of $\neg\exists$ and the $\neg\exists$ is eliminated:

from $a\colon A;\ \forall x\colon A \cdot P(x)$
1   $\neg\exists x\colon A \cdot \neg P(x)$ unfolding (h2)
2   $\neg(\neg P(a))$ $\neg\text{-}\exists\text{-E (h1, 1)}$
infer $P(a)$ $\neg\neg\text{-E (2)}$

One could go on conducting proofs about $\forall$ by expanding its definition in the way just shown, but of course that would lead to unnecessarily long proofs. A theory of useful results about $\forall$ can be built up in much the same way as such a theory was built for $\land$. It is then possible to use rules such as '$\forall$-I' and '$\forall$-E' directly.

As in the case of $\exists$, the theory can be extended to deal with the interaction of $\forall$ and the propositional connectives. Here, instead of a '$\exists$-E/$\exists$-I' technique, the corresponding '$\forall$-I/$\forall$-E' technique is valuable. As an example, consider the following rule, which permits the substitution of a weaker predicate for a stronger one in the body of a universal quantification:

$$\boxed{\forall\text{-subs}} \quad \frac{\forall y\colon A \cdot P(y) \quad x\colon A,\ P(x) \vdash_{\!x} Q(x)}{\forall y\colon A \cdot Q(y)}$$

Beginning the proof, it is apparent that little forward reasoning can be done from the $\forall$ hypothesis since '$\forall$-E' requires an example value. Instead, begin by reasoning backwards using '$\forall$-I':

from $\forall y\colon A \cdot P(y);\ x\colon A,\ P(x) \vdash_{\!x} Q(x)$
1   from $y\colon A$
        ...
    infer $Q(y)$ $\langle$?? justify ??$\rangle$
infer $\forall y\colon A \cdot Q(y)$ $\forall\text{-I (1)}$

Now the example value y is available within Subproof 1 and $P(y)$ can be concluded by '$\forall$-E':

from $\forall y\colon A \cdot P(y);\ x\colon A,\ P(x) \vdash_{\!x} Q(x)$
1   from $y\colon A$
1.1 $P(y)$ $\forall\text{-E (1.h1, h1)}$
    infer $Q(y)$ sequent h2 (1.h1 1.1)
infer $\forall y\colon A \cdot Q(y)$ $\forall\text{-I (1)}$

The same '$\forall$-I/$\forall$-E' technique can be used in many of the proofs of the results relating $\forall$ and the propositional connectives shown in the Directory (Chapter 14).

3.3 Predicate calculus for LPF: proof strategies for quantifiers

The definition of $\forall$ in terms of $\exists$ leads one to suppose that there are analogues of the deMorgan laws for propositional disjunction and conjunction. In the same way as

$$\boxed{\neg\text{-}\wedge\text{-E-deM}} \quad \frac{\neg(e_1 \wedge e_2)}{\neg e_1 \vee \neg e_2}$$

one expects the following to be true:

$$\boxed{\neg\text{-}\forall \to \exists\text{-deM}} \quad \frac{\neg(\forall x: A \cdot P(x))}{\exists x: A \cdot \neg P(x)}$$

Since no rules for $\neg\forall$ have yet been given, the proof must rely on the definition of $\forall$:

from $\neg(\forall x: A \cdot P(x))$
1    $\neg\neg\exists x: A \cdot \neg P(x)$ unfolding (h1)
infer $\exists x: A \cdot \neg P(x)$ $\neg\neg$-E (1)

The complementary deMorgan law:

$$\boxed{\forall \to \neg\text{-}\exists\text{-deM}} \quad \frac{\forall x: A \cdot \neg P(x)}{\neg(\exists x: A \cdot P(x))}$$

has a simple proof by '$\neg$-$\exists$-I':

from $\forall x: A \cdot \neg P(x)$
1   from $y: A$
      infer $\neg P(y)$ $\forall$-E (1.h1, h1)
infer $\neg(\exists x: A \cdot P(x))$ $\neg$-$\exists$-I (1)

and the other two deMorgan laws, shown below, are proved similarly:

$$\boxed{\exists \to \neg\text{-}\forall\text{-deM}} \quad \frac{\exists x: A \cdot \neg P(x)}{\neg(\forall x: A \cdot P(x))} \qquad \boxed{\neg\text{-}\exists \to \forall\text{-deM}} \quad \frac{\neg(\exists x: A \cdot P(x))}{\forall x: A \cdot \neg P(x)}$$

The deMorgan laws can be used to prove useful properties of $\neg\forall$. Consider, for example, the proof of the following rule:

$$\boxed{\neg\text{-}\forall\text{-I-}\neg} \quad \frac{a: A;\ \neg P(a)}{\neg(\forall x: A \cdot P(x))}$$

The proof is straightforward using '$\exists \to \neg\text{-}\forall\text{-deM}$'. Note that it does not have to refer back to the definition of $\forall$:

from $a: A;\ \neg P(a)$
1    $\exists x: A \cdot \neg P(x)$ $\exists$-I (h1, h2)
infer $\neg \forall x: A \cdot P(x)$ $\exists \to \neg\text{-}\forall\text{-deM}$ (1)

3.3.3 N-ary predicates and mixing quantifiers

The rules introduced so far generally concern unary predicates. Each quantifier binds a single variable, so the formula

$\exists y\colon B \cdot P(x,y)$

is a predicate with a single free variable (x), while the following

$\exists x\colon A \cdot \exists y\colon B \cdot P(x,y)$

is a proposition, having no free variables. In cases where the variables are all of the same type, an abbreviated notation may be used informally. Thus the formula

$\exists x\colon A \cdot \exists y\colon A \cdot P(x,y)$

may be abbreviated to

$\exists x,y\colon A \cdot P(x,y)$

Of course, quantifiers can be mixed:

$\forall x\colon A \cdot \exists y\colon B \cdot P(x,y) \wedge Q(y)$

One should be able to develop rules to deal with expressions involving n-ary predicates. Consider the case of binary predicates. The following rules concern values of x for which $P(x,x)$:

$$\boxed{\exists\text{-split}}\ \frac{\exists x\colon A \cdot P(x,x)}{\exists x\colon A \cdot \exists y\colon A \cdot P(x,y)} \qquad \boxed{\forall\text{-fix}}\ \frac{\forall x\colon A \cdot \forall y\colon A \cdot P(x,y)}{\forall x\colon A \cdot P(x,x)}$$

The proofs use the '$\exists$-E/$\exists$-I' and '$\forall$-I/$\forall$-E' strategies. For example, consider the proof of '$\exists$-split'. Applying '$\exists$-E' in backwards reasoning mode, the state of the proof is:

```
     from ∃x: A · P(x,x)
1        from x: A;  P(x,x)
             ...
         infer ∃x: A · ∃y: A · P(x,y)      ⟨?? justify ??⟩
     infer ∃x: A · ∃y: A · P(x,y)          ∃-E (h1, 1)
```

The conclusion of Subproof 1 follows by two applications of '$\exists$-I', one for each of the bound variables:

```
     from ∃x: A · P(x,x)
1        from x: A;  P(x,x)
1.1         ∃y: A · P(x,y)                  ∃-I (1.h1, 1.h2)
         infer ∃x: A · ∃y: A · P(x,y)       ∃-I (1.h1, 1.1)
     infer ∃x: A · ∃y: A · P(x,y)           ∃-E (h1, 1)
```

The application of '$\exists$-I' justifying Line 1.1 instantiates just one occurrence of the free variable x in the binary predicate hypothesis $P(x,x)$, effectively matching the unary pred-

3.3 Predicate calculus for LPF: proof strategies for quantifiers

icate $P(\_)$ in the '∃-I' rule with the unary predicate $P(x, \_)$ in the proof. This form of partial instantiation is intuitively reasonable: if $P(x, x)$ is known then a witness value (namely x) has been produced to justify $\exists y: A \cdot P(x, y)$. Note that one could also conclude $\exists y: A \cdot P(y, x)$ and $\exists y: A \cdot P(y, y)$ by applying the same rule with different pattern matchings to the same hypotheses.

Returning to the derivation of useful rules about n-ary predicates, the following show the ability to reorder quantifiers:

$$\boxed{\exists\text{-}\exists\text{-comm}} \; \frac{\exists x: A \cdot \exists y: B \cdot P(x, y)}{\exists y: B \cdot \exists x: A \cdot P(x, y)} \qquad \boxed{\forall\text{-}\forall\text{-comm}} \; \frac{\forall x: A \cdot \forall y: B \cdot P(x, y)}{\forall y: B \cdot \forall x: A \cdot P(x, y)}$$

$$\boxed{\exists\text{-}\forall \to \forall\text{-}\exists} \; \frac{\exists x: A \cdot \forall y: B \cdot P(x, y)}{\forall y: B \cdot \exists x: A \cdot P(x, y)}$$

These are proved using the usual strategies. Note that the converse of '∃-∀ → ∀-∃' is not true.

The proofs of many of the rules discussed so far in this section involve stripping away and adding quantifiers one-by-one using the appropriate introduction and elimination rules. After a while, this process can seem repetitive for rules involving many quantifiers. This suggests that some derived rules could simplify the proofs. For example, the following rule describes substitution of weaker predicates in formulae with two existential quantifiers :

$$\boxed{\exists\exists\text{-subs}} \; \frac{\exists x: A \cdot \exists y: B \cdot P(x, y) \quad x: A, \; y: B, \; P(x, y) \vdash_{x, y} Q(x, y)}{\exists x: A \cdot \exists y: B \cdot Q(x, y)}$$

A proof using the rules introduced so far is shown below. Note how the quantifiers are introduced and eliminated one by one:

```
from ∃x: A · ∃y: B · P(x, y); x: A, y: B, P(x, y) ⊢ₓ,ᵧ Q(x, y)
1       from x: A; ∃y: B · P(x, y)
1.1         from y: B; P(x, y)
1.1.1           Q(x, y)                         sequent h2 (1.h1, 1.1.h1, 1.1.h2)
1.1.2           ∃y: B · Q(x, y)                 ∃-I (1.1.h1, 1.1.1)
        infer ∃x: A · ∃y: B · Q(x, y)           ∃-I (1.h1, 1.1.2)
    infer ∃x: A · ∃y: B · Q(x, y)               ∃-E (1.h2, 1.1)
infer ∃x: A · ∃y: B · Q(x, y)                   ∃-E (h1, 1)
```

The following rules allow the existential quantifiers to be removed and added in one go, almost as though they were a single quantifier binding two variables:

$$\boxed{\exists\exists\text{-I}} \; \frac{a: A; \; b: B; \; P(a, b)}{\exists x: A \cdot \exists y: B \cdot P(x, y)} \qquad \boxed{\exists\exists\text{-E}} \; \frac{\exists x: A \cdot \exists y: B \cdot P(x, y) \quad x: A, \; y: B, \; P(x, y) \vdash_{x, y} e}{e}$$

Given these two rules, the proof of '∃∃-subs' is simpler:

from $\exists x\colon A \cdot \exists y\colon B \cdot P(x,y); \; x\colon A, \; y\colon B, \; P(x,y) \vdash_{x,y} Q(x,y)$
1   from $x\colon A; \; y\colon B; \; P(x,y)$
1.1 $Q(x,y)$ sequent h2 (1.h1, 1.h2, 1.h3)
    infer $\exists x\colon A \cdot \exists y\colon B \cdot Q(x,y)$ ∃∃-I (1.h1, 1.h2, 1.1)
infer $\exists x\colon A \cdot \exists y\colon B \cdot Q(x,y)$ ∃∃-E (h1, 1)

The same approach simplifies proofs of the other substitution rules relating '∃∃' and the propositional connectives ($\wedge$, $\vee$, etc.). The rules '∃-∃-comm' and '∃-split' can also be proved using '∃∃-I' and '∃∃-E'. The rules '∃∃-I' and '∃∃-E' are themselves proved by the more pedestrian rules for the single quantifier. A similar approach is of benefit in dealing with multiple occurrences of '$\forall$'.

Finally in this section, a note on quantification over empty types. A universally quantified expression can be true if the type is empty: if there are no values of type A then certainly $P(x)$ is true for all x in A. One cannot therefore generally conclude $\exists x\colon A \cdot P(x)$ from $\forall x\colon A \cdot P(x)$. The rule governing this property has a hypothesis to ensure that the type in question is inhabited:

$$\boxed{\forall \to \exists} \; \frac{\forall x\colon A \cdot P(x); \; inhabited(A)}{\exists x\colon A \cdot P(x)}$$

The constant *inhabited* is simply defined as follows:

$$inhabited(T) \stackrel{\text{def}}{=} \exists x\colon T \cdot \text{true}$$

A type is non-empty if some value of the type is known to exist. To show this by '∃-I' involves producing a witness value.

3.3.4 Definedness of quantified expressions

In Chapter 2, the symbol δ, indicating definedness of an expression, was introduced. When should quantified expressions be considered to be defined? Recall that a logical expression e is defined (written $\delta(e)$) if it is either true or false, i.e. one can prove $e \vee \neg e$. Consider now the definedness of the expression $\exists x\colon A \cdot P(x)$. From the rules already defined, if a witness value a can be produced to show $P(a)$, then certainly $\exists x\colon A \cdot P(x)$ follows by '∃-I', and hence $\delta(\exists x\colon A \cdot P(x))$ by 'δ-I'. Conversely, if it can be shown that a witness value does not exist, then $\neg \exists x\colon A \cdot P(x)$ follows by '$\neg$-∃-I' and once again $\delta(\exists x\colon A \cdot P(x))$ is shown by 'δ-I-$\neg$'. However, there is a third case: the predicate P is known to be defined at every value in the type A, but one has insufficient information to either produce or refute the existence of a witness value at which P is true. In this case, one cannot prove either $\exists x\colon A \cdot P(x)$ or $\neg \exists x\colon A \cdot P(x)$, but one does know that one or the other is true, and so $\delta(\exists x\colon A \cdot P(x))$ is known. To cover this third case, the following additional axiom is introduced:

$$\boxed{\delta\text{-}\exists\text{-inherit}} \; \frac{x\colon A \vdash_x \delta P(x)}{\delta(\exists x\colon A \cdot P(x))} \; \text{Ax}$$

From this, the corresponding result for $\forall$ can be proved:

$$\boxed{\delta\text{-}\forall\text{-inherit}}\ \frac{y\colon A\ \vdash_y\ \delta P(y)}{\delta(\forall x\colon A \cdot P(x))}$$

by appealing to the definition of $\forall$.

3.4 Reasoning about equality: substitution and chains of equality

There are many ways of referring to the same value. For example, the natural number '9' is the same number as that denoted by the expression '3^2' or '$2^2 + 2 \times 3 - 1$', or any of a multitude of other expressions. If a property P is known to hold for the value denoted by expression e_1 (written $P(e_1)$) then it should be possible to conclude $P(e_2)$ for any e_2 which is equal to e_1.

Within the logical frame used here, the equality symbol is a binary predicate, taking two expressions as its arguments. Its properties are given by just a few axioms, the simplest of which states that equality is reflexive:

$$\boxed{\text{=-self-I}}\ \frac{a\colon A}{a = a}\ \textbf{Ax}$$

The typing hypothesis may seem unusual. In LPF, equality (called *weak equality* in [BCJ84]) is defined only over denoting terms and is polymorphic (i.e. is defined for all types).

The value of equality lies in the ability to substitute equal values in predicates. This is captured by a collection of substitution rules, the first of which permits substitution of the expression on the left of an equality by the expression on the right:

$$\boxed{\text{=-subs-right(a)}}\ \frac{a\colon A;\ a = b;\ P(a)}{P(b)}\ \textbf{Ax}$$

This axiom's name is suffixed '(a)' because the a in the rule is typed. Like other such rules, it has a '(b)' form, a derived result, presented later. A complementary axiom describes substitution by the expression on the left of the equality:

$$\boxed{\text{=-subs-left(b)}}\ \frac{b\colon A;\ a = b;\ P(b)}{P(a)}\ \textbf{Ax}$$

The following axiom asserts that weak equality is defined when *both* of the operands are denoting:

$$\boxed{\delta\text{-=-I}}\ \frac{a\colon A;\ b\colon A}{\delta(a = b)}\ \textbf{Ax}$$

The axiom above states that equality is defined when both the arguments of '=' are of the same type. What about equality between values of differing types? In the proof theory for VDM presented here, values of different types can be ascribed a common supertype (the union of their own types) so that equality is defined, although one may not have enough information to work out whether the equality is true or false. This point is discussed when type constructors are introduced in Section 4.2 and revisited as an advanced topic in Section 13.3.

The requirement in LPF that the arguments of equality be denoting leads to an abundance of typing hypotheses in rules relating to equality. Such hypotheses are tiresome, but straightforward, to discharge in proofs. A mechanised proof support system could take advantage of static type checking to reduce the need to manually discharge typing assumptions.

If the axiomatisation of equality presented so far reflects intuition, it should be possible to derive the three main properties of equality: reflexivity, symmetry and transitivity. Reflexivity is an axiom already. The first rule for symmetry is:

$$\boxed{\text{=-symm(a)}} \; \frac{a:A; \; a = b}{b = a}$$

The proof is straightforward. Begin by writing down the hypotheses and conclusion in the usual way:

>from $a:A$; $a = b$
>...
>infer $b = a$ ⟨?? justify ??⟩

Given the axioms for equality, it is a safe bet that this proof will involve the application of substitution. What predicate should form the subject of the substitution? The conclusion of the proof suggests '$\_ = a$' as a possibility. This would allow the conclusion of the proof to match the conclusion of '=-subs-right(a)', provided $P(a)$ (i.e. $a = a$) is available. This follows immediately by reflexivity of equality. The final proof is therefore:

>from $a:A$; $a = b$
>1 $a = a$ =-self-I (h1)
>infer $b = a$ =-subs-right(a) (h1, h2, 1)

A similar rule, with a similar proof, allows for the case where b is known to have a type:

$$\boxed{\text{=-symm(b)}} \; \frac{b:A; \; a = b}{b = a}$$

Note that the typing assertion '$\_ : \_$' is itself a predicate, so substitution of equals can be applied to it too, giving rules about simple inheritance of type across equality:

$$\boxed{\text{=-type-inherit-left}} \; \frac{a:A; \; b = a}{b:A} \qquad \boxed{\text{=-type-inherit-right}} \; \frac{b:A; \; b = a}{a:A}$$

These are simply proved by applying the substitution rules, with the typing hypothesis used twice. For example, '=-type-inherit-left' has the proof:

>from $a:A$; $a = b$
>infer $b:A$ =-subs-right(a) (h1, h2, h1)

The symmetry and type inheritance properties of equality allow the proof of two additional substitution rules which complement the substitution axioms given above:

3.4 Reasoning about equality: substitution and chains of equality

$$\boxed{\text{=-subs-left(a)}} \frac{a:A;\ a=b;\ P(b)}{P(a)} \qquad \boxed{\text{=-subs-right(b)}} \frac{b:A;\ a=b;\ P(a)}{P(b)}$$

The proofs of these rules are very straightforward and use the type inheritance rules introduced above. For example, '=-subs-left(a)' is proved as follows:

from $a:A;\ a = b;\ P(b)$
1    $b:A$ =-type-inherit-right (h1, h2)
infer $P(a)$ =-subs-left(b) (1, h2, h3)

The proof of '=-subs-right(b)' is similar.

Another important property of equality is its transitivity. For example:

$$\boxed{\text{=-trans(a)}} \frac{a:A;\ a=b;\ b=c}{a=c}$$

Transitivity follows directly from the rules of substitution. In applying the rules, the predicate P is set to correspond to equality with a third value. For example:

from $a:A;\ a = b;\ b = c$
infer $a = c$ =-subs-left(a) (h1, h2, h3)

A variety of transitivity rules are provided in the Directory (Chapter 14) to cope with various combinations of typing hypotheses and variously commuted equalities.

Finally in this section on equality, an example of some equality rules at work. This is inspired by the squaring function on page 67 of [Jon90]. A function sq which squares natural numbers has been defined recursively. The axioms corresponding to its definition are:

$$\boxed{\text{sq-def-0}} \frac{}{sq(0)=0} \text{Ax} \qquad \boxed{\text{sq-def-}\neg 0} \frac{n:\mathbf{N};\ \neg(n=0)}{sq(n)=sq(n-1)+2\times n-1} \text{Ax}$$

The proof that sq actually implements its specification (i.e. it returns the square of its argument), is inductive over the natural numbers, but for this example the reader need only be concerned with a part of the proof: the induction step. This requires a proof that, if sq is correct at n, then it is correct at $n + 1$, i.e.

$$\boxed{sq\text{-ind-step}} \frac{n:\mathbf{N};\ sq(n)=n^2}{sq(n+1)=(n+1)^2}$$

Although the class of natural numbers, $\mathbf{N}$, has not yet been formally introduced, the reader should be able to construct a straightforward *informal* argument that 'sq-ind-step' holds. Begin by laying out the skeleton of the proof:

from $n:\mathbf{N};\ sq(n) = n^2$
   ...
infer $sq(n+1) = (n+1)^2$ ⟨?? justify ??⟩

Expand the definition of *sq*:

from $n: \mathbf{N}$; $sq(n) = n^2$
1 $sq(n+1) = sq((n+1)-1) + 2 \times (n+1) - 1$ *sq*-def-$\neg 0$
...
infer $sq(n+1) = (n+1)^2$ ⟨?? justify ??⟩

Simplify the right hand side of the equality, appealing to the properties of natural numbers:

from $n: \mathbf{N}$; $sq(n) = n^2$
1 $sq(n+1) = sq((n+1)-1) + 2 \times (n+1) - 1$ *sq*-def-$\neg 0$
2 $ = sq(n) + 2 \times (n+1) - 1$ $\mathbf{N}$, 1
3 $ = sq(n) + 2 \times n + 1$ $\mathbf{N}$, 2
...
infer $sq(n+1) = (n+1)^2$ ⟨?? justify ??⟩

The second hypothesis allows $sq(n)$ to be rewritten as n^2. Then the conclusion follows by again appealing generally to the natural numbers:

from $n: \mathbf{N}$; $sq(n) = n^2$
1 $sq(n+1) = sq((n+1)-1) + 2 \times (n+1) - 1$ *sq*-def-$\neg 0$
2 $ = sq(n) + 2 \times (n+1) - 1$ $\mathbf{N}$, 1
3 $ = sq(n) + 2 \times n + 1$ $\mathbf{N}$, 2
4 $ = n^2 + 2 \times n + 1$ h3, 3
infer $ = (n+1)^2$ $\mathbf{N}$, 4

The informal proof shows clearly the "chain of equality" involved in Lines 1–4. When this proof is made formal, the application of **N** has to be clarified and the chain of equality is seen as a sequence of applications of substitution, transitivity and type inheritance rules. For example, consider Line 1. To formalize this, the hypotheses of the '*sq*-def-$\neg 0$' rule have to be discharged:

from $n: \mathbf{N}$; $sq(n) = n^2$
1 $n+1: \mathbf{N}$ Lemma 1 (h1)
2 $\neg(n+1 = 0)$ Lemma 2 (h1)
3 $sq(n+1) = sq((n+1)-1) + 2 \times (n+1) - 1$ *sq*-def-$\neg 0$ (1, 2)
...
infer $sq(n+1) = (n+1)^2$ ⟨?? justify ??⟩

The reader has no information to hand about the theory of natural numbers. When a formal proof is conducted in such a state of ignorance, it is good practice to record the properties on which one relies as *lemmas* to be proved at a later stage. The assumed properties of Lines 1 and 2 are recorded as follows:

3.4 Reasoning about equality: substitution and chains of equality

$$\boxed{\text{Lemma 1}}\;\dfrac{n:\mathbb{N}}{n+1:\mathbb{N}} \qquad\qquad \boxed{\text{Lemma 2}}\;\dfrac{n:\mathbb{N}}{\neg(n+1=0)}$$

The ability to record precisely the limits of one's reliance on other theories is an advantage of formal proof over rigorous argument. Carrying on with the example, the first simplification of Line 3 replaces the expression $(n+1)-1$ by n. One of the substitution rules is used:

from $n:\mathbb{N}$; $sq(n)=n^2$
1. $n+1:\mathbb{N}$ Lemma 1 (h1)
2. $\neg(n+1=0)$ Lemma 2 (h1)
3. $sq(n+1) = sq((n+1)-1) + 2\times(n+1) - 1$ sq-def-$\neg 0$ (1, 2)
4. $(n+1)-1 = n$ Lemma 3 (h1)
5. $sq(n+1) = sq(n) + 2\times(n+1) - 1$ =-subs-right(b) (h1, 4, 3)
   ...
infer $sq(n+1) = (n+1)^2$ ⟨?? justify ??⟩

where 'Lemma 3' is:

$$\boxed{\text{Lemma 3}}\;\dfrac{n:\mathbb{N}}{(n+1)-1 = n}$$

The proof is completed in a similar way. The remaining lemmas are as follows:

$$\boxed{\text{Lemma 4}}\;\dfrac{n:\mathbb{N}}{2\times(n+1)-1 = 2\times n+1} \qquad \boxed{\text{Lemma 5}}\;\dfrac{n:\mathbb{N}}{2\times n+1:\mathbb{N}}$$

$$\boxed{\text{Lemma 6}}\;\dfrac{n:\mathbb{N}}{n^2:\mathbb{N}} \qquad \boxed{\text{Lemma 7}}\;\dfrac{n:\mathbb{N}}{(n+1)^2 = n^2+2\times n+1}$$

The completed proof is as follows:

from $n:\mathbb{N}$; $sq(n)=n^2$
1. $n+1:\mathbb{N}$ Lemma 1 (h1)
2. $\neg(n+1=0)$ Lemma 2 (h1)
3. $sq(n+1) = sq((n+1)-1) + 2\times(n+1) - 1$ sq-def-$\neg 0$ (1, 2)
4. $(n+1)-1 = n$ Lemma 3 (h1)
5. $sq(n+1) = sq(n) + 2\times(n+1) - 1$ =-subs-right(b) (h1, 4, 3)
6. $2\times(n+1) - 1 = 2\times n + 1$ Lemma 4 (h1)
7. $2\times n+1:\mathbb{N}$ Lemma 5 (h1)
8. $sq(n+1) = sq(n) + 2\times n + 1$ =-subs-right(b) (7, 6, 5)
9. $n^2:\mathbb{N}$ Lemma 6 (h1)
10. $sq(n):\mathbb{N}$ =-type-inherit-left (9, h2)
11. $sq(n+1) = n^2 + 2\times n + 1$ =-subs-right(a) (10, h2, 8)
12. $(n+1)^2 = n^2 + 2\times n + 1$ Lemma 7 (h1)
13. $(n+1)^2:\mathbb{N}$ Lemma 6 (1)
infer $sq(n+1) = (n+1)^2$ =-trans-right(b) (13, 11, 12)

In this example, it is possible to have considerable confidence in the informal proof. Formalizing it is a tedious exercise, and one which would benefit from machine assistance. Furthermore, the final form of the proof tends to hide the chain of equality which forms the proof's basis. A machine-based proof-support mechanism should allow the "chain of equality" style of reasoning while ensuring that the underlying lemmas are recorded and the substitution rules correctly applied.

The "chain of equality" style of reasoning centres on the rewriting of terms. In this example, the rewriting has been chiefly to simplify the right hand side of an equality. The more general case of rewriting terms on both sides of an equality is discussed when it arises in an example from the theory of finite sequences (Section 8.5.4).

3.5 Extensions to typed predicate LPF with equality

Given all the logical constructs introduced so far, it is possible to add more operators to the language. These range from the simple abbreviation for inequality (Section 3.5.1) to the unique choice operator axiomatised in terms of the unique form of existential quantification (Sections 3.5.2 and 3.5.3). Having equality in the logic also permits the definition of conditionals (Section 3.5.4). A convenient notational extension to allow quantification over finite sets is introduced at a later stage (Section 6.4).

3.5.1 Inequality

The commonly used notation for inequality, $e_1 \neq e_2$, can be formalized through a simple definition:

$$e_1 \neq e_2 \stackrel{\text{def}}{=} \neg (e_1 = e_2)$$

3.5.2 Unique existential quantification

The "exists unique" quantifier '∃!' records the fact that exactly one value satisfies a predicate. The quantifier is defined as follows:

$$\exists! x{:}A \cdot P(x) \stackrel{\text{def}}{=} \exists x{:}A \cdot P(x) \wedge \forall y{:}A \cdot P(y) \Rightarrow y = x$$

As with other defined constructs, it is possible to build up a theory of unique quantification which obviates folding and unfolding its definition in proofs. Example derived rules are:

$$\boxed{\exists!\text{-E}} \frac{\exists! x{:}A \cdot P(x) \quad y{:}A,\ P(y),\ \forall z{:}A \cdot P(z) \Rightarrow z = y \vdash_y e}{e}$$

$$\boxed{\exists!\text{-I}} \frac{a{:}A;\ P(a);\ \forall y{:}A \cdot P(y) \Rightarrow y = a}{\exists! x{:}A \cdot P(x)}$$

In Section 2.5 it was indicated that '$\delta\text{-=-I}$' could form the basis of useful case distinctions in proofs. An example of this arises in the proof of properties about the ∃! quantifier. The following rule asserts that if two witness values satisfy a uniquely quantified predicate,

3.5 Extensions to typed predicate LPF with equality

then the witnesses must be equal:

$$\boxed{\exists!\text{-same}} \; \frac{a\!:\!A;\; b\!:\!A;\; P(a);\; P(b);\; \exists!\, x\!:\!A \cdot P(x)}{a = b}$$

Its proof proceeds by such a distinction.

from $a\!:\!A;\; b\!:\!A;\; P(a);\; P(b);\; \exists!\, x\!:\!A \cdot P(x)$
1 $\delta(a = b)$ $\delta\text{-=-I (h1, h2)}$
2 from $\neg (a = b)$
2.1 $a \neq b$ folding 2.h1
2.2 $\neg \exists!\, x\!:\!A \cdot P(x)$ $\neg\text{-}\exists!\text{-I (h1, h2, h3, h4, 2.1)}$
  infer $a = b$ contradiction (h5, 2.2)
infer $a = b$ $\delta\text{-E (1, triv, 2)}$

Observe that the first limb of the case distinction relies on the trivially true subproof that $a = b \vdash a = b$.

3.5.3 Unique choice

The ι (iota) operator allows the selection of the unique element from a class of values satisfying the predicate. Thus the expression

$\iota x\!:\!A \cdot P(x)$

is read as "that x of type A satisfying $P(x)$". In terms of the logical frame, the ι symbol is a binder. Unlike $\exists!$, it is defined by axioms rather than direct definition, because it is necessary to record the requirement that there should exist only one element satisfying the predicate:

$$\boxed{\iota\text{-form}} \; \frac{\exists!\, x\!:\!A \cdot P(x)}{(\iota y\!:\!A \cdot P(y))\!:\!A} \; \textbf{Ax} \qquad \boxed{\iota\text{-I}} \; \frac{\exists!\, x\!:\!A \cdot P(x)}{P(\iota y\!:\!A \cdot P(y))} \; \textbf{Ax}$$

As usual for definitions of operators yielding values of a given type rather than truth values, the definition consists of a *formation axiom* giving the type of expressions formed from the operator and an *introduction axiom* showing when the operator can be used in a proof.

Choice in the case where more than one value satisfies P is discussed as an advanced topic (Section 13.7.1).

3.5.4 Conditionals

The "if a then b else c" construction describes simple choice. If the *discriminator* a is true, the expression evaluates to b:

$$\boxed{\text{condition-true}} \; \frac{b\!:\!A;\; a}{(\text{if } a \text{ then } b \text{ else } c) = b} \; \textbf{Ax}$$

When the discriminator is false, it evaluates to c:

$$\boxed{\text{condition-false}}\ \frac{c\!:\!A;\ \neg a}{(\text{if } a \text{ then } b \text{ else } c) = c}\ \text{Ax}$$

In order to be denoting, the discriminator must be defined, but the alternatives b and c need only be denoting when they apply. The following formation rule is provable from the axioms above (and the rules for equality):

$$\boxed{\text{ITE-form-sqt}}\ \frac{\delta a \quad a \vdash b\!:\!A \quad \neg a \vdash c\!:\!A}{(\text{if } a \text{ then } b \text{ else } c)\!:\!A}$$

3.6 Summary

It is worth briefly reviewing the main points of this chapter:

- Propositional logic limits ability to reason about arbitrary values. A *predicate* involving a number of *free variables* allows properties of values or relationships between values to be expressed.

- The quantifiers $\exists$ and $\forall$ *bind* the free variables in predicates, quantifying them over classes of values or *types*.

- Proof strategies for the quantifiers have been shown ('$\exists$-E / $\exists$-I' and '$\forall$-I / $\forall$-E').

- As in Chapter 2, rules have been given for defined constructs, reducing the need to fold/unfold their definitions in proofs.

- Rules (e.g. the deMorgan laws and the '$\exists\exists$' rules) have also been given for common kinds of formula, which again simplify proofs involving these formulae.

- Equality is defined on denoting values of the same type (extension to equality between values of different types is discussed in Section 4.2).

- Axioms and derived rules show equality to be reflexive, symmetric and transitive. Substitution of equal values and type inheritance are supported.

- The "chain of equality" style of reasoning has been illustrated: the chain of equality becomes a succession of application of substitution, transitivity and type inheritance rules when formalised.

- The calculus has been extended with definitions of inequality, unique quantification, unique choice and conditionals.

3.7 Exercises

1. Distribution of $\exists$ over $\wedge$ and $\vee$

Use the '$\exists$-E/$\exists$-I' strategy to prove the following results:

3.7 Exercises

$$\boxed{\exists\text{-}\Leftrightarrow\text{-subs}} \quad \frac{\exists x: A \cdot P(x) \quad x: A \vdash_x P(x) \Leftrightarrow Q(x)}{\exists x: A \cdot Q(x)}$$

$$\boxed{\exists\text{-}\wedge\text{-E-left}} \quad \frac{\exists x: A \cdot P(x) \wedge Q(x)}{\exists x: A \cdot Q(x)} \qquad \boxed{\exists\text{-}\wedge\text{-E-right}} \quad \frac{\exists x: A \cdot P(x) \wedge Q(x)}{\exists x: A \cdot P(x)}$$

Use these rules to show that existential quantification distributes over conjunction:

$$\boxed{\exists\text{-}\wedge\text{-dist-expand}} \quad \frac{\exists x: A \cdot P(x) \wedge Q(x)}{(\exists y: A \cdot P(y)) \wedge (\exists z: A \cdot Q(z))}$$

The corresponding property for disjunction has a slightly more complex proof, but follows the same style: reason forwards by '∃-E' and perform a case distinction ('∨-E') on the $P(x) \vee Q(x)$ due to the hypotheses.

$$\boxed{\exists\text{-}\vee\text{-dist-expand}} \quad \frac{\exists x: A \cdot P(x) \vee Q(x)}{(\exists x: A \cdot P(x)) \vee (\exists x: A \cdot Q(x))}$$

2. Quantifier pair rules

Prove the following rules about double universal quantification:

$$\boxed{\forall\forall\text{-I}} \quad \frac{x:A,\ y:B \vdash_{x,y} P(x,y)}{\forall x: A \cdot \forall y: B \cdot P(x,y)} \qquad \boxed{\forall\forall\text{-E}} \quad \frac{a:A;\ b:B;\ \forall x: A \cdot \forall y: B \cdot P(x,y)}{P(a,b)}$$

The following rule describes the substitution of a predicate in the body of an expression quantified by ∃∀:

$$\boxed{\exists\forall\text{-subs}} \quad \frac{\exists x: A \cdot \forall y: B \cdot P(x,y) \quad x:A,\ y:B,\ P(x,y) \vdash_{x,y} Q(x,y)}{\exists x: A \cdot \forall y: B \cdot Q(x,y)}$$

Prove the rule by application of the '∃-E / ∃-I' and '∀-I / ∀-E' strategies. Posit a rule for '∃∀-I' and use it to (slightly) simplify the proof.

3. Equality and Conditionals

Suppose that an operator *fac* is defined to represent the factorial calculation:

$$fac(i) \stackrel{\text{def}}{=} \text{if } i = 0 \text{ then } 1 \text{ else } fac(i-1) \times i$$

Part of the proof that this is denoting involves showing that, if *fac(n)* denotes a natural number, then *fac(n + 1)* also denotes a natural number:

$$\frac{n: \mathbb{N};\ fac(n): \mathbb{N}}{fac(n+1): \mathbb{N}}$$

This rule is proved informally as follows:

from $n:\mathbb{N}$; $fac(n):\mathbb{N}$
1   $(n+1)-1 = n$ $\mathbb{N}$, h1
2   $fac((n+1)-1):\mathbb{N}$ h2, 1
3   $(fac((n+1)-1) \times (n+1)):\mathbb{N}$ $\mathbb{N}$, 2, h1
4   (if $n+1 = 0$ then 1 else $fac((n+1)-1) \times (n+1)$)   conditionals, 3
infer $fac(n+1):\mathbb{N}$ defn. of fac, 4

Formalise the proof. There are a number of ways of doing this. One is to unfold the conclusion and then apply 'ITE-form-sqt'. Remember to record any assumptions about natural numbers as lemmas.

4. Conditionals

The following rule is a stronger version of the formation rule for conditionals. Prove it from the weaker one.

$$\boxed{\text{ITE-form}} \quad \frac{\delta a;\ b:A;\ c:A}{(\text{if } a \text{ then } b \text{ else } c):A}$$

Chapter 4

Basic Type Constructors

4.1 Introduction

The logic developed so far has been concerned primarily with reasoning about arbitrary assertions: propositions or predicates. Although the concept of values drawn from a type has been introduced (Section 3.2), the reader has only so far seen primitive types such as the natural numbers N. Recall, however, that the logic being developed here is intended for the interpretation of VDM specifications. Such specifications are based on models of system states built using a rich repertoire of types and type constructors (e.g. sequences, maps, sets). The logic developed so far needs to be extended to allow interpretation of these types. The rest of Part I of this book describes such an extension.

In this chapter, basic constructors for building more elaborate types from basic components are introduced. The reader also has the opportunity to practice some of the proof skills gained so far on examples based on these constructors.

4.2 Union types

A simple way to build a more complex type from basic ones is to join them together by constructing their union. In VDM-SL, the type definition

$T = T1 \mid T2$

means that the type T is composed of all the values of types $T1$ and $T2$[1]. The union is *non-disjoint* in that any values common to $T1$ and $T2$ appear only once in the union type T: they are not tagged or otherwise distinguished. The axioms describing type union are straightforward. Introduction axioms simply state that an element of one type is an element of the union of that type with any other. Separate axioms allow the new type to be added on either side of the original type:

$$\boxed{\text{|-I-left}} \; \frac{b:B}{b:(A \mid B)} \; \mathbf{Ax} \qquad \boxed{\text{|-I-right}} \; \frac{a:A}{a:(A \mid B)} \; \mathbf{Ax}$$

---

[1] In VDM-SL, a union type may be composed of an arbitrary number of types. Here the discussion is restricted to binary unions, since the union constructor _ | _ is a constant in terms of the logical framework used, and constants have fixed arities.

These axioms may suggest to the reader a similarity between type union and propositional disjunction ($\vee$): if $e:(A \mid B)$ then $e:A$ or $e:B$. The elimination rule for union bears this out, being similar in principle to the '$\vee$-E' rule, but dealing with a predicate rather than a proposition. If some property P holds for all elements of types A and B, then it holds for any element of their union:

$$\boxed{\text{|-E}} \quad \frac{\begin{array}{l} u:(A \mid B) \\ a:A \vdash_a P(a) \\ b:B \vdash_b P(b) \end{array}}{P(u)} \text{ Ax}$$

The union operator is associative and commutative, as one would expect. Consider associativity, described by the two rules shown below:

$$\boxed{\text{|-ass-left}} \ \frac{a:(A \mid B) \mid C}{a:A \mid (B \mid C)} \qquad \boxed{\text{|-ass-right}} \ \frac{a:A \mid (B \mid C)}{a:(A \mid B) \mid C}$$

The proofs are straightforward and use the elimination rule '|-E' as the basis for case distinction. Consider as an example the proof of '|-ass-left'. Begin by writing down the hypotheses and conclusion. The hypothesis suggests the form of a case distinction based on '|-E'. The proof so far is therefore:

```
from a:(A | B) | C
1     from b:(A | B)
         ...
         infer b:A | (B | C)              ⟨?? justify ??⟩
2     from c:C
         ...
         infer c:A | (B | C)              ⟨?? justify ??⟩
      infer a:A | (B | C)                 |-E (h1, 1, 2)
```

The first subproof (Subproof 1) suggests a nested case distinction formed by a further application of '|-E':

```
from a:(A | B) | C
1     from b:(A | B)
1.1      from d:A
            ...
            infer d:A | (B | C)           ⟨?? justify ??⟩
1.2      from d:B
            ...
            infer d:A | (B | C)           ⟨?? justify ??⟩
         infer b:A | (B | C)              |-E (1.h1, 1.1, 1.2)
2     from c:C
         ...
         infer c:A | (B | C)              ⟨?? justify ??⟩
      infer a:A | (B | C)                 |-E (h1, 1, 2)
```

4.3 Cartesian product types

The subproofs are completed by simple application of the introduction rules:

```
from a: (A | B) | C
1     from b: (A | B)
1.1       from d: A
              infer d: A | (B | C)              |-I-right (1.1.h1)
1.2       from d: B
1.2.1           d: (B | C)                      |-I-right (1.2.h1)
              infer d: A | (B | C)              |-I-left (1.2.1)
          infer b: A | (B | C)                  |-E (1.h1, 1.1, 1.2)
2     from c: C
2.1         c: (B | C)                          |-I-left (2.h1)
          infer c: A | (B | C)                  |-I-left (2.1)
      infer a: A | (B | C)                      |-E (h1, 1, 2)
```

The parallel with disjunction in propositional LPF continues in that '|-ass-right' can be proved using '|-ass-left' and commutativity, in much the same way as '∨-ass-right' follows from '∨-ass-left' (see Exercise 2 in Section 2.7).

Union types are of importance in ensuring the definedness of equality. Recall that in Section 3.4, the following rule for definedness of equality was introduced:

$$\boxed{\delta\text{-=-I}} \quad \frac{a: A; \ b: A}{\delta(a = b)} \ \text{Ax}$$

This requires both arguments of an equality not merely to be denoting, but to have the same type. It was indicated that the more general result shown below holds:

$$\boxed{\delta\text{-=-I-gen}} \quad \frac{a: A; \ b: B}{\delta(a = b)}$$

This can be proved from 'δ-=-I' by straightforward application of the union type introduction rules. If $a: A$ and $b: B$ then both a and b are members of a common supertype $A \mid B$ and so equality between them is defined:

```
from a: A; b: B
1     a: (A | B)                                |-I-right (h1)
2     b: (A | B)                                |-I-left (h2)
infer δ(a = b)                                  δ-=-I (1, 2)
```

Equality being *defined* does not imply that the rest of the theory of A and B actually gives enough information to determine whether the equality is true or false. Equality between elements of disjoint types is discussed further in Section 13.3.

4.3 Cartesian product types

The Cartesian product type $A \times B$ is the class of all ordered pairs (a, b) of elements of A and B respectively. For an arbitrary pair p of type $A \times B$, the elements of the pair are extracted by the selectors fst and snd for the first and second elements respectively.

Three operators on elements of the cartesian product type have just been described: two *selectors* (fst and snd) and a *constructor* (_,_). Axioms are given to fix the definitions of these operators. In each case, a *formation* axiom indicates when an application of the operator is well-formed, while a *definition* axiom gives its meaning in terms of other operators. For example, consider fst. Its formation axiom states that its argument is a pair and fst returns an element of the first type of the product:

$$\boxed{\text{fst-form}} \quad \frac{p: A \times B}{\text{fst } p: A} \quad \textbf{Ax}$$

The corresponding definition axiom relates fst to the pair constructor by defining fst to be the first element of the pair:

$$\boxed{\text{fst-defn}} \quad \frac{(a,b): A \times B}{\text{fst } (a,b) = a} \quad \textbf{Ax}$$

The axioms for the other selector are analogous:

$$\boxed{\text{snd-form}} \quad \frac{p: A \times B}{\text{snd } p: B} \quad \textbf{Ax} \qquad \boxed{\text{snd-defn}} \quad \frac{(a,b): A \times B}{\text{snd } (a,b) = b} \quad \textbf{Ax}$$

The pair constructor has formation and definition axioms relating it to the selectors as follows:

$$\boxed{\text{pair-form}} \quad \frac{a:A;\ b:B}{(a,b): A \times B} \quad \textbf{Ax} \qquad \boxed{\text{pair-defn}} \quad \frac{p: A \times B}{(\text{fst } p, \text{snd } p) = p} \quad \textbf{Ax}$$

Two pairs are equal if their corresponding components are equal:

$$\boxed{\text{pair-=-merge}} \quad \frac{p_1: A \times B;\ p_2: A \times B;\ \text{fst } p_1 = \text{fst } p_2 \wedge \text{snd } p_1 = \text{snd } p_2}{p_1 = p_2}$$

and vice-versa:

$$\boxed{\text{pair-=-split}} \quad \frac{p_1: A \times B;\ p_1 = p_2}{\text{fst } p_1 = \text{fst } p_2 \wedge \text{snd } p_1 = \text{snd } p_2}$$

These results can be proved from the definitions given so far and the properties of equality from Chapter 3. Consider the first, 'pair-=-split'. The structure of the conclusion suggests proof by '$\wedge$-I':

> from $p_1: A \times B;\ p_1 = p_2$
>
> ...
>
> 1   fst $p_1 = $ fst p_2 ⟨?? justify ??⟩
>
> 2   snd $p_1 = $ snd p_2 ⟨?? justify ??⟩
>
> infer fst $p_1 = $ fst $p_2 \wedge $ snd $p_1 = $ snd p_2 $\wedge$-I (1, 2)

Consider the equality in Line 1. From the first hypothesis, fst is well-formed on p_1. Reflexivity of equality gives fst $p_1 = $ fst p_1 and since p_1 and p_2 are equal, substitution gives fst $p_1 = $ fst p_2. A similar argument works for the second conjunct of the conclusion, yielding the proof:

4.3 Cartesian product types

from $p_1: A \times B$; $p_1 = p_2$
1   fst $p_1: A$ fst-form (h1)
2   fst p_1 = fst p_1 =-self-I (1)
3   fst p_1 = fst p_2 =-subs-right(a) (h1, h2, 2)
4   snd $p_1: B$ snd-form (h1)
5   snd p_1 = snd p_1 =-self-I (4)
6   snd p_1 = snd p_2 =-subs-right(a) (h1, h2, 5)
infer fst p_1 = fst $p_2 \land$ snd p_1 = snd p_2 $\land$-I (3, 6)

This proof raises an interesting point about proof technique. Notice how the arguments of Lines 3–5 and 4–6 follow the same pattern. This suggests that it may be worth abstracting a more general rule which can be used in similar circumstances in other proofs. In this case, the following rule about substitution of equals in value expressions is suggested:

$$\boxed{\text{=-extend(a)}} \quad \frac{a: A; \; a = b; \; E(a): B}{E(a) = E(b)}$$

Using this rule, the above proof would become:

from $p_1: A \times B$; $p_1 = p_2$
1   fst $p_1: A$ fst-form (h1)
2   fst p_1 = fst p_2 =-extend(a) (h1, h2, 1)
3   snd $p_1: B$ snd-form (h1)
4   snd p_1 = snd p_2 =-extend(a) (h1, h2, 3)
infer fst p_1 = fst $p_2 \land$ snd p_1 = snd p_2 $\land$-I (2, 4)

The proof of '=-extend(a)' itself encapsulates the use of '=-self-I' which was repeated in the original proof:

from $a: A$; $a = b$; $E(a): B$
1    $E(a) = E(a)$ =-self-I (h3)
infer $E(a) = E(b)$ =-subs-right(a) (h1, h2, 1)

Note that the proof of '=-extend(a)' would not be possible without the hypothesis that $E(a)$ is denoting. If $E(a)$ is non-denoting, the conclusion could be ill-formed (given that weak equality is undefined when either or both of its arguments are undefined).

It is also worth noting some differences between this approach to Cartesian products and the product types of VDM-SL. The present form of VDM-SL allows arbitrarily long product types (e.g. $T_1 \times \ldots \times T_n$), the elements of which are n-tuples rather than pairs. Element selectors like fst and snd are not provided. In the formalism described here, the number of components is fixed, so to model VDM-SL exactly, a separate constructor would be needed for each arity, with additional selectors (third, fourth etc.). "Associated" product types such as $(A \times B) \times C$ can also be described in the formalism used here, since such types are classes of pairs, the first elements of which are themselves pairs. However, the logical frame used here prevents a completely general theory of arbitrarily long product types being written, except insofar as long tuples could be "encoded" as pairs, the second element of which is a tuple until the last pair is reached (thus $mk\text{-}(a,b,c,d)$ of type $A \times B \times C \times D$ is interpreted as $(a,(b,(c,d)))$ of type $A \times (B \times (C \times D))$).

VDM-SL uses a tuple constructor called $mk\text{-}(\_)$. Thus an element of type $A \times B$ would be written $mk\text{-}(a,b)$. Since this notation is used primarily for tool support involving automatic parsing of specifications, it is not employed here.

Section 4.2 above showed the use of type union to construct a common supertype so that equality is defined on elements of different types. A similar approach to constructing supertypes is needed for reasoning about types built using the other constructors. For example, the following rules allow a pair to be an element of a larger type:

$$\boxed{\text{pair-|-extend-left}} \ \dfrac{p: A \times B}{p: (A \mid C) \times B} \qquad \boxed{\text{pair-|-extend-right}} \ \dfrac{p: A \times B}{p: A \times (B \mid C)}$$

These are both derived rules with straightforward proofs, relying on the formation and definition rules for the Cartesian product type. For example, the proof of the first rule above is as follows:

from $p: A \times B$
1   fst $p: A$ fst-form (h1)
2   fst $p: (A \mid C)$ |-I-right (1)
3   snd $p: B$ snd-form (h1)
4   (fst p, snd p): $(A \mid C) \times B$ pair-form (2, 3)
5   (fst p, snd p) $= p$ pair-defn (h1)
infer $p: (A \mid C) \times B$ =-type-inherit-right (4, 5)

There are similar rules for the other type constructors described in this and subsequent chapters (see the exercises in Section 4.8).

4.4 Optional types

An optional type (written $[A]$) extends a type A with the additional value nil. It can be thought of as a union type between the main type and a type containing only the nil value. The first axiom states that nil belongs to any optional type:

$$\boxed{\text{nil-form}} \ \dfrac{}{\text{nil}: [A]} \ \mathbf{Ax}$$

The second axiom shows an optional type being introduced. The optional type $[A]$ is a supertype of A:

$$\boxed{\text{opt-I}} \ \dfrac{a: A}{a: [A]} \ \mathbf{Ax}$$

Finally, an axiom for the elimination of the optional type, which shows the parallel with union types: constructing an optional type $[A]$ is just like forming a union between A and a type containing only the value nil:

$$\boxed{\text{opt-E}}\ \dfrac{a\colon [A];\ P(\text{nil});\ b\colon A \vdash_b P(b)}{P(a)}\ \text{Ax}$$

This permits proof of another rule, allowing elimination of the optional type when dealing with non-nil values:

$$\boxed{\text{opt-E-}\neq\text{nil}}\ \dfrac{a\colon [A];\ a \neq \text{nil}}{a\colon A}$$

4.5 Subtypes

The subtype of A inhabited by only those elements satisfying a predicate P is written $\ll x\colon A \mid P(x) \gg$. The subtyping construction binds a variable in the unary predicate which forms its body. Subtyping properties are given by just three axioms. The first returns a value to its supertype:

$$\boxed{\text{supertype}}\ \dfrac{a\colon \ll x\colon A \mid P(x) \gg}{a\colon A}\ \text{Ax}$$

The elimination axiom allows the instantiation of the predicate on any value of the subtype:

$$\boxed{\text{subtype-E}}\ \dfrac{a\colon \ll x\colon A \mid P(x) \gg}{P(a)}\ \text{Ax}$$

The introduction axiom asserts that a value of the supertype satisfying the predicate inhabits the subtype:

$$\boxed{\text{subtype-I}}\ \dfrac{a\colon A;\ P(a)}{a\colon \ll x\colon A \mid P(x) \gg}\ \text{Ax}$$

The predicate part of the subtype construction can be weakened:

$$\boxed{\text{subtype-subs}}\ \dfrac{a\colon \ll x\colon A \mid P(x) \gg \quad y\colon A,\ P(y) \vdash_y Q(y)}{a\colon \ll x\colon A \mid Q(x) \gg}$$

The proof uses the axioms of subtyping:

from $a\colon \ll x\colon A \mid P(x) \gg;\ y\colon A,\ P(y) \vdash_y Q(y)$
1 $a\colon A$ supertype (h1)
2 $P(a)$ subtype-E (h1)
3 $Q(a)$ sequent-E-gen (1, 2, h2)
infer $a\colon \ll x\colon A \mid Q(x) \gg$ subtype-I (1, 3)

Line 3 involves a rule which generalises the application of a sequent hypothesis with sequent variables. Until now, sequents have only been applied directly in proofs: the local variable of the sequent is matched only against local variables in the proof, not to metavariables or other expressions. The more general application of sequents is described by *sequent elimination* rules, which can be proved from the more restricted form of sequent application. The most basic sequent elimination rule is 'sequent-E-basic':

$$\text{sequent-E-basic} \quad \frac{a:A; \ x:A \vdash_x P(x)}{P(a)}$$

It is proved simply by using the $\forall$ quantifier to capture a as a variable:

from $a:A; \ x:A \vdash_x P(x)$
1    $\forall x:A \cdot P(x)$ $\forall$-I (h2)
infer $P(a)$ $\forall$-E (h1, 1)

The subtype constructor allows this to be conveniently generalised to the following rule:

$$\text{sequent-E-gen} \quad \frac{a:A; \ P(a); \ x:A, \ P(x) \vdash_x Q(x)}{Q(a)}$$

Its proof uses 'sequent-E-basic', with the P property captured in a subtype of A:

from $a:A; \ P(a); \ x:A, \ P(x) \vdash_x Q(x)$
1      $a: \ll x:A \mid P(x) \gg$ subtype-I (h1, h2)
2   from $y: \ll x:A \mid P(x) \gg$
2.1 $y:A$ supertype (2.h1)
2.2 $P(y)$ subtype-E (2.h1)
        infer $Q(y)$ sequent h2 (2.1, 2.2)
infer $Q(a)$ sequent-E-basic (1, 2)

Other rules describing the replacement of the predicate part of the subtyping construct are considered in the exercises (Section 4.8).

4.6 A note on composite types

This chapter has introduced the basic type constructors needed to reason about VDM specifications. Later chapters deal with the more elaborate constructors such as sets, sequences and maps. *Composite types* also play a vital role in VDM specification. They are essentially tagged tuples. A VDM-SL type definition of the form:

Comp :: *a* : *A*
           b : *B*
           c : *C*

defines a constructor *mk-Comp* which builds a *Comp* from an *A*, a *B* and a *C*; and three selector functions *a*, *b* and *c*, which extract the relevant fields from a *Comp*. The constructor and selectors can be defined by formation and definition axioms. For example:

$$\text{mk-Comp-form} \quad \frac{p:A; \ q:B; \ r:C}{mk\text{-}Comp(p,q,r): Comp} \quad \textbf{Ax}$$

4.7 Summary

$$\boxed{\textit{mk-Comp-def}} \ \frac{\sigma\colon Comp}{\textit{mk-Comp}(\sigma.a, \sigma.b, \sigma.c) = \sigma} \ \textbf{Ax}$$

It is not possible within the logical frame used here to give a completely general theory of composite types. However, it is possible to give a theory for each composite type definition in a particular specification. This is considered in detail in Chapter 10, which deals with the means whereby a theory can be built for a given specification.

4.7 Summary

- Basic type constructors from VDM-SL have been modelled. Axioms and definitions have been given for type union, Cartesian product types and optional types. The type constructors are represented by constants in the logical framework, so they have fixed arity, in this respect differing slightly from their full VDM-SL counterparts.

- The axioms of the subtype constructor have been introduced. This is used to model types restricted by invariants in VDM-SL.

- No general theory of composite types is given within the logical framework used in this book. Each composite type in a specification is dealt with on its own. This is discussed in depth in Chapter 10.

- The union type constructor _ | _ can be used to extend types in proofs. This allows operators such as equality to be defined on elements drawn from different types.

- The section on Cartesian product types showed how spotting a repeated line of reasoning in a proof often suggests a more general result.

4.8 Exercises

1. Type extension rules

Section 4.3 discusses the type extension rules for Cartesian product types. Prove the following related rules for the other constructors of this chapter:

$$\boxed{\textit{opt-|-extend-right}} \ \frac{a\colon [A]}{a\colon [A \mid B]}$$

$$\boxed{\textit{subtype-|-extend-right}} \ \frac{a\colon \ll x\colon A \mid P(x) \gg}{a\colon \ll x\colon (A \mid B) \mid P(x) \gg}$$

Hint: In proving 'opt-|-extend-right', use $\delta(a = \textsf{nil})$ and a case distinction.

2. Relating subtypes, type union and logical disjunction

Prove the following rule relating subtyping involving logical disjunction to union types:

$$\text{subtype-v-to-|} \quad \frac{a: \ll x:A \mid P(x) \vee Q(x) \gg}{a: (\ll x:A \mid P(x) \gg \mid \ll x:A \mid Q(x) \gg)}$$

3. Sequent elimination rules

Section 4.5 shows the use of subtyping in the proof of a rule for generalised application of a sequent. Construct a proof of the following sequent elimination rule, which deals with sequents having two variables:

$$\text{sequent-E-gen-2} \quad \frac{a:A; \; b:B; \; P(a); \; Q(b) \quad x:A, \; y:B, \; P(x), \; Q(y) \vdash_{x,y} R(x,y)}{R(a,b)}$$

Hint: Follow the pattern of proof of the one-variable rule, by first proving the basic version:

$$\text{sequent-E-basic-2} \quad \frac{a:A; \; b:B \quad x:A, \; y:B \vdash_{x,y} P(x,y)}{P(a,b)}$$

using straightforward application of the introduction and elimination rules for double universal quantifiers (see Exercise 2 in Section 3.7).

Chapter 5

Numbers

5.1 Introduction

Amongst the basic data types provided in VDM-SL are various classes of numbers: the natural numbers 0, 1, 2, 3, ... and the positive natural numbers 1, 2, 3, ..., written respectively as $\mathbb{N}$ and $\mathbb{N}_1$; the integers (positive and negative), denoted by $\mathbb{Z}$; the rationals, comprising all positive and negative fractions and represented by the symbol $\mathbb{Q}$; and the real numbers, including all numbers, both rational and irrational, and denoted by the symbol $\mathbb{R}$. By and large these data types are so familiar and their properties are taken for granted to such an extent that it is very difficult to contemplate constructing fully formal proofs about them. For instance, it is generally accepted as being "obvious" that if some number n_1 is greater than some other number n_2 then $n_1 + 1$ is greater than $n_2 + 1$, even though the proof of this fact is by no means immediate (see Exercise 2). In view of this, this chapter does not attempt to give a full axiomatisation of all classes of numbers; rather it uses the natural numbers and the positive natural numbers as a familiar basis around which to discuss not only some widely applicable aspects of the axiomatisation of theories but also some general proof techniques.

The chapter begins by discussing how to construct a model of the values of a data type based on the ideas of generators and induction, using the natural numbers $\mathbb{N}$ as an example. Section 5.3 explores ways of defining operators on the data type axiomatically and shows how properties of such operators can be proved by induction. Section 5.4 goes on to discuss further aspects of proof by induction, illustrating how induction can be applied to rules in which the hypotheses involving the chosen induction variable are not all simple typing assertions. Finally, Section 5.5 illustrates how the technique of direct definition, used in Sections 2.4 and 3.3.2 above in the definition of logical operators like $\land$ and $\forall$, can be applied to the definition of subtypes and of general operators on data types. The positive natural numbers $\mathbb{N}_1$ and the familiar ordering relations on numbers (>, <, etc.) serve as examples here. This section also discusses some potential problems with using definitions.

5.2 Axiomatising the natural numbers

The goal in formalizing a theory is to come up with a set of basic axioms and definitions which express sufficiently many properties of the domain being formalized to allow reasoning to take place. It is important to aim for a small set of independent axioms, to increase confidence in their correctness. There are two ways of doing this: first, by keeping the number of primitive concepts to a minimum and by using direct definitions as much as possible, and second, by defining orthogonal (non-interfering) concepts as far as possible so as to minimize the chance of unintended interactions.

The first stage in this process is to consider the various new types that are to be introduced in the theory. Here, two different types are required, the natural numbers **N** and the positive natural numbers N_1. However, the fact that the values of the latter are a subset of the values of the former indicates that the positive natural numbers should be defined as a subtype of the natural numbers (see Section 5.5). Thus, only one new primitive type is required, the natural numbers **N**.

The next step is to consider how elements of the new primitive type(s) can be generated. A good way of doing this for a data type with an implicit ordering like the natural numbers is to give a definition of the "smallest" member of the data type and of an operator which steps from one element of the data type to the next. In the case of the natural numbers, the smallest element of the data type is the number zero (0) and the stepping function is the function succ which simply adds one to any given natural number ($succ(n) \equiv n + 1$). These concepts are formalised by giving formation axioms for each. The first states that zero is a natural number:

$$\boxed{\text{0-form}} \quad \frac{}{0:N} \text{ Ax}$$

the second that, if n is a natural number then so is $succ(n)$:

$$\boxed{\text{succ-form}} \quad \frac{n:N}{succ(n):N} \text{ Ax}$$

Clearly any given natural number can be constructed by adding one to zero sufficiently many times (alternatively by applying succ to 0 sufficiently many times). In addition, this process only yields natural numbers. Zero and the successor function therefore form a set of *generators* for the natural numbers. This means that an *induction rule* can be formulated.

The induction rule also makes use of the implicit ordering relation. The basic idea behind it is that if it is possible to prove on the one hand that some property P holds for the smallest element of the data type and, on the other hand, that if P holds for some given, arbitrary element of the data type then it also holds for the next element of the data type, then that is sufficient to ensure that P holds for all elements of the data type. The first of these two cases is called the *base case* of the induction, and for the natural numbers involves showing that P holds for 0 (i.e. that $P(0)$ is true). The second case is called the *induction step*, which, for the natural numbers, corresponds to showing that if P holds for some arbitrary value k then it also holds for $succ(k)$ (i.e. that $P(succ(k))$ is true on the assumption that $P(k)$ is true; $P(k)$ is called the *induction hypothesis* here.). The induction rule for natural numbers is formalised in the following axiom:

5.2 Axiomatising the natural numbers

$$\boxed{\text{N-indn}} \quad \frac{n: \mathsf{N}; \quad P(0)}{P(n)} \quad \frac{k: \mathsf{N}, \; P(k) \vdash_k P(\text{succ}(k))}{} \quad \text{Ax}$$

Induction is sometimes also called the "stepping stone principle" because its operation can be pictured in terms of a line of stepping stones. The first stone corresponds to the base case of the induction, and the induction step corresponds to stepping from one stone to the next. In essence, the induction principle says that if the first stone can be reached (corresponding in the proof to showing that the required property P holds for the base case) and if from any arbitrary stone it is possible to reach the next stone (corresponding in the proof to the induction step), then it is possible to reach any given stone simply by starting at the first stone and stepping from one stone to the next sufficiently many times.

The induction rule is a great labour-saving device because it effectively makes it possible to prove that some property is true for all elements of the data type by considering only two cases, the base case and the induction step. Its use is illustrated in various places below.

When developing an axiomatisation of a theory, it is important to know when to stop, that is when the set of axioms is sufficient to provide a complete description of the data type(s) being modelled. A useful technique for determining this is to check whether the axioms are consistent with other unintended models.

In the case of the natural numbers, the intended model is a semi-infinite chain starting at zero and with the successor function providing the means of stepping from one node of the chain to the next (see Figure 5.1). The first three axioms given above are consistent with this picture – '0-form' defines 0 to be a natural number; 'succ-form' states that if n is a natural number then so is $\text{succ}(n)$; and the model clearly embodies the stepping-stone interpretation of induction directly. However, they do not rule out another interpretation, shown in Figure 5.2, in which 0 is the only element of N and $\text{succ}(0) = 0$. (The induction rule is consistent with this interpretation because if 0 is the only member of N then the only possible valid instantiation for the induction variable n is 0 for which instantiation the rule becomes trivially true as its conclusion becomes the same as the hypothesis $P(0)$.) The axioms given so far are therefore not sufficient to provide the intended model of the natural numbers.

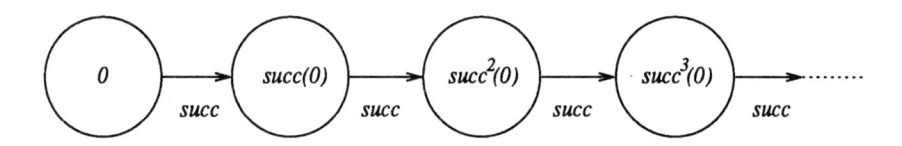

Figure 5.1: The desired model for N with 0 and succ.

Part of this problem can be avoided by adding another axiom stating that 0 and $\text{succ}(n)$ are distinct for all natural numbers n:

$$\boxed{\text{succ} \neq 0} \quad \frac{n: \mathsf{N}}{\text{succ}(n) \neq 0} \quad \text{Ax}$$

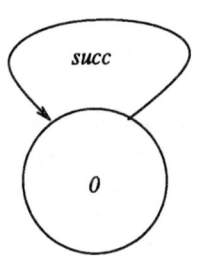

Figure 5.2: A possible model of the axioms with succ(0) = 0

However, the model depicted in Figure 5.3, in which there are only two distinct elements 0 and succ(0) of **N** (with succ(succ(0)) = succ(0)), is still a valid interpretation of the axioms which means that even with this extra one they are still not adequate.

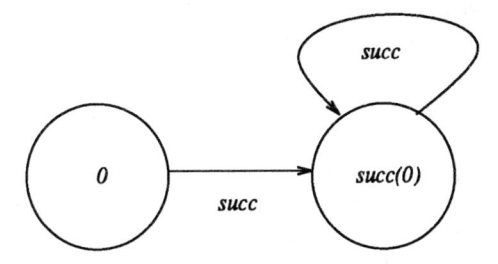

Figure 5.3: A possible model of the first four axioms for zero and the successor function.

One way of eliminating this unwanted model is to add another axiom stating that succ(n) and n are different for any natural number n:

$$\frac{n:\mathbf{N}}{\text{succ}(n) \neq n}\text{-Ax}$$

but, although this rules out all models with only two values (because 0, succ(0) and succ(succ(0)) all have to be different), it still admits a model in which these three values are the only possible values, with succ(succ(succ(0))) = succ(0) (see Figure 5.4).

Another axiom would then be needed to eliminate the models with only three different elements, and so on. This stepwise approach thus requires an infinite number of axioms so is clearly unsatisfactory.

This leads one to the suspicion that there is a more fundamental property which could be stated which captures the fact that applying the successor function repeatedly to 0 generates a new value each time. The best way of doing this is to recognize that the successor function has to be injective (one-to-one): that is, succ yields different values when applied to different arguments. This can be stated via the following axiom:

5.3 Axiomatisation of addition and proof by induction 75

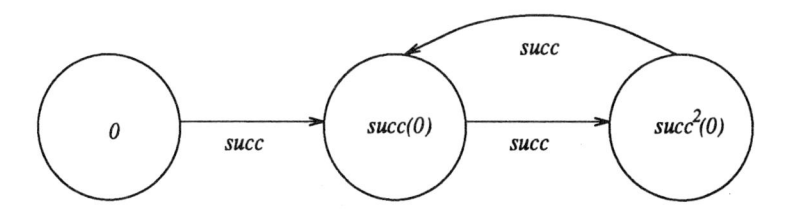

Figure 5.4: Another possible model, with succ(x) ≠ x for all elements x of the model.

$$\boxed{\text{succ-1-1}}\ \frac{n_1:\mathsf{N};\ n_2:\mathsf{N};\ \text{succ}(n_1) = \text{succ}(n_2)}{n_1 = n_2}\ \text{Ax}$$

This axiom eliminates all the unwanted finite models illustrated above as it rules out any loops (because no two links in the diagrams may terminate in the same node). On the other hand, it is consistent with the intended model of the natural numbers under the successor function, the semi-infinite chain depicted in Figure 5.1. However, the question still remains: are these axioms sufficient to allow all the desired operators on the natural numbers to be defined and their expected properties to be proved? The best way of settling this issue is to attempt to define some of these operators and to attempt to prove their required properties. This is done in the next section.

5.3 Axiomatisation of addition and proof by induction

Having developed a set of axioms which consistently model the values that natural numbers can take and rule out all the unwanted models that one can think of, the next step is to formulate axioms describing operators acting on those values.

With a data type defined in terms of generators and an induction rule, the basic principle behind axiomatising operators on that data type is to formulate an axiom defining the operator for each of the generators. The idea behind this approach is that any element of the data type can be expressed as some combination of the generators, so that these axioms, together with the induction rule, are sufficient to define the operator completely. However, care must be taken to ensure that the axioms are chosen so as to mesh appropriately with the induction rule in order that proofs about the operators, which are carried out using induction, are facilitated. All these principles are illustrated by considering the axiomatisation of addition on the natural numbers and how the axioms can be used to prove additional rules by induction.

The first step is to define addition for the two generators of the natural numbers, 0 and succ. However, there are potentially several different axioms that one could write down here. For 0, these might be:

$$\boxed{\text{+-defn-0-left}}\ \frac{n:\mathsf{N}}{0+n = n} \qquad \boxed{\text{+-defn-0-right}}\ \frac{n:\mathsf{N}}{n+0 = n}$$

whilst for succ there are a number of possibilities, including:

$$\boxed{\text{+-defn-succ-left}}\ \dfrac{n_1\!:\!\mathsf{N};\ n_2\!:\!\mathsf{N}}{\mathsf{succ}(n_1) + n_2 = \mathsf{succ}(n_1 + n_2)}$$

$$\boxed{\text{+-defn-succ-right}}\ \dfrac{n_1\!:\!\mathsf{N};\ n_2\!:\!\mathsf{N}}{n_1 + \mathsf{succ}(n_2) = \mathsf{succ}(n_1 + n_2)}$$

$$\boxed{\text{+-defn-succ-left-rev}}\ \dfrac{n_1\!:\!\mathsf{N};\ n_2\!:\!\mathsf{N}}{\mathsf{succ}(n_1) + n_2 = \mathsf{succ}(n_2 + n_1)}$$

$$\boxed{\text{+-defn-succ-left-switch}}\ \dfrac{n_1\!:\!\mathsf{N};\ n_2\!:\!\mathsf{N}}{\mathsf{succ}(n_1) + n_2 = n_1 + \mathsf{succ}(n_2)}$$

$$\boxed{\text{+-defn-succ-left-switch-rev}}\ \dfrac{n_1\!:\!\mathsf{N};\ n_2\!:\!\mathsf{N}}{\mathsf{succ}(n_1) + n_2 = \mathsf{succ}(n_2) + n_1}$$

$$\boxed{\text{+-defn-succ-right-rev}}\ \dfrac{n_1\!:\!\mathsf{N};\ n_2\!:\!\mathsf{N}}{n_1 + \mathsf{succ}(n_2) = \mathsf{succ}(n_2 + n_1)}$$

$$\boxed{\text{+-defn-succ-right-switch}}\ \dfrac{n_1\!:\!\mathsf{N};\ n_2\!:\!\mathsf{N}}{n_1 + \mathsf{succ}(n_2) = \mathsf{succ}(n_1) + n_2}$$

$$\boxed{\text{+-defn-succ-right-switch-rev}}\ \dfrac{n_1\!:\!\mathsf{N};\ n_2\!:\!\mathsf{N}}{n_1 + \mathsf{succ}(n_2) = n_2 + \mathsf{succ}(n_1)}$$

How does one go about choosing which should be axioms and which are derivable?

A good way of getting some hints on this is to look at the proofs of some of the other properties one would expect to be able to derive from the chosen axioms. The most obvious of these for addition is the formation rule:

$$\boxed{\text{+-form}}\ \dfrac{n_1\!:\!\mathsf{N};\ n_2\!:\!\mathsf{N}}{(n_1 + n_2)\!:\!\mathsf{N}}$$

which states that the result of adding two natural numbers is itself a natural number. As indicated above, such properties are proved using the induction rule, so consider the first step in the proof of the formation rule, namely the application of the induction rule.

The natural number induction rule 'N-indn' is typical of all induction rules in that it has a hypothesis of the form $a\!:\!A$, which assigns a type to the *induction variable a*, and a conclusion of the form $P(a)$, the *induction goal*, which represents an arbitrary expression involving the induction variable. When applying an induction rule it is imperative that both the induction variable and the induction goal should be determined. The induction goal, being the conclusion of the rule, should be chosen from amongst the current goals of the proof. The induction variable should be some subterm of the selected induction goal which is known to be, or which can be proved to be, of the correct type.

Applying these principles to the proof of '+-form' using natural number induction, the induction goal has to be the overall conclusion of the proof $(n_1 + n_2)\!:\!\mathsf{N}$ as this is the only goal, and the induction variable n has to be some subterm of this expression which is of the correct type N. There are therefore two possible choices for the induction variable, namely n_1 and n_2. (Terms constructed by applying succ to either n_1 or n_2 would also be known to be of the correct type but these can be ruled out as there is no subterm of

5.3 Axiomatisation of addition and proof by induction

$(n_1 + n_2)$: N involving succ.) Consider each of the two possible cases separately.

If n_1 is chosen as the induction variable, the metavariable P in the induction rule must be chosen so that $P(n_1)$ matches the induction goal $(n_1 + n_2)$: N, which means that $P(\_)$ must[1] be $(\_ + n_2)$: N. Instantiating the induction rule in this way yields:

$$\frac{n_1 : \mathsf{N}; \quad (0 + n_2) : \mathsf{N} \quad k : \mathsf{N}, \ (k + n_2) : \mathsf{N} \vdash_k (\mathrm{succ}(k) + n_2) : \mathsf{N}}{(n_1 + n_2) : \mathsf{N}}$$

applying which to the proof of '+-form' leads to the following partial proof:

```
from n₁: N;  n₂: N
    ...
1    (0 + n₂): N                      ⟨?? justify ??⟩
2    from k: N;  (k + n₂): N
        ...
        infer (succ(k) + n₂): N        ⟨?? justify ??⟩
    infer (n₁ + n₂): N                 N-indn (h1, 1, 2)
```

This proof represents induction *over* or *on* n_1, with Line 1 corresponding to the base case of the induction and Subproof 2 corresponding to the induction step. Looking first at the base case, proving this clearly depends on being able to rewrite $0 + n_2$ to n_2, from which the required result follows because the type of n_2 is known (hypothesis h2). This suggests that the rule '+-defn-0-left' is required as an axiom defining addition on zero.

Turning now to consider the induction step, a similar argument suggests that being able to justify the conclusion of Subproof 2 relies on being able to rewrite the expression $\mathrm{succ}(k) + n_2$ to some expression whose type can be inferred, this latter being determined by considering the combinations of k, n_2 and succ whose type is known within Subproof 2. Now the right-hand side of the equality in the conclusion of each of the suggested axioms involves addition, and since the formation rule for addition is the subject of the current proof it is not yet available for use. The only way of constructing some term which involves addition and whose type is known is thus by applying a more fundamental operator to some term involving addition whose type is already known. The only such term is $k+n_2$, and the only available function of the correct signature is the successor function. Altogether, then, this argues that Subproof 2 can be completed by rewriting $\mathrm{succ}(k) + n_2$ to $\mathrm{succ}(k + n_2)$, pointing to the need to choose '+-defn-succ-left' as an axiom defining addition on the successor function. With these two axioms the proof of the formation rule can be completed:

---

[1] In fact there is strictly another possible instantiation of P, namely when it is independent of its parameter (i.e. with $P(\_) \equiv (n_1 + n_2)$: N). This instantiation is *never* useful, however – when P is independent of its parameter $P(0)$ in the hypotheses of the induction rule is identical to $P(n)$ in the conclusion, so the rule becomes trivially true and nothing is to be gained by using it.

from n_1: N; n_2: N
1     $0 + n_2 = n_2$ +-defn-0-left (h2)
2     $(0 + n_2)$: N   =-type-inherit-left (h2, 1)
3   from k: N; $k + n_2$: N
3.1 $\text{succ}(k + n_2)$: N   succ-form (3.h2)
3.2 $\text{succ}(k) + n_2 = \text{succ}(k + n_2)$ +-defn-succ-left (3.h1, h2)
       infer $(\text{succ}(k) + n_2)$: N   =-type-inherit-left (3.1, 3.2)
infer $(n_1 + n_2)$: N   N-indn (h1, 2, 3)

Consider now what would have happened if n_2 had been chosen as the induction variable in this proof instead of n_1. In this case, the first stage in the proof (after applying the induction rule) would have been:

from n_1: N; n_2: N
    ...
1     $(n_1 + 0)$: N   ⟨?? justify ??⟩
2   from k: N; $(n_1 + k)$: N
       ...
       infer $(n_1 + \text{succ}(k))$: N   ⟨?? justify ??⟩
infer $(n_1 + n_2)$: N   N-indn (h1, 1, 2)

From this point, the argument would be entirely analogous to the one given above, except that it would lead to the conclusion that '+-defn-0-right' and '+-defn-succ-right' should be chosen as axioms. The question now arises, are both pairs required as axioms or is one pair sufficient?

The way to determine this is to attempt to prove one pair of rules from the other. Consider, for instance, trying to prove '+-defn-0-right' from '+-defn-0-left' and '+-defn-succ-left'. The proof again proceeds by induction, the first step being:

from n: N
    ...
1     $0 + 0 = 0$ ⟨?? justify ??⟩
2   from k: N; $k + 0 = k$
       ...
       infer $\text{succ}(k) + 0 = \text{succ}(k)$ ⟨?? justify ??⟩
infer $n + 0 = n$ N-indn (h1, 1, 2)

Here, Line 1 (the base case) can be justified directly using the rule '+-defn-0-left' together with '0-form'. In Subproof 2 (the induction step), the induction hypothesis $k + 0 = k$ can be used to substitute $k + 0$ for k in the right-hand side of the equality in the conclusion of the subproof, whence the rule '+-defn-succ-left' is sufficient to complete the proof:

5.4 More on proof by induction

from n: N
1   0: N   0-form
2    $0 + 0 = 0$ +-defn-0-left (1)
3   from k: N; $k + 0 = k$
3.1 $\text{succ}(k) + 0 = \text{succ}(k + 0)$ +-defn-succ-left (3.h1, 1)
    infer $\text{succ}(k) + 0 = \text{succ}(k)$ =-subs-right(b) (3.h1, 3.h2, 3.1)
infer $n + 0 = n$ N-indn (h1, 2, 3)

The rule '+-defn-succ-right' can be proved in a similar fashion, indicating that it is sufficient to take '+-defn-0-left' and '+-defn-succ-left' as axioms:

$$\boxed{\text{+-defn-0-left}} \; \frac{n:\mathsf{N}}{0+n=n} \; \text{Ax} \qquad \boxed{\text{+-defn-succ-left}} \; \frac{n_1:\mathsf{N};\; n_2:\mathsf{N}}{\text{succ}(n_1) + n_2 = \text{succ}(n_1 + n_2)} \; \text{Ax}$$

The symmetry of the rules means that one could equally have chosen '+-defn-0-right' and '+-defn-succ-right' as axioms. The real correlation is that the induction variable should be chosen to be the same variable used in the defining axioms as the basis for the case distinction on the generators.

Other rules about addition, for example the commutativity and associativity rules

$$\boxed{\text{+-comm}} \; \frac{n_1:\mathsf{N};\; n_2:\mathsf{N}}{n_1 + n_2 = n_2 + n_1} \qquad \boxed{\text{+-ass}} \; \frac{n_1:\mathsf{N};\; n_2:\mathsf{N};\; n_3:\mathsf{N}}{(n_1 + n_2) + n_3 = n_1 + (n_2 + n_3)}$$

can be proved in a similar fashion, and the general techniques illustrated in this section can be applied similarly to the axiomatisation of other operators, e.g. multiplication (see Exercise 1).

5.4 More on proof by induction

In the previous section the rules on which proof by induction was demonstrated were all somewhat special in that their hypotheses were all simple typing assertions. This section investigates proof by induction for rules where this is not the case.

Consider, for example, the rule

$$\boxed{+ = 0\text{-E}} \; \frac{n_1:\mathsf{N};\; n_2:\mathsf{N};\; n_1 + n_2 = 0}{n_1 = 0 \wedge n_2 = 0}$$

which states that if the sum of two natural numbers is zero then each of the numbers must itself be zero. Applying the induction rule as described above with n_1 chosen as the induction variable[2] leads to the following partial proof:

---

[2] Since the rule is symmetric in n_1 and n_2 because both $\wedge$ and $+$ are commutative there is no loss of generality in making this choice.

from $n_1: \mathbb{N}$; $n_2: \mathbb{N}$; $n_1 + n_2 = 0$

...

1    $0 = 0 \land n_2 = 0$ ⟨?? justify ??⟩

2   from $k: \mathbb{N}$; $k = 0 \land n_2 = 0$

       ...

    infer $\text{succ}(k) = 0 \land n_2 = 0$ ⟨?? justify ??⟩

infer $n_1 = 0 \land n_2 = 0$ N-indn (h1, 1, 2)

Looking at the induction step (Subproof 2) of this proof, the induction hypothesis states that both k and n_2 are zero, from which it must be proved that both $\text{succ}(k)$ and n_2 are zero. This is clearly false – it is known (from the rule 'succ $\neq$ 0' as well as from basic understanding of numbers) that $\text{succ}(k)$ cannot be zero. This means that the proof cannot be completed from this point.

The problem is that applying induction as above effectively amounts to attempting to show that the chosen induction goal, in this case the assertion $n_1 = 0 \land n_2 = 0$, is true for all values of the induction variable, namely n_1, which is patently false. Rather, the assertion $n_1 = 0 \land n_2 = 0$ is true for all values of n_1 satisfying the condition $n_1 + n_2 = 0$, the non-typing hypothesis of the rule. This hypothesis therefore has to be brought into the induction in some way before the proof can be carried out successfully.

The way to do this is to first of all apply the rule '$\Rightarrow$-E-left' to it and the overall goal. This yields the following partial proof:

from $n_1: \mathbb{N}$; $n_2: \mathbb{N}$; $n_1 + n_2 = 0$

...

1    $n_1 + n_2 = 0 \Rightarrow n_1 = 0 \land n_2 = 0$ ⟨?? justify ??⟩

infer $n_1 = 0 \land n_2 = 0$ $\Rightarrow$-E-left (1, h3)

This might seem like a retrograde step – it goes against one of the heuristics for selecting useful rules because the new goal it generates is more complicated than the original one. However, this is necessary to bring the non-typing hypothesis into play.

Now applying the induction rule with the assertion on Line 1 as the induction goal and n_1 as the induction variable leads to:

from $n_1: \mathbb{N}$; $n_2: \mathbb{N}$; $n_1 + n_2 = 0$

...

1    $0 + n_2 = 0 \Rightarrow 0 = 0 \land n_2 = 0$ ⟨?? justify ??⟩

2   from $k: \mathbb{N}$; $k + n_2 = 0 \Rightarrow k = 0 \land n_2 = 0$

       ...

    infer $\text{succ}(k) + n_2 = 0 \Rightarrow \text{succ}(k) = 0 \land n_2 = 0$ ⟨?? justify ??⟩

3    $n_1 + n_2 = 0 \Rightarrow n_1 = 0 \land n_2 = 0$ N-indn (h1, 1, 2)

infer $n_1 = 0 \land n_2 = 0$ $\Rightarrow$-E-left (3, h3)

5.5 Using direct definitions

The conclusion of the induction step is now an implication whose left-hand side is false because $\text{succ}(k) + n_2$ cannot be zero (though this still needs to be proved). The base case (Line 1) can also be discharged because both sides of the implication can effectively be simplified to $n_2 = 0$. The completed proof is:

from $n_1: \mathbb{N}$; $n_2: \mathbb{N}$; $n_1 + n_2 = 0$
1	$0 + n_2 = n_2$	+-defn-0-left (h2)
2	$0: \mathbb{N}$	0-form
3	$0 = 0$	=-self-I (2)
4	$\delta(n_2 = 0)$	δ-=-I (h2, 2)
5	from $n_2 = 0$	
	infer $0 = 0 \land n_2 = 0$	$\land$-I (3, 5.h1)
6	$n_2 = 0 \Rightarrow 0 = 0 \land n_2 = 0$	$\Rightarrow$-I (4, 5)
7	$0 + n_2 = 0 \Rightarrow 0 = 0 \land n_2 = 0$	=-subs-left(b) (h2, 1, 6)
8	from $k: \mathbb{N}$; $k + n_2 = 0 \Rightarrow k = 0 \land n_2 = 0$	
8.1	$(k + n_2): \mathbb{N}$	+-form (8.h1, h2)
8.2	$\text{succ}(k) + n_2 = \text{succ}(k + n_2)$	+-defn-succ-left (8.h1, h2)
8.3	$\text{succ}(k + n_2) \neq 0$	succ $\neq 0$ (8.1)
8.4	$\text{succ}(k + n_2): \mathbb{N}$	succ-form (8.1)
8.5	$\text{succ}(k) + n_2 \neq 0$	=-subs-left(b) (8.4, 8.2, 8.3)
8.6	$\neg (\text{succ}(k) + n_2 = 0)$	unfolding (8.5)
	infer $\text{succ}(k) + n_2 = 0 \Rightarrow \text{succ}(k) = 0 \land n_2 = 0$	$\Rightarrow$-I-right-vac (8.6)
9	$n_1 + n_2 = 0 \Rightarrow n_1 = 0 \land n_2 = 0$	$\mathbb{N}$-indn (h1, 7, 8)
infer $n_1 = 0 \land n_2 = 0$		$\Rightarrow$-E-left (9, h3)

It is worth remembering that this "trick" of using '$\Rightarrow$-E-left' as the first step is necessary when proving rules about other data types when those rules have hypotheses involving the chosen induction variable which are not all simple typing assertions (see for instance Section 7.6).

5.5 Using direct definitions

In Section 5.2 addition was defined axiomatically — by giving axioms which describe its basic properties — and other properties were derived from these axioms and the axioms for natural numbers. Wherever possible, however, it is preferable to give a definition of a new concept directly in terms of other already defined concepts – the advantage of this is not only that it keeps the number of axioms to a minimum but also that adding a new definition to a theory cannot compromise the soundness of that theory: a consistent theory remains consistent when a new definition is added to it. (Problems of retaining consistency when adding new axioms are discussed in Section 6.7 in relation to the axiomatisation of set comprehension.)

This section concentrates on defining the positive natural numbers and the familiar ordering relations on numbers. As stated above, the fact that the first of these should be defined as a subtype is suggested by the fact that the possible values of $\mathbb{N}_1$ form a subset of those of the natural numbers N. This involves formulating some (total) predicate on the natural numbers which is true for the positive natural numbers and false for all other natural numbers. There are two obvious candidates: $n \neq 0$ and $n > 0$.

Using the first of these predicates, the positive natural numbers N_1 can be defined via:

$$N_1 \stackrel{\text{def}}{=} \ll n:N \mid n \neq 0 \gg$$

then the ordering relation > can be defined in terms of this via:

$$n > m \stackrel{\text{def}}{=} \exists k:N_1 \cdot m + k = n$$

With the second predicate, however, the ordering relation would have to be defined in terms of 0, + and succ. This might be done via:

$$n > m \stackrel{\text{def}}{=} \exists k:N \cdot m + \text{succ}(k) = n$$

with the positive natural numbers then being defined as:

$$N_1 \stackrel{\text{def}}{=} \ll n:N \mid n > 0 \gg$$

However, these definitions are more complicated than the first pair given above, which are therefore to be preferred.

The reverse relation "less than" (<) can be defined directly in terms of > via:

$$n < m \stackrel{\text{def}}{=} m > n$$

The fact that N_1 is defined as a subtype means that the properties of subtypes (see Section 4.5) can be used to deduce:

$$\boxed{N_1\text{-supertype}} \; \frac{n:N_1}{n:N} \qquad \boxed{N_1\text{-E}} \; \frac{n:N_1}{n \neq 0}$$

The first of these is very important because it means that all the properties of the natural numbers, for instance the axioms and derived rules for addition, are valid for the positive natural numbers as well. This is one of the major advantages of defining types using the subtype construct. Of course, other rules which are special to the positive natural numbers can be developed, for instance an induction rule for N_1 (see Exercise 3).

Unfortunately there is no such labour saving when operators are given by definition rather than axiomatically. Proofs about > therefore rely on folding and unfolding of the definition, though they may make use of existing rules about the operators used in that definition. For instance, the proof that > is a total relation on the natural numbers:

$$\boxed{\delta\text{->}} \; \frac{n_1:N;\; n_2:N}{\delta(n_1 > n_2)}$$

uses the rules 'δ-$\exists$-inherit' and 'δ-=-I' for the definedness of the existential quantifier and equality and is straightforward (left as an exercise for the reader). Other properties that can be proved are that > is irreflexive and transitive:

$$\boxed{\text{>-irreflexive}} \; \frac{n:N}{\neg(n>n)} \qquad \boxed{\text{>-trans}} \; \frac{n_1:N;\; n_2:N;\; n_3:N;\; n_1 > n_2;\; n_2 > n_3}{n_1 > n_3}$$

5.5 Using direct definitions

and that it defines a total ordering on the natural numbers (see Exercise 4).

A final point which is worth making at this stage is that, although definitions are a very useful way of defining new operators, care must be taken when formulating them to ensure that unwanted interpretations have not been included. One way in which this can happen is when the definition contains a polymorphic operator like equality. For instance, one might try to define the relation "greater than or equal to" ($\geq$) verbatim via:

$$n \geq m \stackrel{\text{def}}{=} n > m \vee n = m$$

The problem with this is that the polymorphism of the right-hand disjunct is partially "inherited" into the definition of $\geq$: since the rule '=-self-I' implies that any denoting term is equal to itself, the above definition implies in turn that any denoting term is greater than or equal to itself. This definition is therefore defining the operator $\geq$ outside its normal range (namely the theory of numbers) which may not be what was intended when the definition was formulated[3].

In this particular case this is not a problem as an alternative definition can be formulated which does not rely on equality:

$$n \geq m \stackrel{\text{def}}{=} \exists k: \mathbf{N} \cdot m + k = n$$

Again the definition of the reverse relation is straightforward:

$$n \leq m \stackrel{\text{def}}{=} m \geq n$$

It is not always possible to find a reasonable alternative to the intuitive definition, however. Consider, for instance the double relation $\_ \leq \_ \leq \_$. This might be defined via:

$$n_1 \leq n_2 \leq n_3 \stackrel{\text{def}}{=} n_1 \leq n_2 \wedge n_2 \leq n_3$$

but again there is a problem because the value of the whole definition may be determined by only one part of it, namely if one of the conjuncts is false. In that case, the whole definition is false even if the other conjunct is undefined, more particularly even if the third parameter is not of the correct type (for example the above definition would imply that the expression true $\leq 4 \leq 2$ is false and not undefined as one might expect or wish).

In such a situation, the preferred solution is to define the operator axiomatically:

$$\boxed{\leq \text{-} \leq \text{-defn}} \ \frac{i: \mathbf{N};\ j: \mathbf{N};\ k: \mathbf{N}}{i \leq j \leq k \Leftrightarrow i \leq j \wedge j \leq k} \ \text{Ax}$$

Note here that, although the same intuitive definition is effectively being used in such a rule, the problem described above does not arise – the type of the parameters is enforced by the typing hypotheses of the rule. (See also the discussion of the proper subset relation in Section 6.5.1.)

In conclusion, it is worth pointing out in passing that recursive definitions do not present any special problems provided the recursion is well-founded. These are discussed in Section 8.5.

---

[3] Indeed this goes against the philosophy adopted in this book which would say that $\geq$ should be undefined if its arguments are not of the correct type.

5.6 Summary

This chapter has discussed:

- How to determine a set of axioms for modelling a data type.
- A basic introduction to the principle of induction.
- Examples of proofs using induction.
- How to axiomatise operators in terms of generators.
- Proof by induction using the '$\Rightarrow$-E-left' "trick".
- Some advantages and some problems with using definitions.

5.7 Exercises

1. The axiomatisation of multiplication

Use the techniques described in Section 5.3 to develop an axiomatisation of multiplication on the natural numbers in terms of 0 and succ. Prove the formation rule for multiplication from the axioms chosen.

2. The successor function preserves the > relationship

Prove the rule:

$$\boxed{\text{succ- >-inherit}} \ \frac{n_1:\mathsf{N};\ n_2:\mathsf{N};\ n_1 > n_2}{\text{succ}(n_1) > \text{succ}(n_2)}$$

3. An induction rule for N_1

The arguments used in formulating the induction rule for natural numbers could just as easily be applied to the positive natural numbers, yielding the following induction rule for N_1:

$$\boxed{\mathsf{N}_1\text{-indn}} \ \frac{n:\mathsf{N}_1;\ P(\text{succ}(0))\quad k:\mathsf{N}_1,\ P(k) \vdash_k P(\text{succ}(k))}{P(n)}$$

However, because the positive natural numbers form a subset of the natural numbers, this rule can be proved from the properties of the natural numbers. Construct the proof.

4. The relation > defines a total ordering on N

Prove that > is a total ordering on N:

$$\boxed{\text{>-total-order}} \ \frac{n_1:\mathsf{N};\ n_2:\mathsf{N}}{n_1 > n_2 \lor n_1 = n_2 \lor n_2 > n_1}$$

Chapter 6

Finite Sets

6.1 Introduction

A set is essentially just a collection of objects. There is no concept of order associated with the objects in the collection, and no concept of multiple occurrences of an object in the collection. This means that it is only possible to express the notion of whether or not a particular object belongs to a set (is an element or member of a set), and not how many times it occurs nor where it occurs.

In VDM, the notation $s: A\text{-set}$ is used to represent the assertion that s is a *finite* set, each of whose elements is of type A. Thus, for example, the set $\{13, 4, 7\}$ is of type $\mathbb{N}$-set as each of its elements is a natural number (is of type $\mathbb{N}$).

This chapter begins by showing how an axiomatisation of finite sets can be given in terms of generators and an induction rule. A worked example shows how the induction rule can be used to prove properties of finite sets, and illustrates too how to develop derived rules to correspond to the sort of arguments one uses in informal reasoning. The notion of quantification introduced in Chapter 3 is then extended to cover quantification over sets. The next section introduces the idea of a subset and shows an example of where problems can arise when giving definitions of new constructs instead of defining them axiomatically. This section also deals with set equality and cardinality and shows how a useful set of derived rules can be generated by considering special cases of a general derived rule. The standard set constructors are then introduced, and an example proof shows how reasoning about set equality is done in practice. The final section introduces the notion of set comprehension and points out potential pitfalls, due to considerations of finiteness and definedness, that can arise when trying to decide on a reasonable set of axioms for constructs defined by comprehension. Some examples involving reasoning about set comprehension expressions are also discussed.

6.2 Generators for sets; set membership; set induction

As explained in Section 5.2, an ordered data type like the natural numbers can be axiomatised in terms of generators by defining the smallest element of the data type together with a function which steps from one element of the data type to the next. Any element of the data type can then be uniquely expressed as the stepping function applied to the base element the appropriate number of times, and an induction rule for the data type can be formulated on this basis.

In fact, this technique is not just applicable to data types like the natural numbers which are completely ordered: it can also be applied to data types like finite sets which are only partially ordered. Here, the idea is to define a set of operators (the generators) in such a way that every element of the data type can be expressed in some not necessarily unique way as a finite combination of these operators. In general this means introducing a concept to denote the smallest (or the largest) member of the data type, together with one or more stepping functions, each of which adds (or removes) one new level of complexity to any given element of the data type.

Applying these principles to the axiomatisation of finite sets, the smallest member of the data type is the empty set, represented by the symbol $\{\}$, and only a single stepping function is needed, the function *add* which adds an element to a set. These form a pair of generators for finite sets because any finite set is either empty or can be expressed as a finite series of applications of *add* to the empty set. Thus, for example, the set $\{13, 4, 7\}$ of natural numbers can be expressed as $add(13, add(4, add(7, \{\})))$. This decomposition is not unique, however, as any permutation of the order of the applications of *add* produces the same result.

Developing an axiomatisation of these operators follows the principles outlined in Section 5.2 in relation to developing an axiomatisation of the natural numbers in terms of 0 and succ. First, the formation rules for the generators are given. For the empty set, which represents an empty collection of arbitrary type, the formation rule is:

$$\boxed{\{\}\text{-form}} \ \frac{}{\{\}: A\text{-set}} \ \text{Ax}$$

Note how the polymorphism of the empty set is captured by making the type A of the set a metavariable.

The function *add* adds an element to a set, with the expression $add(b, s)$ representing the result of adding the element b to the set s. If the set s is of type A-set and the element b is of type A the resulting set $add(b, s)$ is also of type A-set. The formation rule for *add* is therefore:

$$\boxed{\text{add-form}} \ \frac{a: A; \ s: A\text{-set}}{add(a, s): A\text{-set}} \ \text{Ax}$$

The next step is to formalise the notion of membership of a set. This is expressed by the symbol '$\in$', so that the expression $a \in s$ represents the assertion that some object a is an element of the set s. The negation of this relation, namely that a particular object is not an element of a given set, is denoted by the symbol '$\notin$', defined simply as:

$$a \notin s \ \stackrel{\text{def}}{=} \ \neg(a \in s)$$

Since a set is completely defined by the collection of elements it contains, defining the membership relation for a newly-defined set is sufficient to define the set itself. Thus, the empty set contains no elements, which can be formalised by saying that some arbitrary object a is not a member of the empty set:

$$\boxed{\{\}\text{-is-empty}} \ \frac{a: A}{a \notin \{\}} \ \text{Ax}$$

6.3 Proof using set induction

Further, an object a is a member of the set $add(b,s)$ if, and only if, either a is already a member of the set s or a is the same as the new element being added (namely b). The set $add(b,s)$ is therefore defined by the membership rule:

$$\boxed{\in\text{-add-defn}}\quad \frac{a:A;\ b:A;\ s:A\text{-set}}{a \in add(b,s) \Leftrightarrow a = b \vee a \in s}\quad \text{Ax}$$

This technique of defining sets by giving a formation rule and a membership rule is also used later to define operators on sets (see Section 6.6).

Finally, the fact that $\{\ \}$ and add form a set of generators for finite sets means that they also form the basis for an induction rule. Generally, such an induction rule is founded on the principle that in order to show that some property P holds for all elements of the data type it is sufficient to show first (the base case) that P holds for the base element of the data type and second (the induction step) that if P holds for an arbitrary element e of the data type then it also holds for each of the generators applied to e. For finite sets, the base case corresponds to showing that P holds for the empty set, the induction step to proving that if P holds for some arbitrary set s' then it also holds for the set $add(a,s')$ where a is some arbitrary new element. The induction rule for finite sets is therefore:

$$\boxed{\text{set-indn}}\quad \frac{s:A\text{-set};\ P(\{\ \})\qquad a:A,\ s':A\text{-set},\ P(s'),\ a \notin s' \vdash_{a,s'} P(add(a,s'))}{P(s)}\quad \text{Ax}$$

Note the additional local hypothesis $a \notin s'$ in the sequent hypothesis (corresponding to the induction step) in this rule, which ensures that the element a is not already in the set s'. This hypothesis is not strictly necessary but can be assumed without any loss of generality. This is because if a is already in the set s' adding it again has no effect as there is no concept of multiple membership of a set. In this situation the sequent becomes trivially true because $add(a,s')$ is the same as s', hence, by substitution of equality, its local conclusion $P(add(a,s'))$ is the same as its assumption $P(s')$. The extra local hypothesis therefore simply rules out the case where the sequent hypothesis is automatically true.

6.3 Proof using set induction

As an example of a proof using set induction, consider the rule '$\in\text{-}\vee\text{-}\notin$':

$$\boxed{\in\text{-}\vee\text{-}\notin}\quad \frac{a:A;\ s:A\text{-set}}{a \in s \vee a \notin s}$$

This states that, given an arbitrary object a and an arbitrary set s, either a is an element of s or a is not an element of s. The proof of this relies on set induction and the properties of add. It is presented in some detail here in order to give some idea of how induction proofs about sets are performed.

Using the 'set-indn' rule to prove '$\in\text{-}\vee\text{-}\notin$' yields two subgoals. The first of these is the base case of the induction and requires that the expression $a \in \{\ \} \vee a \notin \{\ \}$ should be shown to be true. The other subgoal is the induction step. The induction assumption is that $a \in s' \vee a \notin s'$ is true for some arbitrary set s'. From this, the goal is to show that $a \in add(b,s') \vee a \notin add(b,s')$ is true for some arbitrary new element b. After applying this rule the proof looks like:

from $a: A$; $s: A$-set
   ...
1   $a \in \{\} \vee a \notin \{\}$ ⟨?? justify ??⟩
2   from $b: A$; $s': A$-set; $a \in s' \vee a \notin s'$; $b \notin s'$
       ...
       infer $a \in add(b, s') \vee a \notin add(b, s')$ ⟨?? justify ??⟩
infer $a \in s \vee a \notin s$ set-indn (h2, 1, 2)

Proving the base case (Line 1) is easy: the rule '{ }-is-empty' implies that $a \notin \{\}$, whence $a \in \{\} \vee a \notin \{\}$ follows directly by '∨-I-left'.

Proving the induction step (Subproof 2) is somewhat more complicated but not difficult. The first thing to note is that the goal effectively amounts to showing that a either is or is not in the set $add(b, s')$ from the assumption (the third local hypothesis of the induction step) that a either is or is not in the set s'. Reasoning informally to start with, it is clear first of all that if a is in the set s' then it is also in the larger set $add(b, s')$. If a is not in s', however, it is impossible to tell immediately whether or not it is in the set $add(b, s')$ as this depends on whether or not a is the same as b. This all suggests that a good strategy for approaching this proof is to reason using two case distinctions. The first of these case distinctions is on whether or not a is in the set s', the second on whether or not a is equal to b. Note that this second case distinction is only needed in the case where a is not in s', however. The first case distinction comes from applying the '∨-E' rule to the third local hypothesis of the induction step ($a \in s' \vee a \notin s'$), whilst the second arises from the rule '=-cases' from the theory of equality.

Performing these two steps yields the following (still incomplete) proof:

from $a: A$; $s: A$-set
1       $a \notin \{\}$ { }-is-empty (h1)
2       $a \in \{\} \vee a \notin \{\}$ ∨-I-left (1)
3   from $b: A$; $s': A$-set; $a \in s' \vee a \notin s'$; $b \notin s'$
3.1   from $a \in s'$
               ...
               infer $a \in add(b, s') \vee a \notin add(b, s')$ ⟨?? justify ??⟩
3.2   from $a \notin s'$
3.2.1   from $a = b$
                    ...
                    infer $a \in add(b, s') \vee a \notin add(b, s')$ ⟨?? justify ??⟩
3.2.2   from $a \neq b$
                    ...
                    infer $a \in add(b, s') \vee a \notin add(b, s')$ ⟨?? justify ??⟩
                infer $a \in add(b, s') \vee a \notin add(b, s')$ =-cases (h1, 3.h1, 3.2.1, 3.2.2)
            infer $a \in add(b, s') \vee a \notin add(b, s')$ ∨-E (3.h3, 3.1, 3.2)
infer $a \in s \vee a \notin s$ set-indn (h2, 2, 3)

6.3 Proof using set induction

At this stage one would like to complete each of the subproofs (3.1, 3.2.1 and 3.2.2), corresponding to the cases described above, in a way that mirrors the informal argument. However, this was based on an intuitive understanding of the notion of set membership, in particular of the circumstances under which the element a is a member of the set $add(b,s)$, which does not correspond directly to the only available inference rule describing this relationship, namely the rule '$\in$-add-defn'. This suggests that the next stage in the proof of '$\in$-$\vee$-$\notin$' should be the development of a series of lemmas which express the membership properties of *add* in a way which parallels the way one reasons about this construct. This essentially amounts to promoting one side of the equivalence in the conclusion of the membership rule '$\in$-add-defn', possibly negated, to become a hypothesis of a new rule whilst making the other side of the equivalence, negated where appropriate, its conclusion. As part of the process the properties of conjunction, disjunction, and negation thereof are used to simplify propositional expressions. This gives rise to the following series of rules relating properties of a, b and s directly to assertions about whether or not a is a member of the set $add(b,s)$:

$$\boxed{\in\text{-add-E}} \quad \frac{a\!:\!A;\ b\!:\!A;\ s\!:\!A\text{-set};\ a \in add(b,s)}{a = b \vee a \in s}$$

$$\boxed{\in\text{-add-I-elem}} \quad \frac{a\!:\!A;\ s\!:\!A\text{-set}}{a \in add(a,s)}$$

$$\boxed{\in\text{-add-I-set}} \quad \frac{a\!:\!A;\ b\!:\!A;\ s\!:\!A\text{-set};\ a \in s}{a \in add(b,s)}$$

$$\boxed{\notin\text{-add-I}} \quad \frac{a\!:\!A;\ b\!:\!A;\ s\!:\!A\text{-set};\ a \neq b;\ a \notin s}{a \notin add(b,s)}$$

$$\boxed{\notin\text{-add-E-left}} \quad \frac{a\!:\!A;\ b\!:\!A;\ s\!:\!A\text{-set};\ a \notin add(b,s)}{a \notin s}$$

$$\boxed{\notin\text{-add-E-right}} \quad \frac{a\!:\!A;\ b\!:\!A;\ s\!:\!A\text{-set};\ a \notin add(b,s)}{a \neq b}$$

A useful variant of the second of these is:

$$\boxed{\in\text{-add-I-elem-=}} \quad \frac{a\!:\!A;\ s\!:\!A\text{-set};\ a = b}{a \in add(b,s)}$$

The proof of each of these rules is trivial, following simply from '$\in$-add-defn' and the appropriate rule for introduction or elimination of equivalence. They are left as an exercise for the interested reader.

Returning to the abandoned proof of '$\in$-$\vee$-$\notin$', the missing details in the incomplete subproofs are now easy to complete. In Subproofs 3.1 and 3.2.1 the first step is to prove that a is in the set $add(b,s')$ (using the rules '$\in$-add-I-set' and '$\in$-add-I-elem-=' respectively), then the required conclusion follows by using the rule '$\vee$-I-right' in both cases. In Subproof 3.2.2 the rule '$\notin$-add-I' is used to prove that a is not in $add(b,s')$, then the required conclusion follows from the '$\vee$-I-left' rule. The completed proof is thus:

from $a: A$; $s: A$-set
1	$a \notin \{\}$		$\{\}$-is-empty (h1)
2	$a \in \{\} \lor a \notin \{\}$		$\lor$-I-left (1)
3	from $b: A$; $s': A$-set; $a \in s' \lor a \notin s'$; $b \notin s'$		
3.1	from $a \in s'$		
3.1.1	$a \in add(b, s')$		$\in$-add-I-set (h1, 3.h1, 3.h2, 3.1.h1)
	infer $a \in add(b, s') \lor a \notin add(b, s')$		$\lor$-I-right (3.1.1)
3.2	from $a \notin s'$		
3.2.1	from $a = b$		
3.2.1.1	$a \in add(b, s')$		$\in$-add-I-elem-= (h1, 3.h2, 3.2.1.h1)
	infer $a \in add(b, s') \lor a \notin add(b, s')$		$\lor$-I-right (3.2.1.1)
3.2.2	from $a \neq b$		
3.2.2.1	$a \notin add(b, s')$		$\notin$-add-I (h1, 3.h1, 3.h2, 3.2.2.h1, 3.2.h1)
	infer $a \in add(b, s') \lor a \notin add(b, s')$		$\lor$-I-left (3.2.2.1)
	infer $a \in add(b, s') \lor a \notin add(b, s')$		=-cases (h1, 3.h1, 3.2.1, 3.2.2)
	infer $a \in add(b, s') \lor a \notin add(b, s')$		$\lor$-E (3.h3, 3.1, 3.2)
infer $a \in s \lor a \notin s$			set-indn (h2, 2, 3)

From this result and the definitions of $\notin$ and δ it is easy to prove the related rule:

$$\boxed{\delta\text{-}\in} \; \frac{a: A; \; s: A\text{-set}}{\delta(a \in s)}$$

stating that set membership is well-defined.

6.4 Quantification over sets

When dealing with a specification involving sets in some way it is often desirable to assert that some predicate $P(x)$ holds for some or for all elements x of one of those sets. This can be done using the universal and existential quantifiers introduced in Chapter 3 by asserting on the one hand that there is some x of the appropriate type A such that x is an element of the set s and $P(x)$ is true:

$$\exists x: A \cdot x \in s \land P(x)$$

and on the other hand that for each x of type A, if x is an element of the set s then $P(x)$ is true:

$$\forall x: A \cdot x \in s \Rightarrow P(x)$$

These expressions are rather clumsy, however, and reasoning about them can easily get rather cumbersome. To simplify things, therefore, the notion of quantification is extended to include quantification over sets. The assertion that there is some element x in the set s for which $P(x)$ is true is then written

$$\exists x \in s \cdot P(x)$$

and the assertion that $P(x)$ is true for every element of the set s is written

$$\forall x \in s \cdot P(x)$$

6.4 Quantification over sets

It is tempting to formalise these notions by simply giving axioms asserting the equivalence of the two sets of expressions given above, for example

$$\frac{s : A\text{-set}}{\exists x \in s \cdot P(x) \Leftrightarrow \exists x : A \cdot x \in s \wedge P(x)} \text{Ax}$$

but this is incorrect as it allows one to deduce *undefined* $\Leftrightarrow$ *undefined* when the predicate $P(x)$ is undefined. Instead, following the procedure set out in Chapter 3, axioms are defined for the introduction and elimination of the existential quantifier over sets and of its negation:

$$\boxed{\exists\text{-E-set}} \quad \frac{s : A\text{-set};\ \exists x \in s \cdot P(x)}{e} \text{Ax}$$
$$\frac{y : A,\ y \in s,\ P(y) \vdash_y e}{e}$$

$$\boxed{\exists\text{-I-set}} \quad \frac{a : A;\ s : A\text{-set};\ a \in s;\ P(a)}{\exists x \in s \cdot P(x)} \text{Ax}$$

$$\boxed{\neg\text{-}\exists\text{-E-set}} \quad \frac{a : A;\ s : A\text{-set};\ a \in s;\ \neg(\exists x \in s \cdot P(x))}{\neg P(a)} \text{Ax}$$

$$\boxed{\neg\text{-}\exists\text{-I-set}} \quad \frac{s : A\text{-set};\ x : A,\ x \in s \vdash_x \neg P(x)}{\neg(\exists y \in s \cdot P(y))} \text{Ax}$$

Then, continuing the parallel, universal quantification over sets is defined in terms of existential quantification over sets via:

$$\forall x \in s \cdot P(x) \stackrel{\text{def}}{=} \neg \exists x \in s \cdot \neg P(x)$$

and introduction and elimination rules for this can be derived:

$$\boxed{\forall\text{-I-set}} \quad \frac{s : A\text{-set};\ y : A,\ y \in s \vdash_y P(y)}{\forall x \in s \cdot P(x)}$$

$$\boxed{\forall\text{-E-set}} \quad \frac{a : A;\ s : A\text{-set};\ a \in s;\ \forall x \in s \cdot P(x)}{P(a)}$$

In a similar way, unique existential quantification over sets can be defined by the obvious extension of the definition given in Section 3.5.2:

$$\exists! x \in s \cdot P(x) \stackrel{\text{def}}{=} \exists x \in s \cdot P(x) \wedge \forall y \in s \cdot P(y) \Rightarrow y = x$$

and the counterparts of the introduction and elimination rules can be proved:

$$\boxed{\exists!\text{-I-set}} \quad \frac{a : A;\ s : A\text{-set};\ a \in s;\ P(a);\ \forall y \in s \cdot P(y) \Rightarrow y = a}{\exists! x \in s \cdot P(x)}$$

$$\boxed{\exists!\text{-E-set}} \quad \frac{s : A\text{-set};\ \exists! x \in s \cdot P(x)}{e}$$
$$\frac{y : A,\ y \in s,\ P(y),\ \forall x \in s \cdot P(x) \Rightarrow x = y \vdash_y e}{}$$

Finally, the unique choice operator ι over sets can be defined via axioms analogous to those given in Section 3.5.3:

$$\boxed{\iota\text{-form-set}} \frac{s:A\text{-set}; \ \exists!\, x \in s \cdot P(x)}{(\iota y \in s \cdot P(y)): A} \ \text{Ax} \qquad \boxed{\iota\text{-I-set}} \frac{s:A\text{-set}; \ \exists!\, x \in s \cdot P(x)}{P(\iota y \in s \cdot P(y))} \ \text{Ax}$$

Note that no axiom of the form

$$\boxed{\delta\text{-}\exists\text{-inherit-set}} \frac{s:A\text{-set}; \ x:A, \ x \in s \vdash_x \delta P(x)}{\delta(\exists x \in s \cdot P(x))}$$

analogous to the rule 'δ-$\exists$-inherit', is required as this is provable from the above axioms (see Exercise 3).

Rules relating quantification over sets to the corresponding expressions in terms of quantifications over types are also derivable from the axioms and rules given above. These are also the subject of Exercise 3.

6.5 Subsets; set equality; cardinality

6.5.1 Subset and proper subset

A set s_1 is said to be a *subset* of a set s_2 (written $s_1 \subseteq s_2$) if any object which is a member of the set s_1 is also a member of the set s_2. This property is expressed via the '$\subseteq$-defn' rule:

$$\boxed{\subseteq\text{-defn}} \frac{s_1:A\text{-set}; \ s_2:A\text{-set}}{s_1 \subseteq s_2 \Leftrightarrow \forall a \in s_1 \cdot a \in s_2} \ \text{Ax}$$

A simple specialisation of this rule can be obtained by considering the special case in which both s_1 and s_2 are the same set s. Then the universal quantification reduces to true, so the left-hand side of the equivalence must also be identically true in this case. This leads to the following rule stating that any set s is a subset of itself:

$$\boxed{\subseteq\text{-self}} \frac{s:A\text{-set}}{s \subseteq s}$$

Since one sometimes wishes to talk about sets which are strictly smaller than other sets, the related notion of *proper subset* is introduced. This is written $s_1 \subset s_2$ and denotes the assertion that s_1 is a subset of s_2 but is not equal to it.

It is tempting to define proper subset directly in terms of subset using the above idea, via:

$$s_1 \subset s_2 \stackrel{\text{def}}{=} s_1 \subseteq s_2 \wedge s_1 \neq s_2$$

but this leads to problems due to the polymorphism of inequality. For example, $7 = 7$ is certainly true in the theory of natural numbers, from which it follows (using simple propositional arguments) that $7 \subseteq 7 \wedge 7 \neq 7$ is false. The above definition would then imply that $7 \subset 7$ is false. However, this goes against the interpretation that proper subset describes relationships between sets, which would require it to be undefined when the arguments are not of the correct type (cf. the discussion of $\geq$ in Section 5.5).

The problem with the above definition can therefore be attributed to the fact that it is impossible to attach to it the information that it should only be used when s_1 and s_2 are

6.5 Subsets; set equality; cardinality

sets. This means that if proper subset is to be defined in this intuitive way it has to be defined axiomatically:

$$\boxed{\subset\text{-defn}} \quad \frac{s_1\colon A\text{-set};\ s_2\colon A\text{-set}}{s_1 \subset s_2 \Leftrightarrow s_1 \subseteq s_2 \wedge s_1 \neq s_2} \text{ Ax}$$

Note, however, that it is possible to make use of the intuitive meaning of proper subset embodied in the above incorrect definition; the only difference here is that the hypotheses of the rule can hold the required typing information on the parameters.

6.5.2 Set equality

Two sets s_1 and s_2 are equal if they have exactly the same collection of elements. This can be expressed using the notion of subset introduced above: s_1 and s_2 are equal if s_1 is a subset of s_2 and if s_2 is a subset of s_1 – the first of these conditions ensures that any element of the set s_1 is also an element of the set s_2, the second condition the converse. The rule '=-set-defn' expressing equality of sets thus has the form:

$$\boxed{\text{=-set-defn}} \quad \frac{s_1\colon A\text{-set};\ s_2\colon A\text{-set}}{s_1 = s_2 \Leftrightarrow s_1 \subseteq s_2 \wedge s_2 \subseteq s_1} \text{ Ax}$$

A good way of deciding on useful variants of a rule is to consider special cases of its parameters. Here, one might think about taking s_2 to be the empty set. Naïve substitution into '=-set-defn' yields:

$$\frac{s_1\colon A\text{-set};\ \{\,\}\colon A\text{-set}}{s_1 = \{\,\} \Leftrightarrow s_1 \subseteq \{\,\} \wedge \{\,\} \subseteq s_1}$$

Since it is known (from '{ }-form') that the empty set is a set of arbitrary type, the second hypothesis is always true and can therefore be removed. Next, consider the clause $\{\,\} \subseteq s_1$ in the conclusion of this rule. This can in turn be simplified by considering the special case of the '⊆-defn' rule where s_1 is the empty set. This yields the rule

$$\frac{\{\,\}\colon A\text{-set};\ s_2\colon A\text{-set}}{\{\,\} \subseteq s_1 \Leftrightarrow \forall a \in \{\,\} \cdot a \in s_2}$$

The first hypothesis is always true as above, so can be removed. Moreover, universal quantification over the empty set is identically true for any predicate, so the right-hand side of the equivalence in the conclusion of the above rule reduces to 'true' and can therefore be removed as well. This (after renaming s_2 to s) gives a rule stating that the empty set is a subset of any set:

$$\boxed{\{\,\}\text{-is-subset}} \quad \frac{s\colon A\text{-set}}{\{\,\} \subseteq s}$$

Returning now to the consideration of the special case of '=-set-defn', this rule can be used to reduce the right-hand side of the conjunction to 'true', and then the conjunction as a whole can be replaced simply by its left conjunct. This, after renaming s_1 to s, yields:

$$\frac{s\colon A\text{-set}}{s = \{\,\} \Leftrightarrow s \subseteq \{\,\}}$$

Using the properties of equivalence this can be reduced to the following rule for deducing that some set is empty:

$$\frac{s\colon A\text{-set};\ s \subseteq \{\,\}}{s = \{\,\}}$$

The process could, of course, stop here, but using this rule to prove that some set is empty would mean proving instead that the set is a subset of the empty set which in turn would require manipulation of the equivalence in the conclusion of the '$\subseteq$-defn' rule. The point here is that this manipulation would have to be done every time the equality rule was used. Thus it is better (in the sense of saving repeating work) to perform these manipulations on the basic rule and remove the expression involving subset from the hypotheses by rewriting it in some way.

The first step in this process is to use the properties of equivalence to promote the left-hand side of the '$\subseteq$-defn' rule to a hypothesis in the same way as was described above for the lemmas relating membership and the *add* operator (see Section 6.3). This yields a rule of the form

$$\frac{s_1\colon A\text{-set};\ s_2\colon A\text{-set};\ \forall a \in s_1 \cdot a \in s_2}{s_1 \subseteq s_2}$$

for introducing subsets, which, after application of the rule '$\forall$-I-set' to its third hypothesis, can be converted to

$$\boxed{\subseteq\text{-I}}\ \frac{s_1\colon A\text{-set};\ s_2\colon A\text{-set} \\ a\colon A,\ a \in s_1 \vdash_a a \in s_2}{s_1 \subseteq s_2}$$

Considering the special case of this rule where s_2 is the empty set, the conclusion of the sequent hypothesis reduces to 'false' (by the '$\{\,\}$-is-empty' rule), which, combined with the fact that the 'δ-$\in$' rule implies that its premise is defined, means that its premise must also be false. This yields the following version of the above rule for showing that some set is a subset of the empty set:

$$\frac{s\colon A\text{-set} \\ a\colon A \vdash_a a \notin s}{s \subseteq \{\,\}}$$

Finally, combining this with the last version of the rule aimed at deducing that some set is equal to the empty set, yields

$$\boxed{=\text{-}\{\,\}\text{-I}}\ \frac{s\colon A\text{-set} \\ a\colon A \vdash_a a \notin s}{s = \{\,\}}$$

Of course one can take this process further, for example rewriting the rule '=-set-defn' using the familiar properties of equivalence together with the rule '$\subseteq$-I' to produce a version of the general set equality rule which doesn't simply reduce the problem to reasoning about subset:

6.5 Subsets; set equality; cardinality

$$\boxed{\text{=-set-I-sqt}} \quad \frac{s_1\colon A\text{-set};\ s_2\colon A\text{-set}}{a\colon A,\ a\in s_1 \vdash_a a\in s_2 \\ b\colon A,\ b\in s_2 \vdash_b b\in s_1}{s_1 = s_2}$$

All this might seem very informal, but it is worth remembering that this is the sort of reasoning one ought to be using both to develop new rules and to convince oneself that a given rule is provable before starting out on the formal proof. In fact given an argument like any of the above it can easily be formalised as the steps described simply correspond to intuitive application of one or more inference rules. The basic idea behind the process described above is that in general it is helpful to develop a set of rules which express the properties of some new construct (in this case set equality) directly in terms of some old, well-understood and above all *primitive* construct about which reasoning can be performed directly and naturally (in the example above set membership). That the formal proofs bear a close relationship to the informal argument can be seen from the following proof of the '⊆-I' rule:

from $s_1\colon A$-set; $s_2\colon A$-set; $a\colon A,\ a\in s_1 \vdash_a a\in s_2$
1    $s_1 \subseteq s_2 \Leftrightarrow \forall x \in s_1 \cdot x \in s_2$ ⊆-defn (h1, h2)
2    $\forall x \in s_1 \cdot x \in s_2$ ∀-I-set (h1, h3)
infer $s_1 \subseteq s_2$ ⇔-E-right (1, 2)

6.5.3 Cardinality

The *cardinality* of a set is defined to be the number of elements it contains. This is a meaningful concept as all VDM sets are assumed to be finite. Thus, the cardinality of the empty set is 0, whereas the cardinality of a set of the form $add(a,s)$ for some set s and some element a not already in s is simply one greater than the cardinality of the set s. These properties are expressed via the rules 'card-defn-{ }' and 'card-defn-add':

$$\boxed{\text{card-defn-}\{\ \}} \quad \frac{}{\text{card}\{\ \} = 0} \ \mathbf{Ax}$$

$$\boxed{\text{card-defn-add}} \quad \frac{a\colon A;\ s\colon A\text{-set};\ a\notin s}{\text{card}\,add(a,s) = \text{succ}(\text{card}\,s)} \ \mathbf{Ax}$$

From these it is simple to show (using set induction) that the cardinality of a set is a natural number:

$$\boxed{\text{card-form}} \quad \frac{s\colon A\text{-set}}{\text{card}\,s : \mathbb{N}}$$

Other rules for cardinality can be found in Chapter 14.

6.6 Other set constructors

The simplest sets other than the empty set are unit sets, that is sets which contain only a single element. The easiest way of describing unit sets is by defining them directly in terms of the empty set and the *add* operator via:

$$\{a\} \stackrel{\text{def}}{=} add(a, \{\})$$

From this it is easy to show (using the formation rules 'add-form' and '{ }-form' for *add* and the empty set) that $\{a\}$ represents a set:

$$\boxed{\{a\}\text{-form}} \quad \frac{a:A}{\{a\}:A\text{-set}}$$

Other operators which construct new sets from existing sets are defined axiomatically by giving a formation rule and a rule defining the membership properties of the constructed set. These include set union, set intersection, set difference, distributed union and intersection, and power set.

The union of two sets s_1 and s_2, written $s_1 \cup s_2$, is the set formed by adding together all the elements of s_1 and all the elements of s_2. An element a is therefore a member of this set if it is a member of either s_1 or s_2. In addition, if both s_1 and s_2 are of type A-set then the resulting set $s_1 \cup s_2$ is also of type A-set. The rules '$\cup$-form' and '$\in$-$\cup$-defn' defining set union therefore have the form:

$$\boxed{\cup\text{-form}} \quad \frac{s_1:A\text{-set};\ s_2:A\text{-set}}{s_1 \cup s_2 : A\text{-set}} \quad \text{Ax}$$

$$\boxed{\in\text{-}\cup\text{-defn}} \quad \frac{a:A;\ s_1:A\text{-set};\ s_2:A\text{-set}}{a \in s_1 \cup s_2 \Leftrightarrow a \in s_1 \vee a \in s_2} \quad \text{Ax}$$

The intersection of two sets s_1 and s_2, written $s_1 \cap s_2$, is the set formed by selecting those elements which are common to both s_1 and s_2. An object a is thus a member of the set $s_1 \cap s_2$ if it is a member both of s_1 and of s_2. Again, if both s_1 and s_2 are of type A-set, the resulting set $s_1 \cap s_2$ is also of type A-set. Set intersection is therefore defined by the rules '$\cap$-form' and '$\in$-$\cap$-defn':

$$\boxed{\cap\text{-form}} \quad \frac{s_1:A\text{-set};\ s_2:A\text{-set}}{s_1 \cap s_2 : A\text{-set}} \quad \text{Ax}$$

$$\boxed{\in\text{-}\cap\text{-defn}} \quad \frac{a:A;\ s_1:A\text{-set};\ s_2:A\text{-set}}{a \in s_1 \cap s_2 \Leftrightarrow a \in s_1 \wedge a \in s_2} \quad \text{Ax}$$

The difference $s_1 \setminus s_2$ of two sets s_1 and s_2 represents those objects which are elements of the set s_1 but which are not elements of the set s_2. This directly defines the membership rule '$\in$-diff-defn'. The form of the formation rule 'diff-form' follows the pattern of those given above for union and intersection:

$$\boxed{\in\text{-diff-defn}} \quad \frac{a:A;\ s_1:A\text{-set};\ s_2:A\text{-set}}{a \in s_1 \setminus s_2 \Leftrightarrow a \in s_1 \wedge a \notin s_2} \quad \text{Ax}$$

$$\boxed{\text{diff-form}} \quad \frac{s_1:A\text{-set};\ s_2:A\text{-set}}{s_1 \setminus s_2 : A\text{-set}} \quad \text{Ax}$$

6.6 Other set constructors

The distributed union '$\bigcup$' and distributed intersection '$\bigcap$' operators can best be thought of as being generalisations of the standard union and intersection operators to an arbitrary number of sets. Distributed union takes a set of sets s as its single argument and returns the set constructed by taking the union of all the elements in all the sets in s. Thus, if the argument s is of type A-set-set the resulting set $\bigcup s$ is of type A-set. Furthermore an object is an element of the set $\bigcup s$ if it is an element of some set in s. This leads to the following rules defining distributed union:

$$\boxed{\bigcup\text{-form}} \quad \frac{s: A\text{-set-set}}{\bigcup s: A\text{-set}} \ \text{Ax} \qquad \boxed{\in\text{-}\bigcup\text{-defn}} \quad \frac{a: A; \ s: A\text{-set-set}}{a \in \bigcup s \Leftrightarrow \exists t \in s \cdot a \in t} \ \text{Ax}$$

Distributed intersection similarly takes a set of sets s as its argument, this time returning the set formed by taking the intersection of all the sets in s. Again, one would expect the distributed intersection $\bigcap s$ to be of type A-set if s is of type A-set-set, and one might also expect some object to be a member of the set $\bigcap s$ if it is a member of all sets in s. There is a problem here, however, in that, if the set s is empty, any object is automatically a member of every set in s (by universal quantification over an empty domain) and hence any object would also be a member of the distributed intersection over the empty set ($\bigcap\{\ \}$). Since this collection of objects may be infinite, this contradicts the restriction that all sets must be finite, leading one to the conclusion that the expression $\bigcap\{\ \}$ cannot represent a set. This case has therefore to be ruled out in the axiomatisation, and the defining rules for distributed intersection are thus:

$$\boxed{\bigcap\text{-form}} \quad \frac{s: A\text{-set-set}; \ s \neq \{\ \}}{\bigcap s: A\text{-set}} \ \text{Ax} \qquad \boxed{\in\text{-}\bigcap\text{-defn}} \quad \frac{a: A; \ s: A\text{-set-set}; \ s \neq \{\ \}}{a \in \bigcap s \Leftrightarrow \forall t \in s \cdot a \in t} \ \text{Ax}$$

The last set constructor of this form is the power set, written $\mathcal{F}s$. This represents the set of all subsets of the set s (including the empty set and the set s itself). Thus, if s is of type A-set, its power set is of type A-set-set. Furthermore, some set s' of type A-set is a member of the power set of s if it is a subset of s. The power set constructor is therefore defined by the following pair of rules:

$$\boxed{\text{pow-form}} \quad \frac{s: A\text{-set}}{\mathcal{F}s : A\text{-set-set}} \ \text{Ax} \qquad \boxed{\in\text{-pow-defn}} \quad \frac{s_1: A\text{-set}; \ s_2: A\text{-set}}{s_1 \in \mathcal{F}s_2 \Leftrightarrow s_1 \subseteq s_2} \ \text{Ax}$$

6.6.1 Relating *add* and union

It should be clear from the definitions given earlier in this chapter that some redundancy has been introduced as the expressions $add(a, s)$, $\{a\} \cup s$, and $s \cup \{a\}$ all represent the result of adding the element a to the set s. Thus one would expect to be able to prove the following rules:

$$\boxed{\text{add} \to \cup} \quad \frac{a: A; \ s: A\text{-set}}{add(a, s) = \{a\} \cup s} \qquad \frac{a: A; \ s: A\text{-set}}{\{a\} \cup s = s \cup \{a\}}$$

However, it is also clear from the symmetry (in s_1 and s_2) of the rules defining union that union is commutative:

$$\boxed{\cup\text{-comm}}\ \frac{s_1\colon A\text{-set};\ s_2\colon A\text{-set}}{s_1 \cup s_2 = s_2 \cup s_1}$$

so that the second of the rules above is simply a specialisation of this more general commutativity rule to the case where s_1 is a unit set. Its proof is therefore straightforward and follows immediately from '$\cup$-comm' and '$\{a\}$-form'.

The proof of 'add $\rightarrow \cup$' is longer and is typical of proofs where one is trying to show that two sets are equal.

Although several rules for showing that two sets are equal were introduced in Section 6.5.2 (and indeed others can be found in Chapter 14), it should be clear from the accompanying discussion that one of the most useful in practice tends to be the sequent form '=-set-I-sqt'. Applying this to the proof of 'add $\rightarrow \cup$' gives:

from $a\colon A;\ s\colon A$-set
  ...
1   $add(a,s)\colon A$-set   ⟨?? justify ??⟩
2   $\{a\} \cup s\colon A$-set   ⟨?? justify ??⟩
3   from $b\colon A;\ b \in add(a,s)$
      ...
      infer $b \in \{a\} \cup s$ ⟨?? justify ??⟩
4   from $c\colon A;\ c \in \{a\} \cup s$
      ...
      infer $c \in add(a,s)$ ⟨?? justify ??⟩
infer $add(a,s) = \{a\} \cup s$ =-set-I-sqt (1, 2, 3, 4)

The typing assertions (Lines 1 and 2) are easy to discharge using the formation rules for *add*, union, and unit sets ('add-form', '$\cup$-form', and '$\{a\}$-form'). The strategy for the two subproofs is to work on the second hypothesis of each to reduce it to atomic statements about properties of b, a and s or c, a and s respectively using elimination rules for membership of the appropriate composite set, then to combine these using the introduction versions of the membership rules as appropriate to deduce the conclusion of the subproof. This requires the development of the series of rules describing the membership properties of union and unit sets analogous to those for *add* discussed in Section 6.3. The ones relevant here are

$$\boxed{\in\text{-}\cup\text{-E}}\ \frac{a\colon A;\ s_1\colon A\text{-set};\ s_2\colon A\text{-set};\ a \in s_1 \cup s_2}{a \in s_1 \lor a \in s_2}$$

$$\boxed{\in\text{-}\cup\text{-I-left}}\ \frac{a\colon A;\ s_1\colon A\text{-set};\ s_2\colon A\text{-set};\ a \in s_2}{a \in s_1 \cup s_2}$$

$$\boxed{\in\text{-}\cup\text{-I-right}}\ \frac{a\colon A;\ s_1\colon A\text{-set};\ s_2\colon A\text{-set};\ a \in s_1}{a \in s_1 \cup s_2}$$

$$\boxed{\in\text{-}\{a\}\text{-E}}\ \frac{a\colon A;\ b\colon A;\ b \in \{a\}}{b = a} \qquad \boxed{\in\text{-}\{a\}\text{-I-=}}\ \frac{a\colon A;\ b = a}{b \in \{a\}}$$

6.7 Set comprehension

Note that because the conclusion of the first of the above elimination rules contains a disjunction, some intermediate reasoning by cases is also required. This leads to the following complete proof:

from $a:A$; $s:A$-set
1    $add(a,s):A$-set   add-form (h1, h2)
2    $\{a\}:A$-set $\{a\}$-form (h1)
3    $\{a\} \cup s:A$-set $\cup$-form (2, h2)
4   from $b:A$; $b \in add(a,s)$
4.1 $b = a \vee b \in s$ $\in$-add-E (4.h1, h1, h2, 4.h2)
4.2   from $b = a$
4.2.1 $b \in \{a\}$ $\in$-$\{a\}$-I-= (h1, 4.2.h1)
         infer $b \in \{a\} \cup s$ $\in$-$\cup$-I-right (4.h1, 2, h2, 4.2.1)
4.3   from $b \in s$
         infer $b \in \{a\} \cup s$ $\in$-$\cup$-I-left (4.h1, 2, h2, 4.3.h1)
     infer $b \in \{a\} \cup s$ $\vee$-E (4.1, 4.2, 4.3)
5   from $c:A$; $c \in \{a\} \cup s$
5.1 $c \in \{a\} \vee c \in s$ $\in$-$\cup$-E (5.h1, 2, h2, 5.h2)
5.2   from $c \in \{a\}$
5.2.1 $c = a$ $\in$-$\{a\}$-E (h1, 5.h1, 5.2.h1)
         infer $c \in add(a,s)$ $\in$-add-I-elem-= (5.h1, h2, 5.2.1)
5.3   from $c \in s$
         infer $c \in add(a,s)$ $\in$-add-I-set (5.h1, h1, h2, 5.3.h1)
     infer $c \in add(a,s)$ $\vee$-E (5.1, 5.2, 5.3)
infer $add(a,s) = \{a\} \cup s$ =-set-I-sqt (1, 3, 4, 5)

6.7 Set comprehension

Quite often it is useful to define a set implicitly by stating some property that all its elements are to satisfy. This idea is expressed via the following *set comprehension* expression:

$$\{x:A \mid P(x)\}$$

which denotes all objects x of type A for which $P(x)$ is true.

Care is needed when trying to write down formation and membership rules for this construct, however. First, since VDM imposes the restriction that a set must be finite, it is necessary to ensure that the formation rule does not allow the construction of infinite sets, and second, it is imperative that the new axioms are consistent with the properties of sets which follow from the axioms given so far.

The first of these potential pitfalls becomes clear when one considers a particular example of the set comprehension expression in which $P(x)$ is everywhere 'true' and the type A is the natural numbers. Then the expression reduces to

$$\{x:\mathbb{N} \mid \text{true}\}$$

which is to be interpreted as those natural numbers for which 'true' is true, which in turn amounts to all the natural numbers. The problem is that the natural numbers are infinite, so that the above construct cannot be regarded as a set.

The obvious solution here is to insist that there are only finitely many objects x for which $P(x)$ is true. One way of doing this might be to introduce some new primitive concept embodying this notion of finiteness, but a neater way is to use the finiteness property of sets and insist that there must be some set s which contains all those elements x satisfying $P(x)$. This method effectively amounts to showing that there is some set of which the set comprehension expression is a subset. This leads to a hypothesis to the formation rule for set comprehension of the form

$$\exists s: A\text{-}set \cdot \forall y: A \cdot P(y) \Rightarrow y \in s$$

The second problem is somewhat more subtle. On the basis of the interpretation of the set comprehension expression given above, it is tempting to define membership via the predicate

$$a \in \{x: A \mid P(x)\} \Leftrightarrow P(a)$$

which states that an element a is a member of the set $\{x: A \mid P(x)\}$ if $P(a)$ is true and not a member of the set if $P(a)$ is false. The problem here is that, assuming the set comprehension expression does indeed represent a set, the rule 'δ-$\in$' given above (see Section 6.3) implies that the left-hand side of the above equivalence is either true or false, from which it follows by simple propositional logic that the right-hand side must also be either true or false. To put this another way, from the above membership predicate together with the rule 'δ-$\in$' it is possible to prove $\delta P(a)$ on the sole assumption that the set comprehension expression $\{x: A \mid P(x)\}$ denotes a set. To avoid an inconsistency, therefore, it is necessary to insist that the set comprehension expression only denotes a set if the characteristic predicate $P(x)$ is everywhere well-defined, that is if

$$\forall x: A \cdot \delta P(x)$$

This assertion then becomes an additional hypothesis of the formation rule, the correct version of which is:

$$\boxed{\text{those-form}}\ \frac{\forall x: A \cdot \delta P(x) \quad \exists s: A\text{-}set \cdot \forall y: A \cdot P(y) \Rightarrow y \in s}{\{x: A \mid P(x)\}: A\text{-}set}$$

The membership rule, with the predicate given above as its conclusion, requires the same hypotheses in order to ensure that the set comprehension expression occurring therein is well-formed:

$$\boxed{\in\text{-those-defn}}\ \frac{a: A \quad \forall x: A \cdot \delta P(x) \quad \exists s: A\text{-}set \cdot \forall y: A \cdot P(y) \Rightarrow y \in s}{a \in \{y: A \mid P(y)\} \Leftrightarrow P(a)}$$

In fact VDM admits a more general form of set comprehension than the one described above. This is written

$$\{f(x) \mid x: A \cdot P(x)\}$$

6.7 Set comprehension

and stands for all objects of the form $f(x)$ generated from those objects x which satisfy the predicate $P(x)$[1]. Of course, considerations of finiteness and consistency must be taken into account here just as for the simplified case described above. Here, however, one requires the additional constraint that $f(x)$ must be well-formed for each x satisfying the characteristic predicate P. This leads to formation and membership rules of the form:

$$\text{set-comp-form} \quad \frac{\begin{array}{c} \forall x{:}A \cdot \delta P(x) \\ x{:}A,\ P(x) \vdash_{\overline{x}} f(x){:}B \\ \exists s{:}B\text{-set} \cdot \forall y{:}A \cdot P(y) \Rightarrow f(y) \in s \end{array}}{\{f(x) \mid x{:}A \cdot P(x)\}{:}B\text{-set}} \quad \text{Ax}$$

$$\in\text{-set-comp-defn} \quad \frac{\begin{array}{c} b{:}B \\ \forall x{:}A \cdot \delta P(x) \\ x{:}A,\ P(x) \vdash_{\overline{x}} f(x){:}B \\ \exists s{:}B\text{-set} \cdot \forall y{:}A \cdot P(y) \Rightarrow f(y) \in s \end{array}}{b \in \{f(x) \mid x{:}A \cdot P(x)\} \Leftrightarrow \exists a{:}A \cdot P(a) \wedge b = f(a)} \quad \text{Ax}$$

Note that these axioms do not insist that there are only a finite number of values of x satisfying the characteristic predicate $P(x)$, rather that these values of x generate a finite number of different values of $f(x)$. The first condition would be too restrictive as it is perfectly possible for the number of different values of $f(x)$ to be finite even if the number of possible values of x is infinite.

The simple form of set comprehension described above can now be thought of as a special case of this more general form, namely the case where $f(x) \equiv x$, with the formal definition

$$\{x{:}A \mid P(x)\} \stackrel{\text{def}}{=} \{x \mid x{:}A \cdot P(x)\}$$

The formation rule 'those-form' and the membership rule '∈-those-defn' for this simple form can be proved from the rules 'set-comp-form' and '∈-set-comp-defn' for the generalised form given above (see Exercise 4).

The notation can be further extended so that the quantification ranges over a set instead of a type. This is written[2]

$$\{f(x) \mid x \in s \cdot P(x)\}$$

It is defined axiomatically via

$$\text{set-comp-defn-set} \quad \frac{\begin{array}{c} s{:}A\text{-set} \\ \forall x \in s \cdot \delta P(x) \\ x{:}A,\ x \in s,\ P(x) \vdash_{\overline{x}} f(x){:}B \\ \exists t{:}B\text{-set} \cdot \forall y \in s \cdot P(y) \Rightarrow f(y) \in t \end{array}}{\{f(x) \mid x \in s \cdot P(x)\} = \{f(x) \mid x{:}A \cdot x \in s \wedge P(x)\}} \quad \text{Ax}$$

A simplified form of the notation omits the predicate $P(x)$ when it is identically true:

$$\{f(x) \mid x \in s\} \stackrel{\text{def}}{=} \{f(x) \mid x \in s \cdot \text{true}\}$$

---

[1] This notation can be further extended in the obvious way to allow f and P to depend on more than one variable.
[2] Again, the extension to more than one variable is obvious.

Its formation rule, which is derivable from the more general rules given above, is relatively simple:

$$\text{set-comp-form-set-ident} \quad \frac{s\colon A\text{-set} \quad x\colon A,\ x\in s \vdash_x f(x)\colon B \quad \exists t\colon B\text{-set}\cdot \forall y\in s\cdot f(y)\in t}{\{f(x)\mid x\in s\}\colon B\text{-set}}$$

This can be further simplified to:

$$\text{set-comp-form-set-ident-global} \quad \frac{s\colon A\text{-set} \quad x\colon A \vdash_x f(x)\colon B}{\{f(x)\mid x\in s\}\colon B\text{-set}}$$

when $f(x)$ is of type B for all x of type A (i.e. not just for those x in the set s) as finiteness is ensured by the rule

$$\text{finite-set-image} \quad \frac{s\colon A\text{-set};\ x\colon A \vdash_x f(x)\colon B}{\exists t\colon B\text{-set}\cdot \forall x\in s\cdot f(x)\in t}$$

Finally, for completeness, a shorthand notation for the case where the quantification is over a type and where the predicate is identically true can be defined via:

$$\{f(x)\mid x\colon A\} \stackrel{\text{def}}{=} \{f(x)\mid x\colon A\cdot \text{true}\}$$

though its usefulness is limited as it is only finite if the type A is finite or if $f(x)$ takes the same value for all but a finite number of elements of A.

6.8 Reasoning about set comprehension

The fact that the formation and membership rules for set comprehension contain finiteness and definedness hypotheses which have to be discharged when reasoning about set comprehension expressions can not only make this task seem somewhat daunting but can also lead to much repetition of work if the proofs are not structured sensibly into lemmas. The following example illustrates how this can be done.

A common specialisation of set comprehension is the *interval (of numbers)* or *set range* expression. This is written $\{i,\ldots,j\}$ and denotes those natural numbers lying between the natural numbers i and j inclusive, so that, for example, the interval $\{4,\ldots,7\}$ denotes the set $\{4,5,6,7\}$[3].

Intervals can be defined directly in terms of set comprehension via:

$$\{i,\ldots,j\} \stackrel{\text{def}}{=} \{n\colon \mathbb{N}\mid i\le n\le j\}$$

Reasoning informally to begin with, it is easy to see that the characteristic predicate in the above set comprehension expression is well-defined for all natural numbers i and j, and that there are finitely many values of n which satisfy it. This indicates that the expression

---

[3]In fact VDM has a wider notion of intervals than this whereby i and j can be real rather than natural numbers, with the expression $\{i,\ldots,j\}$ then denoting those *integers* lying between i and j. To describe this would require a significant extension to the limited theory of numbers presented in Chapter 5, however, so this more general form is not discussed here.

6.8 Reasoning about set comprehension

does indeed represent a set and suggests that the following formation and membership rules for intervals should be valid:

$$\boxed{\text{interval-form}} \; \frac{i:\mathsf{N};\; j:\mathsf{N}}{\{i,\ldots,j\}:\mathsf{N}\text{-set}} \qquad \boxed{\in\text{-interval-defn}} \; \frac{i:\mathsf{N};\; j:\mathsf{N};\; k:\mathsf{N}}{k \in \{i,\ldots,j\} \Leftrightarrow i \le k \le j}$$

Turning now to consider the formal proofs of these rules, it is clear that the first step in each must be expanding the definition of the interval, after which the formation or membership rule for set comprehension ('those-form' and '∈-those-defn') can be applied as appropriate. The point to note here is that the hypotheses of these two rules are identical, so that after these steps the proofs of both the formation and membership rules for intervals reduce to discharging the same definedness and finiteness hypotheses. Whilst it is true that there is not much to be lost by repeating the justification of the definedness hypothesis, this being a simple consequence of the properties of natural numbers (in particular the rule 'δ-$\le$-$\le$'), the finiteness hypothesis is a different matter entirely as its proof is far from immediate. The best strategy at this point is therefore to state a new lemma asserting the finiteness property required. This has the form:

$$\boxed{\text{interval-finite}} \; \frac{i:\mathsf{N};\; j:\mathsf{N}}{\exists s:\mathsf{N}\text{-set} \cdot \forall y:\mathsf{N} \cdot i \le y \le j \Rightarrow y \in s}$$

The proofs about intervals are now easy to complete. That for the formation rule is:

from $i:\mathsf{N};\; j:\mathsf{N}$
1 from $x:\mathsf{N}$
1.1 $\delta(i \le x \le j)$ δ-$\le$-$\le$ (h1, 1.h1, h2)
  infer $\forall x:\mathsf{N} \cdot \delta(i \le x \le j)$ $\forall$-I (1)
2 $\exists s:\mathsf{N}\text{-set} \cdot \forall y:\mathsf{N} \cdot i \le y \le j \Rightarrow y \in s$ interval-finite (h1, h2)
3 $\{n:\mathsf{N} \mid i \le n \le j\}:\mathsf{N}\text{-set}$ those-form (1, 2)
infer $\{i,\ldots,j\}:\mathsf{N}\text{-set}$ folding (3)

That for the membership rule is similar, differing only in the last two lines:

from $i:\mathsf{N};\; j:\mathsf{N};\; k:\mathsf{N}$
1 from $x:\mathsf{N}$
1.1 $\delta(i \le x \le j)$ δ-$\le$-$\le$ (h1, 1.h1, h2)
  infer $\forall x:\mathsf{N} \cdot \delta(i \le x \le j)$ $\forall$-I (1)
2 $\exists s:\mathsf{N}\text{-set} \cdot \forall y:\mathsf{N} \cdot i \le y \le j \Rightarrow y \in s$ interval-finite (h1, h2)
3 $k \in \{n:\mathsf{N} \mid i \le n \le j\} \Leftrightarrow i \le k \le j$ $\in$-those-defn (h3, 1, 2)
infer $k \in \{i,\ldots,j\} \Leftrightarrow i \le k \le j$ folding (3)

The lemma 'interval-finite' can be proved by induction (left as an exercise for the reader).

6.9 Summary

This chapter has dealt with the following topics:

- Proof using set induction.
- Quantification over sets.
- Constructing useful variants of a rule by considering special cases of its metavariables.
- Ensuring finiteness and definedness of constructs defined by comprehension.
- Reasoning about set comprehension expressions.

6.10 Exercises

1. A non-empty set is inhabited

Use set induction to show that a set which is non-empty contains some element:

$$\boxed{\text{non-empty-set-inhabited}}\ \frac{s\colon A\text{-set};\ s \neq \{\,\}}{\exists a\colon A \cdot a \in s}$$

2. Distributed union

Show that the distributed union of the empty set is the empty set:

$$\boxed{\bigcup\text{-defn-}\{\,\}}\ \frac{}{\bigcup\{\,\} = \{\,\}}$$

3. Relating quantification over sets and quantification over types

Use the rules and definitions given in Section 6.4 to prove the following rules relating existential and universal quantifications over sets and the corresponding quantification over types:

$$\boxed{\exists \to \exists\text{-set}}\ \frac{s\colon A\text{-set};\ \exists x\colon A \cdot x \in s \wedge P(x)}{\exists x \in s \cdot P(x)} \qquad \boxed{\exists\text{-set} \to \exists}\ \frac{s\colon A\text{-set};\ \exists x \in s \cdot P(x)}{\exists x\colon A \cdot x \in s \wedge P(x)}$$

$$\boxed{\forall \to \forall\text{-set}}\ \frac{s\colon A\text{-set};\ \forall x\colon A \cdot x \in s \Rightarrow P(x)}{\forall x \in s \cdot P(x)} \qquad \boxed{\forall\text{-set} \to \forall}\ \frac{s\colon A\text{-set};\ \forall x \in s \cdot P(x)}{\forall x\colon A \cdot x \in s \Rightarrow P(x)}$$

Prove also the definedness rule for existential quantification over sets:

$$\boxed{\delta\text{-}\exists\text{-inherit-set}}\ \frac{s\colon A\text{-set};\ x\colon A,\ x \in s \vdash_x \delta P(x)}{\delta(\exists x \in s \cdot P(x))}$$

6.10 Exercises

4. The simplified form of set comprehension

Prove the formation and membership rules for the simplified form of set comprehension:

$$\boxed{\text{those-form}} \;\; \frac{\forall x\colon A \cdot \delta P(x) \quad \exists s\colon A\text{-set} \cdot \forall y\colon A \cdot P(y) \Rightarrow y \in s}{\{x\colon A \mid P(x)\}\colon A\text{-set}}$$

$$\boxed{\in\text{-those-defn}} \;\; \frac{a\colon A \quad \forall x\colon A \cdot \delta P(x) \quad \exists s\colon A\text{-set} \cdot \forall y\colon A \cdot P(y) \Rightarrow y \in s}{a \in \{y\colon A \mid P(y)\} \Leftrightarrow P(a)}$$

from the general forms 'set-comp-form' and '∈-set-comp-defn' and its derivatives.

Chapter 7

Finite Maps

7.1 Introduction

A map can best be thought of as a collection of *associations* or *maplets* recording some relationship between objects, with, for example, the maplet associating the object b with the object a being written $a \mapsto b$. Here, a is called the *domain value* of the maplet $a \mapsto b$ and b the *range value*. Just as for sets, there is no concept of order associated with the collection, but there is a restriction that no two maplets in the collection may have the same domain value but different range values, that is a map cannot contain both the maplet $a \mapsto b$ and the maplet $a \mapsto c$ when $c \neq b$.

In VDM, the notation $m: A \xrightarrow{m} B$ represents the assertion that m is a *finite* map whose *domain type* is A and whose *range type* is B, that is a finite collection of maplets each of which associates an object of type B with an object of type A. As an example, the map $\{1 \mapsto \text{false}, 2 \mapsto \text{true}, 3 \mapsto \text{true}, 4 \mapsto \text{false}\}$ is of type $\mathbb{N} \xrightarrow{m} \mathbb{B}$ as the domain value of each maplet is a natural number (of type $\mathbb{N}$) and the corresponding range value is a boolean value (of type $\mathbb{B}$; see Chapter 9 for the full description of the boolean data type). Note that it is possible for a map to associate the same range value with two different domain values, as in this example.

The first section of this chapter gives a basic axiomatisation of finite maps in terms of generators, analogous to the axiomatisation of sets in terms of the generators *add* and { } discussed above in Chapter 6, and presents the corresponding induction principle. Together, these form the basis of the next section, which illustrates various ways of axiomatising operators in terms of generators. Next, a worked example is presented which illustrates how one can often structure a proof by spotting that a particular step represents an instance of some more general lemma, perhaps belonging in a more fundamental theory. The following section discusses the use of subsidiary definitions when defining new operators as specialisations of other operators, illustrating this by developing a theory of map union from properties of map override. The penultimate section then shows how to define polymorphic subtypes, using bijective or one-one maps as an example, and also shows how to formulate new induction rules on these subtypes. The chapter closes with a discussion of map comprehension, with the problems of ensuring finiteness and definedness encountered when considering set comprehension expressions (see Section 6.7) again coming to the fore.

7.2 Basic axiomatisation

By analogy with the discussion of sets in Chapter 6, axiomatising maps in terms of generators requires the introduction of a primitive object representing the empty map (written $\{\mapsto\}$) and an operator for adding a new maplet to an existing map (written *addm*). Again, the empty map represents the empty collection of maplets of arbitrary type (strictly of arbitrary domain type and arbitrary range type). Its properties are embodied in the formation rule '$\{\mapsto\}$-form':

$$\boxed{\{\mapsto\}\text{-form}} \quad \frac{}{\{\mapsto\}: A \xrightarrow{m} B} \text{ Ax}$$

The situation is slightly more complicated with the operator *addm*, however, as the restriction that no two maplets may have the same domain value means that one cannot in general simply add an arbitrary maplet to an existing map.

There are potentially two ways one could proceed here, depending on how one interprets the functionality of *addm*. One possibility is to say that the expression $addm(a \mapsto b, m)$, which adds the maplet $a \mapsto b$ to the map m, only represents a map if m does not already contain a maplet whose domain value is a or if m contains the maplet $a \mapsto b$ already (in which case $addm(a \mapsto b, m)$ simply yields m). This ensures that the condition of non-repeating domain values is maintained, and leads to a formation rule for *addm* having a hypothesis ensuring that the relevant condition is met. In terms of the map domain and map application operators to be introduced later (see Section 7.3), this has the form:

$$\frac{a: A; \; b: B; \; m: A \xrightarrow{m} B; \; a \in \text{dom}\, m \Rightarrow m(a) = b}{addm(a \mapsto b, m): A \xrightarrow{m} B} \text{ Ax}$$

The problem with this sort of treatment is that it is inextricably linking the definition of *addm* with the definitions of map domain and map application, and since these concepts will have to be defined in terms of *addm*, this sort of link can easily lead to tortuous circularities in reasoning. Not only that, but every other rule involving *addm* would need similar hypotheses to ensure the well-formedness of each occurrence of *addm*, thus making those rules much more cumbersome to use.

The other way of interpreting *addm* is to say that the expression $addm(a \mapsto b, m)$ always denotes a map, but does not simply add the new maplet $a \mapsto b$ to the map m, rather having a value depending on the value of m. Again, there are two possible interpretations in the case when m already contains a maplet of the form $a \mapsto c$ for some c: either one could say that $addm(a \mapsto b, m)$ does nothing in that case, or one could say that it replaces (or overwrites) the maplet $a \mapsto c$ with $a \mapsto b$ (of course there is no difference between the two interpretations if c is the same as b). Both these approaches lead to the same simple formation rule for *addm*:

$$\boxed{\text{addm-form}} \quad \frac{a: A; \; b: B; \; m: A \xrightarrow{m} B}{addm(a \mapsto b, m): A \xrightarrow{m} B} \text{ Ax}$$

the differences between them showing up in the basic axioms defining the properties of *addm*.

In fact it generally turns out to be easier to write axioms for other operators defined in terms of the generators if the element being explicitly added is actually present in the composite object being constructed, as this enables one to reason about something whose

7.3 Axiomatisation using generators

explicit form is known. This argues for choosing the interpretation that $addm(a \mapsto b, m)$ overwrites any maplet of the form $a \mapsto c$ already present in the map m. This property is captured axiomatically by considering the effect of successive applications of $addm$ with maplets having the same domain value. This yields a rule of the form:

$$\boxed{\text{addm-overwrite}} \ \frac{a\!:\!A;\ b_1\!:\!B;\ b_2\!:\!B;\ m\!:\!A \xrightarrow{m} B}{addm(a \mapsto b_1, addm(a \mapsto b_2, m)) = addm(a \mapsto b_1, m)} \ \text{Ax}$$

Lastly, it is necessary to describe the unordered property of a map. Again this can be done by considering the effect of successive applications of $addm$, this time with the maplets having different domain values. The lack of ordering is then expressed by saying that the order of application of the two $addm$'s is unimportant:

$$\boxed{\text{addm-comm}} \ \frac{a\!:\!A;\ b\!:\!B;\ c\!:\!A;\ d\!:\!B;\ m\!:\!A \xrightarrow{m} B;\ a \neq c}{addm(a \mapsto b, addm(c \mapsto d, m)) = addm(c \mapsto d, addm(a \mapsto b, m))} \ \text{Ax}$$

Clearly any finite map can be expressed as a finite series of applications of $addm$ to the empty map, with each application adding a different maplet. This suggests formulating an induction rule based on the principle that, if some property P can be shown to hold for the empty map and, further, if by assuming that P holds for some arbitrary map m it can be shown that P also holds for the map constructed by adding a new maplet $a \mapsto b$ to m, then P holds for all finite maps. The only problem with the above statement is how to express the fact that a new maplet is being added in the induction step as there is no analogue of the set membership operator $\in$ for maps. The key to this is to realise that it is sufficient to insist that there is no maplet already in m with the same domain value (namely a) as that of the maplet being added. This leads to the introduction of the notion of the *domain* of a map (written $\operatorname{dom} m$), this being simply the set of all the domain values of all the maplets in the map. Its defining axioms are given in the next section.

Now the fact that a new maplet is being added in the induction step can be expressed using simple set membership, namely by saying that the domain value of the new maplet is not in the domain of the map. The induction rule for finite maps therefore has the form

$$\boxed{\text{map-indn}} \ \frac{m_0\!:\!A \xrightarrow{m} B;\ P(\{\mapsto\})}{a\!:\!A,\ b\!:\!B,\ m\!:\!A \xrightarrow{m} B,\ P(m),\ a \notin \operatorname{dom} m \vdash_{a,b,m} P(addm(a \mapsto b, m))} \ \text{Ax}$$
$$P(m_0)$$

Note that, as for the local hypothesis $a \notin s'$ in the induction step of the induction rule for sets ('set-indn'), the local hypothesis $a \notin \operatorname{dom} m$ is not strictly necessary: it simply rules out a case which can be reached by other means (namely by adding the maplet $a \mapsto b$ to the map obtained by removing the maplet with domain value a from m).

7.3 Axiomatisation using generators

A common way of axiomatising operators on data-types defined via generators is to give a series of axioms which define the operator for the base element (here, the empty map) and for each of the generators (here, the maplet addition function $addm$). The parallel with the induction principle is clear, and it should therefore come as no surprise to learn that proofs about operators defined in this manner generally proceed by induction.

A simple example of how to proceed is provided by the domain operator dom. As explained above, this represents the set of all the domain values of all the maplets in a map. Considering first the base case, since the empty map contains no maplets the set of all the domain values, and hence the domain itself, must be the empty set. This leads to the following rule:

$$\boxed{\text{dom-defn-}\{\mapsto\}} \quad \frac{}{\text{dom}\,\{\mapsto\} = \{\,\}} \quad \textbf{Ax}$$

Turning now to the *addm* case, the idea is to define the domain of a map of the form $addm(a \mapsto b, m)$ for an arbitrary map m and an arbitrary maplet $a \mapsto b$ (with a and b being of the appropriate type, of course). These parameters, together with their types, then form the hypotheses of the definition rule, the conclusion of which will be of the form $\text{dom}\,addm(a \mapsto b, m) = \ldots$. It remains to be decided what expression should form the right-hand side of this equality.

One point worth noting is that, to maintain the parallel with the induction rule (and incidentally to make the proofs about domain more tractable), this expression should only depend on a, b and $\text{dom}\,m$. To put this another way, the aim is to express the domain of the extended map in terms of the domain of the smaller map.

Because the value of $addm(a \mapsto b, m)$ may depend on whether or not the map m already contains a maplet whose domain value is a, both these cases must be considered when determining the value of $\text{dom}\,addm(a \mapsto b, m)$. In the first of these cases, the maplet $a \mapsto b$ replaces an existing maplet of the form $a \mapsto c$ for some c, so the domain of the extended map is the same as the domain of the smaller map (so that $\text{dom}\,addm(a \mapsto b, m) = \text{dom}\,m$). In the second case, a maplet with a new domain value is added to m so the domain of the extended map is simply formed by adding this new value (a) to the domain of m (so that $\text{dom}\,addm(a \mapsto b, m) = add(a, \text{dom}\,m)$). However, the first case can also be described by this same expression – in that case a is already in the set $\text{dom}\,m$, so adding it again has no effect. Thus, the appropriate rule defining domain for the generator is:

$$\boxed{\text{dom-defn-addm}} \quad \frac{a:A; \ b:B; \ m:A \xrightarrow{m} B}{\text{dom}\,addm(a \mapsto b, m) = add(a, \text{dom}\,m)} \quad \textbf{Ax}$$

Note here that the fact that $\text{dom}\,addm(a \mapsto b, m)$ can be expressed as $add(a, \text{dom}\,m)$ irrespective of whether or not a is in $\text{dom}\,m$ is important as it effectively "decouples" the definition of domain and the induction rule for maps – although the basic properties of domain have to be proved by induction these proofs do not rely on the last hypothesis of the induction step ($a \notin \text{dom}\,m$). This is illustrated by considering the proof of the formation rule for domain:

$$\boxed{\text{dom-form}} \quad \frac{m:A \xrightarrow{m} B}{\text{dom}\,m: A\text{-set}}$$

Note how the induction step (Subproof 4) uses the rule 'dom-defn-addm' and does not depend on hypothesis 4.h5.

7.3 Axiomatisation using generators

from $m: A \xrightarrow{m} B$
1     $\{\}: A\text{-set}$ $\{\}$-form
2     $\text{dom}\{\mapsto\} = \{\}$ dom-defn-$\{\mapsto\}$
3     $\text{dom}\{\mapsto\}: A\text{-set}$ =-type-inherit-left (1, 2)
4   from $a: A;\ b: B;\ m_1: A \xrightarrow{m} B;\ \text{dom}\, m_1: A\text{-set};\ a \notin \text{dom}\, m_1$
4.1 $\text{dom}\, addm(a \mapsto b, m_1) = add(a, \text{dom}\, m_1)$ dom-defn-addm (4.h1, 4.h2, 4.h3)
4.2 $add(a, \text{dom}\, m_1): A\text{-set}$ add-form (4.h1, 4.h4)
      infer $\text{dom}\, addm(a \mapsto b, m_1): A\text{-set}$ =-type-inherit-left (4.2, 4.1)
infer $\text{dom}\, m: A\text{-set}$ map-indn (h1, 3, 4)

A similar technique can be used to develop a set of axioms describing the *range* (rng) of a map, that is the set of all the range values of all the maplets in a map. Again, the base case is simple as this set is empty

$$\boxed{\text{rng-defn-}\{\mapsto\}}\quad \frac{}{\text{rng}\{\mapsto\} = \{\}}\ \mathbf{Ax}$$

and the case for the generator involves determining the value of the defining expression (which is here $\text{rng}\, addm(a \mapsto b, m)$) in the two cases $a \notin \text{dom}\, m$ and $a \in \text{dom}\, m$. For the first of these two cases, a new maplet is being added to the map m and, although m might or might not already contain a maplet with the same range value b but with a different domain value (e.g. $c \mapsto b$ for some c different from a), the properties of set addition once more allow both these cases to be described by the same expression, namely $add(b, \text{rng}\, m)$.

Going on to consider the value of $\text{rng}\, addm(a \mapsto b, m)$ in the case where $a \in \text{dom}\, m$ is not so simple, however. The condition $a \in \text{dom}\, m$ means that m contains a maplet of the form $a \mapsto c$ for some c, which is overwritten when the maplet $a \mapsto b$ is added. However, although overwriting $a \mapsto c$ with $a \mapsto b$ certainly means that b is a member of the range of the extended map $addm(a \mapsto b, m)$, whether or not c is present depends on whether or not m contains some other maplet of the form $d \mapsto c$ for some d. The problem here is that there is no obvious way to describe this situation using the map operators introduced so far.

However, the basis for axiomatising an operator using generators is that the axioms should be sufficient to define the operator for all maps. Thus, the same principle used in formulating the induction step of the induction rule, namely that any map can be expressed as a finite series of applications of *addm* to the empty map with each application adding a maplet with a *distinct* domain value, can be used here. This means that an operator is completely defined by giving its value for the empty map and its value for the map $addm(a \mapsto b, m)$ for arbitrary values of a, b and m but assuming that a is not already in the domain of m (cf. the premises of the sequent representing the induction step in the induction rule 'map-indn'). The rule 'rng-defn-addm-$\notin$'

$$\boxed{\text{rng-defn-addm-}\notin}\quad \frac{a: A;\ b: B;\ m: A \xrightarrow{m} B;\ a \notin \text{dom}\, m}{\text{rng}\, addm(a \mapsto b, m) = add(b, \text{rng}\, m)}\ \mathbf{Ax}$$

is therefore sufficient to complete the definition of the range operator, and the relevant formation rule can be proved from it (by induction):

$$\boxed{\text{rng-form}}\ \dfrac{m\colon A \xrightarrow{m} B}{\operatorname{rng} m\colon B\text{-set}}$$

One might wonder whether there is ever any point in attempting to write a single defining rule covering both the cases $a \notin \operatorname{dom} m$ and $a \in \operatorname{dom} m$, as was done for the domain operator above. In fact there is, as the resulting rule has fewer hypotheses than the corresponding rules covering only one of these cases and can therefore be applied more widely. This is not to say that rules representing the individual cases would never be used, of course – for instance, if one wanted to deal in some proof with an expression of the form $\operatorname{dom} addm(a \mapsto b, m)$ and it was known that a was in the domain of m then one or two lines of reasoning could be saved by using a specialisation of the rule 'dom-defn-addm' of the form

$$\boxed{\text{dom-defn-addm-}\in}\ \dfrac{a\colon A;\ b\colon B;\ m\colon A \xrightarrow{m} B;\ a \in \operatorname{dom} m}{\operatorname{dom} addm(a \mapsto b, m) = \operatorname{dom} m}$$

instead of the general form 'dom-defn-addm' directly. This rule can easily be proved from 'dom-defn-addm' using the properties of sets and equality.

The next question is how one might formulate and prove a similar rule for the range operator. The key to the former is to notice that the map formed by adding the maplet $a \mapsto b$ to a map m which already contains a maplet of the form $a \mapsto c$ is the same as the map which would be formed by adding the same maplet $a \mapsto b$ to the map m from which the maplet $a \mapsto c$ has been removed. This operation is described by the *domain subtraction* operator. The discussion of the range operator resumes after introducing this and the analogous *domain restriction* operator.

Domain subtraction, which is written $s \triangleleft m$, represents the map formed by removing from the map m those maplets whose domain value is in the set s. For example, the domain subtraction expression $\{1, 4, 7\} \triangleleft \{2 \mapsto \text{true}, 3 \mapsto \text{false}, 4 \mapsto \text{true}\}$ represents the map $\{2 \mapsto \text{true}, 3 \mapsto \text{false}\}$. Note that the set s can contain elements which do not occur in the domain of the map m, as in this example.

The axiomatisation of domain subtraction proceeds in the standard manner. Consider first the case where the map m is empty. Here, whichever set s is chosen no maplets can be removed by the domain subtraction since there are none in the empty map, so the defining rule is simply

$$\boxed{\triangleleft\text{-defn-}\{\mapsto\}}\ \dfrac{s\colon A\text{-set}}{s \triangleleft \{\mapsto\} = \{\mapsto\}}\ \mathbf{Ax}$$

Note that the fact that s must be a set but can be of arbitrary type is captured by the hypothesis $s\colon A\text{-set}$.

Turning now to the *addm* case, the expression $s \triangleleft addm(a \mapsto b, m)$ has to be evaluated for an arbitrary maplet $a \mapsto b$, an arbitrary map m and an arbitrary set s, all of appropriate type ($a\colon A$, $b\colon B$, $m\colon A \xrightarrow{m} B$, $s\colon A\text{-set}$ for arbitrary types A and B). Since domain subtraction involves removing any maplets whose domain value is in the set s, the value of this expression depends on whether or not the new maplet being added to m is going to be removed by the domain subtraction, i.e. on whether or not $a \in s$. These two cases must therefore be considered separately. Further, in each case one must consider the two subcases corresponding to whether or not a is in the domain of m.

It is sometimes helpful when evaluating this sort of defining expression to think "pro-

7.3 Axiomatisation using generators

grammatically". Thus, considering the case $a \in s$, in the first subcase ($a \in \text{dom}\,m$) the maplet $a \mapsto b$ is first added to the map m, overwriting an existing maplet $a \mapsto c$, then it is removed by the domain subtraction. The same effect can be achieved by removing the maplet $a \mapsto c$ directly from m by domain subtraction without first adding the maplet $a \mapsto b$, so this first subcase is described simply by the expression $s \vartriangleleft\!\!\!- m$. In the second subcase ($a \notin \text{dom}\,m$) the new maplet $a \mapsto b$ is first added to m then immediately removed by the domain subtraction, so it might as well never have been added in the first place and this second subcase can also be described by the expression $s \vartriangleleft\!\!\!- m$. This leads to the following rule describing the case $a \in s$:

$$\boxed{\vartriangleleft\!\!\!-\text{-defn-addm-}\in} \quad \frac{a\!:\!A;\ b\!:\!B;\ m\!:\!A \xrightarrow{m} B;\ s\!:\!A\text{-set};\ a \in s}{s \vartriangleleft\!\!\!-\ addm(a \mapsto b, m) = s \vartriangleleft\!\!\!- m} \quad \text{Ax}$$

Turning now to the case $a \notin s$, the first subcase again replaces the maplet $a \mapsto c$ with the maplet $a \mapsto b$ which is not removed by the domain subtraction. This effect can be emulated by first applying the domain subtraction to m, during which process the maplet $a \mapsto c$ survives because a is not in s, then overwriting the resulting map with the maplet $a \mapsto b$. (Recall that in all these cases of developing axiomatisations in terms of generators the object is to express the operator applied to $addm(a \mapsto b, m)$ in terms of a, b and the operator applied to m.) This subcase can therefore be described by the expression $addm(a \mapsto b, s \vartriangleleft\!\!\!- m)$. This expression also describes the second subcase because $addm(a \mapsto b, m)$ adds a completely new maplet to m and this is not affected by the domain subtraction so the order of application can be commuted. Thus, the case $a \notin s$ is described by the rule

$$\boxed{\vartriangleleft\!\!\!-\text{-defn-addm-}\notin} \quad \frac{a\!:\!A;\ b\!:\!B;\ m\!:\!A \xrightarrow{m} B;\ s\!:\!A\text{-set};\ a \notin s}{s \vartriangleleft\!\!\!-\ addm(a \mapsto b, m) = addm(a \mapsto b, s \vartriangleleft\!\!\!- m)} \quad \text{Ax}$$

This completes the definition of domain subtraction.

The axiomatisation of the domain restriction operator proceeds entirely analogously. This is written $s \vartriangleleft m$ and denotes the result of removing those maplets from the map m whose domain value is not in the set s (alternatively of preserving only those maplets whose domain value is in s). Its defining rules are

$$\boxed{\vartriangleleft\text{-defn-}\{\mapsto\}} \quad \frac{s\!:\!A\text{-set}}{s \vartriangleleft \{\mapsto\} = \{\mapsto\}} \quad \text{Ax}$$

$$\boxed{\vartriangleleft\text{-defn-addm-}\in} \quad \frac{a\!:\!A;\ b\!:\!B;\ m\!:\!A \xrightarrow{m} B;\ s\!:\!A\text{-set};\ a \in s}{s \vartriangleleft addm(a \mapsto b, m) = addm(a \mapsto b, s \vartriangleleft m)} \quad \text{Ax}$$

$$\boxed{\vartriangleleft\text{-defn-addm-}\notin} \quad \frac{a\!:\!A;\ b\!:\!B;\ m\!:\!A \xrightarrow{m} B;\ s\!:\!A\text{-set};\ a \notin s}{s \vartriangleleft addm(a \mapsto b, m) = s \vartriangleleft m} \quad \text{Ax}$$

Formation rules for both these operators

$$\boxed{\vartriangleleft\!\!\!-\text{-form}} \quad \frac{m\!:\!A \xrightarrow{m} B;\ s\!:\!A\text{-set}}{s \vartriangleleft\!\!\!- m\!:\!A \xrightarrow{m} B} \qquad \boxed{\vartriangleleft\text{-form}} \quad \frac{m\!:\!A \xrightarrow{m} B;\ s\!:\!A\text{-set}}{s \vartriangleleft m\!:\!A \xrightarrow{m} B}$$

can easily be proved from their defining rules (by induction).

It is now possible to formulate a rule defining the range operator in the case where the maplet being added overwrites an existing maplet with the same domain value, as the notion of removing a maplet from a map can be expressed using domain subtraction and the unit set (as $\{a\} \triangleleft m$). The required rule is therefore

$$\boxed{\text{rng-defn-addm-}\in} \quad \frac{a:A;\ b:B;\ m:A \xrightarrow{m} B;\ a \in \text{dom}\,m}{\text{rng}\,addm(a \mapsto b, m) = add(b, \text{rng}(\{a\} \triangleleft m))}$$

Its proof is covered in detail in Section 7.4.

Operators analogous to domain subtraction and restriction can also be defined for range. Thus, range subtraction which is written $m \triangleright s$, represents the result of removing from the map m every maplet whose range value is in the set s, whilst range restriction, written $m \triangleright s$, similarly represents the result of removing the maplets whose range value is not in s. In both these cases s must be of type B-set if m is of type $A \xrightarrow{m} B$.

Axioms for these operators are developed in a way similar to that described above for the corresponding domain operators except that this time the top-level case distinction for the $addm$ rules is whether or not the range value of the added maplet is in the subtracting (or restricting) set. Also, the trick of domain subtracting the unit set to remove unwanted maplets, which was described above in connection with the formulation of the rule 'rng-defn-addm-∈', has to be used. This yields the following defining rules

$$\boxed{\triangleright\text{-defn-}\{\mapsto\}} \quad \frac{s:B\text{-set}}{\{\mapsto\} \triangleright s = \{\mapsto\}} \text{ Ax}$$

$$\boxed{\triangleright\text{-defn-addm-}\in} \quad \frac{a:A;\ b:B;\ m:A \xrightarrow{m} B;\ s:B\text{-set};\ b \in s}{addm(a \mapsto b, m) \triangleright s = \{a\} \triangleleft (m \triangleright s)} \text{ Ax}$$

$$\boxed{\triangleright\text{-defn-addm-}\notin} \quad \frac{a:A;\ b:B;\ m:A \xrightarrow{m} B;\ s:B\text{-set};\ b \notin s}{addm(a \mapsto b, m) \triangleright s = addm(a \mapsto b, m \triangleright s)} \text{ Ax}$$

$$\boxed{\triangleright\text{-defn-}\{\mapsto\}} \quad \frac{s:B\text{-set}}{\{\mapsto\} \triangleright s = \{\mapsto\}} \text{ Ax}$$

$$\boxed{\triangleright\text{-defn-addm-}\in} \quad \frac{a:A;\ b:B;\ m:A \xrightarrow{m} B;\ s:B\text{-set};\ b \in s}{addm(a \mapsto b, m) \triangleright s = addm(a \mapsto b, m \triangleright s)} \text{ Ax}$$

$$\boxed{\triangleright\text{-defn-addm-}\notin} \quad \frac{a:A;\ b:B;\ m:A \xrightarrow{m} B;\ s:B\text{-set};\ b \notin s}{addm(a \mapsto b, m) \triangleright s = \{a\} \triangleleft (m \triangleright s)} \text{ Ax}$$

from which the formation rules

$$\boxed{\triangleright\text{-form}} \quad \frac{m:A \xrightarrow{m} B;\ s:B\text{-set}}{m \triangleright s: A \xrightarrow{m} B} \qquad \boxed{\triangleright\text{-form}} \quad \frac{m:A \xrightarrow{m} B;\ s:B\text{-set}}{m \triangleright s: A \xrightarrow{m} B}$$

can be proved (again by induction).

The last operator to be dealt with in this section is *map application*, written $m(c)$ and denoting the range value of that maplet belonging to the map m whose domain value is c. This clearly has to be treated somewhat differently from all the examples discussed so far as it certainly cannot be defined for the empty map (as this contains no maplets). Map application therefore represents a partial function which is not well-defined for all

7.4 Extraction and abstraction of lemmas

maps. More specifically, the expression $m(c)$ is only well-defined if c is in the domain of the map m. Note that this condition automatically ensures that the map m is non-empty.

In actuality, this example is not so different from the earlier ones as it might appear. These all proceeded with the aim of developing a series of rules defining a particular operator for all maps, using as a basis for this the fact that any map can be written as a (possibly empty) series of applications of the generator *addm* to the empty map. Taking a broader view, however, one could instead think of this process as developing a series of rules defining an operator for all those maps for which it is well-defined, with all the operators considered so far being well-defined for all maps (*total* functions). This is in fact the correct way of looking at things and forms the basis for the treatment of partial operators.

For the case of map application, it is therefore necessary to construct a series of rules which define $m(c)$ for all values of m and c for which the expression is well-defined, namely when $c \in \text{dom}\, m$ with m non-empty. Now the most general way of representing a non-empty map is as *addm* applied to some other map, say as $addm(a \mapsto b, m)$, and the element c is in the domain of this map if c is the same as a or if c is in the domain of m but is different from a. In the first of these cases the range value associated with the appropriate domain value is b, whilst in the second case it is simply the map m applied directly to c (note that the fact that c has been assumed to be in the domain of m in this case means that the expression $m(c)$ is well-defined). The basic rules defining map application are therefore

$$\boxed{\text{at-defn-addm-=}} \quad \frac{a\colon A;\ b\colon B;\ m\colon A \xrightarrow{m} B}{addm(a \mapsto b, m)(a) = b} \ \text{Ax}$$

$$\boxed{\text{at-defn-addm-}\neq} \quad \frac{a\colon A;\ b\colon B;\ c\colon A;\ m\colon A \xrightarrow{m} B;\ c \neq a;\ c \in \text{dom}\, m}{addm(a \mapsto b, m)(c) = m(c)} \ \text{Ax}$$

The proof of the formation rule

$$\boxed{\text{at-form}} \quad \frac{a\colon A;\ m\colon A \xrightarrow{m} B;\ a \in \text{dom}\, m}{m(a)\colon B}$$

proceeds in the by now familiar way.

Map application is the final ingredient required for the definition of equality on maps. The basic idea here is that two maps m_1 and m_2 are equal if they contain the same collection of maplets. This condition is satisfied if the domains of the two maps are equal and if, for all domain values in the maps, the result of applying m_1 to some domain value is the same as applying m_2 to that domain value. This property is encapsulated in the defining rule

$$\boxed{\text{=-map-defn}} \quad \frac{m_1\colon A \xrightarrow{m} B;\ m_2\colon A \xrightarrow{m} B}{\text{dom}\, m_1 = \text{dom}\, m_2;\ \forall a \in \text{dom}\, m_1 \cdot m_1(a) = m_2(a)} \ \text{Ax}$$
$$m_1 = m_2$$

7.4 Extraction and abstraction of lemmas

Quite often when developing a proof, whether a proof about maps or one about something entirely different, one reaches a point where the particular step under consideration actually represents an instance of a rule which could itself have been proved from the other rules available but which simply had not been thought of up to then. This step could, of course, be completed "in-line" in the current proof, but doing so would mean not only that one would be losing generality by proving an instance of a useful rule instead of the more basic form but also that work would have to be duplicated if some later proof also contained a step representing an instance of this same rule. Not only that, but proofs constructed in this manner would be longer and more complicated, and hence more difficult to understand, than they need be. Thus, although the technique of matching knowns and goals against the hypotheses and the conclusion of available rules is often useful when it comes to deciding how to progress in a proof, it should not be applied indiscriminately. Rather one should additionally consider whether it might be possible to formulate some new rule which would help with the current proof and which might be useful in later proofs too. These "subsidiary" rules or lemmas can arise naturally in the course of constructing a proof, but can also come to light simply by considering the plan of the proof. Both these situations are illustrated by considering two different approaches to proving the rule 'rng-defn-addm-$\in$' introduced in the previous section.

In the first approach it is assumed that the proof is begun by searching for matching rules. Of the available rules about maps only 'map-indn' offers any chance of progress, but, as has already been seen in Section 5.4, the presence of the non-typing hypothesis $a \in \text{dom}\, m$ means that this cannot be applied immediately as the appropriate instance of this hypothesis is required in the induction step of the proof. This means that the trick of applying '$\Rightarrow$-E-left' to transform the goal into an implication is needed again. The first stage of the proof is therefore:

from $a:A$; $b:B$; $m:A \xrightarrow{m} B$; $a \in \text{dom}\, m$
...
1 $a \in \text{dom}\, m \Rightarrow \text{rng}\, addm(a \mapsto b, m) = add(b, \text{rng}(\{a\} \triangleleft m))$ ⟨?? justify ??⟩
infer $\text{rng}\, addm(a \mapsto b, m) = add(b, \text{rng}(\{a\} \triangleleft m))$ $\Rightarrow$-E-left (1, h4)

Now the induction rule can be applied. The base case of the induction involves showing that $a \in \text{dom}\,\{\mapsto\} \Rightarrow \text{rng}\, addm(a \mapsto b, \{\mapsto\}) = add(b, \text{rng}(\{a\} \triangleleft \{\mapsto\}))$ which is entirely trivial because the left-hand side of the implication is false.

One point worth noting here is that, although this step corresponds to a single deduction as far as one's intuition is concerned, justifying it actually requires several lines of proof: first, 'dom-defn-$\{\mapsto\}$' and '$\{\,\}$-is-empty' would have to be used to deduce $\text{dom}\,\{\mapsto\} = \{\,\}$ and $\neg(a \in \{\,\})$ respectively, then the desired result follows from these by substitution of equals. This suggests defining a new rule embodying this step:

$$\boxed{\neg\text{-}\in\text{-dom-}\{\mapsto\}\text{-I}} \quad \frac{a:A}{\neg(a \in \text{dom}\,\{\mapsto\})}$$

which has a proof as outlined above and which can be used directly in the justification of the base case in the proof of 'rng-defn-addm-$\in$' as shown:

7.4 Extraction and abstraction of lemmas

from $a: A$; $b: B$; $m: A \xrightarrow{m} B$; $a \in \text{dom}\, m$
1    $\neg (a \in \text{dom}\, \{\mapsto\})$ $\neg$-$\in$-dom-$\{\mapsto\}$-I (h1)
2    $a \in \text{dom}\, \{\mapsto\} \Rightarrow$
       $\text{rng}\, addm(a \mapsto b, \{\mapsto\}) = add(b, \text{rng}\, (\{a\} \triangleleft \{\mapsto\}))$ $\Rightarrow$-I-right-vac (1)
3   from $a_1: A$; $b_1: B$; $m_1: A \xrightarrow{m} B$;
     $a \in \text{dom}\, m_1 \Rightarrow \text{rng}\, addm(a \mapsto b, m_1) = add(b, \text{rng}\, (\{a\} \triangleleft m_1))$;
     $a_1 \notin \text{dom}\, m_1$
     ...
     infer $a \in \text{dom}\, addm(a_1 \mapsto b_1, m_1) \Rightarrow$
          $\text{rng}\, addm(a \mapsto b, addm(a_1 \mapsto b_1, m_1)) =$
              $add(b, \text{rng}\, (\{a\} \triangleleft addm(a_1 \mapsto b_1, m_1)))$ ⟨?? justify ??⟩
4    $a \in \text{dom}\, m \Rightarrow$
       $\text{rng}\, addm(a \mapsto b, m) = add(b, \text{rng}\, (\{a\} \triangleleft m))$ map-indn (h3, 2, 3)
infer $\text{rng}\, addm(a \mapsto b, m) = add(b, \text{rng}\, (\{a\} \triangleleft m))$ $\Rightarrow$-E-left (4, h4)

Turning now to the induction step (Subproof 3 in the above incomplete proof) the first step is to use '$\Rightarrow$-I' to justify the conclusion, generating $\delta(a \in \text{dom}\, addm(a_1 \mapsto b_1, m_1))$ as a new goal, together with a new subproof having $a \in \text{dom}\, addm(a_1 \mapsto b_1, m_1)$ as its hypothesis and $\text{rng}\, addm(a \mapsto b, addm(a_1 \mapsto b_1, m_1)) = add(b, \text{rng}\, (\{a\} \triangleleft addm(a_1 \mapsto b_1, m_1)))$ as its conclusion (the left- and right-hand sides of the implication respectively). The definedness goal is straightforward to justify, and could also be split off as a lemma

$$\boxed{\delta\text{-}\in\text{-dom-addm-I}} \quad \frac{a_1: A;\ a_2: A;\ b: B;\ m: A \xrightarrow{m} B}{\delta(a_1 \in \text{dom}\, addm(a_2 \mapsto b, m))}$$

In the subproof, the hypothesis can be used to deduce that either $a = a_1$ or $a \in \text{dom}\, m_1$, again via a lemma

$$\boxed{\in\text{-dom-addm-E}} \quad \frac{a_1: A;\ a_2: A;\ b: B;\ m: A \xrightarrow{m} B;\ a_1 \in \text{dom}\, addm(a_2 \mapsto b, m)}{a_1 = a_2 \lor a_1 \in \text{dom}\, m}$$

or a different lemma, making use of the induction hypothesis $a_1 \notin \text{dom}\, m_1$, might be used to deduce additionally that a_1 must be different from a in the second case

$$\boxed{\in\text{-dom-addm-E-}\notin} \quad \frac{a_1: A;\ a_2: A;\ b: B;\ m: A \xrightarrow{m} B \\ a_1 \in \text{dom}\, addm(a_2 \mapsto b, m);\ a_2 \notin \text{dom}\, m}{a_1 = a_2 \lor a_1 \in \text{dom}\, m \land a_2 \neq a_1}$$

Either way there are two cases to consider, $a = a_1$ and $a \neq a_1 \land a \in \text{dom}\, m_1$. In the first of these cases, after substituting a_1 for a in the required goal the rule 'addm-overwrite' can be used to rewrite $addm(a_1 \mapsto b, addm(a_1 \mapsto b_1, m_1))$ to $addm(a_1 \mapsto b, m_1)$ in the left-hand side of the equality, then the resulting term $\text{rng}\, addm(a_1 \mapsto b, m_1)$ can be rewritten to $add(b, \text{rng}\, m_1)$ using the rule 'rng-defn-addm-$\notin$' because $a_1 \notin \text{dom}\, m_1$. Similarly the right-hand side of the equality can be rewritten to $add(b, \text{rng}\, (\{a_1\} \triangleleft m_1))$ using '$\triangleleft$-defn-addm-$\in$' (because $a_1 \in \{a_1\}$). It therefore remains to be shown that $add(b, \text{rng}\, m_1) = add(b, \text{rng}\, (\{a_1\} \triangleleft m_1))$.

One could of course proceed to show this directly, but the similarity in the structure of the two sides of the equality is an indication that some more general rule might be found.

In such a situation, the aim is to find the smallest subterms of each expression which are equal in the current context, and the appropriate strategy is to look first at those subterms which are different on the two sides of the equation. If these can be shown to be equal then their equality represents the required rule. If not, larger and larger containing terms must be considered until a provable equality is discovered.

In the current example, the subterms which are different on the two sides of the equation are m_1 and $\{a_1\} \triangleleft m_1$, and since it is known that $a_1 \notin \text{dom}\, m_1$ these two subterms are equal. This suggests proving a lemma of the form

$$\boxed{\triangleleft\text{-defn-}\{a\}\text{-}\notin}\quad \frac{a:A;\ m:A \xrightarrow{m} B;\ a \notin \text{dom}\, m}{\{a\} \triangleleft m = m}$$

whence the required equality follows easily by substitution.

In the remaining subproof ($a \neq a_1 \wedge a \in \text{dom}\, m_1$) the left-hand side of the equality in the goal can be rewritten to $\text{rng}\, addm(a_1 \mapsto b_1, addm(a \mapsto b, m_1))$ using the rule 'addm-comm', then the fact that $a_1 \notin \text{dom}\, addm(a \mapsto b, m_1)$ (because $a_1 \neq a$ and $a_1 \notin \text{dom}\, m_1$) can be used, together with the rule 'rng-defn-addm-$\notin$', to yield $add(b_1, \text{rng}\, addm(a \mapsto b, m_1))$. Meanwhile the right-hand side of the equality can be rewritten in a similar manner, first to the expression $add(b, \text{rng}\, addm(a_1 \mapsto b_1, \{a\} \triangleleft m_1)$ using a lemma

$$\boxed{\triangleleft\text{-defn-addm-}\{a\}\text{-}\neq}\quad \frac{a_1:A;\ a_2:A;\ b:B;\ m:A \xrightarrow{m} B;\ a_1 \neq a_2}{\{a_1\} \triangleleft addm(a_2 \mapsto b, m) = addm(a_2 \mapsto b, \{a_1\} \triangleleft m)}$$

which is easily proved from '$\triangleleft$-defn-addm-$\notin$', thence to $add(b, add(b_1, \text{rng}\,(\{a\} \triangleleft m_1)))$, again using the fact that $a_1 \notin \text{dom}\,(\{a\} \triangleleft m_1)$ together with the rule 'rng-defn-addm-$\notin$'. Substitution of the induction hypothesis and the commutativity of add (rule 'add-comm' from set theory; see Chapter 6) completes the proof.

An alternative proof of the rule 'rng-defn-addm-$\in$' might involve trying to identify useful new lemmas right at the start. In that case, the earlier discussion, which led to the observation that overwriting an existing maplet in a map using $addm$ yields the same map as would be obtained by applying $addm$ to the map from which the maplet to be overwritten has been removed, suggests that a useful lemma might be

$$\boxed{\text{addm-defn-}\triangleleft\text{-}\{a\}\text{-=}}\quad \frac{a:A;\ b:B;\ m:A \xrightarrow{m} B}{addm(a \mapsto b, m) = addm(a \mapsto b, \{a\} \triangleleft m)}$$

The conclusion can be rewritten to $\text{rng}\, addm(a \mapsto b, \{a\} \triangleleft m) = add(b, \text{rng}\,(\{a\} \triangleleft m))$ using this lemma, and this follows directly from the rule 'rng-defn-addm-$\notin$' in conjunction with a lemma stating that a is not in the domain of $\{a\} \triangleleft m$:

$$\boxed{\notin\text{-dom-}\triangleleft\text{-I-}\{a\}}\quad \frac{a:A;\ m:A \xrightarrow{m} B}{a \notin \text{dom}\,(\{a\} \triangleleft m)}$$

The completed proof is:

7.5 Using subsidiary definitions

from $a:A$; $b:B$; $m:A \xrightarrow{m} B$; $a \in \text{dom}\, m$
1    $addm(a \mapsto b, m): A \xrightarrow{m} B$ addm-form (h1, h2, h3)
2    $\{a\}: A\text{-set}$ $\{a\}$-form (h1)
3    $(\{a\} \triangleleft\!\!- m): A \xrightarrow{m} B$ $\triangleleft\!\!-$-form (h3, 2)
4    $a \notin \text{dom}(\{a\} \triangleleft\!\!- m)$ $\notin$-dom-$\triangleleft\!\!-$-I-$\{a\}$ (h1, h3)
5    $addm(a \mapsto b, m) = addm(a \mapsto b, \{a\} \triangleleft\!\!- m)$ addm-defn-$\triangleleft\!\!-\{a\}$-= (h1, h2, h3)
6    $\text{rng}\, addm(a \mapsto b, \{a\} \triangleleft\!\!- m) = add(b, \text{rng}(\{a\} \triangleleft\!\!- m))$ rng-defn-addm-$\notin$ (h1, h2, 3, 4)
infer $\text{rng}\, addm(a \mapsto b, m) = add(b, \text{rng}(\{a\} \triangleleft\!\!- m))$ =-subs-left(a) (1, 5, 6)

Note that, although this proof is significantly shorter than the first attempt discussed above, all the work has been factored out into the lemma 'addm-defn-$\triangleleft\!\!-\{a\}$-='. This is of course good technique, especially if that lemma can be similarly proved in a few lines by applying similar principles to identify other useful lemmas, as it leads to much clearer and much more manageable proofs. Not only that but the new lemmas identified in this way are likely to be useful in future proofs, thus making those proofs easier to discover and correspondingly simpler.

Note also that the above proof does not actually depend on the final hypothesis $a \in \text{dom}\, m$. That hypothesis can therefore be removed yielding a proof of the stronger rule:

$$\boxed{\text{rng-defn-addm}} \quad \frac{a:A;\ b:B;\ m:A \xrightarrow{m} B}{\text{rng}\, addm(a \mapsto b, m) = add(b, \text{rng}(\{a\} \triangleleft\!\!- m))}$$

7.5 Using subsidiary definitions

Just as one generalises the generator *add* of set theory to obtain the binary set union operator which represents the result of adding each element of one set to another set, so one can also generalise *addm* on maps to obtain the notion of *map override*, written $m_1 \dagger m_2$ and denoting the result of overwriting the map m_1 with each maplet from the map m_2. Map override can be axiomatised in terms of the generators for finite maps exactly as described in Section 7.3 above, and is in fact described by the rules

$$\boxed{\dagger\text{-defn-}\{\mapsto\}\text{-right}} \quad \frac{m:A \xrightarrow{m} B}{m \dagger \{\mapsto\} = m} \ \text{Ax}$$

$$\boxed{\dagger\text{-defn-addm}} \quad \frac{a:A;\ b:B;\ m_1:A \xrightarrow{m} B;\ m_2:A \xrightarrow{m} B}{m_1 \dagger addm(a \mapsto b, m_2) = addm(a \mapsto b, m_1 \dagger m_2)} \ \text{Ax}$$

It shares many of the properties of set union, for example idempotence, associativity, and that the empty generator is an identity for it

$$\boxed{\dagger\text{-self}} \quad \frac{m:A \xrightarrow{m} B}{m \dagger m = m} \qquad \boxed{\dagger\text{-ass}} \quad \frac{m_1:A \xrightarrow{m} B;\ m_2:A \xrightarrow{m} B;\ m_3:A \xrightarrow{m} B}{(m_1 \dagger m_2) \dagger m_3 = m_1 \dagger (m_2 \dagger m_3)}$$

$$\boxed{\dagger\text{-defn-}\{\mapsto\}\text{-left}} \quad \frac{m:A \xrightarrow{m} B}{\{\mapsto\} \dagger m = m}$$

but is not in general commutative due to the fact that the maplet addition may replace maplets in the map m_1 with those from m_2 having the same domain values. It is commutative, however, in the special case where every value a which is common to the domains of the two maps m_1 and m_2 has the same associated range value in both maps, that is if $m_1(a) = m_2(a)$ for every a in $\mathrm{dom}\, m_1 \cap \mathrm{dom}\, m_2$. Two maps which satisfy this condition are said to be *compatible*, and they can be combined using a commutative *map merge* operator $\uplus$ which is a specialisation of the override operator and which is a direct analogue of set union.

From the description given above one can easily formulate an axiomatisation of map merge via a rule

$$\frac{m_1: A \xrightarrow{m} B;\ m_2: A \xrightarrow{m} B;\ \forall a \in \mathrm{dom}\, m_1 \cap \mathrm{dom}\, m_2 \cdot m_1(a) = m_2(a)}{m_1 \uplus m_2 = m_1 \dagger m_2}\text{Ax}$$

where the third hypothesis represents the condition that the two maps must be compatible for the map merge to be defined. However, this rather cumbersome compatibility hypothesis means that proofs using this rule will involve reasoning about that long expression. This is avoided by introducing a subsidiary definition representing the notion of map compatibility into the theory. A set of rules describing its essential properties can then be developed, and these can in turn be used to reason about map merge.

Because of the inability to record essential typing information, map compatibility cannot be introduced by direct definition and must instead be defined axiomatically. The appropriate rule simply makes use of the defining predicate introduced above and is

$$\boxed{\text{compatible-defn}}\ \frac{m_1: A \xrightarrow{m} B;\ m_2: A \xrightarrow{m} B}{compatible(m_1, m_2) \Leftrightarrow \forall a \in \mathrm{dom}\, m_1 \cap \mathrm{dom}\, m_2 \cdot m_1(a) = m_2(a)}\text{Ax}$$

Simple introduction and elimination rules can then be proved from this using the basic properties of equivalence:

$$\boxed{\text{compatible-I}}\ \frac{m_1: A \xrightarrow{m} B;\ m_2: A \xrightarrow{m} B \\ \forall a \in \mathrm{dom}\, m_1 \cap \mathrm{dom}\, m_2 \cdot m_1(a) = m_2(a)}{compatible(m_1, m_2)}$$

$$\boxed{\text{compatible-E}}\ \frac{m_1: A \xrightarrow{m} B;\ m_2: A \xrightarrow{m} B;\ compatible(m_1, m_2)}{\forall a \in \mathrm{dom}\, m_1 \cap \mathrm{dom}\, m_2 \cdot m_1(a) = m_2(a)}$$

The next step is to develop a library of rules about compatibility. Obvious ones, suggested by the fact that the defining predicate is symmetric in m_1 and m_2 and is also trivially true if either m_1 or m_2 is the empty map, are

$$\boxed{\text{compatible-comm}}\ \frac{m_1: A \xrightarrow{m} B;\ m_2: A \xrightarrow{m} B;\ compatible(m_1, m_2)}{compatible(m_2, m_1)}$$

$$\boxed{\text{compatible-defn-}\{\mapsto\}\text{-left}}\ \frac{m: A \xrightarrow{m} B}{compatible(\{\mapsto\}, m)}$$

$$\boxed{\text{compatible-defn-}\{\mapsto\}\text{-right}}\ \frac{m: A \xrightarrow{m} B}{compatible(m, \{\mapsto\})}$$

7.5 Using subsidiary definitions

Also it is clear that the defining predicate is everywhere well-defined, suggesting a rule of the form

$$\boxed{\delta\text{-compatible}} \quad \frac{m_1: A \xrightarrow{m} B; \; m_2: A \xrightarrow{m} B}{\delta(compatible(m_1, m_2))}$$

Two other useful rules, which are perhaps not quite so obvious but which arise naturally as lemmas when addressing proofs about map merge, are:

$$\boxed{\text{compatible-}\dagger\text{-I-left}} \quad \frac{m_1: A \xrightarrow{m} B; \; m_2: A \xrightarrow{m} B; \; m_3: A \xrightarrow{m} B \quad compatible(m_1, m_3); \; compatible(m_2, m_3)}{compatible(m_1 \dagger m_2, m_3)}$$

$$\boxed{\text{compatible-}\dagger\text{-I-right}} \quad \frac{m_1: A \xrightarrow{m} B; \; m_2: A \xrightarrow{m} B; \; m_3: A \xrightarrow{m} B \quad compatible(m_1, m_2); \; compatible(m_1, m_3)}{compatible(m_1, m_2 \dagger m_3)}$$

The main point to note here is that, although one of these rules has to be proved using the basic definition of compatibility, the other can be proved much more easily by making use of the first in conjunction with the commutativity property of compatibility. Thus, assuming 'compatible-†-I-left' has been proved from basic principles, the proof of 'compatible-†-I-right' is:

from $m_1: A \xrightarrow{m} B$; $m_2: A \xrightarrow{m} B$; $m_3: A \xrightarrow{m} B$;
$\quad compatible(m_1, m_2); \; compatible(m_1, m_3)$

1	$m_2 \dagger m_3: A \xrightarrow{m} B$	†-form (h2, h3)
2	$compatible(m_2, m_1)$	compatible-comm (h1, h2, h4)
3	$compatible(m_3, m_1)$	compatible-comm (h1, h3, h5)
4	$compatible(m_2 \dagger m_3, m_1)$	compatible-†-I-left (h2, h3, h1, 2, 3)
infer	$compatible(m_1, m_2 \dagger m_3)$	compatible-comm (1, h1, 4)

Now the map merge operator can be defined in terms of compatibility via the rule

$$\boxed{\uplus\text{-defn}} \quad \frac{m_1: A \xrightarrow{m} B; \; m_2: A \xrightarrow{m} B; \; compatible(m_1, m_2)}{m_1 \uplus m_2 = m_1 \dagger m_2} \; \mathbf{Ax}$$

and its properties follow easily from the properties of compatibility and those of map override. Thus, for example, rules defining compatibility and override for the empty map ('compatible-defn-$\{\mapsto\}$-left', 'compatible-defn-$\{\mapsto\}$-right', '†-defn-$\{\mapsto\}$-left' and '†-defn-$\{\mapsto\}$-right') lead to counterparts '$\uplus$-defn-$\{\mapsto\}$-left' and '$\uplus$-defn-$\{\mapsto\}$-right' defining map merge with the empty map:

$$\boxed{\uplus\text{-defn-}\{\mapsto\}\text{-left}} \quad \frac{m: A \xrightarrow{m} B}{\{\mapsto\} \uplus m = m} \qquad \boxed{\uplus\text{-defn-}\{\mapsto\}\text{-right}} \quad \frac{m: A \xrightarrow{m} B}{m \uplus \{\mapsto\} = m}$$

and rules defining compatibility of map override ('compatible-†-I-left' and 'compatible-†-I-right'), together with the associativity rule for map override ('†-ass'), lead to an associativity rule for map merge:

$$\boxed{\uplus\text{-ass}} \quad \frac{m_1: A \xrightarrow{m} B;\ m_2: A \xrightarrow{m} B;\ m_3: A \xrightarrow{m} B}{compatible(m_1, m_2);\ compatible(m_2, m_3);\ compatible(m_1, m_3)}$$

The proofs of all these rules follow a similar pattern, as illustrated by the following proof of '$\uplus$-ass':

from $m_1: A \xrightarrow{m} B;\ m_2: A \xrightarrow{m} B;\ m_3: A \xrightarrow{m} B;\ compatible(m_1, m_2);$
$\quad compatible(m_2, m_3);\ compatible(m_1, m_3)$

1	$m_1 \dagger m_2: A \xrightarrow{m} B$	$\dagger$-form (h1, h2)
2	$m_2 \dagger m_3: A \xrightarrow{m} B$	$\dagger$-form (h2, h3)
3	$m_1 \dagger (m_2 \dagger m_3): A \xrightarrow{m} B$	$\dagger$-form (h1, 2)
4	$m_2 \uplus m_3 = m_2 \dagger m_3$	$\uplus$-defn (h2, h3, h5)
5	$m_1 \uplus m_2 = m_1 \dagger m_2$	$\uplus$-defn (h1, h2, h4)
6	$compatible(m_1, m_2 \dagger m_3)$	compatible-$\dagger$-I-right (h1, h2, h3, h4, h6)
7	$m_1 \uplus (m_2 \dagger m_3) = m_1 \dagger (m_2 \dagger m_3)$	$\uplus$-defn (h1, 2, 6)
8	$compatible(m_1 \dagger m_2, m_3)$	compatible-$\dagger$-I-left (h1, h2, h3, h6, h5)
9	$(m_1 \dagger m_2) \uplus m_3 = (m_1 \dagger m_2) \dagger m_3$	$\uplus$-defn (1, h3, 8)
10	$(m_1 \dagger m_2) \dagger m_3 = m_1 \dagger (m_2 \dagger m_3)$	$\dagger$-ass (h1, h2, h3)
11	$(m_1 \dagger m_2) \uplus m_3 = m_1 \dagger (m_2 \dagger m_3)$	=-trans(c) (3, 9, 10)
12	$(m_1 \dagger m_2) \uplus m_3 = m_1 \uplus (m_2 \dagger m_3)$	=-trans-right(c) (3, 11, 7)
13	$(m_1 \uplus m_2) \uplus m_3 = m_1 \uplus (m_2 \dagger m_3)$	=-subs-left(b) (1, 5, 12)
infer	$(m_1 \uplus m_2) \uplus m_3 = m_1 \uplus (m_2 \uplus m_3)$	=-subs-left(b) (2, 4, 13)

The proof of the commutativity of map merge would seem at first sight to require a different strategy as map override is not commutative in general. However, a little thought reveals that, by formulating a more specialised rule which relies on the fact that map override is commutative if the two maps are compatible

$$\boxed{\dagger\text{-comm}} \quad \frac{m_1: A \xrightarrow{m} B;\ m_2: A \xrightarrow{m} B;\ compatible(m_1, m_2)}{m_1 \dagger m_2 = m_2 \dagger m_1}$$

the same strategy illustrated above can be followed. The proof of the commutativity of map merge

$$\boxed{\uplus\text{-comm}} \quad \frac{m_1: A \xrightarrow{m} B;\ m_2: A \xrightarrow{m} B;\ compatible(m_1, m_2)}{m_1 \uplus m_2 = m_2 \uplus m_1}$$

is then easy. The rule '$\dagger$-comm' is proved by induction.

7.6 Polymorphic subtypes and associated induction rules

It is quite common when writing a specification to define an invariant on a type definition or on a state declaration which effectively amounts to a statement that only those elements of the type which have a particular property are of interest. In many cases these invariants contain clauses which place restrictions on basic data-types or straightforward type constructors, for example that a particular natural number should be non-zero, and

7.6 Polymorphic subtypes and associated induction rules

some of these restrictions can be quite common, occurring in a whole range of different and unrelated specifications. Identifying these common restrictions and developing new theories for the subclasses of the basic types they correspond to can save a lot of work as the rules describing the properties of the subclass of the type are useful when it comes to proving properties of all specifications which use it. One example of a restriction to a basic type has already been seen in Chapter 5, where the data-type $\mathbf{N}_1$ corresponding to the positive natural numbers was introduced. This section illustrates how to define a subclass of a type constructor.

The basic idea here is to formulate a predicate on the basic type constructor which characterises the required property of the subclass, then the new type constructor is defined as a subtype (see Chapter 4) of the basic type constructor with that predicate. As an example, consider the type of *bijective* or *one-one* maps. A bijective map is one in which no two maplets have the same range value, which can be stated as a predicate

$$\forall a, b \in \text{dom}\, m \cdot m(a) = m(b) \Rightarrow a = b$$

where the shorthand notation for multiple quantifiers has been used.

On the basis of the lessons learned in the previous section, it makes sense to introduce a subsidiary definition to represent this predicate to save having to manipulate the complicated expression when reasoning about bijective maps and to bring the formal theory into line with one's fundamental understanding. Thus, a predicate *is-1-1* is introduced and is defined axiomatically via the rule

$$\boxed{\text{is-1-1-defn}}\ \dfrac{m\colon A \xrightarrow{m} B}{\textit{is-1-1}(m) \Leftrightarrow \forall x, y \in \text{dom}\, m \cdot m(x) = m(y) \Rightarrow x = y}\ \mathbf{Ax}$$

The bijective map type, written $A \xleftrightarrow{m} B$, can then be defined in terms of this via

$$A \xleftrightarrow{m} B \stackrel{\text{def}}{=} \ll m\colon A \xrightarrow{m} B \mid \textit{is-1-1}(m) \gg$$

Note that the definition is polymorphic as it is parameterised on the types A and B.

From this definition and the properties of subtypes it is easy to prove the following basic rules about bijective maps:

$$\boxed{\text{bimap-supertype}}\ \dfrac{m\colon A \xleftrightarrow{m} B}{m\colon A \xrightarrow{m} B} \qquad \boxed{\text{bimap-E}}\ \dfrac{m\colon A \xleftrightarrow{m} B}{\textit{is-1-1}(m)}$$

$$\boxed{\text{bimap-form}}\ \dfrac{m\colon A \xrightarrow{m} B;\ \textit{is-1-1}(m)}{m\colon A \xleftrightarrow{m} B}$$

One could of course stop here and convert every proof involving bijective maps into a proof involving only maps in general by using these three rules together with primitive introduction and elimination rules for the predicate *is-1-1*:

$$\boxed{\text{is-1-1-I}}\ \dfrac{m\colon A \xrightarrow{m} B \quad \forall x, y \in \text{dom}\, m \cdot m(x) = m(y) \Rightarrow x = y}{\textit{is-1-1}(m)}$$

$$\boxed{\text{is-1-1-E}}\ \dfrac{m\colon A \xrightarrow{m} B;\ \textit{is-1-1}(m)}{\forall x, y \in \text{dom}\, m \cdot m(x) = m(y) \Rightarrow x = y}$$

This approach leads to much repetition of work, however, and it is far better to develop a theory of bijective maps in their own right.

A particularly useful strategy when constructing a theory describing some subtype of a type which has an associated induction rule is to develop a specialisation of the induction rule for that subtype. In general, formulating this rule amounts to putting additional constraints on the induction step (in the form of extra premises in the sequent hypothesis which represents it in the rule) to ensure that it steps from one value of the subtype to the next. Also it is necessary to modify the typing information throughout the rule, and possibly the base case as well if the base case for the main type is not a member of the subtype. For bijective maps, it is easy to see that the induction step can be restricted to step only between bijective maps if an additional constraint is imposed to the effect that the range value of the maplet being added should not already be in the range of the map. It is also easy to see that the base case need not be altered because the empty map is bijective. The induction rule for bijective maps is therefore

$$\text{bimap-indn} \quad \frac{m_0: A \xleftrightarrow{m} B; \; P(\{\mapsto\}) \quad\quad a: A, \; b: B, \; m: A \xleftrightarrow{m} B, \quad P(m), \; a \notin \text{dom}\, m, \; b \notin \text{rng}\, m \vdash_{a,b,m} P(addm(a \mapsto b, m))}{P(m_0)}$$

This rule can be proved from the ordinary induction rule for maps as follows. The first stage is to apply the rules 'bimap-supertype' and 'bimap-E' to the typing hypothesis to deduce $m_0: A \xrightarrow{m} B$ and $is\text{-}1\text{-}1(m_0)$ respectively. The ordinary map induction rule can then be applied after $is\text{-}1\text{-}1(m_0)$ has been introduced into the induction step using the standard technique of applying '$\Rightarrow$-E-left'. Doing all this leads to

from $m_0: A \xleftrightarrow{m} B; \; P(\{\mapsto\})$
 $\quad a: A, \; b: B, \; m: A \xleftrightarrow{m} B, \; P(m), \; a \notin \text{dom}\, m, \; b \notin \text{rng}\, m \vdash_{a,b,m} P(addm(a \mapsto b, m))$
1 $\quad m_0: A \xrightarrow{m} B$ \hfill bimap-supertype (h1)
2 $\quad is\text{-}1\text{-}1(m_0)$ \hfill bimap-E (h1)
 $\quad \ldots$
3 $\quad is\text{-}1\text{-}1(\{\mapsto\}) \Rightarrow P(\{\mapsto\})$ \hfill ⟨?? justify ??⟩
4 $\quad$ from $a_1: A; \; b_1: B; \; m_1: A \xrightarrow{m} B; \; is\text{-}1\text{-}1(m_1) \Rightarrow P(m_1); \; a_1 \notin \text{dom}\, m_1$
 $\quad\quad \ldots$
 $\quad$ infer $is\text{-}1\text{-}1(addm(a_1 \mapsto b_1, m_1)) \Rightarrow P(addm(a_1 \mapsto b_1, m_1))$ \hfill ⟨?? justify ??⟩
5 $\quad is\text{-}1\text{-}1(m_0) \Rightarrow P(m_0)$ \hfill map-indn (1, 3, 4)
infer $P(m_0)$ \hfill $\Rightarrow$-E-left (5, 2)

The base case (Line 3) is easy to complete, following directly from the hypothesis $P(\{\mapsto\})$ by vacuous implication introduction (rule '$\Rightarrow$-I-left-vac'). Moreover it is clear that the induction step has to make use of the sequent hypothesis, and, since the right-hand side of the implication in the conclusion of the induction step is the same expression that appears as the conclusion of the sequent hypothesis (after suitably renaming variables), this suggests that an appropriate strategy is to first apply '$\Rightarrow$-I' to the conclusion of the induction step, then to use the sequent hypothesis to justify the conclusion of the resulting subproof. This yields

7.6 Polymorphic subtypes and associated induction rules

from $m_0: A \xleftrightarrow{m} B$; $P(\{\mapsto\})$
    $a:A,\ b:B,\ m:A \xleftrightarrow{m} B,\ P(m),\ a \notin \text{dom}\,m,\ b \notin \text{rng}\,m \vdash_{a,b,m} P(addm(a \mapsto b, m))$

1	$m_0: A \xrightarrow{m} B$	bimap-supertype (h1)
2	$is\text{-}1\text{-}1(m_0)$	bimap-E (h1)
3	$is\text{-}1\text{-}1(\{\mapsto\}) \Rightarrow P(\{\mapsto\})$	$\Rightarrow$-I-left-vac (h2)
4	from $a_1:A;\ b_1:B;\ m_1:A \xrightarrow{m} B;\ is\text{-}1\text{-}1(m_1) \Rightarrow P(m_1);\ a_1 \notin \text{dom}\,m_1$	
	...	
4.1	$\delta(is\text{-}1\text{-}1(addm(a_1 \mapsto b_1, m_1)))$	$\langle ??\ \text{justify}\ ??\rangle$
4.2	from $is\text{-}1\text{-}1(addm(a_1 \mapsto b_1, m_1))$	
	...	
4.2.1	$m_1: A \xleftrightarrow{m} B$	$\langle ??\ \text{justify}\ ??\rangle$
4.2.2	$b_1 \notin \text{rng}\,m_1$	$\langle ??\ \text{justify}\ ??\rangle$
4.2.3	$P(m_1)$	$\langle ??\ \text{justify}\ ??\rangle$
	infer $P(addm(a_1 \mapsto b_1, m_1))$ sequent h3 (4.h1, 4.h2, 4.2.1, 4.2.3, 4.h5, 4.2.2)	
	infer $is\text{-}1\text{-}1(addm(a_1 \mapsto b_1, m_1)) \Rightarrow P(addm(a_1 \mapsto b_1, m_1))$	$\Rightarrow$-I (4.1, 4.2)
5	$is\text{-}1\text{-}1(m_0) \Rightarrow P(m_0)$	map-indn (1, 3, 4)
infer $P(m_0)$		$\Rightarrow$-E-left (5, 2)

Now Line 4.2.1 follows from 'bimap-form', generating a new goal $is\text{-}1\text{-}1(m_1)$. This, together with the induction hypothesis $is\text{-}1\text{-}1(m_1) \Rightarrow P(m_1)$, justifies Line 4.2.3. The remaining goals can easily be made the subject of lemmas about $is\text{-}1\text{-}1$ following the strategies discussed in Section 7.4. The finished proof is:

from $m_0: A \xleftrightarrow{m} B$; $P(\{\mapsto\})$
    $a:A,\ b:B,\ m:A \xleftrightarrow{m} B,\ P(m),\ a \notin \text{dom}\,m,\ b \notin \text{rng}\,m \vdash_{a,b,m} P(addm(a \mapsto b, m))$

1	$m_0: A \xrightarrow{m} B$	bimap-supertype (h1)
2	$is\text{-}1\text{-}1(m_0)$	bimap-E (h1)
3	$is\text{-}1\text{-}1(\{\mapsto\}) \Rightarrow P(\{\mapsto\})$	$\Rightarrow$-I-left-vac (h2)
4	from $a_1:A;\ b_1:B;\ m_1:A \xrightarrow{m} B;\ is\text{-}1\text{-}1(m_1) \Rightarrow P(m_1);\ a_1 \notin \text{dom}\,m_1$	
4.1	$addm(a_1 \mapsto b_1, m_1): A \xrightarrow{m} B$	addm-form (4.h1, 4.h2, 4.h3)
4.2	$\delta(is\text{-}1\text{-}1(addm(a_1 \mapsto b_1, m_1)))$	δ-is-1-1 (4.1)
4.3	from $is\text{-}1\text{-}1(addm(a_1 \mapsto b_1, m_1))$	
4.3.1	$is\text{-}1\text{-}1(m_1)$ is-1-1-addm-E-$\notin$-map (4.h1, 4.h2, 4.h3, 4.3.h1, 4.h5)	
4.3.2	$m_1: A \xleftrightarrow{m} B$	bimap-form (4.h3, 4.3.1)
4.3.3	$b_1 \notin \text{rng}\,m_1$ is-1-1-addm-E-$\notin$-rng (4.h1, 4.h2, 4.h3, 4.3.h1, 4.h5)	
4.3.4	$P(m_1)$	$\Rightarrow$-E-left (4.h4, 4.3.1)
	infer $P(addm(a_1 \mapsto b_1, m_1))$ sequent h3 (4.h1, 4.h2, 4.3.2, 4.3.4, 4.h5, 4.3.3)	
	infer $is\text{-}1\text{-}1(addm(a_1 \mapsto b_1, m_1)) \Rightarrow P(addm(a_1 \mapsto b_1, m_1))$	$\Rightarrow$-I (4.2, 4.3)
5	$is\text{-}1\text{-}1(m_0) \Rightarrow P(m_0)$	map-indn (1, 3, 4)
infer $P(m_0)$		$\Rightarrow$-E-left (5, 2)

The following lemmas have been used:

$$\boxed{\delta\text{-is-1-1}}\;\frac{m\colon A \xrightarrow{m} B}{\delta(\textit{is-1-1}(m))}$$

$$\boxed{\textit{is-1-1-addm-E-}\notin\textit{-rng}}\;\frac{a\colon A;\; b\colon B;\; m\colon A \xrightarrow{m} B \\ \textit{is-1-1}(\textit{addm}(a \mapsto b, m));\; a \notin \textit{dom}\, m}{b \notin \textit{rng}\, m}$$

$$\boxed{\textit{is-1-1-addm-E-}\notin\textit{-map}}\;\frac{a\colon A;\; b\colon B;\; m\colon A \xrightarrow{m} B \\ \textit{is-1-1}(\textit{addm}(a \mapsto b, m));\; a \notin \textit{dom}\, m}{\textit{is-1-1}(m)}$$

This induction rule can now be used to prove new rules about bijective maps.

7.7 Map comprehension

The notion of set comprehension described above in Section 6.7 effectively provides a means of defining a set implicitly by giving a predicate which all its members should satisfy. A similar mechanism, *map comprehension*, allows maps to be defined in an analogous way.

The map comprehension expression[1]

$$\{f(a) \mapsto g(a) \mid a\colon A \cdot P(a)\}$$

represents the collection of maplets with domain value $f(a)$ and range value $g(a)$ for all values a satisfying the predicate $P(a)$. Just as the analogous set comprehension expression does not necessarily represent a set, so this map comprehension expression does not necessarily represent a map. The first condition that has to be satisfied if the above expression is to denote a map of type $B \xrightarrow{m} C$ is that $f(a)$ and $g(a)$ must respectively be of types B and C for all values of a satisfying $P(a)$. This leads to hypotheses of the form:

$$a\colon A,\; P(a) \vdash_a f(a)\colon B \qquad\qquad a\colon A,\; P(a) \vdash_a g(a)\colon C$$

The next constraint arises as a result of the condition that no two maplets in a map may have the same domain value but different range values. This effectively means that if there are two (or more) distinct values a_1 and a_2 which satisfy the defining predicate $P(a)$ and which are equal under f (i.e. if $f(a_1) = f(a_2)$) then they must also be equal under g (i.e. $g(a_1) = g(a_2)$). This is expressed by a hypothesis

$$\forall a_1, a_2\colon A \cdot P(a_1) \land P(a_2) \land f(a_1) = f(a_2) \Rightarrow g(a_1) = g(a_2)$$

Two final constraints arise in a similar way to the corresponding ones on the set comprehension expression. The first is that the predicate $P(a)$ must be well-defined for all values of a in order that the contents of the map be well-defined. The second is that the number of maplets in the map must be finite. Note that this latter condition is expressed by saying that the number of different possible domain values (that is values of $f(a)$) is

---

[1] Again, the extension to the case where f, g and P involve more than one variable is obvious.

7.7 Map comprehension

finite, making the domain of the map finite. That the range of the map is also finite is a consequence of this (see Exercise 5 below). Together these constraints give rise to two more hypotheses:

$$\forall x: A \cdot \delta P(x)$$

$$\exists s: B\text{-set} \cdot \forall a: A \cdot P(a) \Rightarrow f(a) \in s$$

The formation rule for map comprehension is therefore:

$$\text{map-comp-form} \frac{\begin{array}{c} \forall x: A \cdot \delta P(x) \\ x: A, \ P(x) \vdash_{\overline{x}} f(x): B \\ x: A, \ P(x) \vdash_{\overline{x}} g(x): C \\ \exists s: B\text{-set} \cdot \forall y: A \cdot P(y) \Rightarrow f(y) \in s \\ \forall a_1, a_2: A \cdot P(a_1) \land P(a_2) \land f(a_1) = f(a_2) \Rightarrow g(a_1) = g(a_2) \end{array}}{\{f(x) \mapsto g(x) \mid x: A \cdot P(x)\}: B \xrightarrow{m} C} \text{Ax}$$

Of course defining the formation rule alone is not sufficient to define map comprehension entirely – that only allows one to show that some map comprehension expression denotes some map, but says nothing about which map that might be. The latter is best defined by linking map comprehension to the definition of map equality. Since this is defined in terms of domain and map application, defining both of these for the map comprehension expression is sufficient to define it completely.

The domain of the map comprehension expression is very easy to define, being simply the set of all possible values of $f(a)$. This is expressed most easily using set comprehension:

$$\text{dom-defn-map-comp} \frac{\begin{array}{c} \forall x: A \cdot \delta P(x) \\ x: A, \ P(x) \vdash_{\overline{x}} f(x): B \\ x: A, \ P(x) \vdash_{\overline{x}} g(x): C \\ \exists s: B\text{-set} \cdot \forall y: A \cdot P(y) \Rightarrow f(y) \in s \\ \forall a_1, a_2: A \cdot P(a_1) \land P(a_2) \land f(a_1) = f(a_2) \Rightarrow g(a_1) = g(a_2) \end{array}}{\text{dom}\{f(x) \mapsto g(x) \mid x: A \cdot P(x)\} = \{f(x) \mid x: A \cdot P(x)\}} \text{Ax}$$

Map application is harder to define, however, and needs to make use of the unique choice operator of Section 3.5.3. This description works because it is known from the discussion of the formation rule above that all values of a which generate the correct domain value yield the same range value. The rule describing the application of a map comprehension expression is therefore:

$$\text{at-defn-map-comp} \frac{\begin{array}{c} b: B \\ \forall x: A \cdot \delta P(x) \\ x: A, \ P(x) \vdash_{\overline{x}} f(x): B \\ x: A, \ P(x) \vdash_{\overline{x}} g(x): C \\ \exists s: B\text{-set} \cdot \forall y: A \cdot P(y) \Rightarrow f(y) \in s \\ \forall a_1, a_2: A \cdot P(a_1) \land P(a_2) \land f(a_1) = f(a_2) \Rightarrow g(a_1) = g(a_2) \\ b \in \text{dom}\{f(x) \mapsto g(x) \mid x: A \cdot P(x)\} \end{array}}{\begin{array}{c} \{f(x) \mapsto g(x) \mid x: A \cdot P(x)\}(b) = \\ \iota c: C \cdot \forall x: A \cdot P(x) \land b = f(x) \Rightarrow c = g(x) \end{array}} \text{Ax}$$

Other forms of the notation, analogous to those given for set comprehension at the end of Section 6.7, can be formalised. Thus, the variant of the general form in which the quantification ranges over a set instead of a type, which is written

$$\{f(x) \mapsto g(x) \mid x \in s \cdot P(x)\}$$

is defined axiomatically via:

$$\text{map-comp-defn-set} \quad \frac{\begin{array}{c} s\colon A\text{-set} \\ \forall x \in s \cdot \delta P(x) \\ x\colon A,\ x \in s,\ P(x) \vdash_{\overline{x}} f(x)\colon B \\ x\colon A,\ x \in s,\ P(x) \vdash_{\overline{x}} g(x)\colon C \\ \exists t\colon B\text{-set} \cdot \forall y \in s \cdot P(y) \Rightarrow f(y) \in t \\ \forall a_1, a_2 \in s \cdot P(a_1) \wedge P(a_2) \wedge f(a_1) = f(a_2) \Rightarrow g(a_1) = g(a_2) \end{array}}{\begin{array}{c} \{f(x) \mapsto g(x) \mid x \in s \cdot P(x)\} = \\ \{f(x) \mapsto g(x) \mid x\colon A \cdot x \in s \wedge P(x)\} \end{array}} \text{Ax}$$

and the specialisations of both forms to the case where the predicate $P(x)$ is identically true are directly defined by:

$$\{f(x) \mapsto g(x) \mid x \in s\} \stackrel{\text{def}}{=} \{f(x) \mapsto g(x) \mid x \in s \cdot \text{true}\}$$

$$\{f(x) \mapsto g(x) \mid x\colon A\} \stackrel{\text{def}}{=} \{f(x) \mapsto g(x) \mid x\colon A \cdot \text{true}\}$$

Again, the first of these special cases has a relatively simple formation rule, particularly when $f(x)$ is of type B for all x of type A:

$$\text{map-comp-form-set-ident} \quad \frac{\begin{array}{c} s\colon A\text{-set} \\ x\colon A \vdash_{\overline{x}} f(x)\colon B \\ x\colon A,\ x \in s \vdash_{\overline{x}} g(x)\colon C \\ \forall a_1, a_2 \in s \cdot f(a_1) = f(a_2) \Rightarrow g(a_1) = g(a_2) \end{array}}{\{f(x) \mapsto g(x) \mid x \in s\}\colon B \stackrel{m}{\longrightarrow} C}$$

and the usefulness of the second is limited by considerations of finiteness.

7.7.1 Reasoning about map comprehension

As might be expected from the complexity of the axioms, reasoning about the general form of map comprehension described above is even more tortuous than reasoning about set comprehension. Again, the best strategy is to divide the task up into a series of lemmas. In this way, expected properties of map comprehension can be proved, for example that applying the map to a domain element of the form $f(a)$ yields $g(a)$:

$$\text{at-defn-map-comp-}f(a) \quad \frac{\begin{array}{c} a\colon A;\ P(a) \\ \forall x\colon A \cdot \delta P(x) \\ x\colon A,\ P(x) \vdash_{\overline{x}} f(x)\colon B \\ x\colon A,\ P(x) \vdash_{\overline{x}} g(x)\colon C \\ \exists s\colon B\text{-set} \cdot \forall y\colon A \cdot P(y) \Rightarrow f(y) \in s \\ \forall a_1, a_2\colon A \cdot P(a_1) \wedge P(a_2) \wedge f(a_1) = f(a_2) \Rightarrow g(a_1) = g(a_2) \end{array}}{\{f(x) \mapsto g(x) \mid x\colon A \cdot P(x)\}(f(a)) = g(a)}$$

and that the range is formed from the set of possible values of $g(x)$:

$$\boxed{\text{rng-defn-map-comp}} \quad \frac{\begin{array}{c} \forall x\colon A \cdot \delta P(x) \\ x\colon A,\ P(x) \vdash_{\overline{x}} f(x)\colon B \\ x\colon A,\ P(x) \vdash_{\overline{x}} g(x)\colon C \\ \exists s\colon B\text{-set} \cdot \forall y\colon A \cdot P(y) \Rightarrow f(y) \in s \\ \forall a_1, a_2\colon A \cdot P(a_1) \wedge P(a_2) \wedge f(a_1) = f(a_2) \Rightarrow g(a_1) = g(a_2) \end{array}}{\operatorname{rng}\{f(x) \mapsto g(x) \mid x\colon A \cdot P(x)\} = \{g(x) \mid x\colon A \cdot P(x)\}}$$

Reasoning about special cases of map comprehension can be much simpler than this, however. For example, the map comprehension expression

$$\{x \mapsto f(x) \mid x \in s\}$$

is described by the following rules:

$$\boxed{\text{map-comp-form-left-set}} \quad \frac{\begin{array}{c} s\colon A\text{-set} \\ x\colon A,\ x \in s \vdash_{\overline{x}} f(x)\colon B \end{array}}{\{x \mapsto f(x) \mid x \in s\}\colon A \xrightarrow{m} B}$$

$$\boxed{\text{dom-defn-map-comp-left-set}} \quad \frac{\begin{array}{c} s\colon A\text{-set} \\ x\colon A,\ x \in s \vdash_{\overline{x}} f(x)\colon B \end{array}}{\operatorname{dom}\{x \mapsto f(x) \mid x \in s\} = s}$$

$$\boxed{\text{at-defn-map-comp-left-set}} \quad \frac{\begin{array}{c} a\colon A;\ s\colon A\text{-set};\ a \in s \\ x\colon A,\ x \in s \vdash_{\overline{x}} f(x)\colon B \end{array}}{\{x \mapsto f(x) \mid x \in s\}(a) = f(a)}$$

An example of the use of these rules appears in Exercise 4 in Section 12.5.3.

7.8 Summary

Points covered in this chapter include:

- Axiomatising operators on a data type in terms of generators.
- Structuring a proof into lemmas.
- Introducing new concepts to help with reasoning.
- Developing induction rules for subtypes.
- Map comprehension expressions.

7.9 Exercises

1. Map composition and distributed map merge

Two map operators which are sometimes useful but which have not been described above are map composition and distributed map merge.

Map composition, written $m_1 \circ m_2$, represents a map which is constructed from the map m_2 by applying the map m_1 to the range value of each of its maplets (leaving the domain value untouched). For example, the expression

$$\{b_1 \mapsto c_1, b_2 \mapsto c_2, b_3 \mapsto c_3\} \circ \{a_1 \mapsto b_1, a_2 \mapsto b_2\}$$

represents the map

$$\{a_1 \mapsto c_1, a_2 \mapsto c_2\}$$

If the map m_2 is of type $A \xrightarrow{m} B$ and the map m_1 is of type $B \xrightarrow{m} C$ then the composed map $m_1 \circ m_2$ is of type $A \xrightarrow{m} C$. Map composition is a partial function which is only well-defined if $\operatorname{rng} m_2 \subseteq \operatorname{dom} m_1$.

Distributed map merge, written merge s, generalises the binary map merge operator ⊎ introduced above (see Section 7.5) to a set of maps s (compare the set union and the distributed set union operators on sets described in Section 6.6). This represents the map formed by combining all the maplets from all the maps in the set of maps s, and is only well-defined if all the maps in the set are compatible.

(a) Use the techniques described in Section 7.3 of this chapter to develop an axiomatisation of these two operators.

(b) State and prove the appropriate formation rules.

2. The proof of 'addm-defn-⊲-$\{a\}$-='

Use the techniques described in Section 7.4 of this chapter to develop a set of subsidiary lemmas to prove 'addm-defn-⊲-$\{a\}$-='.

3. The proof of 'is-1-1-addm-E-∉-rng'

Prove the rule 'is-1-1-addm-E-∉-rng'. Hint: use '∈-rng-E' and 'contradiction'.

4. Map inverse

The inverse of a one-one map m is written m^{-1} and effectively reverses each maplet in m so that the domain value becomes the range value and vice versa. It is defined axiomatically via:

$$\boxed{\text{inv-defn}} \quad \frac{m: A \xleftrightarrow{m} B}{m^{-1} = \{m(a) \mapsto a \mid a \in \operatorname{dom} m\}} \quad \text{Ax}$$

Prove:

(a) that the range of the inverse map is the domain of the map:

$$\boxed{\text{rng-defn-inv}} \quad \frac{m: A \xleftrightarrow{m} B}{\operatorname{rng}(m^{-1}) = \operatorname{dom} m}$$

(b) that the domain of the inverse map is the range of the map:

$$\boxed{\text{dom-defn-inv}} \quad \frac{m: A \xleftrightarrow{m} B}{\operatorname{dom}(m^{-1}) = \operatorname{rng} m}$$

7.9 Exercises

(c) that the inverse map is of type $B \xleftrightarrow{m} A$ if the map is of type $A \xleftrightarrow{m} B$:

$$\boxed{\text{inv-form}} \; \frac{m: A \xleftrightarrow{m} B}{m^{-1}: B \xleftrightarrow{m} A}$$

5. The range of a map comprehension expression is finite

Prove the rule

$$\boxed{\in\text{-dom-map-comp-I-}f(a)} \; \frac{\begin{array}{c} a:A; \; P(a) \\ \forall x:A \cdot \delta P(x) \\ x:A, \; P(x) \vdash_{\overline{x}} f(x):B \\ x:A, \; P(x) \vdash_{\overline{x}} g(x):C \\ \exists s:B\text{-set} \cdot \forall y:A \cdot P(y) \Rightarrow f(y) \in s \\ \forall a_1, a_2:A \cdot P(a_1) \wedge P(a_2) \wedge f(a_1) = f(a_2) \Rightarrow g(a_1) = g(a_2) \end{array}}{f(a) \in \text{dom}\, \{f(x) \mapsto g(x) \mid x:A \cdot P(x)\}}$$

Use it to prove

$$\boxed{\text{dom-finite}\Rightarrow\text{rng-finite}} \; \frac{\begin{array}{c} \forall x:A \cdot \delta P(x) \\ x:A, \; P(x) \vdash_{\overline{x}} f(x):B \\ x:A, \; P(x) \vdash_{\overline{x}} g(x):C \\ \exists s:B\text{-set} \cdot \forall y:A \cdot P(y) \Rightarrow f(y) \in s \\ \forall a_1, a_2:A \cdot P(a_1) \wedge P(a_2) \wedge f(a_1) = f(a_2) \Rightarrow g(a_1) = g(a_2) \end{array}}{\exists t:C\text{-set} \cdot \forall a:A \cdot P(a) \Rightarrow g(a) \in t}$$

Chapter 8

Finite Sequences

8.1 Introduction

This chapter introduces the theory of finite sequences, sometimes simply called *lists*. A sequence is an ordered collection of elements, with repetitions allowed. In VDM-SL, the expression A^* stands for the type of finite sequences of elements drawn from the type A. For example, $\mathbb{N}^*$ consists of lists of natural numbers, T^{**} consists of lists of lists of values of T, and so on.

Section 8.2 gives the basic axiomatisation of lists in terms of generators and an induction rule. A worked example illustrates the proof of a useful derivative of the induction rule. Section 8.3 introduces the partial hd and tl operators, and equality is defined on lists in Section 8.4. This basic repertoire of operators is expanded in Section 8.5, which also affords opportunities to illustrate a number of proof strategies including rewriting both sides of an equality, the use of lemmas corresponding to limbs of a conditional, and an extension to strategies for proof by induction. Section 8.6 shows how consideration of alternative sets of generators for a data type can simplify some proofs.

8.2 Basic axiomatisation

Lists can be given explicitly by listing their members in order: [4, 3, 3] for example. In order to reason effectively about lists, however, it is necessary to develop a slightly more abstract notation which allows general rules about lists to be formulated independently of their length and contents. To do so, it is first necessary to choose a set of generators for the type of lists.

One particularly simple set of generators for A^* consists of the empty list [ ] and the operator cons which appends a single element onto the front (left-hand end) of a list. For example

$$[5] = \text{cons}(5, [\,])$$
$$[3, 7, 9] = \text{cons}(3, \text{cons}(7, \text{cons}(9, [\,])))$$

Since any finite list can be built up by sufficiently many applications of cons and [ ], these two operators are generators for finite sequences. There are many other possible choices of generator set, one of which is discussed in Section 8.6, but this choice is probably the simplest and most familiar to many people.

The axiomatization of this theory starts with formation rules for the generators:

$$\boxed{\text{[]-form}}\ \frac{}{[\,]:A^*}\ \text{Ax}$$

The empty sequence is polymorphic: the same value [ ] is used to represent the empty list of numbers, the empty list of lists of numbers, the empty list of characters, and so on. The symbol A^+ stands for the type of non-empty lists over A and is defined by

$$A^+ \overset{\text{def}}{=} \ll s:A^* \mid s \neq [\,] \gg$$

The formation axiom for cons states that the generator produces a non-empty sequence:

$$\boxed{\text{cons-form-seq+}}\ \frac{a:A;\ s:A^*}{\text{cons}(a,s):A^+}\ \text{Ax}$$

The following rules can be proved by application of the rules of subtyping (Section 4.5):

$$\boxed{\text{cons-form}}\ \frac{a:A;\ s:A^*}{\text{cons}(a,s):A^*} \qquad \boxed{\text{cons-}\neq\text{-[]}}\ \frac{a:A;\ s:A^*}{\text{cons}(a,s) \neq [\,]}$$

Having chosen a set of generators, the next step is to formulate the appropriate induction rule. Recall that, in the induction rule for natural numbers (Chapter 5), the base case of the induction corresponds to zero and the induction step to going from k to succ(k) for arbitrary k. The rule was valid because every natural number can be generated by applying the successor operator to zero sufficiently many times. The analogous induction rule for lists is

$$\boxed{\text{seq-indn}}\ \frac{s:A^*;\ P([\,])\quad h:A,\ t:A^*,\ P(t) \vdash_{h,t} P(\text{cons}(h,t))}{P(s)}\ \text{Ax}$$

The base case corresponds to the empty list. The induction step corresponds to going from t to cons(h,t) for arbitrary h and t of agreeing types. More precisely, given an arbitrary element h of type A and an arbitrary list t of type A^*, the induction step is to prove that $P(\text{cons}(h,t))$ holds under the assumption that $P(t)$ holds (the induction hypothesis). Examples of the use of 'seq-indn' are given below.

The following "head normal form" rule is a simple consequence of the induction rule:

$$\boxed{\text{seq+-hnf}}\ \frac{s:A^+\quad h:A,\ t:A^* \vdash_{h,t} P(\text{cons}(h,t))}{P(s)}$$

It says that, in order to prove that P holds for any non-empty list s, it suffices to consider lists of the form cons(h,t). The proof of 'seq+-hnf' is by sequence induction. Because the hypothesis $s:A^+$ really represents the two hypotheses $s:A^*$ and $s \neq [\,]$, the '$\Rightarrow$-E-left' strategy of Section 5.4 is employed. Recall that this centres on the use of the induction rule to prove an implication with the non-typing hypotheses appearing as antecedents. In this case, the implication to be proved is

$$s \neq [\,] \Rightarrow P(s)$$

The skeleton of the proof is therefore:

8.2 Basic axiomatisation

from $s: A^+$; $h: A$, $t: A^*$ $\vdash_{h,t} P(\text{cons}(h,t))$
1    $s: A^*$ seq+-supertype (h1)
2    $s \neq [\,]$ seq+-E (h1)
    ...
3    $s \neq [\,] \Rightarrow P(s)$ ⟨?? justify ??⟩
infer $P(s)$ $\Rightarrow$-E-left (3, 2)

Now the object is to prove the implication on Line 3. The assertion on Line 1 allows 'seq-indn' to be applied, yielding the following:

from $s: A^+$; $h: A$, $t: A^*$ $\vdash_{h,t} P(\text{cons}(h,t))$
1    $s: A^*$ seq+-supertype (h1)
2    $s \neq [\,]$ seq+-E (h1)
    ...
3    $[\,] \neq [\,] \Rightarrow P([\,])$ ⟨?? justify ??⟩
4   from $h': A$; $t': A^*$; $t' \neq [\,] \Rightarrow P(t')$
      ...
     infer $\text{cons}(h',t') \neq [\,] \Rightarrow P(\text{cons}(h',t'))$ ⟨?? justify ??⟩
5    $s \neq [\,] \Rightarrow P(s)$ seq-indn (1, 3, 4)
infer $P(s)$ $\Rightarrow$-E-left (5, 2)

The antecedent of the base case on Line 3 is false, suggesting that it should be justified by '$\Rightarrow$-I-right-vac'. The induction step is also straightforward: the sequent hypothesis (h2) is directly applicable to the local assumptions of Subproof 4. The finished proof is as follows:

from $s: A^+$; $h: A$, $t: A^*$ $\vdash_{h,t} P(\text{cons}(h,t))$
1    $s: A^*$ seq+-supertype (h1)
2    $s \neq [\,]$ seq+-E (h1)
3    $[\,]: A^*$ [ ]-form
4    $\neg([\,] \neq [\,])$ $\neg$-$\neq$-self-I (3)
5    $[\,] \neq [\,] \Rightarrow P([\,])$ $\Rightarrow$-I-right-vac (4)
6   from $h': A$; $t': A^*$; $t' \neq [\,] \Rightarrow P(t')$
6.1 $P(\text{cons}(h',t'))$ sequent h2 (6.h1, 6.h2)
     infer $\text{cons}(h',t') \Rightarrow P(\text{cons}(h',t'))$ $\Rightarrow$-I-left-vac (6.1)
7    $s \neq [\,] \Rightarrow P(s)$ seq-indn (1, 5, 6)
infer $P(s)$ $\Rightarrow$-E-left (7, 2)

Note that the induction hypothesis (6.h3) has not been used in the proof. This should make the reader suspicious that the proof need not necessarily be done by induction. In fact, the induction rule has merely been used as a way of introducing names for the head and tail of the list s. The concept of a *destructor* operator allows one to reason directly about the constituent parts of a list in a less contrived way. The next section introduces destructors, while Exercise 1 (Section 8.8) affords a comparison of proofs with and without the use of destructors.

8.3 Destructors

Operators which build new values from other values are called *constructors*. Operators which break constructed values into their constituent parts are called *destructors*. The destructors corresponding to cons are called hd (for *head*) and tl (for *tail*). When applied to a non-empty list, hd returns the leftmost element in the list and tl returns the remainder of the list. For example:

$$\text{hd}\,[x, y, z] = x$$

$$\text{tl}\,[x, y, z] = [y, z]$$

The axioms defining hd and tl are

$$\boxed{\text{hd-defn-cons}}\ \frac{a:A;\ s:A^*}{\text{hd}\,\text{cons}(a, s) = a}\ \text{Ax} \qquad \boxed{\text{tl-defn-cons}}\ \frac{a:A;\ s:A^*}{\text{tl}\,\text{cons}(a, s) = s}\ \text{Ax}$$

The hd and tl operators are not defined on the empty list. From these the following formation rules can be proved using 'seq+-hnf':

$$\boxed{\text{hd-form}}\ \frac{s:A^+}{\text{hd}\,s:A} \qquad \boxed{\text{tl-form}}\ \frac{s:A^+}{\text{tl}\,s:A^*}$$

Destructor operators are the "inverse" of constructor operators in that a value can be reconstructed from its constituent parts. Thus, it is possible to derive the following rule by a simple application of 'seq+-hnf' and the axioms above:

$$\boxed{\text{cons-I}}\ \frac{s:A^+}{\text{cons}(\text{hd}\,s, \text{tl}\,s) = s}$$

8.4 Equality between lists

Two lists are equal if and only if they contain exactly the same elements in exactly the same order. The following rules are consequences of the definitions already given:

$$\boxed{\text{=-seq-defn-cons}}\ \frac{a_1:A;\ a_2:A;\ s_1:A^*;\ s_2:A^*}{\text{cons}(a_1, s_1) = \text{cons}(a_2, s_2) \Leftrightarrow a_1 = a_2 \wedge s_1 = s_2}$$

$$\boxed{\text{=-seq+-defn}}\ \frac{s_1:A^+;\ s_2:A^+}{s_1 = s_2 \Leftrightarrow \text{hd}\,s_1 = \text{hd}\,s_2 \wedge \text{tl}\,s_1 = \text{tl}\,s_2}$$

8.5 Operators on lists

This section gives definitions of some standard operators on lists in VDM-SL and illustrates how to reason about them. Some proof techniques of more general applicability are discussed.

8.5.1 The singleton list

The singleton list constructor [_] denotes lists with only one element. Its direct definition is very simple:

$$[a] \stackrel{\text{def}}{=} \text{cons}(a, [\,])$$

The following rules are proved from the the rules given already by folding the definition of the singleton:

$$\boxed{\text{[a]-form}} \ \frac{a:A}{[a]:A^*} \qquad \boxed{\text{hd-defn-[a]}} \ \frac{a:A}{\text{hd}\,[a] = a} \qquad \boxed{\text{tl-defn-[a]}} \ \frac{a:A}{\text{tl}\,[a] = [\,]}$$

8.5.2 The length of a list

The length of a list is given by the len operator. Its direct definition is as follows:

$$\text{len}\,s \stackrel{\text{def}}{=} \text{if } s = [\,] \text{ then } 0 \text{ else succ}(\text{len}\,(\text{tl}\,s))$$

This definition is "recursive" in the sense that unfolding len s in a proof yields another expression in terms of len. It is important to check that it is well-founded. This can be done by proving the formation rule, which states that the len operator always returns a denoting value:

$$\boxed{\text{len-form}} \ \frac{s:A^*}{\text{len}\,s:\mathbf{N}}$$

The proof proceeds by induction on s:

    from $s:A^*$
       ...
  1   len[ ]: **N**   ⟨?? justify ??⟩
  2   from $h:A$; $t:A^*$; len $t:$ **N**
       ...
       infer len cons$(h, t):$ **N**   ⟨?? justify ??⟩
    infer len $s:$ **N**   seq-indn (h1, 1, 2)

The base case is straightforward, eliminating the conditional in the definition of len because the condition is true:

from $s:A^*$
1   0: **N**   0-form
2   [ ]: A^* [ ]-form
3   (if [ ] = [ ] then 0 else succ(len (tl [ ]))) = 0   condition-true-ident (2, 1)
4   len [ ] = 0   folding (3)
5   len [ ]: **N**   =-type-inherit-left (1, 4)
    ⋮

The induction step is similar. In order to eliminate the conditional, one must show $\neg(\mathrm{cons}(h,t) = [\,])$ and $\mathrm{succ}(\mathrm{len}(\mathrm{tl\,cons}(h,t))):\mathbb{N}$. The former follows from the definition of equality on sequences, and the latter from the induction hypothesis and formation rules of succ, tl and cons. Since the length of a sequence is a natural number, the proof relies on some elementary properties of natural numbers, as discussed in Chapter 5. The rest of the proof is as follows:

from $s:A^*$
⋮
6   from $h:A$; $t:A^*$; len $t:\mathbb{N}$
6.1   tl cons$(h,t) = t$ tl-defn-cons (6.h1, 6.h2)
6.2   len tl cons$(h,t):\mathbb{N}$ =-subs-left(b) (6.h2, 6.1, 6.h3)
6.3   succ(len(tl cons$(h,t))):\mathbb{N}$ succ-form (6.2)
6.4   cons$(h,t) \neq [\,]$ cons-$\neq$-[ ] (6.h1, 6.h2)
6.5 $\neg(\mathrm{cons}(h,t) = [\,])$ unfolding (6.4)
6.6   (if cons$(h,t) = [\,]$ then 0 else succ(len(tl cons$(h,t)))) =$
                succ(len(tl cons$(h,t)))$ condition-false (6.3, 6.5)
6.7   len cons$(h,t) = $ succ(len(tl cons$(h,t)))$ folding (6.6)
     infer len cons$(h,t):\mathbb{N}$ =-type-inherit-left (6.3, 6.7)
infer len $s:\mathbb{N}$ seq-indn (h1, 5, 6)

8.5.3 The set of elements in a list

The operator elems gives the set of elements in a list. It is defined recursively as follows:

$$\mathrm{elems}\,s \stackrel{\mathrm{def}}{=} \text{if } s = [\,] \text{ then } \{\,\} \text{ else } add(\mathrm{hd}\,s, \mathrm{elems}(\mathrm{tl}\,s))$$

The following formation rule is proved in an analogous way to 'len-form' above:

$$\boxed{\text{elems-form}}\;\frac{s:A^*}{\mathrm{elems}\,s:A\text{-set}}$$

8.5.4 List concatenation

The operator $\frown$ concatenates one list onto the front of another list. For example:

$$[9,23,5] \frown [9,4] = [9,23,5,9,4]$$

A direct definition such as

$$s \frown t \stackrel{\mathrm{def}}{=} \text{if } s = [\,] \text{ then } t \text{ else } \mathrm{cons}(\mathrm{hd}\,s, \mathrm{tl}\,s \frown t)$$

is unsatisfactory since it places no type restrictions on t and thus allows nonsensical statements such as $([\,] \frown 0) = 0$ to be deduced. (Similar problems were encountered with the definition of $\subset$ in Chapter 6.) Since $s \frown t$ should be undefined when either s or t is not a list, an axiomatic definition is more appropriate than a direct definition here. The

8.5 Operators on lists

axioms are as follows:

$$\boxed{\frown\text{-defn-[ ]-left}} \quad \frac{s:A^*}{[\,]\frown s = s} \text{ Ax}$$

$$\boxed{\frown\text{-defn-cons-left}} \quad \frac{a:A;\ s_1:A^*;\ s_2:A^*}{\text{cons}(a, s_1)\frown s_2 = \text{cons}(a, s_1 \frown s_2)} \text{ Ax}$$

From these axioms can be derived rules such as

$$\boxed{\frown\text{-form}} \quad \frac{s_1:A^*;\ s_2:A^*}{s_1 \frown s_2:A^*} \qquad \boxed{\frown\text{-defn-[ ]-right}} \quad \frac{s:A^*}{s \frown [\,] = s}$$

and the associativity of $\frown$, as well as the following rules which relate various operators defined so far and the theories of sets and natural numbers:

$$\boxed{\text{len-defn-}\frown} \quad \frac{s_1:A^*;\ s_2:A^*}{\text{len}(s_1 \frown s_2) = \text{len}\, s_1 + \text{len}\, s_2}$$

$$\boxed{\text{elems-defn-}\frown} \quad \frac{s_1:A^*;\ s_2:A^*}{\text{elems}(s_1 \frown s_2) = \text{elems}\, s_1 \cup \text{elems}\, s_2}$$

The proof of 'len-defn-$\frown$' provides an opportunity to discuss the use of the rules introduced so far in the context of a proof based on rewriting of terms. The proof proceeds by induction on s_1:

from $s_1:A^*;\ s_2:A^*$

    ...
1    $\text{len}([\,]\frown s_2) = \text{len}[\,] + \text{len}\, s_2$ ⟨?? justify ??⟩
2   from $h:A;\ t:A^*;\ \text{len}(t\frown s) = \text{len}\, t + \text{len}\, s$

    ...
    infer $\text{len}(\text{cons}(h, t)\frown s_2) = \text{len}\,\text{cons}(h, t) + \text{len}\, s_2$ ⟨?? justify ??⟩
infer $\text{len}(s_1\frown s_2) = \text{len}\, s_1 + \text{len}\, s_2$ seq-indn (h1, 1, 2)

The proofs of both the base case and induction step are essentially done by rewriting the conclusions. For example, if one were presenting an informal proof of the base case, the argument might take the following form. The base case involves proving that

$$\text{len}([\,]\frown s_2) = \text{len}[\,] + \text{len}\, s_2$$

which can be done by first rewriting the left-hand side to $\text{len}\, s_2$ because $[\,]\frown s_2 = s_2$:

$$\text{len}\, s_2 = \text{len}[\,] + \text{len}\, s_2$$

Then the right-hand side rewrites to $0 + \text{len}\, s_2$ because $\text{len}[\,] = 0$, giving the following:

$$\text{len}\, s_2 = 0 + \text{len}\, s_2$$

This final result is known to be true because $\text{len}\, s_2$ is a natural number and $n = 0 + n$ for any natural number n.

In the formal framework used here, each rewriting step is a backwards application of an '=-subs' or related ('=-trans' or '=-type-inherit') rule, with the relevant equality coming from forwards reasoning from the hypotheses. Consider the base case again:

from $s_1: A^*$; $s_2: A^*$
...
1   $\text{len}([\,]\frown s_2) = \text{len}[\,] + \text{len}\, s_2$ ⟨?? justify ??⟩
⋮

The first rewriting is of $\text{len}([\,]\frown s_2)$ to $\text{len}\, s_2$. This is formalised as follows:

from $s_1: A^*$; $s_2: A^*$
...
1   $\text{len}\, s_2 = \text{len}[\,] + \text{len}\, s_2$ ⟨?? justify ??⟩
2   $\text{len}([\,]\frown s_2) = \text{len}[\,] + \text{len}\, s_2$ =-subs-?? (?, 1)
⋮

The validity of the rewriting depends on showing $[\,]\frown s_2 = s_2$, which follows by applying '$\frown$-defn-[ ]-left' to hypothesis h2:

from $s_1: A^*$; $s_2: A^*$
1   $[\,]\frown s_2 = s_2$ $\frown$-defn-[ ]-left (h2)
...
2   $\text{len}\, s_2 = \text{len}[\,] + \text{len}\, s_2$ ⟨?? justify ??⟩
3   $\text{len}([\,]\frown s_2) = \text{len}[\,] + \text{len}\, s_2$ =-subs-left(b) (h2, 1, 2)
⋮

The second rewrite proceeds similarly, using 'len-defn-[ ]':

from $s_1: A^*$; $s_2: A^*$
1   $[\,]\frown s_2 = s_2$ $\frown$-defn-[ ]-left (h2)
2   $0: N$ 0-form
3   $\text{len}[\,] = 0$ len-defn-[ ]
...
4   $\text{len}\, s_2 = 0 + \text{len}\, s_2$ ⟨?? justify ??⟩
5   $\text{len}\, s_2 = \text{len}[\,] + \text{len}\, s_2$ =-subs-left(b) (2, 3, 4)
6   $\text{len}([\,]\frown s_2) = \text{len}[\,] + \text{len}\, s_2$ =-subs-left(b) (h2, 1, 5)
⋮

The base case is completed by appealing to the theory of natural numbers and the formation rule for len, as suggested by the informal argument. The completed formal proof of the base case is:

8.5 Operators on lists

```
       from s₁: A*;  s₂: A*
1         [ ] ⁀ s₂ = s₂                              ⁀-defn-[ ]-left (h2)
2         0: N                                       0-form
3         len [ ] = 0                                len-defn-[ ]
4         len s₂: N                                  len-form (h2)
5         len s₂ = 0 + len s₂                        +-defn-0-left-rev (4)
6         len s₂ = len [ ] + len s₂                  =-subs-left(b) (2, 3, 5)
7         len ([ ] ⁀ s₂) = len [ ] + len s₂          =-subs-left(b) (h2, 1, 6)
           ⋮
```

A similar process leads to completion of the induction step, the goal of which is as follows:

$$\text{len}(\text{cons}(h, t) \frown s_2) = (\text{len cons}(h, t)) + (\text{len } s_2)$$

The left-hand side of this expression can be rewritten to len cons($h, t ⁀ s_2$) by '⁀-defn-cons-left', thence to succ(len ($t ⁀ s_2$)) by 'len-defn-cons', and finally to succ(len t + len s_2) by the induction hypothesis. The right-hand side of the induction goal can be rewritten to succ(len t) + len s_2 by 'len-defn-cons', and thence to succ(len t + len s_2) by '+-defn-succ-left-comm' from the theory of natural numbers. The formal proof of the induction step is as follows:

```
       ⋮
8      from h: A;  t: A*;  len (t ⁀ s₂) = len t + len s₂
8.1       t ⁀ s₂: A*                                        ⁀-form (8.h2, h2)
8.2       cons(h, t ⁀ s₂): A*                               cons-form (8.h1, 8.1)
8.3       cons(h, t) ⁀ s₂ = cons(h, t ⁀ s₂)                 ⁀-defn-cons-left (8.h1, 8.h2, h2)
8.4       len t ⁀ s₂: N                                     len-form (8.1)
8.5       succ len (t ⁀ s₂): N                              succ-form (8.4)
8.6       len cons(h, t ⁀ s₂) = succ len (t ⁀ s₂)           len-defn-cons (8.h1, 8.1)
8.7       len t: N                                          len-form (8.h2)
8.8       succ len t: N                                     succ-form (8.7)
8.9       len cons(h, t) = succ len t                       len-defn-cons (8.h1, 8.h2)
8.10      succ(len t + len s₂) = succ len t + len s₂        +-defn-succ-left-comm (8.7, 4)
8.11      succ(len t + len s₂) = len cons(h, t) + len s₂    =-subs-left(b) (8.8, 8.9, 8.10)
8.12      succ len (t ⁀ s₂) = len cons(h, t) + len s₂       =-subs-left(a) (8.4, 8.h3, 8.11)
8.13      len cons(h, t ⁀ s₂) = len cons(h, t) + len s₂     =-trans(b) (8.5, 8.6, 8.12)
       infer len (cons(h, t) ⁀ s₂) = len cons(h, t) + len s₂   =-subs-left(b) (8.2, 8.3, 8.13)
```

It is interesting to compare this proof based on rewriting terms to the example of a "chain of equality" proof in Section 3.4. The "chain of equality" style of reasoning is a special case of the more general rewriting of terms on both sides of the equality discussed in this section. In fact, the proof in Section 3.4 could be given the same systematic treatment that 'len-defn-⁀' has received here.

8.5.5 Distributed concatenation

The distributed concatenation operator conc, when applied to a sequence of sequences s, returns the concatenation of all the sequences in s. For example:

$$\text{conc } [[1,3],[5],[\,],[3]] = [1,3,5,3]$$

The conc operator is defined recursively in a way by now familiar to the reader:

$$\text{conc } s \stackrel{\text{def}}{=} \text{ if } s = [\,] \text{ then } [\,] \text{ else } (\text{hd} s)\frown \text{conc}(\text{tl} s)$$

The appropriate formation rule is as follows:

$$\boxed{\text{conc-form}} \quad \frac{s: A^{**}}{\text{conc } s: A^*}$$

Its proof by induction is in principle straightforward, but is made difficult to follow by the introduction and elimination of the conditional expressions corresponding to the expansion of conc. The proof is as follows:

from $s: A^{**}$
1 $[\,]: A^*$ []-form
2 (if $[\,] = [\,]$ then $[\,]$ else hd$[\,]\frown$(conc tl$[\,]$)) = $[\,]$ condition-true-ident (1, 1)
3 conc $[\,] = [\,]$ folding (2)
4 conc $[\,]: A^*$ =-type-inherit-left (1, 3)
5 from $h: A^*$; $t: A^{**}$; conc $t: A^*$
5.1 $(h \frown (\text{conc } t)): A^*$ $\frown$-form (5.h1, 5.h3)
5.2 tl cons$(h, t) = t$ tl-defn-cons (5.h1, 5.h2)
5.3 hd cons$(h, t) = h$ hd-defn-cons (5.h1, 5.h2)
5.4 cons$(h, t) \neq [\,]$ cons-$\neq$-[] (5.h1, 5.h2)
5.5 $\neg(\text{cons}(h, t) = [\,])$ unfolding (5.4)
5.6 (if cons$(h, t) = [\,]$ then $[\,]$ else $h\frown$(conc t)) = $(h\frown(\text{conc } t))$
    condition-false (5.1, 5.5)
5.7 (if (cons$(h, t) = [\,])$ then $[\,]$ else $(h\frown(\text{conc } t))): A^*$
    =-type-inherit-left (5.1, 5.6)
5.8 (if (cons$(h, t) = [\,])$ then $[\,]$ else (hd cons$(h, t)\frown(\text{conc } t))): A^*$
    =-subs-left(b) (5.h1, 5.3, 5.7)
5.9 (if (cons$(h, t) = [\,])$ then $[\,]$ else (hd cons$(h, t)\frown(\text{conc tl cons}(h, t)))): A^*$
    =-subs-left(b) (5.h2, 5.2, 5.8)
infer (conc cons$(h, t)): A^*$ folding (5.9)
infer conc $s: A^*$ seq-indn (h1, 4, 5)

In many cases where an operator is defined via a conditional, proofs can be simplified by using lemmas corresponding to the application of the conditional in cases where the condition does and does not hold. In the case of the conc operator, these lemmas are as follows:

8.5 Operators on lists

$$\boxed{\text{conc-defn-[ ]}} \quad \frac{}{\text{conc } [\,] = [\,]}$$

$$\boxed{\text{conc-defn-cons}} \quad \frac{s_1\!:\!A^+;\ s_2\!:\!A^{**}}{\text{conc cons}(s_1, s_2) = s_1 \frown \text{conc } s_2}$$

The proof of 'conc-form' (and any number of other proofs) can now exploit the lemmas, instead of expanding the definition of conc, resulting in the simpler proof shown below:

from $s\!:\!A^{**}$
1    $[\,]\!:\!A^*$ [ ]-form
2   conc [ ] = [ ]   conc-defn-[ ]
3   conc [ ]$:\!A^*$ =-type-inherit-left (1, 2)
4   from $h\!:\!A^+;\ t\!:\!A^{**};\ \text{conc } t\!:\!A^*$
4.1 $(h \frown \text{conc } t)\!:\!A^*$ $\frown$-form (4.h1, 4.h3)
4.2   conc cons$(h, t) = h \frown \text{conc } t$ conc-defn-cons (4.h1, 4.h2)
     infer (conc cons$(h, t))\!:\!A^*$ =-type-inherit-left (4.1, 4.2)
infer conc $s\!:\!A^*$ seq-indn (h1, 3, 4)

8.5.6 Sequence application

When a sequence is *applied* to a non-zero natural number i, the result is the ith element of the sequence. Sequence application is therefore only meaningful for a non-empty sequence and numbers up to the length of the sequence. These restrictions on the use of sequence application mean that, as in the case of sequence concatenation (Section 8.5.4), a direct definition is not appropriate. Instead, application is defined axiomatically. If the (non-empty) sequence is applied to the number 1, the head is returned:

$$\boxed{\text{appl-defn-hd}} \quad \frac{s\!:\!A^+}{s(1) = \text{hd } s} \ \text{Ax}$$

If s is applied to i and i is an index of s not equal to 1, the result is the $(i-1)$th element of the tail of s:

$$\boxed{\text{appl-defn-tl}} \quad \frac{s\!:\!A^+;\ i\!:\!\mathbf{N}_1;\ i \neq 1;\ i \leq \text{len } s}{s(i) = (\text{tl } s)(i - 1)} \ \text{Ax}$$

The formation rule is as follows:

$$\boxed{\text{appl-form}} \quad \frac{s\!:\!A^+;\ i\!:\!\mathbf{N}_1;\ i \leq \text{len } s}{s(i)\!:\!A}$$

The proof of 'appl-form' is not presented in full here. However, it does illustrate an important extension of the '$\Rightarrow$-E-left' strategy for proofs by induction. Using this strategy on 'appl-form', one expects to prove

$$i \leq \text{len } s \Rightarrow s(i)\!:\!A$$

by induction on s. However, an attempt at proving this fails in the induction step because the value of i is related to the sequence s introduced in the global hypothesis of the proof

rather than to the sequence introduced in the induction step. At the induction step, the knowns are:
$$s: A^+; \ i: \mathbf{N}_1; \ i \leq \operatorname{len} s$$

The step itself introduces an h and t along with the induction hypothesis. The skeleton is as follows:

$s: A^+; \ i: \mathbf{N}_1; \ i \leq \operatorname{len} s$
from $h: A; \ t: A^*; \ i \leq \operatorname{len} t \Rightarrow t(i): A$
...

1	$\delta(i \leq \operatorname{len} \operatorname{cons}(h, t))$	⟨?? justify ??⟩
2	from $i \leq \operatorname{len} \operatorname{cons}(h, t)$	
	...	
	infer $\operatorname{cons}(h, t)(i): A$	⟨?? justify ??⟩
	infer $i \leq \operatorname{len} \operatorname{cons}(h, t) \Rightarrow \operatorname{cons}(h, t)(i): A$	$\Rightarrow$-I (1, 2)

⋮

The body of the step proceeds by 'δ-E' on $\delta(i = 1)$. The case where $i = 1$ is completed easily from 'appl-defn-hd'. In the case where $i \neq 1$, the defining axiom 'appl-defn-tl' indicates that $\operatorname{cons}(h, t)(i) = t(i-1)$. However, there is no information relating to $(i-1)$ in the knowns. In particular, the induction hypothesis cannot be applied because it relates i, and not $(i-1)$ to t. This suggests that the induction hypothesis should state that $t(j): A$ for *all* j among the indices of t. The formula to be proved by induction should therefore be $\forall j: \mathbf{N}_1 \cdot j \leq \operatorname{len} s \Rightarrow s(j): A$. The '$\Rightarrow$-E-left' strategy is therefore extended to include a '$\forall$-E'. The reader should bear this extended strategy in mind where metavariables other than the subject of the induction (such as i) are linked to the subject of the induction by hypotheses in the rule to be proved. Employing the extended strategy, the skeleton of the proof is as follows:

from $s: A^+; \ i: \mathbf{N}_1; \ i \leq \operatorname{len} s$
...

1	$\forall j: \mathbf{N}_1 \cdot j \leq \operatorname{len} [\,] \Rightarrow [\,](j): A$	⟨?? justify ??⟩
2	from $h: A; \ t: A^*; \ \forall j: \mathbf{N}_1 \cdot j \leq \operatorname{len} t \Rightarrow t(j): A$	
2.1	from $k: \mathbf{N}_1$	
	...	
2.1.1	$\delta(k \leq \operatorname{len} \operatorname{cons}(h, t))$	⟨?? justify ??⟩
2.1.2	from $k \leq \operatorname{len} \operatorname{cons}(h, t)$	
	...	
	infer $\operatorname{cons}(h, t)(k): A$	⟨?? justify ??⟩
	infer $k \leq \operatorname{len} \operatorname{cons}(h, t) \Rightarrow \operatorname{cons}(h, t)(k): A$	$\Rightarrow$-I (2.1.1, 2.1.2)
	infer $\forall k: \mathbf{N}_1 \cdot k \leq \operatorname{len} \operatorname{cons}(h, t) \Rightarrow \operatorname{cons}(h, t)(k): A$	$\forall$-I (2.1)
3	$\forall j: \mathbf{N}_1 \cdot j \leq \operatorname{len} \operatorname{cons}(h, t) \Rightarrow s(j): A$	seq-indn (1, 2)
4	$i \leq \operatorname{len} \operatorname{cons}(h, t) \Rightarrow s(i): A$	$\forall$-E (h2, 3)
infer $s(i): A$		$\Rightarrow$-E-left (4, h3)

The base case follows vacuously. The induction step is based on 'δ-E' over $\delta(k = 1)$.

8.5.7 The indices of a list

In the rules for sequence application, the fact that i is a valid index for a sequence s is expressed by stating that $i: \mathbf{N}_1$ and $i \leq \operatorname{len} s$. The same fact can be expressed more succinctly by using the inds operator, which returns the set of valid indices. One could give a definition in the style used for sequence length and elements:

$$\operatorname{inds} s \stackrel{\text{def}}{=} \text{if } s = [\,] \text{ then } \{\,\} \text{ else } add(\operatorname{succ}(\operatorname{len}(\operatorname{tl} s)), \operatorname{inds} \operatorname{tl} s)$$

However, a more direct definition can be given in terms of the *set range* construct introduced in Section 6.8:

$$\operatorname{inds} s \stackrel{\text{def}}{=} \{1, \ldots, \operatorname{len} s\}$$

Proofs may now use results from the theory of set range. For example, the proof of the formation rule for inds:

$$\boxed{\text{inds-form}} \; \frac{s: A^*}{\operatorname{inds} s: \mathbf{N}_1\text{-set}}$$

follows directly from the rule 'initial-interval-1-form':

$$\boxed{\text{initial-interval-1-form}} \; \frac{n: \mathbf{N}}{\{1, \ldots, n\}: \mathbf{N}_1\text{-set}}$$

The proof is simple:

from $s: A^*$
1    $\operatorname{len} s: \mathbf{N}$ len-form (h1)
2    $\{1, \ldots, \operatorname{len} s\}: \mathbf{N}_1\text{-set}$ initial-interval-1-form (1)
infer $\operatorname{inds} s: \mathbf{N}_1$ folding (2)

Induction is not required, the base and induction cases having been considered in the proof of the rule from the theory of set range. In particular, where $\operatorname{len} s = 0$, the set range constructor returns $\{\,\}$, as required by the semantics of inds.

8.6 An alternative generator set

The empty sequence $[\,]$ and cons do not form the only possible set of generators for lists. An alternative set is $[\,]$, $[\_]$ and $\frown$. The relevant induction rule using these constructors has two base cases, corresponding to the empty list and singleton lists. The induction step takes two arbitrary lists s_1 and s_2 and, assuming P holds for each of them, requires proof that P holds for their concatenation $s_1 \frown s_2$:

$$\boxed{\text{seq-}\frown\text{-indn}} \quad \frac{s:A^*;\ P([\,])}{a:A \vdash_a P([a])}$$
$$\frac{s_1:A^*,\ s_2:A^*,\ P(s_1),\ P(s_2) \vdash_{s_1,s_2} P(s_1 \frown s_2)}{P(s)}$$

The proof of 'seq-$\frown$-indn' is straightforward and is a good illustration of the use of sequent hypotheses:

from $s:A^*;\ P([\,]);\ a:A \vdash_a P([a]);$
$\quad s_1:A^*,\ s_2:A^*,\ P(s_1),\ P(s_2) \vdash_{s_1,s_2} P(s_1 \frown s_2)$
1   from $h:A;\ t:A^*;\ P(t)$
1.1 $[h]:A^*$ [a]-form (1.h1)
1.2 $P([h])$ sequent h3 (1.h1)
1.3 $P([h] \frown t)$ sequent-E-gen-2 (1.1, 1.h2, 1.2, 1.h3, h4)
1.4 $[h] \frown t:A^*$ $\frown$-form (1.1, 1.h2)
1.5 $\text{cons}(h,t) = [h] \frown t$ [_]-$\frown$-cons (1.h1, 1.h2)
        infer $P(\text{cons}(h,t))$ =-subs-left(b) (1.4, 1.5, 1.3)
infer $P(s)$ seq-indn (h1, h2, 1)

In some cases the new induction rule is more convenient than 'seq-indn'. As an example, consider the proof that the reverse of the reverse of a sequence is the same as the original sequence. The operator for reversing the order of the elements in a sequence can be defined directly[1]:

$rev(s) \stackrel{\text{def}}{=}$ if $s = [\,]$
                    then $[\,]$
                    else $rev(\text{tl}\,s) \frown [\text{hd}\,s]$

The following rules can be proved from the definition:

$$\boxed{\text{rev-form}} \quad \frac{s:A^*}{rev(s):A^*} \qquad \boxed{\text{rev-defn-[]}} \quad \frac{}{rev[\,] = [\,]} \qquad \boxed{\text{rev-defn-[\_]}} \quad \frac{a:A}{rev[a] = [a]}$$

$$\boxed{\text{rev-defn-}\frown} \quad \frac{s_1:A^*;\ s_2:A^*}{rev(s_1 \frown s_2) = rev(s_2) \frown rev(s_1)}$$

The theorem to be proved is formally stated as follows:

$$\boxed{\text{rev-rev-id}} \quad \frac{s:A^*}{rev(rev(s)) = s}$$

Consider the proof using the new induction rule. The base case for the empty list requires showing that $rev(rev([\,])) = [\,]$, which follows from the lemma 'rev-defn-[ ]' and the rules of substitution. The base case for singleton lists requires proving $rev(rev[a]) = [a]$ for an arbitrary element a of type A, which again is straightforward using the 'rev-defn-[_]' lemma above. For the induction step, suppose s_1 and s_2 are arbitrary lists of type A^* and assume the induction hypotheses that $rev(rev(s_1)) = s_1$ and $rev(rev(s_2)) = s_2$. The

---

[1]The rev operator is not strictly part of the VDM-SL language. It is introduced here for illustrative purposes.

following chain of equality completes the proof:

$$\begin{array}{lll} rev(rev(s_1 \frown s_2)) & = rev(rev(s_2) \frown rev(s_1)) & \text{by } rev\text{-defn-}\frown \\ & = rev(rev(s_1)) \frown rev(rev(s_2)) & \text{by } rev\text{-defn-}\frown \\ & = s_1 \frown s_2 & \text{by induction hyps} \end{array}$$

A proof using 'seq-indn' is much more clumsy.

8.7 Summary

- The notions of *constructor* and *destructor* for a data type have been introduced and illustrated on sequences.

- The following operators on sequences have been defined: the singleton list, list length, list elements, concatenation, distributed concatenation, sequence application and indices.

- The definition of operators by recursive direct definition has been illustrated.

- Lemmas describing the limbs of a conditional definition are useful in simplifying proofs using the definition.

- Formalisation of proof by "rewriting" has been shown.

- An alternative generator set has been illustrated for sequences.

Two VDM-SL constructs relating to finite sequences have not been considered: sequence comprehension and the extraction of subsequences. The latter is the subject of an exercise below. Sequence comprehension is complex enough for it to be beyond the scope of this tutorial text. Briefly, the notation

$$[f(n) \mid n:\mathbb{N} \cdot P(n)]$$

is the sequence of $f(n)$ formed from taking each natural number n which satisfies P in order. Thus:

$$[n^2 + 1 \mid n:\mathbb{N} \cdot n < 5] = [1, 2, 5, 10, 17]$$

As well as describing this, an axiomatisation for sequence comprehension should ensure that the result sequence is finite and that $f(n)$ is denoting for each applicable n. Full VDM-SL has a more general form of sequence comprehension, in which n may be drawn from a set of real numbers.

8.8 Exercises

1. Separability of sequences

The induction proof of 'seq+-hnf' as discussed in Section 8.2 does not use the induction hypothesis. Prove the rule using the following lemma instead of 'seq-indn', using only rules introduced in Section 8.2:

$$\boxed{\text{seq-sep}} \quad \frac{s: A^*}{s = [\,] \vee \exists h: A \cdot \exists t: A^* \cdot s = \mathsf{cons}(h, t)}$$

Now prove 'seq-sep' by 'seq-indn', using only the rules of Section 8.2 (i.e. without using hd or tl). The introduction of hd and tl obviates the need to use induction just to provide a name for head and tail components of a list: prove 'seq-sep' using the destructors, basing the proof on a case distinction over $s = [\,]$.

2. Induction on non-empty sequences

Prove the following rule for induction over non-empty sequences using the '$\Rightarrow$-E-left' trick:

$$\boxed{\text{seq+-indn}} \quad \frac{\begin{array}{c} s: A^+ \\ a: A \vdash_a P([a]) \\ h: A,\ t: A^+,\ P(t) \vdash_{h,t} P(\mathsf{cons}(h, t)) \end{array}}{P(s)}$$

The proof is similar to that of 'bimap-indn' in Section 7.6. Also see Exercise 3 in Chapter 5.

3. Subsequences

The expression $s(i, \ldots, j)$ refers to the subsequence of sequence s beginning at index i and ending at j. Write axioms defining the subsequence operator where the indices are natural numbers greater than zero. If the sequence s is empty, $s(i, \ldots, j) = [\,]$. Otherwise, if j exceeds the length of s, the subsequence from i up to the end of s is taken. If $i > j$, then $s(i, \ldots, j) = [\,]$. Consider the various possible cases for i and j, as was done in the axiomatisation of domain and range subtraction and restriction in Section 7.3.

Sketch the proof of a formation rule for the subsequence operator.

Aside: VDM-SL has a wider definition of subsequence than this: i and j can be real rather than natural numbers, with the expression $s(i, \ldots, j)$ denoting those $s(k)$ for which k is a positive integer lying between i and j and less than len s. As with the extension to set range discussed in Section 6.8, to describe this would require a significant extension to the limited theory of numbers presented in Chapter 5, so the more general form is not discussed here.

Chapter 9

Booleans

9.1 Introduction

The boolean data type $\mathbb{B}$ consists of the two values true and false, so that the elements of $\mathbb{B}$ are those propositions which have well-defined values. In logics which admit no concept of undefinedness (such as classical logic), all propositions are well-defined, so that boolean logic is indistinguishable from the basic logic of propositions. In LPF, however, propositions may also be undefined, so that those which are either true or false essentially constitute a subset of all possible propositions, namely those propositions e for which δe is true. All the axioms and rules which hold for propositional LPF, therefore, are also valid for boolean-valued propositions, though those involving δ can generally be simplified.

In specifications there are typically two places where booleans are used – first as a basic data type from which other type definitions or state definitions are constructed, and second as the implicit type of preconditions and postconditions of operation and function definitions and of invariants (see Chapter 10). Proofs involving booleans thus almost invariably involve showing that a given expression is boolean-valued (of type $\mathbb{B}$).

The first section of this chapter gives axioms for booleans and shows that they represent a two-valued subset of propositional LPF. Formation rules for the primitive boolean-valued operators are then discussed, and it is shown how boolean-valued propositions which are constructed from subterms which may become undefined are dealt with. This section is also used to show examples of how conjectures are constructed. The final section illustrates these techniques by working through an example of a well-formedness proof such as typically arises as a proof obligation from a specification.

9.2 Basic axiomatisation

The link to the defined subset of propositional LPF is most easily formed by identifying boolean-valued with definedness (delta) via the two rules:

$$\boxed{\delta \to \mathbb{B}} \; \frac{\delta a}{a : \mathbb{B}} \; \text{Ax} \qquad\qquad \boxed{\mathbb{B} \to \delta} \; \frac{a : \mathbb{B}}{\delta a} \; \text{Ax}$$

These effectively allow one to deduce that any defined proposition is boolean-valued and, conversely, that any boolean-valued proposition is defined.

The link between propositions and values (that is 'true' and 'false') is provided by a third rule

$$\boxed{\Leftrightarrow \rightarrow =} \; \frac{a \Leftrightarrow b}{a = b} \; \text{Ax}$$

which states that boolean values are equal if they are equivalent. Note that this rule does not require typing hypotheses $a:\mathbb{B}$ or $b:\mathbb{B}$ as these are deducible from the equivalence using the rule '$\delta \rightarrow \mathbb{B}$' and the rules

$$\boxed{\Leftrightarrow\text{-E-left-}\delta} \; \frac{e_1 \Leftrightarrow e_2}{\delta e_2} \qquad \boxed{\Leftrightarrow\text{-E-right-}\delta} \; \frac{e_1 \Leftrightarrow e_2}{\delta e_1}$$

from propositional LPF.

Note also that a rule relating equality and equivalence in the other direction

$$\boxed{= \rightarrow \Leftrightarrow} \; \frac{a:\mathbb{B}; \; a = b}{a \Leftrightarrow b}$$

can be proved, though this does require a typing hypothesis $a:\mathbb{B}$ to ensure that the equivalence in its conclusion is well-defined. (Without the typing hypothesis the polymorphism of equality would induce polymorphism in equivalence so that, for example, it would be possible to prove len [ ] $\Leftrightarrow$ 0, which is clearly meaningless.) The proof is straightforward, using '$\mathbb{B} \rightarrow \delta$', '$\Leftrightarrow$-self-I' and substitution of equals:

from $a:\mathbb{B}; \; a = b$
1 δa $\mathbb{B} \rightarrow \delta$ (h1)
2 $a \Leftrightarrow a$ $\Leftrightarrow$-self-I (1)
infer $a \Leftrightarrow b$ =-subs-right(a) (h1, h2, 2)

9.2.1 $\mathbb{B}$ is two-valued

The fact that the type $\mathbb{B}$ has only two values true and false is embodied in the rule '$\mathbb{B}$-eval':

$$\boxed{\mathbb{B}\text{-eval}} \; \frac{a:\mathbb{B}}{a = \text{true} \vee a = \text{false}}$$

The proof is fairly straightforward. Clearly there is only one possible choice for each of the first two steps, namely first to apply '$\mathbb{B} \rightarrow \delta$' to the hypothesis, then to apply 'δ-E' to reason by cases. The first subproof then has a as its local hypothesis, which means that it is necessary to prove $a = \text{true}$. A backwards application of '$\Leftrightarrow \rightarrow =$' yields a new goal of $a \Leftrightarrow \text{true}$, which follows easily from the rules for equivalence in propositional LPF. The other subproof is entirely analogous.

from $a: \mathbb{B}$
1 $\quad \delta a$ $\hfill \mathbb{B} \rightarrow \delta$ (h1)
2 $\quad$ from a
2.1 $\quad\quad$ true $\hfill$ true-I
2.2 $\quad\quad$ $a \Leftrightarrow$ true $\hfill \Leftrightarrow$-I (2.h1, 2.1)
2.3 $\quad\quad$ $a =$ true $\hfill \Leftrightarrow \rightarrow =$ (2.2)
$\quad\quad$ infer $(a =$ true$) \vee (a =$ false$)$ $\hfill \vee$-I-right (2.3)
3 $\quad$ from $\neg a$
3.1 $\quad\quad$ $\neg$ false $\hfill \neg$-false-I
3.2 $\quad\quad$ $a \Leftrightarrow$ false $\hfill \Leftrightarrow$-I-$\neg$ (3.h1, 3.1)
3.3 $\quad\quad$ $a =$ false $\hfill \Leftrightarrow \rightarrow =$ (3.2)
$\quad\quad$ infer $(a =$ true$) \vee (a =$ false$)$ $\hfill \vee$-I-left (3.3)
infer $(a =$ true$) \vee (a =$ false$)$ $\hfill \delta$-E (1, 2, 3)

9.3 Formation rules for boolean-valued operators

As stated above, most of the proofs involving booleans which arise in specifications have to do with showing that a particular expression is boolean-valued. These proofs typically use the derived rules discussed in this section. The conclusion of each of these rules is of the form $x: \mathbb{B}$, where x is some expression. Rules where x only involves propositional operators are dealt with in the first subsection. The second subsection deals with quantifiers and relations.

9.3.1 Basic formation rules for propositional operators

The overall aim of this section is to define a basic set of formation rules for the propositional operators. Each of these rules will have a conclusion of the form $x: \mathbb{B}$, where x is the simplest possible expression that can be constructed out of a particular propositional operator, that is x will contain only one operator and only one occurrence of that operator. Thus, there will be rules with conclusions true: $\mathbb{B}$, $(\neg e): \mathbb{B}$, $(e_1 \wedge e_2): \mathbb{B}$, $(e_1 \Rightarrow e_2): \mathbb{B}$, and so on. It is instructive to look at how to decide what the hypotheses of such rules should be.

First, consider the constants true and false. Their formation rules will have conclusions true: $\mathbb{B}$ and false: $\mathbb{B}$ respectively, and it is clear that these represent true statements in their own right. The rules therefore need no hypotheses and simply take the form

$$\boxed{\text{true-form}} \;\; \frac{}{\text{true}: \mathbb{B}} \qquad\qquad \boxed{\text{false-form}} \;\; \frac{}{\text{false}: \mathbb{B}}$$

It is also clear that the formation rule for negation must have the form

$$\boxed{\neg\text{-form}} \;\; \frac{a: \mathbb{B}}{(\neg a): \mathbb{B}}$$

as the only way to ensure that $\neg e$ is either true or false is to make e either true or false.

The rules for the binary operators are, however, perhaps not quite so obvious. Consider, for example, the formation rule for disjunction ($\vee$). It will have a conclusion of the form $(e_1 \vee e_2): \mathbb{B}$, which amounts to the statement that $e_1 \vee e_2$ is either true or false. It is certainly the case that if both e_1 and e_2 are either true or false then so is $e_1 \vee e_2$, giving a formation rule

$$\boxed{\vee\text{-form}} \quad \frac{e_1: \mathbb{B}; \ e_2: \mathbb{B}}{(e_1 \vee e_2): \mathbb{B}}$$

but is this the best one can do? Well, $e_1 \vee e_2$ is only false if both e_1 and e_2 are false, which is covered by the above case, but it is true if *either* e_1 or e_2 is true even if the other is undefined. On the other hand $e_1 \vee e_2$ is undefined if both e_1 and e_2 are undefined. This suggests a stronger form of the formation rule which requires that one of the arguments is defined but only requires the other to be defined in the case where the first is false. The second hypothesis thus becomes a sequent, and the more general form of the rule has the form:

$$\boxed{\vee\text{-form-sqt}} \quad \frac{e_1: \mathbb{B}; \ \neg e_1 \vdash e_2: \mathbb{B}}{(e_1 \vee e_2): \mathbb{B}}$$

Note that the rule '$\vee$-form' above follows immediately from '$\vee$-form-sqt' as $e_2: \mathbb{B}$ discharges the sequent $e_1 \vdash e_2: \mathbb{B}$ directly (see Exercise 4 in Section 2.7 for a similar example).

The proof of the rule '$\vee$-form-sqt' follows the by now familiar pattern: after reducing the goal to $\delta(e_1 \vee e_2)$ by a backwards application of the rule '$\delta \to \mathbb{B}$', deduce δe_1 from $e_1: \mathbb{B}$ using the rule '$\mathbb{B} \to \delta$', then use 'δ-E' to consider the two cases. The sequent hypothesis is used in the second subproof to deduce $e_2: \mathbb{B}$, which is treated in the same way. Simple propositional logic completes the proof.

from $e_1: \mathbb{B}; \ \neg e_1 \vdash e_2: \mathbb{B}$
1   δe_1 $\mathbb{B} \to \delta$ (h1)
2   from e_1
       infer $\delta(e_1 \vee e_2)$ δ-$\vee$-I-right (2.h1)
3   from $\neg e_1$
3.1 $e_2: \mathbb{B}$ sequent h2 (3.h1)
3.2 δe_2 $\mathbb{B} \to \delta$ (3.1)
3.3   from e_2
           infer $\delta(e_1 \vee e_2)$ δ-$\vee$-I-left (3.3.h1)
3.4   from $\neg e_2$
3.4.1 $\neg(e_1 \vee e_2)$ $\neg$-$\vee$-I (3.h1, 3.4.h1)
           infer $\delta(e_1 \vee e_2)$ δ-I-$\neg$ (3.4.1)
     infer $\delta(e_1 \vee e_2)$ δ-E (3.2, 3.3, 3.4)
4    $\delta(e_1 \vee e_2)$ δ-E (1, 2, 3)
infer $(e_1 \vee e_2): \mathbb{B}$ $\delta \to \mathbb{B}$ (4)

The rules for conjunction and implication are treated similarly to those for disjunction

9.3 Formation rules for boolean-valued operators

given above. Again, there are two forms of each:

$$\boxed{\wedge\text{-form}}\ \frac{e_1:\mathbb{B};\ e_2:\mathbb{B}}{(e_1 \wedge e_2):\mathbb{B}} \qquad \boxed{\wedge\text{-form-sqt}}\ \frac{e_1:\mathbb{B};\ e_1 \vdash e_2:\mathbb{B}}{(e_1 \wedge e_2):\mathbb{B}}$$

$$\boxed{\Rightarrow\text{-form}}\ \frac{e_1:\mathbb{B};\ e_2:\mathbb{B}}{(e_1 \Rightarrow e_2):\mathbb{B}} \qquad \boxed{\Rightarrow\text{-form-sqt}}\ \frac{e_1:\mathbb{B};\ e_1 \vdash e_2:\mathbb{B}}{(e_1 \Rightarrow e_2):\mathbb{B}}$$

Their proofs are simpler, however: first, the conjunction or implication is replaced by its expanded definition, then the proof is completed using the formation rules for negation and disjunction already proved.

The formation rule for equivalence is the odd-one-out in this set as the equivalence is only defined if both its arguments are defined. There is thus only one form of the equivalence formation rule and this has hypotheses stating that both arguments must be boolean-valued:

$$\boxed{\Leftrightarrow\text{-form}}\ \frac{e_1:\mathbb{B};\ e_2:\mathbb{B}}{(e_1 \Leftrightarrow e_2):\mathbb{B}}$$

Its proof is straightforward and follows directly from the definition of equivalence and the (non-sequent forms of the) formation rules for implication and conjunction.

9.3.2 Basic formation rules for quantifiers and relations

The quantifiers $\forall$, $\exists$ and $\exists!$ and relational operators like $\in$ and $<$ are also boolean-valued and have similar formation rules. In the case of the quantifiers it is easy to see that the quantified expression is boolean-valued if its predicate is boolean-valued everywhere. Thus the formation rule for $\forall$ is

$$\boxed{\forall\text{-form}}\ \frac{y:A \vdash_y P(y):\mathbb{B}}{(\forall x:A \cdot P(x)):\mathbb{B}}$$

with similar rules for $\exists!$ and $\exists$.

Versions of these rules dealing with quantification over sets, for example

$$\boxed{\forall\text{-form-set}}\ \frac{s:A\text{-set}}{y:A,\ y \in s \vdash_y P(y):\mathbb{B}}{(\forall x \in s \cdot P(x)):\mathbb{B}}$$

can be derived.

For the relational operators the situation is even simpler as it is known from rules like 'δ-$\in$' (see set theory, Chapter 6) that they are always defined. Thus, rules like

$$\boxed{\in\text{-form}}\ \frac{a:A;\ s:A\text{-set}}{(a \in s):\mathbb{B}}$$

are immediate consequences of the corresponding definedness rule and '$\delta \to \mathbb{B}$'.

9.4 An example of a well-formedness proof obligation

As an example of how proofs involving booleans arise in practice, consider the following simple and partial specification of a parts store:

$Store :: parts \quad : Part \xleftrightarrow{m} PartId^+$
$\qquad\quad configs : Config \xleftrightarrow{m} (Part \xleftrightarrow{m} PartId)$
$\text{inv } (parts, configs) \triangleq \forall m \in \text{rng } configs \cdot \forall n \in \text{dom } m \cdot$
$\qquad n \in \text{dom } parts \wedge m(n) \in \text{elems } parts(n)$

In this specification, the first field of the composite type records the different versions of each part which are available, whilst the second records how particular versions of different parts can be combined. The use of non-empty sequences (see Chapter 8) and one-one maps (see Chapter 7) in the definitions of the fields means that there must be at least one version of each part and that it is not possible to build a configuration using different versions of the same part. The invariant imposes the additional constraint that configurations must be composed of existing parts.

As is explained in more detail in Chapter 10, associated with a type definition which has an invariant there is a proof obligation to ensure the soundness of the definition, namely that the invariant must be a boolean-valued function of its variables. For the example above, this is expressed by the rule

$$\frac{parts: Part \xleftrightarrow{m} PartId^+; \; configs: Config \xleftrightarrow{m} (Part \xleftrightarrow{m} PartId)}{(\forall m \in \text{rng } configs \cdot \forall n \in \text{dom } m \cdot n \in \text{dom } parts \wedge m(n) \in \text{elems } parts(n)): \mathbb{B}}$$

The proof of this rule follows a pattern which is typical of those of "well-formedness" proof obligations in general (invariants, preconditions, postconditions and initialisation conditions; see Chapter 10). The basic strategy is always to reason backwards, first using the formation rules for the boolean-valued operators and quantifiers given earlier in this chapter to eliminate the propositional operators and the quantifiers, then using the formation rules for relations on the resulting subgoals to generate a new set of subgoals which do not involve the boolean data-type, and finally using the standard formation rules for the basic operators on sets, maps, sequences and numbers to complete the proof.

Generally, these proofs are simple in that for a given subgoal there is only one of these rules which can be applied, namely the formation rule associated with the main operator of that subgoal. Thus, returning to the example, the main operator of the overall goal is a universal quantifier over a set, so the first step is to apply the rule '∀-form-set', giving:

from $parts: Part \xleftrightarrow{m} PartId^+; \; configs: Config \xleftrightarrow{m} (Part \xleftrightarrow{m} PartId)$
...
1   $\text{rng } configs: (Part \xleftrightarrow{m} PartId)\text{-set}$ ⟨?? justify ??⟩
2   from $m: Part \xleftrightarrow{m} PartId; \; m \in \text{rng } configs$
    ...
    infer $(\forall n \in \text{dom } m \cdot n \in \text{dom } parts \wedge m(n) \in \text{elems } parts(n)): \mathbb{B}$ ⟨?? justify ??⟩
infer $(\forall m \in \text{rng } configs \cdot \forall n \in \text{dom } m \cdot$
$\qquad n \in \text{dom } parts \wedge m(n) \in \text{elems } parts(n)): \mathbb{B}$ ∀-form-set (1, 2)

9.4 An example of a well-formedness proof obligation

Line 1 follows directly from the formation rule for range on one-one maps ('rng-form-bimap'), and the only other goal again involves showing that a universal quantification over a set is boolean-valued. The rule '∀-form-set' is therefore applied to this, yielding:

from $parts: Part \xleftrightarrow{m} PartId^+$; $configs: Config \xleftrightarrow{m} (Part \xleftrightarrow{m} PartId)$
1   rng $configs: (Part \xleftrightarrow{m} PartId)$-set   rng-form-bimap (h2)
2   from $m: Part \xleftrightarrow{m} PartId$; $m \in$ rng $configs$
     ...
2.1   dom $m: Part$-set   ⟨?? justify ??⟩
2.2   from $n: Part$; $n \in$ dom m
         ...
         infer $(n \in$ dom $parts \land m(n) \in$ elems $parts(n)): \mathbb{B}$ ⟨?? justify ??⟩
     infer $(\forall n \in$ dom $m \cdot$
         $n \in$ dom $parts \land m(n) \in$ elems $parts(n)): \mathbb{B}$ ∀-form-set (2.1, 2.2)
infer $(\forall m \in$ rng $configs \cdot \forall n \in$ dom $m \cdot$
     $n \in$ dom $parts \land m(n) \in$ elems $parts(n)): \mathbb{B}$ ∀-form-set (1, 2)

The first of the resulting subgoals is easy to discharge using the formation rule for domain for one-one maps ('dom-form-bimap'). In the second, however, it must be shown that a conjunction is boolean-valued, and there are thus two formation rules which could be applied, '∧-form' and '∧-form-sqt'. Here, and in all cases where there is a choice between a basic formation rule and its corresponding sequent form, the choice is determined by considering whether or not the separate operands are boolean-valued. If so, then the basic formation rule should be used, if not the sequent form is required. In the case in question, the right-hand operand is clearly undefined, and hence not boolean-valued, if n is not in the domain of the *parts* map as the map application *parts(n)* is undefined in that case, so the sequent form of the rule must be used. This leads to the following partial proof:

from $parts: Part \xleftrightarrow{m} PartId^+$; $configs: Config \xleftrightarrow{m} (Part \xleftrightarrow{m} PartId)$
1   rng $configs: (Part \xleftrightarrow{m} PartId)$-set   rng-form-bimap (h2)
2   from $m: Part \xleftrightarrow{m} PartId$; $m \in$ rng $configs$
2.1   dom $m: Part$-set   dom-form-bimap (2.h1)
2.2   from $n: Part$; $n \in$ dom m
         ...
2.2.1 $(n \in$ dom $parts): \mathbb{B}$ ⟨?? justify ??⟩
2.2.2   from $n \in$ dom $parts$
             ...
             infer $(m(n) \in$ elems $parts(n)): \mathbb{B}$ ⟨?? justify ??⟩
         infer $(n \in$ dom $parts \land m(n) \in$ elems $parts(n)): \mathbb{B}$ ∧-form-sqt (2.2.1, 2.2.2)
     infer $(\forall n \in$ dom $m \cdot$
         $n \in$ dom $parts \land m(n) \in$ elems $parts(n)): \mathbb{B}$ ∀-form-set (2.1, 2.2)
infer $(\forall m \in$ rng $configs \cdot \forall n \in$ dom $m \cdot$
     $n \in$ dom $parts \land m(n) \in$ elems $parts(n)): \mathbb{B}$ ∀-form-set (1, 2)

It is worth noting at this point that there was an important correlation in the step just discussed between the form of the sequent formation rule for conjunction and the order in which the various subterms appear in the expression comprising the invariant, namely that both are written in such a way that any undefinedness always appears in the right-hand conjunct. At the same time, the left-hand conjunct forms a guard to ensure that the right-hand conjunct is defined where the value of the whole expression is not determined solely by the left-hand conjunct. Thus, the formation rule has $e_1 : \mathbb{B}$ and $e_1 \vdash e_2 : \mathbb{B}$ as its hypotheses and the appropriate subterm of the invariant follows the same ordering, being written as $n \in \mathrm{dom}\, parts \land m(n) \in \mathrm{elems}\, parts(n)$. Consider, however, what would have happened if the subterms in the invariant had been written in the opposite order, namely as $m(n) \in \mathrm{elems}\, parts(n) \land n \in \mathrm{dom}\, parts$. The proof up to the previous step would be identical to that already constructed, except that now the second of the two subgoals would be $(m(n) \in \mathrm{elems}\, parts(n) \land n \in \mathrm{dom}\, parts) : \mathbb{B}$. In this simple case, of course, it would be straightforward to prove a "commuted" form of the sequent formation rule

$$\frac{e_2 : \mathbb{B}; \quad e_2 \vdash e_1 : \mathbb{B}}{(e_1 \land e_2) : \mathbb{B}}$$

and then to use this to discharge that subgoal. One might even think that having this additional rule would be an advantage in that the two rules together would mean that the order of the subterms in the specification would be immaterial. In fact this is far from the truth, and the process of adding new formation rules to cope with different combinations of subterms soon gets out of hand.

To see how this happens, suppose that one wishes to show that the expression

$$(m(m(a)) = b \land a \in \mathrm{dom}\, m) \land m(a) \in \mathrm{dom}\, m$$

is boolean-valued, where a and b are both of type A and m is of type $A \xrightarrow{m} A$ for some type A. In this case, although the whole expression is clearly boolean-valued, neither of the separate conjuncts in the main conjunction is itself boolean-valued so neither the standard sequent formation rule '$\land$-form-sqt' nor the commuted form mentioned above can be applied. This means that to deal with this case one would need either to prove a new rule dealing specifically with this particular combination of subterms or to prove rules, for example

$$\frac{((a \land b) \land c) : \mathbb{B}}{(a \land (b \land c)) : \mathbb{B}} \qquad \frac{(a \land b) : \mathbb{B}}{(b \land a) : \mathbb{B}}$$

which allow the associativity and commutativity of conjunction to be used to rewrite the expression into a form to which the original version of the sequent formation rule ('$\land$-form-sqt') can be applied.

The lesson to be learned here is that it is often possible to make the task of proving properties of a specification simpler by giving some thought to the way in which the specification is actually written. The more specific lesson is that when writing invariants, preconditions and postconditions, this simplification is achieved by ordering their subterms in such a way that any undefinedness always appears in the right-hand operand of binary propositional operators, at the same time structuring the left-hand operand to ensure that, in the case where its value does not determine the value of the overall expression, the right-hand operand is well-defined.

9.4 An example of a well-formedness proof obligation

Returning now to the original example proof, the two remaining subgoals are both justified using the relational formation rule '∈-form', yielding:

from $parts: Part \xleftrightarrow{m} PartId^+$; $configs: Config \xleftrightarrow{m} (Part \xleftrightarrow{m} PartId)$
1   rng $configs: (Part \xleftrightarrow{m} PartId)$-set   rng-form-bimap (h2)
2   from $m: Part \xleftrightarrow{m} PartId$; $m \in$ rng $configs$
2.1   dom $m: Part$-set   dom-form-bimap (2.h1)
2.2   from $n: Part$; $n \in$ dom m
               ...
2.2.1   dom $parts: Part$-set   ⟨?? justify ??⟩
2.2.2 $(n \in$ dom $parts): \mathbb{B}$ ∈-form (2.2.h1, 2.2.1)
2.2.3   from $n \in$ dom $parts$
                   ...
2.2.3.1 $m(n): PartId$ ⟨?? justify ??⟩
2.2.3.2   elems $parts(n): PartId$-set   ⟨?? justify ??⟩
               infer $(m(n) \in$ elems $parts(n)): \mathbb{B}$ ∈-form (2.2.3.1, 2.2.3.2)
            infer $(n \in$ dom $parts \land m(n) \in$ elems $parts(n)): \mathbb{B}$ ∧-form-sqt (2.2.2, 2.2.3)
       infer $(\forall n \in$ dom $m \cdot$
               $n \in$ dom $parts \land m(n) \in$ elems $parts(n)): \mathbb{B}$ ∀-form-set (2.1, 2.2)
infer $(\forall m \in$ rng $configs \cdot \forall n \in$ dom $m \cdot$
         $n \in$ dom $parts \land m(n) \in$ elems $parts(n)): \mathbb{B}$ ∀-form-set (1, 2)

and the proof is completed using the formation rules for domain, map application and elements from map theory and sequence theory (see Chapters 7 and 8):

from $parts: Part \xleftrightarrow{m} PartId^+$; $configs: Config \xleftrightarrow{m} (Part \xleftrightarrow{m} PartId)$
1   rng $configs: (Part \xleftrightarrow{m} PartId)$-set   rng-form-bimap (h2)
2   from $m: Part \xleftrightarrow{m} PartId$; $m \in$ rng $configs$
2.1   dom $m: Part$-set   dom-form-bimap (2.h1)
2.2   from $n: Part$; $n \in$ dom m
2.2.1   dom $parts: Part$-set   dom-form-bimap (h1)
2.2.2 $(n \in$ dom $parts): \mathbb{B}$ ∈-form (2.2.h1, 2.2.1)
2.2.3   from $n \in$ dom $parts$
2.2.3.1 $m(n): PartId$ at-form-bimap (2.2.h1, 2.h1, 2.2.h2)
2.2.3.2 $parts(n): PartId^+$ at-form-bimap (2.2.h1, h1, 2.2.3.h1)
2.2.3.3   elems $parts(n): PartId$-set   elems-form-seq+ (2.2.3.2)
               infer $(m(n) \in$ elems $parts(n)): \mathbb{B}$ ∈-form (2.2.3.1, 2.2.3.3)
            infer $(n \in$ dom $parts \land m(n) \in$ elems $parts(n)): \mathbb{B}$ ∧-form-sqt (2.2.2, 2.2.3)
       infer $(\forall n \in$ dom $m \cdot$
               $n \in$ dom $parts \land m(n) \in$ elems $parts(n)): \mathbb{B}$ ∀-form-set (2.1, 2.2)
infer $(\forall m \in$ rng $configs \cdot \forall n \in$ dom $m \cdot$
         $n \in$ dom $parts \land m(n) \in$ elems $parts(n)): \mathbb{B}$ ∀-form-set (1, 2)

9.5 Summary

The following points have been discussed in this chapter:

- The relationship between boolean values and well-defined propositions.
- Taking account of undefinedness in the formulation of formation rules.
- Using sequent forms of formation rules to reason about the well-formedness of partial functions.
- A standard proof strategy for dealing with well-formedness proof obligations.
- How treating undefinedness in specifications and rules systematically can lead to saving work in proofs.

9.6 Exercises

1. Substitution of equivalent values

Substitution of equal values was discussed above in Section 3.4. Analogous rules permit the substitution of equivalent values:

$$\boxed{\Leftrightarrow\text{-subs-left}}\ \frac{a \Leftrightarrow b;\ P(b)}{P(a)} \qquad \boxed{\Leftrightarrow\text{-subs-right}}\ \frac{a \Leftrightarrow b;\ P(a)}{P(b)}$$

Prove these rules.

2. The proof of '⇒-form-sqt'

Prove the rule '⇒-form-sqt'.

Part II

Proof in Practice

Chapter 10

Proofs From Specifications

10.1 Introduction

The preceding chapters have dealt with the construction of proofs about the mathematical objects of the underlying logic and data types used in VDM specifications. These theories provide the basic context where it is meaningful to reason about specifications in general. Building on this platform, it is now relatively straightforward to define the mathematical constructs corresponding to the constructions arising in each individual specification. These further theories provide the context where reasoning about individual specifications can take place. This chapter deals with how these theories are built and how they are used in proofs concerning specifications.

A VDM specification is a formal model which describes the behaviour of a system. Normally, the concern is a software system, but the use of VDM to describe the behaviour of hardware systems, human processes or other systems is not precluded. At the heart of a VDM specification are usually a model for the state of the system and some state-transforming operations. The description of the state model is supported by the language for defining the basic data types and type constructors of earlier chapters; the model for operations is given by the use of predicates which describe possible state transitions.

From a purely syntactic viewpoint, a VDM specification consists of a series of definitions: definitions of types, a state, some functions, constants and some operations. This chapter considers reasoning about each of these forms of definition in turn. Well-formedness and satisfiability of a specification cannot be guaranteed by syntactic correctness alone, and in general can only be shown by construction of proofs. Each VDM specification has a number of associated *proof obligations,* which are statements of properties that must hold true of the specification. Proof obligations also arise in reification, as described in the following chapter.

The main aim of this chapter is to describe the definitions, axioms and proof obligations which arise from a specification. Proof obligations are expressed as rules to be derived from the axioms and definitions. To avoid unnecessary detail, however, the main principles are illustrated on abstract examples. Chapter 12 contains numerous, specific, applications of the approach presented here.

10.2 Type definitions

A substantial part of the design of a VDM specification is the choice of type definitions. The aim is to construct types that "naturally" model the state and the values passed and returned by the operations and to construct a specification that whilst formal is also at a level of abstraction suitable for the reasoning one wishes to perform. The basic types and type constructors described in previous chapters are used to form type expressions which are the building material for the types to be used. Type definitions are used in specifications to name particular types relevant to the problem domain that is being specified.

This section discusses the use of type expressions in simple and composite type definitions and how invariants can be given to restrict these types. Note that composite types and invariants can only be used in type definitions whereas the previous type constructions can be used wherever a type is expected.

Discussion of recursion in type definitions and the construction of induction rules to reason about recursive types is deferred to Section 13.4.

10.2.1 Simple type definitions

A simple type definition associates a new name with some type expression. Consider an example similar to that Chapter 1:

$Frame = Var \xrightarrow{m} Loc$

This specifies the type name *Frame* as a synonym for the type of maps from *Var* to *Loc*. For a simple type definition of this form, there is no need for any explicit formation or definition rules. The corresponding definition in the logical framework is:

$Frame \stackrel{\text{def}}{=} Var \xrightarrow{m} Loc$

in the theory of the specification. Folding and unfolding the type definition can be used to reduce proofs about *Frame*s to proofs about maps. However, not all forms of type definition can be treated in this way and the following sections deal with some of these.

10.2.2 Invariants

Of crucial importance in the definition of sufficiently abstract types for modelling a system is the idea of type invariants. A *type invariant* (or simply *invariant*) is used to restrict the possible values of a type. For example, one may wish to give a model for the even numbers, ordered sequences or possible positions in the game of chess. For such definitions it is convenient to first describe a supertype which includes the values required and then eliminate the unwanted values from that type by giving a property that holds just for the desired values. The invariant is thus a predicate on the values of a type defined by a type expression.

In narrowing down the possible values of the type, the invariant can help the reader of a specification to understand quickly and precisely how the type models the system in question. In particular, when used in a state definition, the invariant can be thought of as an assertion that certain states are unreachable and so can save the reader or verifier of

10.2 Type definitions

the specification needless concern about cases that never occur. In practice, the choice of type model and invariant can be a powerful tool in aiding understanding of the system being specified.

In VDM, the type invariant is considered to be part of the type definition and so asserting type membership is implicitly also asserting that the invariant holds.

Consider a simple example, the type *Even* of even numbers:

$Even = \mathbb{N}$
inv $e \quad \triangleq \quad e \bmod 2 = 0$

It is convenient to introduce a definition for the invariant:

$inv\text{-}Even(n) \stackrel{\text{def}}{=} n \bmod 2 = 0$

particularly when the predicate is long. The type *Even* is treated as a subtype of the natural numbers, with the invariant forming the defining predicate:

$Even \stackrel{\text{def}}{=} \ll e:\mathbb{N} \mid inv\text{-}Even(e) \gg$

From this definition and the rules for subtypes (Section 4.5) it is possible to derive rules that explicitly give properties of the even numbers to be used in proofs. Firstly, instantiating the rule 'subtype-I' for the above definition gives a rule saying that a natural number that satisfies the invariant for *Even* is also an even number:

$$\boxed{Even\text{-form}} \; \frac{n:\mathbb{N}; \;\; inv\text{-}Even(n)}{n:Even}$$

Furthermore, instantiating the rule 'supertype' yields a rule which states that all even numbers are natural numbers, and 'subtype-E' shows that all even numbers satisfy the *inv-Even* predicate:

$$\boxed{Evens\text{-are-Ns}} \; \frac{e:Even}{e:\mathbb{N}} \qquad \boxed{inv\text{-}Even\text{-I}} \; \frac{e:Even}{inv\text{-}Even(e)}$$

These three rules give the defining properties of even numbers. However, as with the primitive types from earlier chapters, it is worthwhile constructing a library of lemmas about the type *Even* that will raise the level of reasoning in proofs. For example, one might prove a lemma stating that the sums and products of even numbers are even. Once a sufficient number of such properties have been shown it should be possible to reason entirely at the level of evenness rather than remainders.

Of course, there is a well-formedness obligation on the type definition which states that the invariant should be total and boolean-valued over the supertype:

$$\boxed{inv\text{-}Even\text{-form}} \; \frac{n:\mathbb{N}}{inv\text{-}Even(n):\mathbb{B}}$$

A simple validation condition that may be proved, without which the definition of a simple type with invariant is unlikely to be useful, is that the type is inhabited:

$$\boxed{Even\text{-inhab}} \; \frac{}{inhabited(Even)}$$

This is not an obligation, as VDM-SL does not insist that every defined type is inhabited.

10.2.3 Composite type definitions

Composite type definitions allow the construction of types that are akin to Cartesian product types, but where the composite type has a named constructor function and each component (or *field*) has a named selector function. For example, one might wish to specify that locations are composed of a segment address and an offset:

$$Loc :: segment : Even$$
$$offset : \mathbf{N}$$

In addition to defining the type name *Loc*, this also defines a constructor for locations *mk-Loc*, and selectors (destructors) for each field $\_.segment$ and $\_.offset$. The type definition also gives rise to formation rules for the constructor and selectors:

$$\boxed{mk\text{-}Loc\text{-form}} \quad \frac{s: Even;\ o: \mathbf{N}}{mk\text{-}Loc(s, o): Loc} \ \mathbf{Ax}$$

$$\boxed{segment\text{-form}} \quad \frac{l: Loc}{l.segment: Even} \ \mathbf{Ax} \qquad \boxed{offset\text{-form}} \quad \frac{l: Loc}{l.offset: \mathbf{N}} \ \mathbf{Ax}$$

These rules can be thought of as defining the following signatures for the constructor and selectors:

$mk\text{-}Loc: Even \times \mathbf{N} \to Loc$
$\_.segment: Loc \to Even$
$\_.offset: Loc \to \mathbf{N}$

Two further axioms give definitions of the selector functions, $\_.segment$ and $\_.offset$, which extract the relevant components of a *Loc*:

$$\boxed{segment\text{-defn}_0} \quad \frac{mk\text{-}Loc(s, o): Loc}{mk\text{-}Loc(s, o).segment = s} \ \mathbf{Ax}$$

$$\boxed{offset\text{-defn}_0} \quad \frac{mk\text{-}Loc(s, o): Loc}{mk\text{-}Loc(s, o).offset = o} \ \mathbf{Ax}$$

Note that the typing assertion $mk\text{-}Loc(s, o): Loc$ is used to ensure that $mk\text{-}Loc(s, o)$ is well-formed, that is $s: Even$ and $o: \mathbf{N}$.

It can be shown from these axioms that each element of a composite type has a unique representation in terms of the *mk*-function for that type, that is, it is possible to prove:

$$\frac{mk\text{-}Loc(s_1, o_1): Loc;\ mk\text{-}Loc(s_2, o_2): Loc}{\underline{mk\text{-}Loc(s_1, o_1) = mk\text{-}Loc(s_2, o_2)}}$$
$$s_1 = s_2 \land o_1 = o_2$$

One further axiom is required to ensure that $\_.segment$ and $\_.offset$ together give enough information to reconstruct a *Loc*:

$$\boxed{mk\text{-}Loc\text{-defn}} \quad \frac{l: Loc}{mk\text{-}Loc(l.segment, l.offset) = l} \ \mathbf{Ax}$$

This ensures that a *Loc* is characterised completely by its *segment* and *offset* selectors, that is, there is no "hidden" information in a *Loc* which the selectors cannot reveal.

10.2 Type definitions

Used judiciously, composite types have a number of advantages over Cartesian products. The field names are available as mnemonics for the components and can be used as selector functions to "extract" the fields without the designer needing to remember the order in which they occur; and the constructor function ensures that values of the composite type cannot be confused with values of the product type that might be used elsewhere.

10.2.4 Composite types with invariants

In the same way that invariants can be used to restrict simple type definitions, they can also be used with composite types. One way that this can be done is to first make a type definition giving a name to the unrestricted type (often a subscript '0' is added to the type name for this "proto-type"). Then the desired type can be defined by giving the invariant as a predicate on the proto-type. The rules for reasoning about such a construct simply reflect its two stage definition. The unrestricted type is defined as a composite type without an invariant, then the restricted type is defined as a simple type with invariant.

An alternative, more direct, approach is often preferred, particularly when it is convenient to write the invariant as a predicate on the separate fields. For this form some adaptation of the rules for composite types is required.

Consider again the above example and suppose that an invariant is added to *Loc*:

Loc :: *segment* : *Even*
       offset : $\mathbb{N}$
inv $mk\text{-}Loc(s, o)$ $\triangleq$ $(s \times 2^4 + o) < 2^{20}$

Here, the invariant is defined in terms of a pattern $mk\text{-}Loc(s, o)$. It could also be defined in terms of a single variable of type *Loc*, though this would be less convenient for the present approach.

As was done for invariants on simple type definitions, it is convenient to introduce a definition:

$inv\text{-}Loc(s, o)$ $\stackrel{\text{def}}{=}$ $(s \times 2^4 + o) < 2^{20}$

which, just as for simple types, should be boolean-valued over the cross-product of the field types:

$$\boxed{inv\text{-}Loc\text{-form}} \; \frac{s\colon Even;\; o\colon \mathbb{N}}{inv\text{-}Even(s, o)\colon \mathbb{B}}$$

The formation axioms for the selectors, '*segment*-form' and '*offset*-form', are as before but there is an extra hypothesis in the formation axiom for the constructor, '$mk\text{-}Loc$-form', which asserts that the invariant holds for the values being composed:

$$\boxed{mk\text{-}Loc\text{-form}} \; \frac{s\colon Even;\; o\colon \mathbb{N};\; inv\text{-}Loc(s, o)}{mk\text{-}Loc(s, o)\colon Loc} \; \text{Ax}$$

Similarly, the introduction axioms '*segment*-defn$_0$', '*offset*-defn$_0$' and '$mk\text{-}Loc$-defn' are as before but an additional axiom for asserting the invariant is required:

$$\boxed{inv\text{-}Loc\text{-I}} \; \frac{mk\text{-}Loc(s, o)\colon Loc}{inv\text{-}Loc(s, o)} \; \text{Ax}$$

Together, these axioms capture the idea that the expression $mk\text{-}Loc(s, o)$ has type Loc precisely when s: $Even$, o: $\mathbb{N}$ and the invariant holds for s and o. They also state that all values of type Loc can be formed in this way.

As for simple types with invariants, it is worthwhile demonstrating that the defined type is inhabited.

Note that the rules of the previous section (before invariants were considered) can be recovered as special cases of the rules of this section where the invariant is universally true.

10.3 The state

As described in Chapter 1, a VDM specification defines a state machine with labelled transitions. The type constructions are used to give a model for the state space and the transition system is implicitly defined by the operations. This section describes how reasoning can be performed about the description of the state.

In VDM, the state is described as a composite type with an optional invariant. The separate fields of the type might be thought of as state variables and the invariant as a description of which states are of interest. As this may be an abstract specification, there is no requirement that these variables should correspond to the variables that will eventually appear in the implementation of the specification. (See data reification in the next chapter.) There may also be an initialisation condition describing the initial states for the system.

Consider the following simple state definition:

state S of
    a : A
    b : B
inv $mk\text{-}S(x, y)$ $\triangleq$ $P(x, y)$
init $mk\text{-}S(x, y)$ $\triangleq$ $Q(x, y)$
end

This defines a state S which consists of two components a and b of types A and B respectively. The invariant and initialisation are given in terms of a pattern $mk\text{-}S(x, y)$ that matches the structure of the state model: the invariant is expressed as a predicate $P(x, y)$ in x and y; similarly for the initialisation $Q(x, y)$.

Clearly, S is a form of composite type with invariant. The same definitions and rules that appear in Section 10.2.4 apply. However, there is an extra dimension introduced by the initialisation predicate.

10.3.1 Initialisation

As for invariants, it is convenient to make a definition for the initialisation predicate. Unlike the definition for the invariant (which is defined as a predicate in the components of the state) the initialisation is defined as a predicate in the entire state. In the VDM-SL definition of S above, the initialisation is defined (like the invariant) via a pattern $mk\text{-}S(x, y)$[1],

10.4 Functions and values

and the definition of *init-S* in the logical framework uses the selector functions:

$$\textit{init-S}(\sigma) \stackrel{\text{def}}{=} Q(\sigma.a, \sigma.b)$$

Obligations for well-formedness and satisfiability of the initialisation predicate are also required. Well-formedness requires that the initialisation predicate be boolean-valued over the state type:

$$\forall \sigma: S \cdot \textit{init-S}(\sigma): \mathbb{B}$$

which can be formulated as a rule:

$$\boxed{\textit{init-S-form}} \quad \frac{\sigma: S}{\textit{init-S}(\sigma): \mathbb{B}}$$

Satisfiability requires the existence of a state for which the initialisation predicate holds:

$$\boxed{\textit{init-S-sat}} \quad \frac{}{\exists \sigma: S \cdot \textit{init-S}(\sigma)}$$

This last condition also demonstrates that the state type is inhabited, and reduces to inhabitedness when there is no initialisation given, that is, when the predicate is simply true.

10.4 Functions and values

In VDM, auxiliary functions are used together with type definitions to model concepts that arise in applications. Proving properties of these functions can help with reasoning about the specification by raising its level from that of the primitive constructs of the language to that of the auxiliary functions. Thus the use of auxiliary constructs in a specification is akin to the use of definitions in mathematics. Some work needs to be done to correctly formulate useful functions, and further work must be done to establish properties of these functions, but then reasoning can be conducted at the level of the defined concepts rather than those used in the definitions.

In VDM, functions can be defined either explicitly by giving an expression that evaluates the result in terms of the parameters, or implicitly by stating a relation between the result and the parameters. *Constants*, or *value expressions*, can be thought of as functions without parameters.

10.4.1 Explicit function definitions

As a first example, consider a simple explicit function definition with no precondition:

$$f: \textit{Even} \times \mathbb{N} \to \mathbb{N}$$
$$f(x,y) \;\triangleq\; x \times 2^4 + y$$

In order to be able to reason about the above function a rule is required that enables "folding" and "unfolding" of its definition. Such a rule is simple to state:

---
[1] See Section 13.6 for further discussion on patterns.

$$\boxed{f\text{-defn}}\ \frac{x\colon\mathsf{Even};\ y\colon\mathsf{N}}{f(x,y) = x \times 2^4 + y}$$

but to give such a rule as an axiom would be dangerous. For example, if the body of the function were ill-formed, then the value of the function might be undefined and the equation in the conclusion would introduce an inconsistency (see the discussion of weak equality in Section 3.4).

Thus, before asserting such an equality, it is necessary to ensure the well-formedness of the function body, that is to show:

$$\boxed{f\text{-wff}}\ \frac{x\colon\mathsf{Even};\ y\colon\mathsf{N}}{(x \times 2^4 + y)\colon\mathsf{N}}$$

Once this has been shown, the 'f-defn' rule given above can be used.

This requirement to show well-formedness before using the definition rule is formalized by giving as an axiom a version of the definition rule with a "one-point" version[2] of well-formedness as an extra hypothesis:

$$\boxed{f\text{-defn}_0}\ \frac{x\colon\mathsf{Even};\ y\colon\mathsf{N};\ (x \times 2^4 + y)\colon\mathsf{N}}{f(x,y) = x \times 2^4 + y}\ \text{Ax}$$

Now the "working version" of the definition rule given above can be justified by proving the general well-formedness rule and using it to discharge the extra hypothesis:

from $x\colon\mathsf{Even};\ y\colon\mathsf{N}$
1    $x \times 2^4 + y\colon\mathsf{N}$ f-wff (h1, h2)
infer $f(x,y) = x \times 2^4 + y$ f-defn$_0$ (h1, h2, 1)

In this way, the well-formedness of the function body has been shown for once and for all and the axiomatic form of the definition rule with the extra hypothesis need never be used again.

Note that even if a parameter is not mentioned in the body of the function, it is still included as a typing hypothesis to maintain strictness. For example, consider a function which only uses the first of its arguments, say:

$g\colon \mathsf{N} \times \mathsf{N} \to \mathsf{N}$
$g(x,y)\ \triangleq\ x \times 2^4$

This gives the axiom:

$$\boxed{g\text{-defn}_0}\ \frac{x\colon\mathsf{N};\ y\colon\mathsf{N};\ (x \times 2^4)\colon\mathsf{N}}{g(x,y) = x \times 2^4}\ \text{Ax}$$

Even though the type-soundness of the body of g only depends on g's first argument, this axiom permits the replacement of $g(e_1, e_2)$ in an expression by $e_1 \times 2^4$ only if both e_1 and e_2 are of type N. Consequently, an expression such as $g(0, 1/0)$ cannot be replaced by 0

---

[2] The term "one-point" is used because in order to deduce (using the axiom 'f-defn$_0$') that $f(x,y)$ is defined for some particular x and y, it is sufficient to show that the body expression is well-formed for those particular values of x and y, i.e. for one point of the domain of f. It is not necessary to show that the body of f is well-defined throughout the (claimed) domain of f.

10.4 Functions and values

and hence the type of $g(x, y)$ cannot be inferred.

This requirement explains why functions are not treated as definitions. Such a function would present a number of problems if interpreted in the obvious way as a definition:

$$g(x,y) \stackrel{\text{def}}{=} x \times 2^4$$

Firstly, at the syntactic level, unfolding the definition would lose information and so it would be impossible to fold it again:

$$g(1,2) = 2^4 = g(1,?).$$

But even if some way were found to circumvent this, at the semantic level such a definition would be non-strict. For example, one could derive:

$$g(1, 1/0) = (1 \times 2^4) : \mathbf{N}$$

even though 1/0 is undefined.

Such problems could perhaps be avoided by some mechanism that introduces a superfluous mention of the unused parameter, for example one might define:

$$g(x,y) \stackrel{\text{def}}{=} \text{let } y = y \text{ in } x \times 2^4$$

but such a "syntactic trick" is unnatural, and the axiomatic interpretation is preferred.

10.4.2 Preconditions

Both explicit and implicit function definitions can have preconditions. The precondition is used to place restrictions upon the domain of applicability of the function, in addition to the typing constraints of the function signature. Function definitions with preconditions say nothing about the behaviour of a function when applied to values that do not satisfy the precondition (the function is not even guaranteed to terminate). To formalize this, the precondition can simply be added to the hypotheses of each of the above axioms and rules.

In order to prevent having to write the precondition expression repeatedly, it is convenient to make a definition for it. If the example given above had a precondition:

$f : \text{Even} \times \mathbf{N} \to \mathbf{N}$
$f(x,y) \;\triangleq\; x \times 2^4 + y$
pre $x < 2^{16} \wedge y < 2^{16}$

the following definition would be made:

$$\textit{pre-f}(x,y) \stackrel{\text{def}}{=} x < 2^{16} \wedge y < 2^{16}$$

and the axiom 'f-defn$_0$' would have the precondition as an extra hypothesis:

$$\boxed{f\text{-defn}_0} \;\; \frac{x : \text{Even}; \; y : \mathbf{N}; \; \textit{pre-f}(x,y); \; (x \times 2^4 + y) : \mathbf{N}}{f(x,y) = x \times 2^4 + y} \;\; \text{Ax}$$

and similarly for the rules 'f-wff' and 'f-defn':

$$\boxed{f\text{-wff}} \frac{x:\mathsf{Even};\ y:\mathsf{N};\ \textit{pre-f}(x,y)}{(x \times 2^4 + y):\mathsf{N}}$$

$$\boxed{f\text{-defn}} \frac{x:\mathsf{Even};\ y:\mathsf{N};\ \textit{pre-f}(x,y)}{f(x,y) = x \times 2^4 + y}$$

Once again, care should be taken to guard against possible ill-formedness of the precondition. It should be total in the arguments to f (that is, over $\textit{Even} \times \mathsf{N}$) and boolean-valued:

$$\boxed{\textit{pre-f}\text{-form}} \frac{x:\mathsf{Even};\ y:\mathsf{N}}{\textit{pre-f}(x,y):\mathbb{B}}$$

Again there is the issue of how to handle the case where a parameter is not mentioned. In this case the approach taken is to make the precondition a definition with fewer parameters, ensuring that wherever the definiendum is used the correct arguments are selected to be used as parameters.

10.4.3 Implicit function definitions

The treatment of implicit functions is not too dissimilar to explicit ones. The same example might have been written implicitly as:

$f\ (x:\mathsf{Even}, y:\mathsf{N})\ r:\mathsf{N}$
pre $x < 2^{16} \wedge y < 2^{16}$
post $r = x \times 2^4 + y$

Definitions are introduced for the precondition and postcondition. The definition for a postcondition is similar to that for the precondition, with an extra parameter for the result:

$$\textit{pre-f}(x,y) \overset{\text{def}}{=} x < 2^{16} \wedge y < 2^{16}$$

$$\textit{post-f}(x,y,r) \overset{\text{def}}{=} r = x \times 2^4 + y$$

Well-formedness amounts to saying that, given arguments of the correct types satisfying the precondition, the postcondition must be a boolean-valued expression:

$$\boxed{\textit{post-f}\text{-form}} \frac{x:\mathsf{Even};\ y:\mathsf{N};\ r:\mathsf{N};\ \textit{pre-f}(x,y)}{\textit{post-f}(x,y,r):\mathbb{B}}$$

A working formation rule can be given, stating that $f(x,y)$ is well-typed if the arguments are of the correct types and satisfy the precondition:

$$\boxed{f\text{-form}} \frac{x:\mathsf{N};\ y:\mathsf{N};\ \textit{pre-f}(x,y)}{f(x,y):\mathsf{N}}$$

with the intention that this should be proven using the axiom '$f\text{-form}_0$' (given later).

As f is implicitly defined, it is not possible, in general, to give a precise value z such that $f(x,y) = z$; f is said to be *under-specified* (see Section 10.4.5.) The most that can be said is that $f(x,y)$ satisfies its postcondition (given the same conditions as above):

10.4 Functions and values

$$\boxed{f\text{-defn}} \frac{x\colon \mathbf{N};\ y\colon \mathbf{N};\ \textit{pre-f}(x,y)}{\textit{post-f}(x,y,f(x,y))}$$

Before these rules can be used, the *satisfiability* proof obligation for f should be discharged (otherwise, there is no guarantee that the expression $f(x,y)$ denotes a value). The satisfiability obligation can be described as the rule:

$$\boxed{f\text{-sat}} \frac{x\colon \mathbf{N};\ y\colon \mathbf{N};\ \textit{pre-f}(x,y)}{\exists r\colon \mathbf{N} \cdot \textit{post-f}(x,y,r)}$$

Proof of satisfiability for this example should present no problems. After some unfolding of definitions, a witness has to be chosen for the application of exists introduction. In effect, this requires one to build an expression which could be an explicit definition of the function. In this example, it is clear that one must choose $x \times 2^4 + y$ as the witness.

Another way that one might be tempted to proof satisfiability could be to choose the expression $f(x,y)$ itself as the witness. The proof would then be completed by recourse to the 'f-defn' rule given above. Of course, such an argument would be quite circular and completely invalid. Clearly, satisfiability must be proved without using the function itself in constructing the witness expression.

In preference to requiring this meta-logical constraint on the proof of satisfiability, as for explicit functions, the working rules 'f-form' and 'f-defn' are not given as axioms. Rather the axioms incorporate "one-point" versions of the satisfiability obligation, as for the explicit function example:

$$\boxed{f\text{-form}_0} \frac{x\colon \mathbf{N};\ y\colon \mathbf{N};\ \textit{pre-f}(x,y);\ \exists r\colon \mathbf{N} \cdot \textit{post-f}(x,y,r)}{f(x,y)\colon \mathbf{N}} \quad \text{Ax}$$

$$\boxed{f\text{-defn}_0} \frac{x\colon \mathbf{N};\ y\colon \mathbf{N};\ \textit{pre-f}(x,y);\ \exists r\colon \mathbf{N} \cdot \textit{post-f}(x,y,r)}{\textit{post-f}(x,y,f(x,y))} \quad \text{Ax}$$

Thus, before any properties of an expression which applies f to a particular x and y can be derived, it must be shown that f is satisfiable for those particular arguments. The working versions can be proved from these using the satisfiability rule 'f-sat'.

10.4.4 Recursive functions and satisfiability

It is interesting to see how the above axiomatisation deals with functions defined using recursion. As might be expected, for these functions reasoning tends to rely on induction. In this section, the proof of satisfiability for a recursively defined function is outlined.

Consider the function *sum* on sequences of natural numbers, defined implicitly via[3]:

sum $(s\colon \mathbf{N}^*)\ r\colon \mathbf{N}$
post if $s = []$ then $r = 0$ else $r = \text{hd}\,s + \textit{sum}(\text{tl}\,s)$

Using the scheme given previously, this generates two axioms and a definition for the post-condition:

$$\boxed{\textit{sum-form}_0} \frac{s\colon \mathbf{N}^*;\ \exists r\colon \mathbf{N} \cdot \textit{post-sum}(s,r)}{\textit{sum}(s)\colon \mathbf{N}} \quad \text{Ax}$$

---

[3] Clearly this function could have been defined explicitly. In fact the same issues arise in either case.

$$\boxed{\textit{sum-defn}_0} \; \frac{s: \mathbf{N}^*; \; \exists r: \mathbf{N} \cdot \textit{post-sum}(s, r)}{\textit{post-sum}(s, \textit{sum}(s))} \; \textbf{Ax}$$

$$\textit{post-sum}(s, r) \stackrel{\text{def}}{=} \text{if } s = [\,] \text{ then } r = 0 \text{ else } r = \text{hd } s + \textit{sum}(\text{tl } s)$$

The task is to prove the following satisfiability obligation:

$$\boxed{\textit{sum-sat}} \; \frac{s: \mathbf{N}^*}{\exists r: \mathbf{N} \cdot \textit{post-sum}(s, r)}$$

From this, the working versions of the formation and definition rules can be proved:

$$\boxed{\textit{sum-form}} \; \frac{s: \mathbf{N}^*}{\textit{sum}(s): \mathbf{N}} \qquad \boxed{\textit{sum-defn}} \; \frac{s: \mathbf{N}^*}{\textit{post-sum}(s, \textit{sum}(s))}$$

As might be expected, the proof proceeds by sequence induction. The point of interest is how the existential hypotheses in the axioms are discharged when they are used in the induction step.

The first stage is to apply sequence induction backwards to the conclusion to give:

from $s: \mathbf{N}^*$
    ...
1    $\exists r: \mathbf{N} \cdot \textit{post-sum}([\,], r)$ ⟨?? justify ??⟩
2   from $h: \mathbf{N}; \; t: \mathbf{N}^*; \; \exists r: \mathbf{N} \cdot \textit{post-sum}(t, r)$
       ...
    infer $\exists r: \mathbf{N} \cdot \textit{post-sum}(\textit{cons}(h, t), r)$ ⟨?? justify ??⟩
infer $\exists r: \mathbf{N} \cdot \textit{post-sum}(s, r)$ seq-indn (h1, 1, 2)

The base case is simple to justify by choosing the witness r to be 0, unfolding the definition of *post-sum* and using 'condition-true'. The induction step is justified by '∃-I' choosing $h + \textit{sum}(t)$ as witness. Progress can also be made by working forwards from the local hypotheses of the induction step by using the '*sum*-defn$_0$' axiom on t. Notice how the local hypothesis generated by the induction step is exactly what is required to be able to discharge the existential hypothesis in '*sum*-defn$_0$'. Performing these two steps gives:

from $s: \mathbf{N}^*$
    ...
1    $\exists r: \mathbf{N} \cdot \textit{post-sum}([\,], r)$ ⟨?? justify ??⟩
2   from $h: \mathbf{N}; \; t: \mathbf{N}^*; \; \exists r: \mathbf{N} \cdot \textit{post-sum}(t, r)$
2.1 $\textit{post-sum}(t, \textit{sum}(t))$ *sum*-defn$_0$ (2.h2, 2.h3)
       ...
2.2 $h + \textit{sum}(t): \mathbf{N}$ ⟨?? justify ??⟩
2.3 $\textit{post-sum}(\textit{cons}(h, t), h + \textit{sum}(t))$ ⟨?? justify ??⟩
    infer $\exists r: \mathbf{N} \cdot \textit{post-sum}(\textit{cons}(h, t), r)$ ∃-I (2.2, 2.3)
infer $\exists r: \mathbf{N} \cdot \textit{post-sum}(s, r)$ seq-indn (h1, 1, 2)

The fact that $h + \textit{sum}(t)$ is a natural number can now be proved using '+-form' and '*sum*-form$_0$'. Note once again, that the existential local hypothesis is exactly what is needed to

10.4 Functions and values

be able to use 'sum-$form_0$'.

The remaining part of this proof, to justify $post$-$sum(cons(h,t), h + sum(t))$ from $post$-$sum(t, sum(t))$ is straightforward once the postconditions are expanded.

One can see now why *one-point* versions of the satisfiability obligations are used to guard the formation and definition axioms. An alternative formulation which could be suggested would be to use the full satisfiability obligation as a sequent hypothesis in the axioms. Although this is perfectly satisfactory for non-recursive functions, the approach does not work for recursive functions. The induction in a proof such as that above becomes trapped in a "satisfiability loop": to show that *sum* is satisfiable at an arbitrary point s, it must be shown to be satisfiable throughout its domain. (See Exercise 5.)

10.4.5 Looseness in function definitions

In VDM, looseness in the definition of functions is interpreted as under-specification (also known as under-determinism) rather than non-determinism. That is to say that it can be assumed that the function always evaluates to the same result even though the precise value may not be fully determined.

This looseness can arise either from the use of implicit functions where the body does not fully determine the result or from the use of loose expression constructs in explicit functions. (Loose expression constructs are discussed in Chapter 13.)

For example, consider the function:

$f\ (x:\mathbf{N}, y:\mathbf{N})\ r:\mathbf{N}$
pre $x \le y$
post $x \le r \land r \le y$.

Clearly it is easy to discharge well-formedness ('$post$-f-form') and satisfiability ('f-sat'). The latter can then be used with 'f-$form_0$' and 'f-$defn_0$' to prove 'f-form' and 'f-defn'. In this example, pre-f can be unfolded in 'f-form' to give:

$$\boxed{f\text{-form}_1}\ \frac{x:\mathbf{N};\ y:\mathbf{N};\ x \le y}{f(x,y):\mathbf{N}}$$

This can be used with '=-self-I' to prove:

$$\boxed{f\text{-deterministic}}\ \frac{x:\mathbf{N};\ y:\mathbf{N};\ x \le y}{f(x,y) = f(x,y)}$$

Thus, applying f to the same values always produces the same (natural number) value, or in other words, f is deterministic.

Similarly, $post$-f can be unfolded in 'f-defn' to obtain:

$$\boxed{f\text{-prop}_1}\ \frac{x:\mathbf{N};\ y:\mathbf{N};\ x \le y}{x \le f(x,y)\ \land\ f(x,y) \le y}$$

This captures the fact that the specification of f is loose: the most that can be said about f is that it returns a number that lies between its arguments.

10.4.6 Polymorphic function definitions

Many of the predefined functions in VDM-SL are *polymorphic*. For example, 'tl' can be applied to sequences of any type X. It is also possible to define new polymorphic functions in VDM-SL, whose signatures can contain one or more type variables.

Polymorphic function definitions must be explicit, and when such a function is applied, any type variables in its definition must be instantiated to specific types (which can be the type variables of an enclosing function). As an example, the following defines a function which returns the last element of a non-empty sequence of items of arbitrary type:

$last\,[@elem]: @elem^+ \to @elem$
$last(l) \;\triangleq\; \text{if len}\, l = 1 \text{ then hd}\, l \text{ else } last[@elem](\text{tl}\, l)$

Here, the phrase '$[@elem]$' in the signature introduces a type variable '$@elem$'. When *last* is applied recursively, this type variable must be instantiated, in this case by itself.

Now *last* can be used to define the function *addlast*, which adds the last elements of two non-empty sequences of natural numbers:

$addlast : \mathbf{N}^+ \times \mathbf{N}^+ \to \mathbf{N}$
$addlast(l_1, l_2) \;\triangleq\; last[\mathbf{N}](l_1) + last[\mathbf{N}](l_2)$

Here the type variable in the definition of *last* is instantiated by $\mathbf{N}$ in each application.

A polymorphic function definition can be handled in the theory of a specification much like any other explicit function definition: the only difference is that the polymorphic type variable becomes a metavariable For example, the formation rule for *last* is:

$$\boxed{last\text{-form}}\;\; \frac{l: Elem^+}{last(l): Elem}$$

where *Elem* is a type metavariable in the rule, not the name of a type defined in the theory.

When proving properties about an application of a polymorphic function, instantiation of the type variable is handled as part of the instantiation of the metavariables in applying (for example) the formation rule. (Consequently, there is no need for the explicit instantiation in VDM-SL polymorphic function application to be duplicated in the logical frame.) An example of this occurs in the following proof of '*addlast*-form':

from $l_1: \mathbf{N}^+$; $l_2: \mathbf{N}^+$
1    $last(l_1): \mathbf{N}$ *last*-form (h1)
2    $last(l_2): \mathbf{N}$ *last*-form (h2)
3    $last(l_1) + last(l_2): \mathbf{N}$ +-form (1, 2)
4    $addlast(l_1, l_2) = last(l_1) + last(l_2)$ *addlast*-defn$_0$ (h1, h2, 3)
infer $addlast(l_1, l_2): \mathbf{N}$ =-type-inherit-left (3, 4)

In the use of the rule '*last*-form' in Line 1, the type metavariable *Elem* is instantiated by $\mathbf{N}$, in the same manner as l is instantiated by l_1.

Note that the logical frame supports the definition of polymorphic types as well as polymorphic functions. For example, it is possible to define a type of non-repeating sequences of an arbitrary element type via:

$$is\text{-}non\text{-}repeating(xs) \stackrel{\text{def}}{=} \forall n_1, n_2 \in \text{inds}\, xs \cdot (xs(n_1) = xs(n_2) \Rightarrow n_1 = n_2)$$

$$NonRepSeq(X) \stackrel{\text{def}}{=} \ll xs{:}X^* \mid is\text{-}non\text{-}repeating(xs) \gg$$

However, such a definition has no direct counterpart in VDM-SL, where only explicit function definitions can be polymorphic. Instead the specification must define a separate type for each instance of the polymorphic type required, for example:

is-non-repeating [@*elem*]: @*elem** → $\mathbb{B}$
is-non-repeating(*l*) $\triangleq$ $\forall n_1, n_2 \in$ inds $xs \cdot (xs(n_1) = xs(n_2) \Rightarrow n_1 = n_2)$

NonRepNatSeq = $\mathbb{N}^*$
inv *ns* $\triangleq$ *is-non-repeating*[$\mathbb{N}$](*ns*)

10.4.7 Value expressions

As stated earlier, value expressions, or constants, can be thought of as special cases of function definitions; simply explicit functions without arguments or precondition. Thus the value expression:

v:T = E

has the following associated axiom:

$$\boxed{v\text{-defn}_0} \; \frac{E{:}T}{v = E} \; \mathbf{Ax}$$

where the hypothesis can be discharged if the expression is well-formed.

As in the case of functions, it is useful to prove well-formedness separately:

$$\boxed{v\text{-form}} \; \frac{}{E{:}T}$$

and then prove a working version of the definition rule:

$$\boxed{v\text{-defn}} \; \frac{}{v = E}$$

10.5 Operations

Operations describe the possible changes in the state. Like functions, they can be given implicitly or explicitly. This section is concerned only with implicit operation definitions.

An implicit operation defines a set of possible state transitions. For each state, the choice of state transition may depend on the values of arguments to the operations. The operation may also return a result. Where there is more than one possible transition from a given state, the operation specification is considered to be truly non-deterministic. That is to say that implementations may deliver different resulting state values each time they are called, even given the same parameters.

Preconditions and postconditions play similar roles to those played in implicit functions except that they constrain the before and after states as well as the parameters and results.

Externals clauses specify the read and write frames of the operations and bind the state variables that appear in the predicates.

The simplest case to consider is an operation with no arguments or result; its only action is to transform the state:

OP
ext rd *r* : *R*
    wr *w* : *W*
pre *Pr(r, w)*
post *Po(r, $\overleftarrow{w}$, w)*

As for implicit functions, definitions are made for the precondition and postcondition:

pre-OP(r, w) $\stackrel{\text{def}}{=}$ *Pr(r, w)*

post-OP(r, $\overleftarrow{w}$, w) $\stackrel{\text{def}}{=}$ *Po(r, $\overleftarrow{w}$, w)*

These definitions can now be used in the conjecture and proof of validation theorems and proof obligations about the specification. Detailed examples appear in the case study.

10.5.1 Satisfiability

As in the case of implicitly specified functions, it is necessary to show that an implicitly specified operation can be implemented. It is desirable to demonstrate this before developing a detailed reification, to avoid wasted effort in trying to implement in inherently unsatisfiable operation specification. The satisfiability obligation is a rule that guarantees that the operation is implementable, without the need to develop a detailed implementation as a demonstration.

The usual satisfiability obligation, written in terms of the whole state $\sigma: \Sigma$ might be given as:

$$\frac{\overleftarrow{\sigma}:\Sigma;\ \textit{pre-OP}(\overleftarrow{\sigma})}{\exists \sigma: \Sigma \cdot \textit{post-OP}(\overleftarrow{\sigma}, \sigma)}$$

However, this formulation has two problems. Firstly, it is not always well-formed, because in general *pre-OP* and *post-OP* can be predicates in only some of the components of the state. But even apart from that problem, the rule has ignored completely the information in the externals clauses of the operation.

A first attempt to rectify these problems might be to restrict the obligation to the components in the read and write frames, for example:

$$\frac{r:R;\ \overleftarrow{w}:W;\ \textit{pre-OP}(r, \overleftarrow{w})}{\exists w: W \cdot \textit{post-OP}(r, \overleftarrow{w}, w)}$$

However, this form is not correct either, for this does not ensure that the operation maintains the invariant.

Thus the obligation should be written in terms of the whole state, but also distinguishing the individual components for the predicates. Supposing that the state is actually composed of the two components already introduced and additionally a third "unread"

10.6 Validation proofs

component, u, then the obligation can be stated as:

$$\frac{r: R;\ \overleftarrow{w}: W;\ u: U;\ inv\text{-}\Sigma(r, \overleftarrow{w}, u);\ pre\text{-}OP(r, \overleftarrow{w})}{\exists w: W \cdot inv\text{-}\Sigma(r, w, u) \land post\text{-}OP(r, \overleftarrow{w}, w)}$$

or, alternatively, using a pattern for the state:

$$\boxed{OP\text{-sat}}\ \frac{mk\text{-}\Sigma(\overleftarrow{r}, \overleftarrow{w}, \overleftarrow{u}): \Sigma;\ pre\text{-}OP(\overleftarrow{r}, \overleftarrow{w})}{\exists mk\text{-}\Sigma(r, w, u): \Sigma \cdot post\text{-}OP(r, \overleftarrow{w}, w) \land r = \overleftarrow{r} \land u = \overleftarrow{u}}$$

where the invariant is hidden by use of the state type Σ. The last two conjuncts arise, of course, because the variables outside the write frame, r and u, must be unchanged. This form of the satisfiability obligation is clearly the component by component version of the usual whole state obligation given earlier.

The astute reader may still be slightly concerned by this formulation. Although it distinguishes between read-only and read-write state components, no distinction is made between the read-only and unread components. In fact this is in agreement with the interpretation of externals clauses in VDM-SL which does not make a semantic distinction between read and unread components. A discussion of the role of the read and write frames in operations, including an alternative formulation of the satisfiability which takes the unread nature of variables not mentioned in the externals clauses into account, can be found in [Bic93].

10.5.2 Parameters and results

In the case where the operation has parameters and a result these are incorporated in the obvious way. For example, if the above operation had additionally a parameter $x: X$ and a result $y: Y$ the satisfiability rule would be:

$$\boxed{OP\text{-sat}}\ \frac{x: X;\ mk\text{-}\Sigma(\overleftarrow{r}, \overleftarrow{w}, \overleftarrow{u}): \Sigma;\ pre\text{-}OP(x, \overleftarrow{r}, \overleftarrow{w})}{\exists y: Y, mk\text{-}\Sigma(r, w, u): \Sigma \cdot\\ post\text{-}OP(x, y, r, \overleftarrow{w}, w) \land r = \overleftarrow{r} \land u = \overleftarrow{u}}$$

10.6 Validation proofs

For any particular specification, there may be some specific propositions about an operation that can be postulated, or more general propositions may be stated about the specification as a whole. Some examples of this kind of validation condition are discussed in the case study in Sections 12.4.3 and 12.4.6.

There are also some other more general properties that it might be useful to show of any specification. For example, one might wish to show that there is always at least one operation that can be applied, i.e. that the disjunction of the preconditions of all the operations is true for all values of the state type. Or one may prove that certain states are unreachable by proposing a stronger invariant on the state and showing that it is maintained by the operations. In this way validation can not only serve to check that a specification exhibits properties that are desired for the system, but also, by helping the understanding of the model given, it can suggest improvements to that model or even alternative models to consider. What appears to be a great deal of extra work - to try an alternative specification - may well pay dividends when proofs are being constructed.

One possibility for validation arises from VDM's implicit maintenance of the invariant by the postconditions. Often there is a choice of how much of the information implicit in the invariant should be repeated in the postcondition. There is often some tension between the most concise form of postcondition that relies on properties of the invariant for its correctness, and a longer, but more explicit, form that includes some redundant information. This choice can be seen as an opportunity to prove the stronger forms from the weaker. Which formulation of the postcondition is chosen may make a significant difference to the complexity of the proofs: the form that most clearly conveys the information may not be the form that will be most useful in proofs. Indeed, the stronger form is more likely to be helpful when the specification is being proved to be a reification of another, and the weaker form when it is itself being reified.

By building a theory of proved properties of a specification in this way, some of the burden of proof that would otherwise arise when trying to justify a refinement, can be discharged in an environment where one only has to consider a single specification. Clearly it is easier to reason in the context of a single specification than that of a refinement which relates a pair of specifications. The following chapter will discuss reasoning about refinements.

10.7 Summary

This chapter has dealt with the following topics:

- Definitions and axioms for reasoning about elements of VDM-SL specifications: type definitions, the state model, explicit and implicit functions, value definitions, and implicit operations.

- Treating type invariants as subtype restrictions integral to the type definition.

- Introducing definitions for invariants, preconditions and postconditions.

- The use of well-formedness guards on definitional axioms.

- Proof obligations: well-formedness; satisfiability of implicit functions and operations.

- Validation proofs, e.g. that a type definition is inhabited (has at least one value).

10.8 Exercises

1. The role played by invariants in proofs

Consider the function *'double'*, defined as:

$double : \mathbb{N} \to Even$
$double(n) \triangleq 2 \times n.$

10.8 Exercises

(a) State and prove the formation rule '*double*-form', analogous to '*f*-form' in Section 10.4.1.

(b) Repeat Exercise 1(a) for the function '*halve*', defined as:

$halve : Even \to \mathbf{N}$
$halve(e) \triangleq \iota n : \mathbf{N} \cdot n + n = e.$

(c) Suppose instead that the above functions had the signatures:

$double: \mathbf{N} \to \mathbf{N}$
$halve: \mathbf{N} \to \mathbf{N}$

How does this affect the proofs of '*double*-form' and '*halve*-form'? What roles did the invariant on *Even* play in the original proofs?

2. A satisfiability proof

Prove the satisfiability obligation for the function f as defined in Section 10.4.3:

$f\ (x: Even, y: \mathbf{N})\ r: \mathbf{N}$
pre $x < 2^{16} \wedge y < 2^{16}$
post $r = x \times 2^4 + y$

$$\boxed{f\text{-sat}}\ \frac{x: \mathbf{N};\ y: \mathbf{N};\ pre\text{-}f(x, y)}{\exists r: \mathbf{N} \cdot post\text{-}f(x, y, r)}$$

Remember that the proof must *not* use '*f*-defn'.

3. An experiment in recursive function definitions

Consider the explicit recursive function definition:

$sum : \mathbf{N}^* \to \mathbf{N}$
$sum(s) \triangleq$ if $s = [\,]$
        then 0
        else hd $s + sum(\text{tl}\ s)$

Suppose that instead of the form suggested by Section 10.4.1, the definition axiom is:

$$\frac{s: \mathbf{N}^*\ ;\ s_1: \mathbf{N}^* \vdash_{s_1}\ (\text{if } s_1 = [\,] \text{ then } 0 \text{ else } \text{hd}\ s_1 + sum(\text{tl}\ s_1)): \mathbf{N}}{sum(s) =\ \text{if } s = [\,] \text{ then } 0 \text{ else } \text{hd}\ s + sum(\text{tl}\ s)}\text{-Ax}$$

where the sequent hypothesis corresponds to showing that the body of *sum* is well-defined for all $\mathbf{N}^*$.

(a) Try to prove that the body of *sum* is well-defined, namely:

$$\frac{s: \mathbf{N}^*}{(\text{if } s = [\,] \text{ then } 0 \text{ else } \text{hd}\ s + sum(\text{tl}\ s)): \mathbf{N}}$$

Why does this fail?

(b) Repeat the attempt, this time using the axiom:

$$\text{sum-defn}_0 \; \frac{s:\mathbf{N}^* \; ; \; (\text{if } s = [\,] \text{ then } 0 \text{ else hd } s + sum(\text{tl } s)):\mathbf{N}}{sum(s) \;=\; \text{if } s = [\,] \text{ then } 0 \text{ else hd } s + sum(\text{tl } s)} \; \text{Ax}$$

4. Alternative definitions of pre- and postconditions

In the semantics of VDM-SL, the pre- and postconditions of an operation are predicates in the whole state of the specification, rather than just the components read and/or written by the operation.

(a) Given the state definition:

state Σ of
    $r \; : \; R$
    $w \; : \; W$
    $u \; : \; U$
inv $mk\text{-}\Sigma(r, w, u) \; \triangleq \; Pi(r, w, u)$
end

and an operation specification as in Section 10.5, that reads r, writes w and ignores u:

    OP
    ext rd $r \; : \; R$
        wr $w \; : \; W$
    pre $Pr(r, w)$
    post $Po(r, \overleftarrow{w}, w)$

how might *pre-OP* and *post-OP* be defined in terms of Σ?

$pre\text{-}OP(\sigma) \; \stackrel{\text{def}}{=} \; \ldots$

$post\text{-}OP(\overleftarrow{\sigma}, \sigma) \; \stackrel{\text{def}}{=} \; \ldots$

Take care not to forget the role of the write frame.

(b) Re-state the obligation '*OP*-sat' (page 10.5.2) in terms of these new definitions.

(c) Repeat (a) and (b) for one of the operations in the case study, and construct the proof of the satisfiability obligation. Compare this against the original.

Chapter 11

Verifying Reifications

11.1 Introduction

Chapter 1 introduced the broad principles of reification. It described how *data reification* and *operation modelling* combine to provide a more concrete specification which is in some way closer of an implementation whilst still exhibiting external behaviour compatible with that of its abstract counterpart. A fuller explanation of the principle of reification can be found in [Jon90]. There are many issues associated with formalising the idea of reification, some of which are discussed here and others as they arise in the case study. The primary objective of this chapter is to describe a set of formally-stated proof obligations for reification, the proof of which provides a sufficient justification for the preservation of external behaviour. The case study in the following chapter provides the major demonstration of how these proof obligations are applied in practice.

There are many ways in which a specification can be reified in order to bring it closer to an acceptable implementation. The example in Section 1.2.3 discussed how a new data model for the state can be chosen in order to bring information required for more efficient implementation of the operations to the fore. It also mentioned how the operations themselves can be refined by the reduction of possible non-termination or the reduction of non-determinacy. Often, more than one of these forms are combined in a reification. In order to record the most general form for the proof obligations that arise in reification, the exposition in this chapter uses an abstract example.

The next section deals with the reification of the state model. It formalises the idea of the *retrieve function* and describes the requirement for *adequacy* of the concrete model. It also deals with reification of the initial states. Section 11.3 considers the operation modelling that arises as a consequence of such a data reification, giving the *domain* and *result* proof obligations in general format. There then follows (Section 11.4) a small example showing how the general proof obligations are specialised for a particular case and giving some example proofs. Section 11.5 discusses rules for reasoning about the satisfaction of implicit functions by explicit definitions. The last section briefly discusses how the form of reification presented here can be insufficiently general in some cases and how this can be overcome.

This chapter, and indeed this book as a whole, restricts attention to what may be termed "data-centred" reification, namely those forms of reification that concentrate upon the consequences of changing data representations. Reification of actions, that is, the process of *operation decomposition* in VDM, is a large enough subject to merit a separate volume in its own right and is not addressed here.

11.2 Data reification

The key element in justifying a data reification in VDM is the retrieve function. This acts as the formal link between the data models of the abstract and concrete specifications. The abstract model was chosen to simplify high-level reasoning about the problem domain; now reification introduces some degree of implementation detail and with this comes an increase in the complexity of reasoning. Demonstrating the validity of a data reification is often a difficult task, however because reification is transitive, it can be performed in several stages where each step introduces a small amount of implementation detail and is relatively simple to justify. Although this does not reduce the complexity of the overall design, it has the benefit of structuring the design and verification process.

Setting aside until the case study (Chapter 12) motivation for how and why one might choose a particular data model, this section describes the form of definitions and obligations introduced by a data reification. This is done by reference to an artificially general pair of specifications which simply introduce names for the components of the state models and operations that are used in the definitions and obligations.

11.2.1 Retrieve functions

Consider the following pair of specifications. For convenience in the definition of the operations that follow, it is assumed that the abstract and concrete states each have three components. The names of these components are chosen to reflect their use in the externals clauses of the example operation in section 11.3, thus r stands for read-only, w for read-write, and u for unread. Arbitrary predicates in the state components are given for invariant and initialisation.

Abstract State	*Concrete State*
state S_a of	state S_c of
$\quad r_a : R_a$	$\quad r_c : R_c$
$\quad w_a : W_a$	$\quad w_c : W_c$
$\quad u_a : U_a$	$\quad u_c : U_c$
inv $mk\text{-}S_a(r_a, w_a, u_a) \triangleq inv_a(r_a, w_a, u_a)$	inv $mk\text{-}S_c(r_c, w_c, u_c) \triangleq inv_c(r_c, w_c, u_c)$
init $mk\text{-}S_a(r_a, w_a, u_a) \triangleq init_a(r_a, w_a, u_a)$	init $mk\text{-}S_c(r_c, w_c, u_c) \triangleq init_c(r_c, w_c, u_c)$
end	end

Note that, although the abstract and concrete state models have the same number of components with similar names, this is not meant to suggest that retrieval need be defined component-wise. More generally, retrieval is defined between the whole states S_c and S_a. It is not intended that there need be any correspondence between the individual components of the states, nor indeed that there be the same number of components in each state.

The first step in showing that S_c is a reification of S_a is to construct a retrieve function. This should have the following form:

11.2 Data reification

$$retr\text{-}S : S_c \to S_a$$
$$retr\text{-}S(s_c\colon S_c) \;\triangleq\; body\text{-}expression$$

The same verification conditions that apply to any function definition (Section 10.4.1) also apply to retrieve functions. In addition, the retrieve function must be total over the concrete state model. This is formalised by the fact that it has no precondition. Note that the invariants of the abstract and concrete models have been "absorbed" within the type definition, as described in Section 10.2.

One extra requirement for a retrieve function is to ensure that the concrete data model is *adequate*. Adequacy requires that every value of the abstract state model has a corresponding value in the concrete model. This obligation can be written as:

$$\boxed{retr\text{-}S\text{-adeq}} \;\; \frac{s_a\colon S_a}{\exists s_c\colon S_c \cdot retr\text{-}S(s_c) = s_a}$$

The importance of demonstrating these properties of the retrieve function cannot be overstated. Attempting their justification can highlight many problems with a design which might not otherwise become apparent until much later. This might not only be the indication of a point of failure, but a proof that is difficult or ungainly may suggest an improvement to the concrete model, the retrieve function, or even in the abstract model. For example, in attempting a proof of adequacy, it may transpire that some abstract values have no concrete counterparts. This might be because the concrete model is inadequate, or it may be that the retrieve function is not correctly defined. However it could also indicate that the abstract model is insufficiently abstract. Such situations are discussed further in Section 11.6.

11.2.2 Reifying initialisation

In addition to showing that the concrete data model is an adequate representation of the abstract one, there is also a constraint on the initialisation conditions. Reifying the initialisation condition is rather like the modelling of an operation but a little simpler. Where unique states are defined by the initialisation predicate, then clearly they must be states which correspond under the retrieve function. That is, the abstract initial state should be the image under the retrieve function of the concrete initial state. Where there are a number of possible initial states that satisfy the initialisation condition, the criterion is that the concrete initialisation should exhibit no more non-determinacy that the abstract. This is formalised by saying that the image under the retrieve function of the set of states satisfying the concrete initialisation must be contained within the states satisfying the abstract one. This is formalised in the following obligation which describes "adequacy of initialisation":

$$\boxed{init\text{-}S\text{-adeq}} \;\; \frac{\begin{array}{c} s_a\colon S_a;\; s_c\colon S_c \\ s_a = retr\text{-}S(s_c) \\ init\text{-}S_c(s_c) \end{array}}{init\text{-}S_a(s_a)}$$

As suggested, this is a special form of the result obligation that arises in operation modelling which is discussed in the next section. (See Exercise 11.8.1.)

11.3 Operation modelling

11.3.1 Modelling behaviour

Once a new state definition is given for the concrete specification, new operations must be defined that model the operations of the abstract specification. In order to preserve external behaviour, there must be a concrete operation for each abstract operation and furthermore the argument and result types of corresponding operations must be the same. However, the body of each operation must be redefined in order to accommodate the new state type.

In some cases the systems described by abstract and concrete specifications behave identically but this is not an absolute requirement. Operation modelling is based on a definition of *satisfaction*. A concrete operation satisfies an abstract one so long as the behaviour of the concrete operation is in a sense compatible with that of the abstract operation. The definition of compatible behaviour is such that a user of the system should not be able to ascertain whether the system is behaving in accordance with the abstract or concrete specification.

As stated earlier, the difference in specified behaviour can arise in two ways. First it can result from an increase in the domain of termination of the operation and second it may arise from a reduction of non-determinism. This leads to a closely-linked pair of proof obligations, the *domain* and *result* obligations. These two obligations are formalised in the next two subsections.

Again in order to explore the most general case, the treatment is based on an abstract example. Consider a pair of corresponding operations acting on the abstract and concrete states given above:

Abstract Operation	*Concrete Operation*
$OP_a\ (a{:}A)\ t{:}T$	$OP_c\ (a{:}A)\ t{:}T$
ext rd $r_a\ :\ R_a$	ext rd $r_c\ :\ R_c$
wr $w_a\ :\ W_a$	wr $w_c\ :\ W_c$
pre $P_a(a, r_a, w_a)$	pre $P_c(a, r_c, w_c)$
post $Q_a(a, t, r_a, \overleftarrow{w_a}, w_a)$	post $Q_c(a, t, r_c, \overleftarrow{w_c}, w_c)$

Note that the operations have corresponding names – albeit with different subscripts – and the same "visible types", that is argument and result types. Sufficient generality for the present discussion is provided by assuming that each operation accesses one state component in read-write mode, one in read-only mode, and does not access the other at all. Recall that there is not necessarily any correspondence between the individual components of the states. Preconditions and postconditions are given as arbitrary predicates over the relevant state components.

11.3.2 Reducing undefinedness

It is enough to show that a concrete operation is *no less defined* than its abstract counterpart. The negative is chosen carefully. An abstract operation specification does not say that the operation cannot be invoked outside of its precondition, only that the consequences of so doing are not defined at this level of abstraction. An implementation of

11.3 Operation modelling

that operation may be defined over a wider domain, but its behaviour over the "extra" domain is not constrained by the abstract specification. Nonetheless, it is essential that the concrete operation should be defined at least wherever the abstract operation is defined. This is captured in the *domain obligation* which states that the concrete precondition must hold whenever the abstract one does. As the two operations are defined over different state models, the retrieve function is used to yield an "abstract view" of the concrete operation's domain. The domain obligation can be stated as follows:

$$\boxed{\textit{OP-dom-obl}}\ \frac{a:A;\ s_c:S_c;\ s_a:S_a}{s_a = \textit{retr-S}(s_c)}\\ \frac{\textit{pre-OP}_a(a, s_a.r_a, s_a.w_a)}{\textit{pre-OP}_c(a, s_c.r_c, s_c.w_c)}$$

This formal statement of the obligation uses one metavariable for each of the concrete and abstract states. An alternative formulation might introduce metavariables r_c, w_c, etc. with hypotheses of the form:

$$\textit{mk-}S_c(r_c, w_c, u_c): S_c$$

A metavariable for the abstract state, together with the hypothesis equating it to the retrieved concrete state, is given here as its use simplifies the statement of the abstract precondition.

One consequence of this "satisfaction-based" approach is that the precondition should not be interpreted as defining a domain outside which the operation *cannot* be invoked. Rather it says that for such invocations any outcome is possible. Requirements of this nature should be described directly in the postcondition by giving the exceptional result of such an invocation.

11.3.3 Reducing non-determinacy

In an abstract specification, the postcondition of an operation may well be "loose". That is, given a particular initial state there may be many possible final states that satisfy the relation. An implementation of this operation has the freedom to reduce this looseness by narrowing the choice of possible states. Indeed, as looseness in operations is interpreted as true non-determinism, an implementation that chooses different final states on different invocations is also valid so long as the postcondition is satisfied.

The looseness available in implicitly-specified operations is a useful tool in developing abstract specifications. However, as progress is made towards an implementation, it is often natural to "tighten up" the postcondition of an operation, moving from a specification of the relationship between the initial and final states towards a description of how the final state can be constructed from the initial state. Another way to state this is to say that the concrete operation may reduce the non-determinacy of its abstract counterpart.

The concrete operation should not break the postcondition of the abstract operation, so it is to be expected that the concrete postcondition should ensure the abstract postcondition (under the retrieve function, naturally). In other words, given a concrete state s_c which satisfies *pre-OP*$_c$, a condition something like the following should hold:

$$\textit{post-OP}_c(\overleftarrow{s_c}, s_c) \Rightarrow \textit{post-OP}_a(\textit{retr-S}(\overleftarrow{s_c}), \textit{retr-S}(s_c))$$

However, recall that in the abstract specification any behaviour is allowed for the operation outside its precondition. Thus it is sufficient to consider only cases where the abstract precondition holds. Taking this into account, and moving to an inference rule presentation, leads to an obligation of the form:

$$\frac{\overleftarrow{s_c}:S_c;\ s_c:S_c \quad pre\text{-}OP_a(retr\text{-}S(\overleftarrow{s_c})) \quad post\text{-}OP_c(\overleftarrow{s_c},s_c)}{post\text{-}OP_a(retr\text{-}S(\overleftarrow{s_c}),retr\text{-}S(s_c))}$$

There are three ways in which this statement is still a little inaccurate. First, it omits consideration of the arguments and result of the operations. However these are trivial to incorporate. Second, the preconditions and postconditions have been given as predicates on the entire state, whereas elsewhere they have been treated as predicates in the separate state components. Third, the permissible final states are determined not only by the postconditions but also by the externals clauses of the operations. In particular, state components outside the "write frame" of each operation must not be changed.

Taking these three considerations into account yields the following form for the result obligation:

$$\boxed{OP\text{-res-obl}}\ \frac{\begin{array}{c} a:A;\ t:T \\ s_a:S_a;\ s_c:S_c;\ s_a = retr\text{-}S(s_c) \\ \overleftarrow{s_a}:S_a;\ \overleftarrow{s_c}:S_c;\ \overleftarrow{s_a} = retr\text{-}S(\overleftarrow{s_c}) \\ pre\text{-}OP_a(a,\overleftarrow{s_a}.r_a,\overleftarrow{s_a}.w_a) \\ post\text{-}OP_c(a,t,s_c.r_c,\overleftarrow{s_c}.w_c,s_c.w_c) \wedge s_c.r_c = \overleftarrow{s_c}.r_c \wedge s_c.u_c = \overleftarrow{s_c}.u_c \end{array}}{post\text{-}OP_a(a,t,s_a.r_a,\overleftarrow{s_a}.w_a,s_a.w_a) \wedge s_a.r_a = \overleftarrow{s_a}.r_a \wedge s_a.u_a = \overleftarrow{s_a}.u_a}$$

Although apparently rather ungainly in the form presented here, this obligation is often relatively concise for particular examples.

11.4 An example reification proof

This section presents a example illustrating the domain and result obligation for a simple specification and implementation. The example concentrates upon an operation *PULL* which removes and returns an element from a collection.

The abstract specification pulls an arbitrary element from a set:

state S_a of
    s : X-set
end

operations

    $PULL_a$ () $x:X$
    ext wr s : X-set
    pre $s \neq \{\ \}$
    post $x \in \overleftarrow{s} \wedge s = \overleftarrow{s} \setminus \{x\}$

Naturally, the full specification would also include other operations.

11.4 An example reification proof

One data reification that might be considered would be to replace the set of X in the state by a sequence and an index into that sequence which defines the element that should be "pulled". An auxiliary function helps to make the definition of the operation concise:

state S_c of
    $l : X^*$
    $i : \mathbb{N}$
inv $mk\text{-}S_c(l, i)$ $\triangleq$ if $l = [\,]$ then $i = 0$ else $i \in$ inds l
end

functions

    $remove : \mathbb{N}_1 \times X^+ \to X^*$
    $remove(i, l)$ $\triangleq$ $l(1, \ldots, i-1) \curvearrowright l(i+1, \ldots, \text{len } l)$
    pre $i \in$ inds l

operations

    $PULL_c\ ()\ x{:}X$
    ext wr $l\ :\ X^*$
        wr $i\ :\ \mathbb{N}$
    pre $i \neq 0$
    post $x = \overleftarrow{l}(\overleftarrow{i}) \land l = remove(\overleftarrow{i}, \overleftarrow{l})$

The postcondition does not specify the new value of i. Thus any new index satisfying the invariant is arbitrarily chosen. The invariant ensures that i is a valid index of l when l is not empty and 0 otherwise. Thus, in the precondition for $PULL_c$, the test for emptiness on l can be replaced by the test whether $i = 0$. Note however, that although this may be a more efficient test to implement, its use in the precondition will increase the complexity of reasoning required to show the domain and result obligations.

It is claimed that the following is a valid retrieve function from S_c to S_a:

    $retr : S_c \to S_a$
    $retr(mk\text{-}S_c(l, i))$ $\triangleq$ $mk\text{-}S_a(\text{elems } l)$

This claim should be supported by constructing well-formedness and adequacy proofs. These are left as simple exercises.

Following the recipe in Section 11.3.2, the domain obligation for modelling $PULL_a$ by $PULL_c$ is:

$$\boxed{PULL\text{-dom-obl}}\ \frac{\begin{array}{c} s_c{:}S_c;\ s_a{:}S_a \\ s_a = retr(s_c) \\ s_a.s \neq \{\,\} \end{array}}{s_c.i \neq 0}$$

In order to discharge this obligation, it is necessary to use the invariant of S_c. Since the empty list has no elements, $s_c.l$ cannot be $[\,]$, and so $s_c.i$ cannot be 0. The following informal sketch of a proof indicates how the domain obligation can be discharged. The reader should by now be able to fill in the formal details:

188   11 Verifying Reifications

from $s_c: S_c$; $s_a: S_a$; $s_a = retr(s_c)$; $s_a.s \neq \{\,\}$
1   $s_a = mk\text{-}S_a(\text{elems}\, s_c.l)$ defn. of $retr$ (h3)
2   $\text{elems}\, s_c.l \neq \{\,\}$ rewriting (1) with (h4)
3   $s_c.l \neq [\,]$ since $\text{elems}\,[\,] = \{\,\}$ (2)
4   $s_c.i \in \text{inds}\, s_c.l$ (3) and $inv\text{-}S_c$
infer $s_c.i \neq 0$ seq index non-zero (3, 4)

The result obligation for *PULL* can be given as follows:

$$x: X;\ mk\text{-}S_a(s): S_a;\ mk\text{-}S_c(l,i): S_c$$
$$mk\text{-}S_a(\overleftarrow{s}): S_a;\ mk\text{-}S_c(\overleftarrow{l},\overleftarrow{i}): S_c$$
$$mk\text{-}S_a(s) = retr(mk\text{-}S_c(l,i));\ mk\text{-}S_a(\overleftarrow{s}) = retr(mk\text{-}S_c(\overleftarrow{l},\overleftarrow{i}))$$

$$\boxed{PULL\text{-res-obl}}\ \frac{\overleftarrow{s} \neq \{\,\};\ x = \overleftarrow{l}(\overleftarrow{i}) \wedge l = remove(\overleftarrow{i},\overleftarrow{l})}{x \in \overleftarrow{s} \wedge s = \overleftarrow{s} \setminus \{x\}}$$

Rather than using one metavariable per state as in the domain obligation above, one metavariable per state component has been used here. Although this makes the proof obligation a little more untidy, it improves the presentation of the proof. Definitions of precondition and postcondition have been expanded. Both $PULL_a$ and $PULL_c$ write the entire state, so there is no need for "rest unchanged" extensions to the postconditions.

An informal partial proof of the result obligation, omitting typing issues and some detail, brings the main issue to light:

from $mk\text{-}S_a(\overleftarrow{s}) = retr(mk\text{-}S_c(\overleftarrow{l},\overleftarrow{i}));\ mk\text{-}S_a(s) = retr(mk\text{-}S_c(l,i));$
$\overleftarrow{s} \neq \{\,\};\ x = \overleftarrow{l}(\overleftarrow{i}) \wedge l = remove(\overleftarrow{i},\overleftarrow{l})$
1   $\overleftarrow{s} = \text{elems}\,\overleftarrow{l}$ (h1), retr-defn, s-defn
2   $s = \text{elems}\, l$ (h2), retr-defn, s-defn
3   $x = \overleftarrow{l}(\overleftarrow{i})$ $\wedge$-E-right (h4)
4   $l = remove(\overleftarrow{i},\overleftarrow{l})$ $\wedge$-E-left (h4)
    ...
5   $\text{elems}\, remove(\overleftarrow{i},\overleftarrow{l}) = \text{elems}\,\overleftarrow{l} \setminus \{\overleftarrow{l}(\overleftarrow{i})\}$ ⟨?? justify ??⟩
6   $s = \overleftarrow{s} \setminus \{x\}$ rewriting (5) with (2, 4, 1, 3)
7   $x \in \overleftarrow{s}$ ⟨?? justify ??⟩
infer $x \in \overleftarrow{s} \wedge s = \overleftarrow{s} \setminus \{x\}$ $\wedge$-I (6, 7)

At this stage it is worth considering how the proof might proceed. Lines 5 and 7 need to be justified. Rewriting Line 7 using the equations in Lines 1 and 3 gives $\overleftarrow{l}(\overleftarrow{i}) \in \text{elems}\,\overleftarrow{l}$. This follows if it can be shown that $\overleftarrow{i} \in \text{inds}\,\overleftarrow{l}$ which follows from the invariant $inv\text{-}S_c(mk\text{-}S_c(\overleftarrow{l},\overleftarrow{i}))$ provided $\overleftarrow{l}$ is not empty. The invariant comes from the typing hypotheses, whereas $\overleftarrow{l}$ not being empty follows by Line 1 and h3.

Now consider informally a strategy for the justification of Line 5:

$$\text{elems } remove(\overleftarrow{i}, \overleftarrow{l}) = \text{elems } \overleftarrow{l} \setminus \{\overleftarrow{l}(\overleftarrow{i})\}$$

For this to hold, $\overleftarrow{l}(\overleftarrow{i})$ must not occur in $remove(\overleftarrow{i}, \overleftarrow{l})$. Developing the reasoning a little further, unfolding the definition of $remove$ gives:

$$\overleftarrow{l}(\overleftarrow{i}) \notin \text{elems}(\overleftarrow{l}(1,\ldots,\overleftarrow{i} \setminus 1) \frown \overleftarrow{l}(\overleftarrow{i}+1,\ldots,\text{len } \overleftarrow{l}))$$

In other words, the $\overleftarrow{i}$ th element of $\overleftarrow{l}$ must not occur anywhere else in $\overleftarrow{l}$. Unfortunately, this is not guaranteed by the concrete specification and the present obligation cannot be proved.

If the state definition S_c is modified by extending the invariant to ensure that l is non-repeating, then the proof can be completed. The invariant is then sufficient to ensure that $remove(\overleftarrow{i}, \overleftarrow{l})$ does not contain $\overleftarrow{l}(\overleftarrow{i})$. It is useful to prove some lemmas concerning non-repeating sequences including the following:

$$\boxed{remove\text{-lemma}} \quad \frac{i: \mathbb{N}_1; \; l: X^*; \; non\text{-}repeating(l); \; i \in \text{inds } l}{non\text{-}repeating(remove(i, l))}$$

Alternatively, the concrete specification could define a type of non-repeating sequences, and then define *remove* over this type (with the same body as before). The above lemma would then be discharged as part of the well-formedness obligation on *remove*. Either way, this would assist in proving that the final concrete state $mk\text{-}S_c(l, i)$ is well-formed, which now involves the extra effort of having to show l is non-repeating.

Ideally, the flaw in the original specification could have been detected earlier, perhaps through careful inspection of the design, or by any other software engineering practice. However, it is not guaranteed that such a design error will be detected by any of these means. Here, the proof process has revealed the error – more exactly, the error was revealed through careful consideration of the possible next stages in the proof. In this sense, the process of developing a proof acts as a filter for sifting out design flaws that can be used alongside other processes such as parsing, type-checking and animation.

A formal proof of some property of a specification or reification is an extremely rigorous argument that the property does indeed hold. However it is always possible that there is an error in the proof itself or even a flaw in the proof system being used which will render it invalid. On the other hand, failure to prove the result may indicate a design flaw, but could equally have occurred because the correct approach to the proof was not tried, or because the proof system itself was incomplete. Thus neither proof nor failure to prove should be considered to be an end in itself. Rather it is the proof *process* that is important as a means to structure and document the justification of a design step.

11.5 Implementing functions

The previous sections have concentrated upon those obligations that arise through data reification. This section considers obligations that arise through the need to provide explicit definitions of implicitly-defined functions.

A VDM specification describes the external behaviour of a system through the set of operations which act upon some internal state. All that can be observed is the outcome of a sequence of operation invocations involving values passed as parameters and returned as results. Given such a viewpoint (cf. [Nip86, Sch86]), the functions of a VDM specification can be considered to be merely "auxiliary", that is, they are defined simply to permit the succinct statement of the predicates in the specification. However, the values passed as arguments to operations can also be constructed through function applications. Thus at some stage in the development, an implicitly defined function may well have to be replaced by an explicit one.

Taking the view that the argument and result types of operations are the "visible" types of the specification and are thus not reified during development, there is no need to consider data reification in function satisfaction. Hence only "direct" satisfaction of implicit functions by explicit ones is of relevance. The issues arising are thus just reduction of undefinedness and increase in determinism.

Again abstract examples are used to convey the general formulation. Consider an implicit specification f_i and a candidate implementation f_e:

Implicit Function	Explicit Function
$f_i(a:A)\ r:R$	$f_e : A \to R$
pre $P_i(a)$	$f_e(a) \triangleq h(a)$
post $Q_i(a,r)$	pre $P_e(a)$

In addition to well-formedness, it is necessary to show the counterpart of the domain obligation, namely that f_e is defined at least whenever f_i is. This is formalised as:

$$\boxed{f_i\text{-}f_e\text{-dom-obl}}\ \frac{a:A;\ \textit{pre-}f_i(a)}{\textit{pre-}f_e(a)}$$

It is also necessary to show that over the domain required by the implicit function, the explicit function satisfies the implicit postcondition:

$$\boxed{f_i\text{-}f_e\text{-satn}}\ \frac{a:A;\ \textit{pre-}f_i(a)}{\textit{post-}f_i(a,f_e(a))}$$

11.6 Implementation bias and unreachable states

Before proceeding to exercise the above techniques in a more realistic example in the next chapter, a brief word of caution about the treatment of reification presented here. It should be noted that there are occasions where, although there is preservation of external behaviour in a reification, it is not possible to define a suitable retrieve function between the data models.

Two situations in which seemingly valid data reifications cannot be justified through the use of a retrieve function are where there are *unreachable states* or *implementation bias* in the abstract model. This section gives a very brief indication of what these terms mean, and one possible route to overcome such difficulties. A useful tutorial on data refinement which covers these matters in far more depth is [Cle93].

Implementation bias in a specification means that different states cannot be distinguished by observing the subsequent external behaviour of the system. Such specifications are unduly biased towards a particular data model in the sense that an alternative model that coalesces the two indistinguishable states would exhibit the same external behaviour. If an abstract specification of a system has implementation bias that is not present in a concrete specification of that system, then no retrieve function can be found between them as different abstract states will correspond to the same concrete state. Such situations can be handled by using relational retrieve associations as described for example in [Nip86], however the resulting proof obligations are somewhat more difficult. An alternative approach is to redesign the abstract specification to remove the implementation bias.

Unreachable states arise where no combination of applications of operations can lead to the establishment of a particular value in the state. If there are unreachable states in the abstract model but, on the other hand, all the states in the concrete specification are reachable then there will be no retrieve function that is both total and adequate[1]. This is because the existence of an adequate retrieve function would imply the existence of a concrete state that corresponds to an unreachable abstract state. However, this concrete state would then need to correspond to the reachable abstract state that arises by undergoing the same sequence of operations that achieves that state in the concrete specification and thus the retrieve function would not in fact be a function. Where there are unreachable states, strengthening the invariant to exclude them does not change the meaning of the specification and is generally a useful technique that helps to convey quickly an understanding of the system. In many cases the stronger invariant also allows simpler postconditions in the operations.

This concludes the presentation of data reification in an abstract setting. The next chapter shows how it is used in practice.

11.7 Summary

This chapter has dealt with the following topics:

- The retrieve function which provides the correspondence between the state models of the abstract and concrete specifications.

- Totality and adequacy of the retrieve function.

- Adequacy of initialisation.

- Operation Modelling which is the definition of operations in the concrete specification which have behaviour compatible with the operations in the abstract specification.

- The characterisation of compatible behaviour by the domain and result obligations which formalise the requirements for reduction in undefinedness and reduction in non-determinism respectively.

---

[1] Strictly speaking the situation is a little more complicated than this. Where there are operations with non-trivial preconditions, their behaviour outside the precondition is completely free and so they could establish any state. This complicates the notion of unreachable states and in some cases, where preconditions are weakened in the concrete specification, does admit the possibility of a valid retrieve function. However the practical advice given here about strengthening the invariant still holds.

- How the process of formalising the reification can lead to the discovery of errors even before fully formal proofs are attempted.
- Implementing implicit functions by explicit ones.
- The concepts of implementation bias and unreachable states.

11.8 Exercises

1. Modelling state initialisation as an operation

In Section 11.2.2 it was stated that the initialisation adequacy obligation can be considered as a special case of the operation modelling result obligation. Suppose that instead of a state initialisation clause for S_a there is a corresponding "abstract initialisation" operation:

$INIT_a$ ()
ext wr r_a : R_a,
        w_a : W_a,
        u_a : U_a
pre true
post $init\text{-}S_a(mk\text{-}S_a(r_a, w_a, u_a))$

Note that $init\text{-}S$ does not mention the previous state $mk\text{-}S_a(\overleftarrow{r_a}, \overleftarrow{w_a}, \overleftarrow{u_a})$.

(a) Define a corresponding operation $INIT_c$ for S_c.

(b) State the result obligation for modelling $INIT_a$ by $INIT_c$.

(c) Derive (i.e. prove) the initialisation adequacy obligation given in Section 11.2.2 from this result obligation.

2. Correcting an incorrect design

Redo the example in Section 11.4 according to one of the suggested corrections:

(a) by strengthening $inv\text{-}S_c$ to add that l is non-repeating, or

(b) by defining the type of non-repeating sequences.

Formulate and prove some lemmas concerning non-repeating sequences. Fill in the details of the domain and result proofs.

3. An alternative formulation of the result obligation

Restate the general result proof obligation in the form given for the result obligation for *PULL* in Section 11.4. (One metavariable per state component, etc.) Show that the two forms are equivalent.

Chapter 12

A Case Study in Air-Traffic Control

12.1 Introduction

The purpose of this chapter is to illustrate, on an example which is neither trivial nor unrealistic, how the techniques of formal proof discussed in Chapters 2 to 11 can be applied in practice to help with the design and the analysis of formal specifications and formal developments. Amongst other things, it is shown how attempting to discharge the proof obligations of a specification or of a development step can reveal errors in the design which may otherwise go undetected until much later in the development process. It is also shown how the formulation and the proof of validation conditions can be used to demonstrate that the essential requirements of a system have been captured by the formal specification, even though they might not be explicit in the specification.

The case study presented here concerns the allocation of aircraft to air-traffic controllers within an Air-Traffic Control (ATC) region. In particular, the specification deals with a simple systems management tool, such as might be used for overseeing communications between pilots and controllers (Fig. 12.1). Such a tool could, for example, act as a supplementary safety system, put in place alongside existing procedures and used to raise an alarm if certain safety constraints are violated. In addition, it could be configured for anything from air-traffic control of a metropolitan airport to a major international ATC centre, so it is to that extent generic. Formal development of this system is a realistic consideration because of its appreciable safety-critical element.

The layout of the chapter follows the basic stages one might go through in a formal development, although it must be stressed that in practice this process is rarely as linear as this layout might suggest. Section 12.2 can be thought of as the initial "requirements definition" of the system, in that it gives an informal description of the air-traffic control system under consideration and describes both its required properties and some simplifying assumptions which are made. This informal model is then formalised in Section 12.3, which gives a VDM state definition and outlines the associated theory and proof obligations. This section also shows how statements taken from the informal requirements can be captured as validation conditions and discusses some representative proofs. The functionality of the ATC subsystem is then given in Section 12.4 via a series of VDM operations on the basic state, and again some proof obligations and their associated proofs are discussed. This section also illustrates how these proofs can help to uncover errors in the specification. Section 12.5 describes a possible data reification of the basic abstract

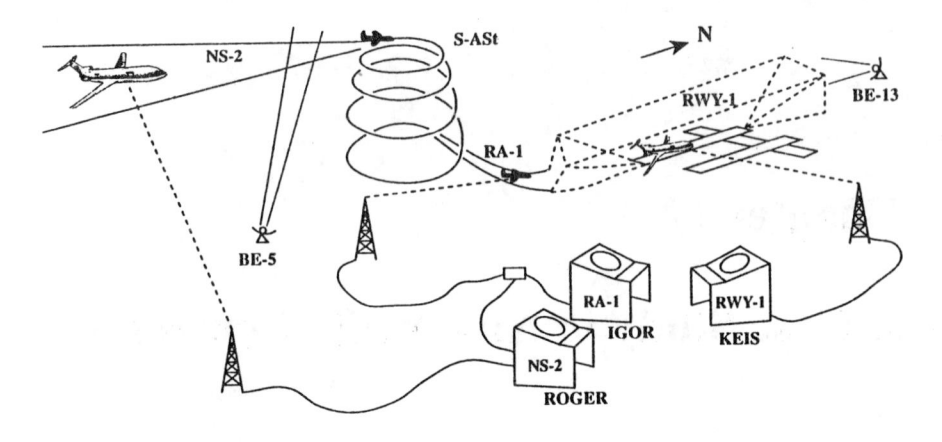

Figure 12.1: Air-traffic control subsystem showing major components: airspaces (e.g. NS-2, RA-1, RWY-1), controllers (Roger, Igor, Keis), and aircraft.

state, and gives a corresponding concrete counterpart of one of the operations from the abstract specification. The theory of the refinement and the proof obligations and their proofs are also discussed. A second possible data reification is outlined in Section 12.6, and the chapter closes with a summary and some concluding remarks.

12.2 The air-traffic control system

12.2.1 Description

In general terms, an air-traffic control system and the air-traffic controllers who run it are responsible for directing aircraft safely through a particular ATC region. It is assumed that this region is subdivided into a number of smaller component airspaces, possibly overlapping physically, each of which is the responsibility of a single controller. It is further assumed that any aircraft within the ATC region as a whole is at any time under the direction of a single controller who is responsible for it whilst it crosses his or her particular airspace. However, as an aircraft moves through the region it will move from one airspace to another, at which points its controller will change.

A number of aspects of a full ATC system are beyond the scope of this case study and so do not feature in the model discussed here, though they might be included in a specification of a more elaborate system. First, only a single ATC region is considered; an additional level of functionality would deal with the transfer of aircraft between regions. Second, details of the physical shape, arrangement, etc. of the airspaces making up the ATC region are omitted at this level of abstraction. The specification is not, therefore, concerned with constraints regarding the movement of aircraft between airspaces, for example that an

12.2 The air-traffic control system

aircraft can only move from one airspace to an adjacent airspace. Third, details of an aircraft's flight data (speed, elevation, etc.) other than its identity are not included.

In addition, at this level of detail it is not specified what is meant by either an "airspace" or a "controller". In particular, no attempt is made to distinguish between different types of airspace or different types of controller. Thus, for example, the abstract term "airspace" may indeed denote a physical region of space, but may equally denote an airport runway and its surrounds or ground areas such as taxiing routes or parking bays. Similarly, "controller" might represent any of airport approach, arrivals, surface movement, departures, tower, or en-route controller.

This is of course a gross simplification of the realities of an air-traffic control system. However, the system described here should not be thought of as a tool which deals with the full complexities of air-traffic control. Rather it should be regarded as a system which could be used in conjunction with existing air-traffic control procedures to oversee and maintain high-level safety properties. Indeed, viewed in this way, the overall picture is not totally unrealistic (cf. [IEE, Cha81, Cho88]).

A single air-traffic controller is therefore responsible for ensuring the safe separation of all the aircraft within his or her allotted airspace and for keeping track of the flight paths, the elevation and the speed of each of those aircraft, while the subsystem is responsible for ensuring that each aircraft is allocated a controller and that the transfer of aircraft into the ATC region from an external region, between airspaces within the region, and out of the region to another region, is all handled correctly. In addition, the subsystem ensures the continuity of control as controllers come on and go off duty, and limits the responsibility of each controller, albeit rather crudely, by placing an upper bound on the number of aircraft that can occupy a given airspace. In this way, it might limit the capacity of an airspace according to its size or its location (for instance it might impose a restriction that at most one aircraft may occupy an airspace containing an airport runway) or change its capacity to take account of changing weather conditions, for example.

12.2.2 Analysis

On the basis of the informal description given above, the following basic components of the subsystem can be identified:

- the controllers currently on duty;
- the airspaces comprising the ATC region;
- the aircraft occupying the ATC region.

The essential relationships between these objects are:

- each airspace has at most one controller;
- each aircraft has exactly one controller;
- each aircraft occupies one airspace;
- the number of aircraft that can occupy any given airspace is limited.

The following terminology is introduced in order to facilitate the description of the functionality and the safety properties of the system:

commissioned An airspace is said to be commissioned if it is a component of the ATC region. This term is preferable to "controlled airspace" which is an official legal term carrying connotations not intended here (for instance, that an aircraft cannot enter a controlled airspace without official clearance). For the purposes of this specification it is assumed that an airspace is commissioned if and only if its capacity is known.

activated An airspace is said to be activated if a controller is assigned to it.

deactivated An airspace is said to be deactivated if it is commissioned but has no assigned controller. For example, an airspace relating in whole or in part to an airport may become deactivated when the airport shuts down for the night.

utilised An airspace is said to be utilised if it is occupied by one or more aircraft. An airspace may be activated but not currently utilised, but not vice versa.

assigned The current controller of a particular airspace is said to be assigned to that airspace. A controller is simply assigned if he or she is the controller of some airspace within the ATC region.

available A controller who is on duty but not currently assigned is said to be available.

known An aircraft is said to be known if it is utilising some airspace in the ATC region.

The basic functionality of the system concerns the assignment of controllers to aircraft and the correct management of these assignments. This behaviour is described by the following operations on the model:

- operations to commission and decommission an airspace, and to reset its capacity;
- operations describing controllers coming on and going off duty;
- operations to activate, deactivate, and reassign control of an airspace;
- operations to add flight data to and remove it from the system, and to hand over flight data from one airspace to another.

Finally, the following are identified as requirements on the system:

R1 Only on-duty controllers can control airspaces.

R2 An airspace can be activated only if it is commissioned.

R3 All utilised airspaces in the ATC region are activated.

R4 The capacity of each utilised airspace is not exceeded.

R5 A controller cannot be assigned to two different airspaces simultaneously.

12.3 Formalisation of the state model

R6 Each known aircraft has a unique controller.

R7 Each known aircraft occupies a unique airspace.

R8 Each activated airspace has a unique controller.

R9 An airspace which is not activated contains no aircraft.

R10 The controller of a known aircraft is on duty.

Note that this is not meant to be an exhaustive list of requirements.

12.3 Formalisation of the state model

12.3.1 The state of the system

The formalisation of the model begins with the introduction of primitive types (or parameters) of the specification corresponding to the basic components of the subsystem identified in Section 12.2.2 above. These are:

- *Controller*, representing all possible air-traffic controllers;
- *Space*, representing all possible airspaces; and
- *Aircraft*, representing all possible aircraft.

Their definitions are unimportant here.

The overall state space of the ATC subsystem then has four state variables constructed from these primitive types:

1. *onduty*: a set of *Controllers*, representing the controllers who are currently on duty, although not necessarily assigned.
2. *control*: a one-one map that records which controller is assigned to which airspace. The domain of the *control* map thus represents the currently activated airspaces, its range those controllers who are currently assigned.
3. *capacity*: a map which gives the number of aircraft each airspace can safely accommodate. Its domain represents the commissioned airspaces.
4. *location*: a map that associates an aircraft with the airspace it currently occupies. The domain of the *location* map represents the known aircraft, while its range denotes the currently utilised airspaces.

The state space, without invariant and initialisation condition as yet, is written in VDM as follows:

state *ATC* **of**
    onduty   : *Controller*-set
    control   : *Space* $\xleftarrow{m}$ *Controller*
    capacity : *Space* $\xrightarrow{m}$ **N**
    location : *Aircraft* $\xrightarrow{m}$ *Space*
inv ...
init ...
end

The invariant on the state has to be sufficiently strong to ensure that all the requirements **R1** to **R10** are actually properties of the formal specification. One way to do this, of course, is to simply make the invariant the conjunction of all the requirements, suitably formalised. The problem with this approach is that, because the requirements are generally not all independent, the invariant then tends to be much larger than necessary, making any proofs which depend on showing that the invariant holds (e.g. satisfiability proofs; see Section 12.4) much longer than they need be. The trick then is to identify some small subset of the requirements, satisfying which is sufficient to ensure that all the other requirements are also satisfied. The invariant is then formed from the conjunction of the subset of the requirements thus chosen, and the remaining requirements become validation conditions on the specification, to be proved at some later stage (see Section 12.3.4).

Here, the first four requirements **R1** to **R4** are chosen as the basic subset from which the invariant is to be constructed, and **R5** to **R10** are treated as validation conditions. On the basis of the description of the relationship between the informal concepts and the various parts of the state components given above, these four requirements are formalised as follows:

R1 Only on-duty controllers can control airspaces:

$$\text{rng}\, control \subseteq onduty$$

R2 An airspace can be activated only if it is commissioned.

$$\text{dom}\, control \subseteq \text{dom}\, capacity$$

R3 All utilised airspaces in the ATC region are activated:

$$\text{rng}\, location \subseteq \text{dom}\, control$$

R4 The capacity of each utilised airspace is not exceeded:

$$\forall s \in \text{rng}\, location \cdot numOfAircraft(s, location) \leq capacity(s)$$

and the invariant is simply the conjunction of these four expressions.

The auxiliary function *numOfAircraft* determines the number of aircraft in an airspace:

  numOfAircraft : *Space* × (*Aircraft* $\xrightarrow{m}$ *Space*) → **N**
  numOfAircraft(*s*, *loc*) $\triangleq$ card(dom(*loc* $\triangleright$ {*s*}))

12.3 Formalisation of the state model

In order to define the initialisation condition on the state, it is assumed that an off-the-shelf ATC subsystem has all fields empty. For this, it is sufficient to insist that the *onduty* set and the *capacity* map are both empty as the state invariant then implies that the *control* and *location* maps must also be empty.

The complete state definition is thus:

state *ATC* of
    onduty : *Controller*-set
    control : *Space* $\xleftarrow{m}$ *Controller*
    capacity : *Space* $\xrightarrow{m}$ $\mathbb{N}$
    location : *Aircraft* $\xrightarrow{m}$ *Space*
inv *mk-ATC*(*cs, con, cap, loc*) $\triangleq$ rng *con* $\subseteq$ *cs* $\wedge$ dom *con* $\subseteq$ dom *cap* $\wedge$
                      rng *loc* $\subseteq$ dom *con* $\wedge$ $\forall s \in$ rng *loc* · *numOfAircraft*(*s, loc*) $\leq$ *cap*(*s*)
init σ $\triangleq$ σ.*onduty* = { } $\wedge$ σ.*capacity* = {$\mapsto$}
end

12.3.2 Axiomatisation of the abstract state

Following the procedures set out in Chapter 10, the theory describing the above state definition consists of:

- type symbols *Space*, *Controller* and *Aircraft* corresponding to the primitive types of the specification;

- a type symbol *ATC* representing the state;

- a symbol *mk-ATC* representing the *mk*-function for the state;

- symbols _.*onduty*, _.*control*, _.*capacity* and _.*location* representing the selector functions for the state components;

- a defined symbol *inv-ATC* for the state invariant, defined via:

  inv-ATC(*cs, con, cap, loc*) $\stackrel{\text{def}}{=}$ rng *con* $\subseteq$ *cs* $\wedge$ dom *con* $\subseteq$ dom *cap* $\wedge$
      rng *loc* $\subseteq$ dom *con* $\wedge$ $\forall s \in$ rng *loc* · *numOfAircraft*(*s, loc*) $\leq$ *cap*(*s*)

- a defined symbol *init-ATC* for the initialisation condition, defined via:

  init-ATC(σ) $\stackrel{\text{def}}{=}$ σ.*onduty* = { } $\wedge$ σ.*capacity* = {$\mapsto$}

- a symbol *numOfAircraft*(_, _) representing the auxiliary function;

- axioms giving the formation and definition rules for the *mk*-function:

$$\boxed{\textit{mk-ATC-form}} \quad \frac{cs: \textit{Controller-set}; \; con: \textit{Space} \xleftarrow{m} \textit{Controller} \quad cap: \textit{Space} \xrightarrow{m} \mathbb{N}; \; loc: \textit{Aircraft} \xrightarrow{m} \textit{Space} \quad \textit{inv-ATC}(cs, con, cap, loc)}{\textit{mk-ATC}(cs, con, cap, loc): \textit{ATC}} \text{Ax}$$

$$\boxed{\textit{mk-ATC-defn}} \quad \frac{\sigma: \textit{ATC}}{\textit{mk-ATC}(\sigma.\textit{onduty}, \sigma.\textit{control}, \sigma.\textit{capacity}, \sigma.\textit{location}) = \sigma} \text{Ax}$$

$$\boxed{\text{inv-ATC-I}}\ \frac{mk\text{-}ATC(cs, con, cap, loc):ATC}{inv\text{-}ATC(cs, con, cap, loc)}\ \text{Ax}$$

- axioms giving the formation and definition rules for each of the selector functions. Those for the selector *onduty* are given below and are typical. Those for the other selectors are analogous and are given in Section 14.11.

$$\boxed{\text{onduty-form}}\ \frac{\sigma:ATC}{\sigma.onduty:\text{Controller-set}}\ \text{Ax}$$

$$\boxed{\text{onduty-defn}}\ \frac{mk\text{-}ATC(cs, con, cap, loc):ATC}{mk\text{-}ATC(cs, con, cap, loc).onduty = cs}\ \text{Ax}$$

- an axiom defining the auxiliary function *numOfAircraft*:

$$\boxed{\text{numOfAircraft-defn}_0}\ \frac{s:Space;\ loc:Aircraft \xrightarrow{m} Space}{numOfAircraft(s, loc) = \text{card}(\text{dom}(loc \triangleright \{s\}))}\ \text{Ax}$$

The proof obligations are stated as rules to be proved in this theory. For the state definition these are:

Proof obligation 1 The auxiliary function *numOfAircraft* is well-defined:

$$\boxed{\text{numOfAircraft-form}}\ \frac{s:Space;\ loc:Aircraft \xrightarrow{m} Space}{numOfAircraft(s, loc):\mathbb{N}}$$

Proof obligation 2 The state invariant is well-defined:

$$\boxed{\text{inv-ATC-form}}\ \frac{cs:\text{Controller-set};\ con:Space \xleftarrow{m} Controller\quad cap:Space \xrightarrow{m} \mathbb{N};\ loc:Aircraft \xrightarrow{m} Space}{inv\text{-}ATC(cs, con, cap, loc):\mathbb{B}}$$

Proof obligation 3 The initialisation condition is well-defined:

$$\boxed{\text{init-ATC-form}}\ \frac{\sigma:ATC}{init\text{-}ATC(\sigma):\mathbb{B}}$$

Proof obligation 4 The initialisation condition is satisfiable:

$$\boxed{\text{init-ATC-sat}}\ \overline{\exists \sigma:ATC\cdot init\text{-}ATC(\sigma)}$$

Requirements **R5** to **R10**, which become validation conditions, are treated just like the proof obligations in that they are stated as rules to be proved in this theory. However, the statements of these validation conditions make use of some of the terminology from Section 12.2.2, which was introduced to help to describe the system in terms corresponding to one's informal thinking. For this reason, it is useful to formalise the appropriate parts of this terminology as additional auxiliary functions in the specification. Thus, an *activated* airspace is one which appears in the domain of the *control* map:

12.3 Formalisation of the state model

$\textit{is-activated} : Space \times ATC \to \mathbb{B}$
$\textit{is-activated}(s, \sigma) \triangleq s \in \text{dom}(\sigma.control)$

and a *known* aircraft is one which is in the domain of the *location* map:

$\textit{is-known} : Aircraft \times ATC \to \mathbb{B}$
$\textit{is-known}(p, \sigma) \triangleq p \in \text{dom}(\sigma.location)$

The controller of some known aircraft can then be defined via the function *controllerOf*:

$\textit{controllerOf} : Aircraft \times ATC \to Controller$
$\textit{controllerOf}(p, \sigma) \triangleq \sigma.control(\sigma.location(p))$
pre $\textit{is-known}(p, \sigma)$

The theory described above must now be extended to incorporate descriptions of each of these new functions. This requires new symbols *is-activated*, *is-known*, and *controllerOf* to represent the functions, a new defined symbol *pre-controllerOf* for the precondition of the auxiliary function *controllerOf*, defined via:

$\textit{pre-controllerOf}(p, \sigma) \stackrel{\text{def}}{=} \textit{is-known}(p, \sigma)$

and a defining axiom for each function (cf. the treatment of *numOfAircraft* above):

$$\boxed{\textit{is-activated-defn}_0}\ \frac{s: Space;\ \sigma: ATC;\ (s \in \text{dom}(\sigma.control)): \mathbb{B}}{\textit{is-activated}(s, \sigma) = (s \in \text{dom}(\sigma.control))}\ \textbf{Ax}$$

$$\boxed{\textit{is-known-defn}_0}\ \frac{p: Aircraft;\ \sigma: ATC;\ (p \in \text{dom}(\sigma.location)): \mathbb{B}}{\textit{is-known}(p, \sigma) = (p \in \text{dom}(\sigma.location))}\ \textbf{Ax}$$

$$\boxed{\textit{controllerOf-defn}_0}\ \frac{p: Aircraft;\ \sigma: ATC;\ \textit{pre-controllerOf}(p, \sigma)\ (\sigma.control(\sigma.location(p))): Controller}{\textit{controllerOf}(p, \sigma) = \sigma.control(\sigma.location(p))}\ \textbf{Ax}$$

Additional well-formedness proof obligations are also required for each of these new functions. These are:

Proof obligation 5 The auxiliary function *is-activated* is well-defined:

$$\boxed{\textit{is-activated-form}}\ \frac{s: Space;\ \sigma: ATC}{\textit{is-activated}(s, \sigma): \mathbb{B}}$$

Proof obligation 6 The auxiliary function *is-known* is well-defined:

$$\boxed{\textit{is-known-form}}\ \frac{p: Aircraft;\ \sigma: ATC}{\textit{is-known}(p, \sigma): \mathbb{B}}$$

Proof obligation 7 The precondition of *controllerOf* is well-defined:

$$\boxed{\textit{pre-controllerOf-form}}\ \frac{p: Aircraft;\ \sigma: ATC}{\textit{pre-controllerOf}(p, \sigma): \mathbb{B}}$$

Proof obligation 8 The auxiliary function *controllerOf* is well-defined:

$$\boxed{controllerOf\text{-form}} \frac{p: Aircraft;\ \sigma: ATC;\ pre\text{-}controllerOf(p, \sigma)}{controllerOf(p, \sigma): Controller}$$

The validation conditions corresponding to requirements **R5** to **R10** can now be formulated as the following rules:

Validation 1 A controller cannot be assigned to two different airspaces simultaneously:

$$\boxed{\text{no-double-assignment}} \frac{\begin{array}{c} s_1: Space;\ s_2: Space;\ \sigma: ATC;\ is\text{-}activated(s_1, \sigma) \\ is\text{-}activated(s_2, \sigma);\ \sigma.control(s_1) = \sigma.control(s_2) \end{array}}{s_1 = s_2}$$

Validation 2 Each known aircraft has a unique controller:

$$\boxed{\text{aircraft-controller-unique}} \frac{p: Aircraft;\ \sigma: ATC;\ is\text{-}known(p, \sigma)}{\exists!\ c: Controller \cdot c = controllerOf(p, \sigma)}$$

Validation 3 Each known aircraft occupies a unique airspace:

$$\boxed{\text{aircraft-in-unique-space}} \frac{p: Aircraft;\ \sigma: ATC;\ is\text{-}known(p, \sigma)}{\exists!\ s: Space \cdot s = \sigma.location(p)}$$

Validation 4 Each activated airspace has a unique controller:

$$\boxed{\text{airspace-controller-unique}} \frac{s: Space;\ \sigma: ATC;\ is\text{-}activated(s, \sigma)}{\exists!\ c: Controller \cdot c = \sigma.control(s)}$$

Validation 5 An airspace which is not activated contains no aircraft:

$$\boxed{\text{not activated} \Rightarrow \text{empty}} \frac{s: Space;\ \sigma: ATC;\ \neg(is\text{-}activated(s, \sigma))}{numOfAircraft(s, \sigma.location) = 0}$$

Validation 6 The controller of a known aircraft is on duty:

$$\boxed{controllerOf\text{-onduty}} \frac{p: Aircraft;\ \sigma: ATC;\ is\text{-}known(p, \sigma)}{controllerOf(p, \sigma) \in \sigma.onduty}$$

The proofs of these proof obligations and validation conditions are discussed in the next two sections.

12.3.3 Internal consistency

Although simply writing a formal specification of a system is likely not only to increase one's understanding of that system but also to reveal some errors in the basic design, errors can still be present, for instance because there may be logical inconsistencies or oversights in one's mental picture of the system. Sometimes such errors can be revealed by statically type-checking the specification using some appropriate tool, but there are two limitations to this process: first, type checking in VDM-SL is not in general completely

12.3 Formalisation of the state model

statically decidable (because it cannot in general be statically checked that invariants hold), and second, there are some areas of verification (for example the satisfiability of operations; see Section 12.4) which simply do not lend themselves to static type checking. A specification can therefore only be shown to be completely error-free (in the sense of containing no logical inconsistencies) if all the proof obligations have been discharged. This section shows how **proof obligations 1** to **8** given in Section 12.3.2 are dealt with.

Proof obligation 1 The auxiliary function *numOfAircraft* is well-defined.

For an explicit, non-recursive[1] function definition like this, the key to proving well-formedness is to first prove a rule asserting the well-formedness of the defining expression. This proof is straightforward, consisting simply of a series of applications of the formation rules for the operators from which that defining expression is constructed. This rule is then used to prove the working version (see Section 10.4.1) of the definition rule, and the required formation rule for the function then follows by simple type inheritance.

Applying this series of steps to the proof of '*numOfAircraft*-form' the rule asserting the well-formedness of the defining expression is:

$$\boxed{numOfAircraft\text{-wff}} \; \frac{s \colon Space; \; loc \colon Aircraft \xrightarrow{m} Space}{\text{card}(\text{dom}(loc \triangleright \{s\})) \colon \mathbb{N}}$$

Its proof follows directly from the formation rules for card, dom, $\triangleright$ and the unit set:

from $s \colon Space; \; loc \colon Aircraft \xrightarrow{m} Space$
1   $\{s\} \colon Space$-set $\{a\}$-form (h1)
2   $loc \triangleright \{s\} \colon Aircraft \xrightarrow{m} Space$ $\triangleright$-form (h2, 1)
3   $\text{dom}(loc \triangleright \{s\}) \colon Aircraft$-set   dom-form (2)
infer $\text{card}(\text{dom}(loc \triangleright \{s\})) \colon \mathbb{N}$ card-form (3)

The working version of the definition rule:

$$\boxed{numOfAircraft\text{-defn}} \; \frac{s \colon Space; \; loc \colon Aircraft \xrightarrow{m} Space}{numOfAircraft(s, loc) = \text{card}(\text{dom}(loc \triangleright \{s\}))}$$

is then easy to prove as the well-formedness rule just proved justifies the third hypothesis of the basic definition rule '*numOfAircraft*-defn$_0$' from the other two:

from $s \colon Space; \; loc \colon Aircraft \xrightarrow{m} Space$
1   $\text{card}(\text{dom}(loc \triangleright \{s\})) \colon \mathbb{N}$ *numOfAircraft*-wff (h1, h2)
infer $numOfAircraft(s, loc) = \text{card}(\text{dom}(loc \triangleright \{s\}))$ *numOfAircraft*-defn$_0$ (h1, h2, 1)

The overall formation rule '*numOfAircraft*-form' then follows directly from these together with the rule '=-type-inherit-left':

---
[1] See the treatment of the function *nonRptng* in Section 12.5.5 for a discussion of recursive functions.

from s: *Space*; loc: *Aircraft* $\xrightarrow{m}$ *Space*
1 card(dom($loc \triangleright \{s\}$)): N   *numOfAircraft*-wff (h1, h2)
2 *numOfAircraft*(s, loc) = card(dom($loc \triangleright \{s\}$))   *numOfAircraft*-defn (h1, h2)
infer *numOfAircraft*(s, loc): N   =-type-inherit-left (1, 2)

Proof obligation 2 The state invariant is well-defined.

The proof that the invariant is boolean-valued follows the pattern described in Section 9.4. After expanding the definition of the invariant, the propositional operators are eliminated using the propositional formation rules of Section 9.3.1. Again, care must be taken to use the sequent forms of these rules where appropriate. Next, the relational formation rules given in Section 9.3.2 are used to eliminate the relational operators, and the proof is completed using the formation rules for the operators on the basic data-types.

from cs: *Controller*-set; con: *Space* $\xleftrightarrow{m}$ *Controller*;
   cap: *Space* $\xrightarrow{m}$ N; loc: *Aircraft* $\xrightarrow{m}$ *Space*
1 rng con: *Controller*-set   rng-form-bimap (h2)
2 (rng $con \subseteq cs$): B $\subseteq$-form (1, h1)
3 dom con: *Space*-set   dom-form-bimap (h2)
4 dom cap: *Space*-set   dom-form (h3)
5 (dom $con \subseteq$ dom cap): B $\subseteq$-form (3, 4)
6 from dom $con \subseteq$ dom cap
6.1 rng loc: *Space*-set   rng-form (h4)
6.2 (rng $loc \subseteq$ dom con): B $\subseteq$-form (6.1, 3)
6.3 from rng $loc \subseteq$ dom con
6.3.1   from s_1: *Space*; $s_1 \in$ rng loc
6.3.1.1   *numOfAircraft*(s_1, loc): N   *numOfAircraft*-form (6.3.1.h1, h4)
6.3.1.2   rng $loc \subseteq$ dom cap $\subseteq$-trans (6.1, 3, 4, 6.3.h1, 6.h1)
6.3.1.3 $s_1 \in$ dom cap $\subseteq$-E (6.3.1.h1, 6.1, 4, 6.3.1.h2, 6.3.1.2)
6.3.1.4 $cap(s_1)$: N   at-form (6.3.1.h1, h3, 6.3.1.3)
    infer (*numOfAircraft*(s_1, loc) $\leq cap(s_1)$): B $\leq$-form (6.3.1.1, 6.3.1.4)
   infer ($\forall s \in$ rng loc · *numOfAircraft*(s, loc) $\leq cap(s)$): B
                          $\forall$-form-set (6.1, 6.3.1)
  infer (rng $loc \subseteq$ dom $con \wedge$
     $\forall s \in$ rng loc · *numOfAircraft*(s, loc) $\leq cap(s)$): B $\wedge$-form-sqt (6.2, 6.3)
7 (dom $con \subseteq$ dom $cap \wedge$ rng $loc \subseteq$ dom $con \wedge$
   $\forall s \in$ rng loc · *numOfAircraft*(s, loc) $\leq cap(s)$): B $\wedge$-form-sqt (5, 6)
8 (rng $con \subseteq cs \wedge$ dom $con \subseteq$ dom $cap \wedge$ rng $loc \subseteq$ dom $con \wedge$
   $\forall s \in$ rng loc · *numOfAircraft*(s, loc) $\leq cap(s)$): B $\wedge$-form (2, 7)
infer *inv-ATC*(cs, con, cap, loc): B   folding (8)

12.3 Formalisation of the state model

Note how the innermost subproof (Subproof 6.3.1) in the proof above relies on the well-formedness rule for *numOfAircraft* proved previously (**proof obligation 1**). This subproof also involves showing that $cap(s)$ is well-defined for all s in rng *loc*, which follows from the facts that rng $loc \subseteq$ dom con and dom $con \subseteq$ dom cap (the third and second conjuncts of the state invariant respectively).

One point worth noting here is that proving the well-formedness of *inv-ATC* has done more to increase confidence in the model than "merely" showing its internal consistency: it has also performed a cross-check on whether or not a suitable subset of the requirements has been chosen to construct the invariant. For example, if either of the requirements **R2** or **R3** had not been included in the state invariant, the oversight would have been revealed in the course of trying to prove the well-formedness of the final conjunct of the invariant (corresponding to the requirement **R4**).

Proof obligation 3 The initialisation condition is well-defined.

The proof of '*init-ATC*-form' is straightforward, relying on the definition of *init-ATC* and the formation rules for equality and for the selector functions:

from $\sigma: ATC$
1    $\sigma.onduty: Controller$-set   *onduty*-form (h1)
2    $\sigma.capacity: Space \xrightarrow{m} \mathbb{N}$ *capacity*-form (h1)
3    $\{\}: Controller$-set $\{\}$-form
4    $\{\mapsto\}: Space \xrightarrow{m} \mathbb{N}$ $\{\mapsto\}$-form
5    $(\sigma.onduty = \{\}): \mathbb{B}$ =-form (1, 3)
6    $(\sigma.capacity = \{\mapsto\}): \mathbb{B}$ =-form (2, 4)
7    $(\sigma.onduty = \{\} \land \sigma.capacity = \{\mapsto\}): \mathbb{B}$ $\land$-form (5, 6)
infer *init-ATC*$(\sigma): \mathbb{B}$ folding (7)

Proof obligation 4 The initialisation condition is satisfiable.

This requires showing the existence of some state satisfying the initialisation condition. Because the initialisation condition effectively implies that the initial state has all fields empty, as already stated above, the easiest way of doing this is by using '$\exists$-I' with *mk-ATC*($\{\}, \{\mapsto\}, \{\mapsto\}, \{\mapsto\}$) as the witness value. This involves showing that this value does in fact satisfy the initialisation condition (Line 19) and also represents a valid state (Line 15). The first of these is easy, relying only on the definition of the initialisation condition, propositional logic, and properties of the selector functions. For the second, it must be shown that the components of *mk-ATC*($\{\}, \{\mapsto\}, \{\mapsto\}, \{\mapsto\}$) are of the correct type (trivial; Lines 1 to 4) and that they satisfy the invariant on *ATC*. This last proceeds by substitution of the definitions of dom $\{\mapsto\}$ and rng $\{\mapsto\}$ from Lines 5 and 6 and simple predicate logic and set theory. The complete proof is:

from
1 $\{\}: Controller$-set $\{\}$-form
2 $\{\mapsto\}: Space \xleftrightarrow{m} Controller$ $\{\mapsto\}$-form-bimap
3 $\{\mapsto\}: Space \xrightarrow{m} \mathbb{N}$ $\{\mapsto\}$-form
4 $\{\mapsto\}: Aircraft \xrightarrow{m} Space$ $\{\mapsto\}$-form
5 dom $\{\mapsto\} = \{\}$ dom-defn-$\{\mapsto\}$
6 rng $\{\mapsto\} = \{\}$ rng-defn-$\{\mapsto\}$
7 $\{\} \subseteq \{\}$ $\{\}$-is-subset (3)
8 rng $\{\mapsto\} \subseteq \{\}$ =-subs-left(b) (1, 6, 7)
9 dom $\{\mapsto\} \subseteq$ dom $\{\mapsto\}$ =-subs-left(b) (1, 5, 7)
10 rng $\{\mapsto\} \subseteq$ dom $\{\mapsto\}$ =-subs-left(b) (1, 5, 8)
11 rng $\{\mapsto\}: Space$-set rng-form (4)
12 from $y: Space;\ y \in$ rng $\{\mapsto\}$
12.1 $\neg (y \in$ rng $\{\mapsto\})$ $\neg$-$\in$-rng-$\{\mapsto\}$-I (12.h1)
   infer $numOfAircraft(y, \{\mapsto\}) \leq \{\mapsto\}(y)$ contradiction (12.h2, 12.1)
13 $\forall s \in$ rng $\{\mapsto\} \cdot numOfAircraft(s, \{\mapsto\}) \leq \{\mapsto\}(s)$ $\forall$-I-set (11, 12)
14 $inv\text{-}ATC(\{\}, \{\mapsto\}, \{\mapsto\}, \{\mapsto\})$ inv-ATC-I-separate (1, 2, 3, 4, 8, 9, 10, 13)
15 $mk\text{-}ATC(\{\}, \{\mapsto\}, \{\mapsto\}, \{\mapsto\}): ATC$ mk-ATC-form (1, 2, 3, 4, 14)
16 $(mk\text{-}ATC(\{\}, \{\mapsto\}, \{\mapsto\}, \{\mapsto\})).onduty = \{\}$ $onduty$-form (15)
17 $(mk\text{-}ATC(\{\}, \{\mapsto\}, \{\mapsto\}, \{\mapsto\})).capacity = \{\mapsto\}$ $capacity$-form (15)
18 $(mk\text{-}ATC(\{\}, \{\mapsto\}, \{\mapsto\}, \{\mapsto\})).onduty = \{\} \land$
     $(mk\text{-}ATC(\{\}, \{\mapsto\}, \{\mapsto\}, \{\mapsto\})).capacity = \{\mapsto\}$ $\land$-I (16, 17)
19 $init\text{-}ATC(mk\text{-}ATC(\{\}, \{\mapsto\}, \{\mapsto\}, \{\mapsto\}))$ folding (18)
infer $\exists \sigma: ATC \cdot init\text{-}ATC(\sigma)$ $\exists$-I (15, 19)

Proof obligations 5, 6, and 8 Each of the auxiliary functions *is-activated*, *is-known* and *controllerOf* is well-defined.

These proof obligations are treated in exactly the same way as the corresponding proof obligation for the function *numOfAircraft* (see **proof obligation 1** above).

Proof obligation 7 The precondition of *controllerOf* is well-defined.

This follows immediately from the well-formedness of *is-known*.

12.3.4 Validation of the state representation

Although discharging the proof obligations on the state shows that the formal model is logically consistent, it does not mean that it actually represents the system described in the informal requirements. In particular, there is no guarantee at this stage that requirements **R5** to **R10** have actually been captured by the invariant, and there is probably already enough complexity present for this not to be obvious. This step from informal requirements to formal specification can, by definition, never be made completely formal because there could easily be additional "requirements" which have simply been overlooked. Nevertheless, showing that the requirements that have been thought of are all

12.3 Formalisation of the state model

consequences of the formal model is a very good way of increasing confidence that the model does actually represent the system required. This is done by transforming the original informal requirements into formal validation conditions, rules representing essentially the formalisation of one's informal intuition about the system. Proving these rules demonstrates formally that the corresponding requirements are logical consequences of the state invariant.

For the ATC system, this informal intuition has been captured in the remaining requirements **R5** to **R10** and the corresponding formal rules have been given in Section 12.3.2. This section discusses the proofs of these rules.

Validation 1 A controller cannot be assigned to two different airspaces simultaneously.

Figure 12.2: A controller cannot be assigned to two different airspaces simultaneously.

Where a boolean-valued auxiliary function like *is-activated* is used in the hypotheses of rules, a useful first step is to prove a lemma formalising the elimination of that function. This saves having to use the definition rule and substitution of equality every time the function appears. In this case the appropriate rule is

$$\boxed{\textit{is-activated-E}} \quad \frac{s: \textit{Space}; \quad \sigma: \textit{ATC}; \quad \textit{is-activated}(s, \sigma)}{s \in \text{dom}(\sigma.\textit{control})}$$

the proof of which simply consists of the two steps mentioned above.

After using this to eliminate both occurrences of *is-activated* (Lines 1 and 2 in the proof below), the overall result is an almost immediate consequence of the fact that the *control* map is one-one. Note how the hypotheses *is-activated*(s_1, σ) and *is-activated*(s_2, σ) are necessary to ensure the well-formedness of $\sigma.control(s_1)$ and $\sigma.control(s_2)$.

from s_1: *Space*; s_2: *Space*; σ: *ATC*; *is-activated*(s_1, σ);
    is-activated(s_2, σ); σ.*control*$(s_1) = \sigma$.*control*(s_2)
1   $s_1 \in \mathrm{dom}(\sigma.control)$ *is-activated*-E (h1, h3, h4)
2   $s_2 \in \mathrm{dom}(\sigma.control)$ *is-activated*-E (h2, h3, h5)
3   $\sigma.control$: *Space* $\xleftrightarrow{m}$ *Controller*   *control*-form (h3)
infer $s_1 = s_2$ bimap-1-1 (h1, h2, 3, 1, 2, h6)

Validation 2   Each known aircraft has a unique controller.

Figure 12.3: Each known aircraft has a unique controller.

This result follows directly from the well-formedness of the function *controllerOf* (see **proof obligation 8**) and the rule '∃!-=-I':

from p: *Aircraft*; σ: *ATC*; *is-known*(p, σ)
1   *pre-controllerOf*(p, σ) folding (h3)
2   *controllerOf*(p, σ): *Controller*   *controllerOf*-form (h1, h2, 1)
infer $\exists!\, c$: *Controller* $\cdot$ $c = controllerOf(p, \sigma)$ ∃!-=-I (2)

12.3 Formalisation of the state model

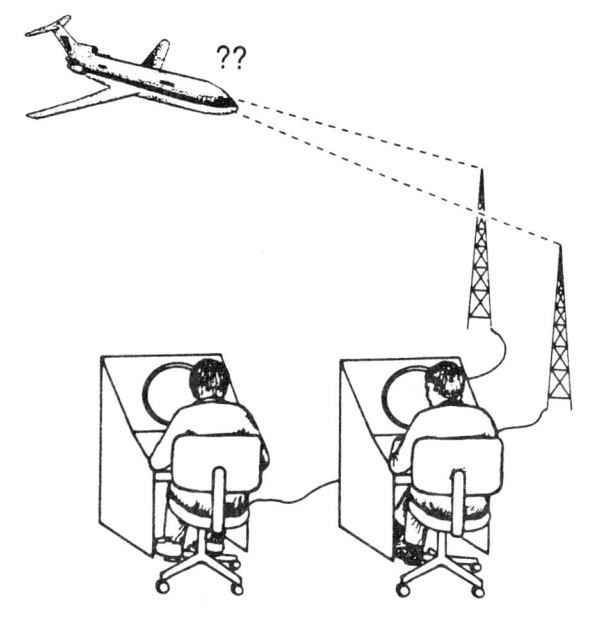

Figure 12.4: Each known aircraft occupies a unique airspace.

Validation 3 Each known aircraft occupies a unique airspace.

This is also a direct consequence of the well-formedness of the right-hand side of the equality in the conclusion and the rule '∃!-=-I':

from p: *Aircraft*; σ: *ATC*; *is-known*(p, σ)
1    $p \in \text{dom}(\sigma.\textit{location})$ *is-known*-E (h1, h2, h3)
2    $\sigma.\textit{location}$: *Aircraft* $\xrightarrow{m}$ *Space*   *location*-form (h2)
3    $\sigma.\textit{location}(p)$: *Space*   at-form (h1, 2, 1)
infer $\exists!\, s$: *Space* $\cdot s = \sigma.\textit{location}(p)$ ∃!-=-I (3)

Validation 4 Each activated airspace has a unique controller.

This proof is entirely analogous to the previous one. It is left as an exercise for the reader.

Validation 5 An airspace which is not activated contains no aircraft.

The first step is to use the definition of *numOfAircraft* (Line 2) and the transitivity of equality to reduce the problem to showing that $\text{card}(\text{dom}(\sigma.\textit{location} \triangleright \{s\})) = 0$. Then simple manipulation using the rules for maps and sets reduces this to showing (Line 9) that $s \notin \text{rng}(\sigma.\textit{location})$, which follows easily from the third conjunct of the state invariant which insists that occupied airspaces have controllers.

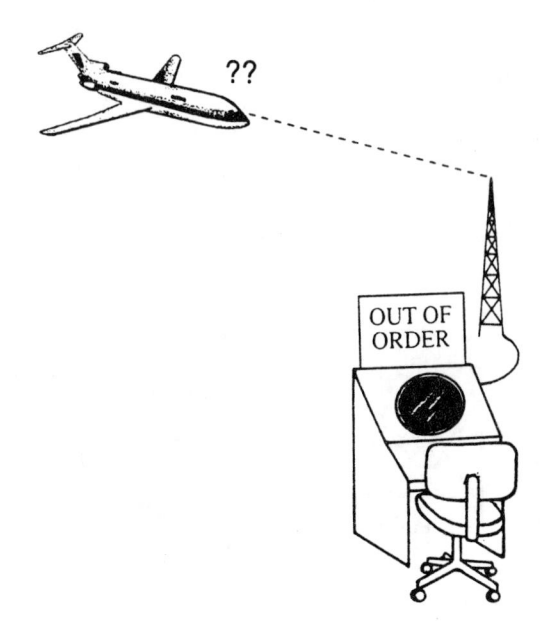

Figure 12.5: An airspace which is not activated contains no aircraft.

from $s: Space$; $\sigma: ATC$; $\neg(is\text{-}activated(s, \sigma))$
1   $\sigma.location: Aircraft \xrightarrow{m} Space$ *location*-form (h2)
2   $numOfAircraft(s, \sigma.location) =$
         $card(dom(\sigma.location \triangleright \{s\}))$ *numOfAircraft*-defn (h1, 1)
3   $numOfAircraft(s, \sigma.location): \mathbb{N}$ *numOfAircraft*-form (h1, 1)
4   $rng(\sigma.location): Space$-set   rng-form (1)
5   $\sigma.control: Space \xleftarrow{m} Controller$ *control*-form (h2)
6   $dom(\sigma.control): Space$-set   dom-form-bimap (5)
7   $rng(\sigma.location) \subseteq dom(\sigma.control)$ *inv-ATC*-I-clause3 (h2)
8   $s \notin dom(\sigma.control)$ $\neg$-*is-activated*-E (h1, h2, h3)
9   $s \notin rng(\sigma.location)$ $\notin$-subset-I (h1, 4, 6, 7, 8)
10 $\sigma.location \triangleright \{s\} = \{\mapsto\}$ $\triangleright$-defn-$\{a\}$-$\notin$ (h1, 1, 9)
11 $dom(\sigma.location \triangleright \{s\}) = \{\}$ dom-$\{\mapsto\}$-I (10)
12 $card(dom(\sigma.location \triangleright \{s\})) = 0$ card=0-I (11)
infer $numOfAircraft(s, \sigma.location) = 0$ =-trans(a) (3, 2, 12)

Exercise 1 A possible variant of this validation condition says that if there is a non-zero number of aircraft in any airspace, then that airspace is activated. Formulate this validation condition as a rule and prove it. □

12.4 Top-level operations

Validation 6 The controller of a known aircraft is on duty.

After applying '*is-known*-E' to the hypotheses and using the definition of *controllerOf* to rewrite the conclusion, this proof reduces to showing that $\sigma.control(\sigma.location(p)) \in \sigma.onduty$ from $p \in \text{dom}(\sigma.location)$. This follows easily, if tediously, from the first and third conjuncts of the invariant (Lines 6 and 13) and the basic properties of subsets and map application (Lines 10 and 14 to 17).

from p: *Aircraft*; σ: *ATC*; *is-known*(p, σ)
1. pre-*controllerOf*(p, σ)   folding (h3)
2. *controllerOf*(p, σ) = $\sigma.control(\sigma.location(p))$ *controllerOf*-defn (h1, h2, h3)
3. $\sigma.control(\sigma.location(p))$: *Controller*   *controllerOf*-wff (h1, h2, 1)
4. $p \in \text{dom}(\sigma.location)$ *is-known*-E (h1, h2, h3)
5. $\sigma.location$: *Aircraft* $\xrightarrow{m}$ *Space*   *location*-form (h2)
6. rng($\sigma.control$) $\subseteq \sigma.onduty$ *inv-ATC*-I-clause1 (h2)
7. $\sigma.onduty$: *Controller*-set   *onduty*-form (h2)
8. $\sigma.control$: *Space* $\xleftrightarrow{m}$ *Controller*   *control*-form (h2)
9. rng($\sigma.control$): *Controller*-set   rng-form-bimap (8)
10. $\sigma.location(p)$: *Space*   at-form (h1, 5, 4)
11. rng($\sigma.location$): *Space*-set   rng-form (5)
12. dom($\sigma.control$): *Space*-set   dom-form-bimap (8)
13. rng($\sigma.location$) $\subseteq$ dom($\sigma.control$)   *inv-ATC*-I-clause3 (h2)
14. $\sigma.location(p) \in$ rng($\sigma.location$) $\in$-rng-I-at (h1, 5, 4)
15. $\sigma.location(p) \in$ dom($\sigma.control$) $\subseteq$-E (10, 11, 12, 14, 13)
16. $\sigma.control(\sigma.location(p)) \in$ rng($\sigma.control$) $\in$-rng-I-at (10, 8, 15)
17. $\sigma.control(\sigma.location(p)) \in \sigma.onduty$ $\subseteq$-E (3, 9, 7, 16, 6)
infer *controllerOf*(p, σ) $\in \sigma.onduty$ =-subs-left(b) (3, 2, 17)

12.4 Top-level operations

To complete the top-level specification of the ATC subsystem, operations by which the state can be changed are specified. As described in Section 12.2.2, these are grouped into four categories:

- operations to commission and decommission an airspace, and to reset its capacity;
- operations describing controllers coming on and going off duty;
- operations to activate and deactivate an airspace, and to reassign control of an airspace;
- operations to add flight data to and remove it from the system, and to hand over flight data from one airspace to another.

Each operation requires symbols to be added to the basic theory outlined in Section 12.3 to represent the precondition (if any) and the postcondition of the operation. However, no additional axioms are required. In addition, each operation gives rise to proof obligations to show that both its precondition and its postcondition are well-formed (boolean-valued) and that it is satisfiable.

One such satisfiability obligation is discussed in Section 12.4.1, and another in Section 12.4.2 where it is shown how failure to discharge the satisfiability proof can reveal errors in the specification. Validation conditions similar to those discussed in Section 12.3.4 are also useful at the level of the operations to ensure that the functionality they describe matches one's informal intuition, and some of these are also discussed here.

12.4.1 Commissioning an airspace

The first operation is for commissioning a new airspace s, with capacity n:

Commission $(s: Space, n: \mathbb{N})$
ext wr *capacity* : $Space \xrightarrow{m} \mathbb{N}$
pre $s \notin \text{dom}\, capacity$
post $capacity = \overleftarrow{capacity} \dagger \{s \mapsto n\}$

The precondition simply says that the airspace is not already commissioned.

As indicated above, defined symbols representing the operation's precondition and postcondition are added to the theory:

pre-Commission$(s, cap) \stackrel{\text{def}}{=} s \notin \text{dom}\, cap$

post-Commission$(s, n, \overleftarrow{cap}, cap) \stackrel{\text{def}}{=} cap = \overleftarrow{cap} \dagger \{s \mapsto n\}$

each of which has an associated well-formedness proof obligation:

Proof obligations 9 and 10 The precondition and the postcondition of the operation *Commission* are well-formed.

$$\boxed{\textit{pre-Commission-form}} \quad \frac{\begin{array}{c} s: Space;\ \ n: \mathbb{N};\ \ cs: Controller\text{-set} \\ con: Space \xleftrightarrow{m} Controller;\ \ cap: Space \xrightarrow{m} \mathbb{N} \\ loc: Aircraft \xrightarrow{m} Space;\ \ inv\text{-}ATC(cs, con, cap, loc) \end{array}}{\textit{pre-Commission}(s, cap): \mathbb{B}}$$

$$\boxed{\textit{post-Commission-form}} \quad \frac{\begin{array}{c} s: Space;\ \ n: \mathbb{N};\ \ cs: Controller\text{-set} \\ con: Space \xleftrightarrow{m} Controller;\ \ \overleftarrow{cap}: Space \xrightarrow{m} \mathbb{N} \\ cap: Space \xrightarrow{m} \mathbb{N};\ \ loc: Aircraft \xrightarrow{m} Space \\ inv\text{-}ATC(cs, con, \overleftarrow{cap}, loc);\ \ \textit{pre-Commission}(s, \overleftarrow{cap}) \end{array}}{\textit{post-Commission}(s, n, \overleftarrow{cap}, cap): \mathbb{B}}$$

In this particular case, it is fairly obvious that these well-formedness conditions are satisfied, so the proofs of these rules are not discussed here. The interested reader can easily apply the techniques described in Section 9.4 to construct them.

The final proof obligation associated with this operation is the satisfiability obligation, which states that there must always be at least one state configuration satisfying the op-

12.4 Top-level operations

eration's postcondition whenever the operation can legitimately be applied (i.e. when the system is in some legal state and when the operation's parameters satisfy its precondition in that state):

Proof obligation 11 The operation *Commission* is satisfiable.

$$\boxed{\textit{Commission-sat}} \quad \frac{\begin{array}{c} s\colon \textit{Space};\ n\colon \mathsf{N};\ cs\colon \textit{Controller}\text{-set} \\ con\colon \textit{Space} \xleftarrow{m} \textit{Controller};\ \overleftarrow{cap}\colon \textit{Space} \xrightarrow{m} \mathsf{N} \\ loc\colon \textit{Aircraft} \xrightarrow{m} \textit{Space};\ \textit{inv-ATC}(cs, con, \overleftarrow{cap}, loc) \\ \textit{pre-Commission}(s, \overleftarrow{cap}) \end{array}}{\exists cap\colon \textit{Space} \xrightarrow{m} \mathsf{N} \cdot \\ \textit{post-Commission}(s, n, \overleftarrow{cap}, cap) \wedge \textit{inv-ATC}(cs, con, cap, loc)}$$

The first step in all these satisfiability proofs is to unfold the definition of the postcondition in the conclusion. After that, there are generally two ways of proceeding: either a witness value (see Section 3.3.1) must be explicitly given which satisfies the existential quantification, or some appropriate induction rule might be used. In this case, the fact that the postcondition is a simple equality means that it effectively defines the appropriate witness value for the new value of the *capacity* field directly, namely that it must be

$$\overleftarrow{capacity} \dagger \{s \mapsto n\}$$

Because of this, the appropriate rule to use is '∃-I-1pt'. The proof (below) then reduces to showing that making this change to the *capacity* field preserves both the type of the *capacity* field (Line 10) and the state invariant (Line 17).

The first of these goals is easy to discharge using the basic formation rules for the operators involved (map override and unit map). For the second, the fact that the first and third clauses of the invariant do not involve the *capacity* field means these will be unaffected when it is changed and will therefore still be true after the change (Lines 11 and 13). It is thus only necessary to show that the other two clauses of the invariant are similarly preserved by the change, that is:

- an airspace can be activated only if it is commissioned (Line 12);
- the capacity of each utilised airspace is not exceeded (Line 16).

The first of these follows easily from the corresponding (second) conjunct of the invariant on the state prior to the application of the operation (Line 4) and the fact that overriding a map with another cannot reduce its domain. For the second, the first step is to apply '∀-I-set', resulting in Subproof 15. Then the precondition of the operation, expanded in Line 3, can be used in conjunction with the second and third conjuncts of the invariant on the state before the operation is applied (Lines 4 and 13) to show that $s \notin \mathrm{rng}\, loc$ (Line 14), which, taken together with the second hypothesis of Subproof 15, means that y is different from s (Line 15.2). The properties of map override then allow $(\overleftarrow{cap} \dagger \{s \mapsto n\})(y)$ to be rewritten as $\overleftarrow{cap}(y)$ (Line 15.6), and the proof is completed using the fourth conjunct of the invariant (Line 8) and simple predicate calculus.

from $s\colon Space$; $n\colon \mathbb{N}$; $cs\colon Controller$-set; $con\colon Space \xleftrightarrow{m} Controller$;
$\overleftarrow{cap}\colon Space \xrightarrow{m} \mathbb{N}$; $loc\colon Aircraft \xrightarrow{m} Space$;
$inv\text{-}ATC(cs, con, \overleftarrow{cap}, loc)$; $pre\text{-}Commission(s, \overleftarrow{cap})$

1	$con\colon Space \xrightarrow{m} Controller$	bimap-supertype (h4)
2	rng $loc\colon Space$-set	rng-form (h6)
3	$s \notin \mathrm{dom}\,\overleftarrow{cap}$	unfolding (h8)
4	$\mathrm{dom}\,con \subseteq \mathrm{dom}\,\overleftarrow{cap}$	inv-ATC-E-clause2 (h3, h4, h5, h6, h7)
5	$\mathrm{dom}\,con\colon Space$-set	dom-form-bimap (h4)
6	$\mathrm{dom}\,\overleftarrow{cap}\colon Space$-set	dom-form (h5)
7	$s \notin \mathrm{dom}\,con$	$\notin$-subset-I (h1, 5, 6, 4, 3)
8	$\forall x \in \mathrm{rng}\,loc \cdot numOfAircraft(x, loc) \leq \overleftarrow{cap}(x)$	
		inv-ATC-E-clause4 (h3, h4, h5, h6, h7)
9	$\{s \mapsto n\}\colon Space \xrightarrow{m} \mathbb{N}$	$\{a \mapsto b\}$-form (h1, h2)
10	$\overleftarrow{cap} \dagger \{s \mapsto n\}\colon Space \xrightarrow{m} \mathbb{N}$	$\dagger$-form (h5, 9)
11	rng $con \subseteq cs$	inv-ATC-E-clause1 (h3, h4, h5, h6, h7)
12	$\mathrm{dom}\,con \subseteq \mathrm{dom}\,(\overleftarrow{cap} \dagger \{s \mapsto n\})$	$\dagger$-preserves-dom-$\subseteq$ (1, h5, 9, 4)
13	rng $loc \subseteq \mathrm{dom}\,con$	inv-ATC-E-clause3 (h3, h4, h5, h6, h7)
14	$s \notin \mathrm{rng}\,loc$	$\notin$-subset-I (h1, 2, 5, 13, 7)
15	from $y\colon Space$; $y \in \mathrm{rng}\,loc$	
15.1	$\quad numOfAircraft(y, loc) \leq \overleftarrow{cap}(y)$	$\forall$-E-set (15.h1, 2, 15.h2, 8)
15.2	$\quad \neg(y = s)$	$\in$-$\notin$-contr (15.h1, h1, 2, 15.h2, 14)
15.3	$\quad y \in \mathrm{dom}\,con$	$\subseteq$-E (15.h1, 2, 5, 15.h2, 13)
15.4	$\quad y \in \mathrm{dom}\,\overleftarrow{cap}$	$\subseteq$-E (15.h1, 5, 6, 15.3, 4)
15.5	$\quad \overleftarrow{cap}(y)\colon \mathbb{N}$	at-form (15.h1, h5, 15.4)
15.6	$\quad (\overleftarrow{cap} \dagger \{s \mapsto n\})(y) = \overleftarrow{cap}(y)$	
		at-defn-$\dagger$-$\{a \mapsto b\}$-$\neq$ (h1, h2, 15.h1, h5, 15.4, 15.2)
	infer $numOfAircraft(y, loc) \leq (\overleftarrow{cap} \dagger \{s \mapsto n\})(y)$	
		=-subs-left(b) (15.5, 15.6, 15.1)
16	$\forall x \in \mathrm{rng}\,loc \cdot numOfAircraft(x, loc) \leq (\overleftarrow{cap} \dagger \{s \mapsto n\})(x)$	$\forall$-I-set (2, 15)
17	$inv\text{-}ATC(cs, con, \overleftarrow{cap} \dagger \{s \mapsto n\}, loc)$	
		inv-ATC-I-separate (h3, h4, 10, h6, 11, 12, 13, 16)
18	$\exists cap\colon Space \xrightarrow{m} \mathbb{N} \cdot$	
	$\quad cap = \overleftarrow{cap} \dagger \{s \mapsto n\} \land inv\text{-}ATC(cs, con, cap, loc)$	$\exists$-I-1pt (10, 17)
	infer $\exists cap\colon Space \xrightarrow{m} \mathbb{N} \cdot$	
	$\quad post\text{-}Commission(s, n, \overleftarrow{cap}, cap) \land inv\text{-}ATC(cs, con, cap, loc)$	folding (18)

12.4.2 Resetting the capacity of an airspace

Next, consider an operation for resetting the capacity of an airspace. A first attempt to specify this might simply mimic the *Commission* operation given above:

ResetCapacity $(s: Space, n: \mathbb{N})$
ext wr *capacity* : $Space \xrightarrow{m} \mathbb{N}$
pre $s \in \text{dom}\, capacity$
post *capacity* $= \overleftarrow{capacity} \dagger \{s \mapsto n\}$

The appropriate satisfiability proof obligation for this operation is

$$\boxed{\textit{ResetCapacity-sat}} \quad \frac{\begin{array}{c} s: Space;\ n: \mathbb{N};\ cs: Controller\text{-set};\ con: Space \xleftarrow{m} Controller \\ \overleftarrow{cap}: Space \xrightarrow{m} \mathbb{N};\ loc: Aircraft \xrightarrow{m} Space \\ inv\text{-}ATC(cs, con, \overleftarrow{cap}, loc);\ pre\text{-}ResetCapacity(s, \overleftarrow{cap}) \end{array}}{\exists cap: Space \xrightarrow{m} \mathbb{N} \cdot \\ post\text{-}ResetCapacity(s, n, \overleftarrow{cap}, cap) \land inv\text{-}ATC(cs, con, cap, loc)}$$

with *pre-ResetCapacity* and *post-ResetCapacity* defined via

$pre\text{-}ResetCapacity(s, cap) \stackrel{\text{def}}{=} s \in \text{dom}\, cap$

$post\text{-}ResetCapacity(s, n, \overleftarrow{cap}, cap) \stackrel{\text{def}}{=} cap = \overleftarrow{cap} \dagger \{s \mapsto n\}$

The proof proceeds as in the previous example: after expanding the definition of the postcondition and using '∃-I-1pt' to supply the witness value for the existential quantification directly from the equality in the postcondition, the proof again reduces to showing that making the given change to the *capacity* field preserves both its type and the state invariant. The parallel with the previous example continues, the latter goal again reducing to having to show that:

- an airspace can be activated only if it is commissioned (Line 3 in the proof below);

- the capacity of each utilised airspace is not exceeded (Line 7).

Considering now the second of these two subgoals, the next step which immediately suggests itself is to apply '∀-I-set', as before. However, since the precondition in this example is the negation of that in the previous example it cannot be used to yield $y \neq s$ as was done there. But the value of the expression $(\overleftarrow{cap} \dagger \{s \mapsto n\})(y)$ in the conclusion of Subproof 6 depends on whether or not $y = s$. This suggests that the next step should be to set up a case distinction on these two alternatives, this time using the rule '=-cases' which unifies into a single rule the combined application of 'δ-=-I' and 'δ-E' illustrated in Section 3.5.2. Substituting $y = s$ from the hypothesis of the first of the two subproofs generated by this case distinction into its conclusion, and using the properties of map application to rewrite the resulting subgoal, then leads to the partial proof below:

from $s: Space$; $n: \mathbb{N}$; $cs: Controller$-set; $con: Space \xleftarrow{m} Controller$;
$\overline{cap}: Space \xrightarrow{m} \mathbb{N}$; $loc: Aircraft \xrightarrow{m} Space$;
$inv\text{-}ATC(cs, con, \overline{cap}, loc)$; $pre\text{-}ResetCapacity(s, \overline{cap})$
...

1	$\overline{cap} \dagger \{s \mapsto n\}: Space \xrightarrow{m} \mathbb{N}$	⟨?? justify ??⟩
2	$\text{rng } con \subseteq cs$	⟨?? justify ??⟩
3	$\text{dom } con \subseteq \text{dom}(\overline{cap} \dagger \{s \mapsto n\})$	⟨?? justify ??⟩
4	$\text{rng } loc \subseteq \text{dom } con$	⟨?? justify ??⟩
5	$\text{rng } loc: Space\text{-set}$	⟨?? justify ??⟩
6	from $y: Space$; $y \in \text{rng } loc$	
6.1	from $y = s$	
6.1.1	$(\overline{cap} \dagger \{s \mapsto n\})(s) = n$	at-defn-$\dagger$-$\{a \mapsto b\}$-= (h1, h2, h5)
	...	
6.1.2	$numOfAircraft(s, loc) \leq n$	⟨?? justify ??⟩
6.1.3	$numOfAircraft(s, loc) \leq (\overline{cap} \dagger \{s \mapsto n\})(s)$	
		=-subs-left(b) (h2, 6.2.1, 6.2.2)
	infer $numOfAircraft(y, loc) \leq (\overline{cap} \dagger \{s \mapsto n\})(y)$	
		=-subs-left(b) (h1, 6.2.h1, 6.2.3)
6.2	from $y \neq s$	
	...	
	infer $numOfAircraft(y, loc) \leq (\overline{cap} \dagger \{s \mapsto n\})(y)$	⟨?? justify ??⟩
	infer $numOfAircraft(y, loc) \leq (\overline{cap} \dagger \{s \mapsto n\})(y)$	=-cases (6.h1, h1, 6.1, 6.2)
7	$\forall x \in \text{rng } loc \cdot numOfAircraft(x, loc) \leq (\overline{cap} \dagger \{s \mapsto n\})(x)$	$\forall$-I-set (5, 6)
8	$inv\text{-}ATC(cs, con, \overline{cap} \dagger \{s \mapsto n\}, loc)$	$inv\text{-}ATC$-I-separate (h3, h4, 1, h6, 2, 3, 4, 7)
9	$\exists cap: Space \xrightarrow{m} \mathbb{N} \cdot cap = \overline{cap} \dagger \{s \mapsto n\} \wedge inv\text{-}ATC(cs, con, cap, loc)$	
		$\exists$-I-1pt (1, 8)
	infer $\exists cap: Space \xrightarrow{m} \mathbb{N} \cdot$	
	$post\text{-}ResetCapacity(s, n, \overline{cap}, cap) \wedge inv\text{-}ATC(cs, con, cap, loc)$	folding (9)

From this point it is clear that Subproof 6.1 can only be completed if it is possible to prove that $numOfAircraft(s, loc) \leq n$, but the only hypotheses available which give any information about s and n are the typing hypotheses on the two variables and the precondition.

At this stage, if not before, it would probably occur to the verifier that the proof cannot be completed, and that in fact the precondition on the operation must be strengthened to say that the reset value n cannot be less than the number of aircraft currently occupying the space s. This leads to a revised specification of the operation:

ResetCapacity ($s: Space$, $n: \mathbb{N}$)
  ext rd *location* : $Aircraft \xrightarrow{m} Space$
    wr *capacity* : $Space \xrightarrow{m} \mathbb{N}$
  pre $s \in \text{dom } capacity \wedge numOfAircraft(s, location) \leq n$
  post $capacity = \overleftarrow{capacity} \dagger \{s \mapsto n\}$

12.4 Top-level operations

and a corresponding change in the proof obligation:

$$\boxed{\textit{ResetCapacity-sat}} \frac{\begin{array}{c} s\colon Space;\ n\colon \mathbb{N};\ cs\colon Controller\text{-set} \\ con\colon Space \xleftrightarrow{m} Controller;\ \overline{cap}\colon Space \xrightarrow{m} \mathbb{N} \\ loc\colon Aircraft \xrightarrow{m} Space;\ inv\text{-}ATC(cs, con, \overline{cap}, loc) \\ pre\text{-}ResetCapacity(s, n, \overline{cap}, loc) \end{array}}{\exists cap\colon Space \xrightarrow{m} \mathbb{N} \cdot \\ post\text{-}ResetCapacity(s, n, \overline{cap}, cap) \wedge inv\text{-}ATC(cs, con, cap, loc)}$$

Note how the failed proof not only revealed that the precondition needed to be strengthened, but also indicated what additional condition needed to be added to it. In fact, attempting to discharge the satisfiability proof obligation for an operation is a good way of checking that no preconditions or parts of preconditions have been overlooked.

Another point worth noting here is that it is not necessary to start a new proof because an error in the precondition has been discovered: all of the steps done so far are still valid if the definition of the precondition is changed since none of them depend on it. Thus, the only change that has to be made is that extra arguments have to be added to *pre-ResetCapacity* in the hypotheses of the proof. Having made this change the proof can proceed by simply extending the proof constructed so far.

12.4.3 Decommissioning an airspace

The operation *Decommission* is for decommissioning an airspace, that is for removing from the system an airspace which is no longer operational. For example, it might be desirable to subdivide an existing airspace into new, smaller airspaces to accommodate increased demand in the ATC region, which could be achieved by first decommissioning the airspace and then commissioning new airspaces appropriately.

This operation might be specified as follows:

Decommission ($s\colon Space$)
  ext rd *control* : $Space \xleftrightarrow{m} Controller$
    wr *capacity* : $Space \xrightarrow{m} \mathbb{N}$
  pre $s \in (\text{dom}\,capacity \setminus \text{dom}\,control)$
  post $capacity = \{s\} \triangleleft \overline{capacity}$

Here, intuition would probably suggest that it should be meaningless to apply this operation to a utilised airspace, although it might not be immediately obvious that this is actually a property of the specification. The way to show this, then, is to formalise the validation property as a rule and to prove the rule:

Validation 7 A utilised airspace cannot be decommissioned.

$$\boxed{\textit{Decommission-lemma}} \frac{s\colon Space;\ mk\text{-}ATC(cs, con, cap, loc)\colon ATC;\ s \in \text{rng}\,loc}{\neg\,pre\text{-}Decommission(s, con, cap)}$$

The proof of this is fairly straightforward: after expanding the definition of the precondition it relies simply on the properties of sets and the third clause of the invariant. The completed proof is:

from $s\colon Space;\ mk\text{-}ATC(cs, con, cap, loc)\colon ATC;\ s \in \text{rng}\, loc$

1	$con\colon Space \xleftrightarrow{m} Controller$	*control*-form-mk (h2)
2	$cap\colon Space \xrightarrow{m} \mathbb{N}$	*capacity*-form-mk (h2)
3	$loc\colon Aircraft \xrightarrow{m} Space$	*location*-form-mk (h2)
4	rng $loc\colon Space$-set	rng-form (3)
5	dom $con\colon Space$-set	dom-form-bimap (1)
6	dom $cap\colon Space$-set	dom-form (2)
7	rng $loc \subseteq$ dom con	*inv-ATC*-I-mk-clause3 (h2)
8	$s \in$ dom con	$\subseteq$-E (h1, 4, 5, h3, 7)
9	$s \notin (\text{dom}\, cap \setminus \text{dom}\, con)$	$\notin$-diff-I-left (h1, 6, 5, 8)
10	$\neg(s \in (\text{dom}\, cap \setminus \text{dom}\, con))$	unfolding (9)

infer $\neg\, pre\text{-}Decommission(s, con, cap)$ folding (10)

12.4.4 Controllers coming on duty

Turning attention now to controllers, the next operation registers the fact that a controller has "clocked on" (come on duty). It simply adds c to the *onduty* set. There is a precondition to say that c is not already on duty. Note that this precondition is not the weakest which permits the postcondition to be satisfied. It rather records an additional requirement, namely a limitation on the use of the *ClockOn* operation.

ClockOn (*c*: *Controller*)
ext wr *onduty* : *Controller*-set
pre $c \notin onduty$
post $onduty = \overleftarrow{onduty} \cup \{c\}$

12.4.5 Controllers going off duty

The corresponding operation for "clocking-off" (going off duty) has a precondition which says that the controller clocking off must be on duty but may not be currently assigned:

ClockOff (*c*: *Controller*)
ext wr *onduty* : *Controller*-set
    rd *control* : $Space \xleftrightarrow{m} Controller$
pre $c \in onduty \setminus \text{rng}\, control$
post $onduty = \overleftarrow{onduty} \setminus \{c\}$

A controller will become deassigned when the airspace under his or her control is either assigned to some other controller via the operation *Reassign* (see Section 12.4.7) or becomes deactivated as a result of the operation *Deactivate* (see Section 12.4.8).

12.4 Top-level operations

12.4.6 Activating an airspace

Turning next to operations for assigning controllers to airspaces, the first deals with an airspace being activated, for example when an airport opens for the day. Recall that in this abstract model an airspace is activated if and only if it is under someone's control, so that the operation simply needs to assign the airspace to a controller. But how should the controller be chosen? Or rather, since this is a specification and not an implementation, what are the precise requirements for the choice?

To give a little variety to the specification, the operation is left loosely specified at this level of abstraction. At a later stage in the development, a richer model of the state could be defined, which would include, say, information pertinent to the choice of controller, taking into account such things as rosters, seniority, qualifications or whatever. Such detail would swamp the specification if introduced too early, making verification of correctness properties far more complicated. Here the primary interest is to ensure that the choice of controller does not violate any of the requirements built into the state invariant.

The operation has a precondition stating that airspace s is commissioned but not currently activated and that there should be a controller available. The latter can be stated as $\text{rng } control \neq onduty$ because it is known that $\text{rng } control \subseteq onduty$. The specification is:

Activate $(s: Space)\ c: Controller$
ext rd *onduty* : *Controller*-set
     wr *control* : $Space \xleftrightarrow{m} Controller$
     rd *capacity* : $Space \xrightarrow{m} \mathbb{N}$
pre $s \in (\text{dom } capacity \setminus \text{dom } control) \land \text{rng } control \neq onduty$
post $control = \overleftarrow{control} \dagger \{s \mapsto c\}$

Another validation condition that might occur to the designer at this point is that the controller allocated to the new airspace as a result of this operation should have been available at the time, that is both on duty and unassigned:

Validation 8 It is a consequence of the specification of *Activate* that the controller chosen by the operation was available at the time the operation was invoked.

$$\boxed{Activate\text{-lemma}}\ \frac{s: Space;\ \ c: Controller \\ mk\text{-}ATC(cs, \overleftarrow{con}, cap, loc): ATC;\ \ mk\text{-}ATC(cs, con, cap, loc): ATC \\ pre\text{-}Activate(s, cs, \overleftarrow{con}, cap);\ post\text{-}Activate(s, c, \overleftarrow{con}, con)}{c \in (cs \setminus \text{rng } \overleftarrow{con})}$$

Intuitively, the hypotheses of this rule record everything that is known about the state of the system after execution of the operation. In principle, the proof of the validation might depend on any or all of these hypotheses.

Exercise 2 Prove the above validation. **Hint:** Use the fact that both $\overleftarrow{con}$ and con are one-one. □

12.4.7 Reassigning control of an airspace

The next operation is for assigning a new controller to an already activated airspace, for example when a controller wants to clock off or simply take a break. Once again, there is a precondition that a controller is available, but the actual choice of controller is left loosely specified:

Reassign (*s*: *Space*) *c*: *Controller*
ext rd *onduty* : *Controller*-set
 wr *control* : *Space* $\xleftrightarrow{m}$ *Controller*
pre $s \in \text{dom}\,control \land \text{rng}\,control \neq onduty$
post $control = \overline{control} \dagger \{s \mapsto c\} \land c \neq \overline{control}(s)$

Note that the postcondition says that the original controller should not be re-chosen, since this would after all defeat the purpose of the operation.

12.4.8 Deactivating an airspace

The next operation is for deactivating an airspace, for example if an airport closes down for the night:

Deactivate (*s*: *Space*)
ext wr *control* : *Space* $\xleftrightarrow{m}$ *Controller*
 rd *location* : *Aircraft* $\xrightarrow{m}$ *Space*
pre $s \in (\text{dom}\,control \setminus \text{rng}\,location)$
post $control = \{s\} \triangleleft \overline{control}$

The precondition says that *s* must not be utilised at the time. Note that the operation simply deactivates *s* without decommissioning it.

12.4.9 Adding new flight data to the system

The last three operations concern flight handling. The first of these describes the arrival of a new aircraft *p* into the ATC region, at airspace *s*. For example, *s* might be the taxiway from the terminal to the runway in the case of a departing flight, or *s* might be one of the "frontier" corridors for incoming flights.

There are three parts to the precondition: *s* is already under someone's control; *p* is a *new* aircraft, unknown in the current state; and *s* is not already at its full capacity.

AddFlight (*p*: *Aircraft*, *s*: *Space*)
ext rd *control* : *Space* $\xleftrightarrow{m}$ *Controller*
 rd *capacity* : *Space* $\xrightarrow{m}$ ℕ
 wr *location* : *Aircraft* $\xrightarrow{m}$ *Space*
pre $s \in \text{dom}\,control \land p \notin \text{dom}\,location \land$
 $numOfAircraft(s, location) < capacity(s)$
post $location = \overline{location} \dagger \{p \mapsto s\}$

12.4.10 Handing over a flight

The next operation handles the case of an aircraft p already in the ATC region and preparing to move from one airspace to another, s say. In addition to the requirements in the precondition for *AddFlight* above, p should not already be in airspace s.

Handover $(p:Aircraft, s:Space)$
ext rd *control* : $Space \xleftrightarrow{m} Controller$
    rd *capacity* : $Space \xrightarrow{m} \mathbb{N}$
    wr *location* : $Aircraft \xrightarrow{m} Space$
pre $s \in \text{dom}\, control \land p \in \text{dom}\, location \land location(p) \neq s \land$
    $numOfAircraft(s, location) < capacity(s)$
post $location = \overleftarrow{location} \dagger \{p \mapsto s\}$

12.4.11 Removing flight data from the system

The last operation allows an aircraft to leave the ATC region, for example when an arriving flight has landed and docked at its gate, or when a departing flight has reached the outgoing frontier of the region.

RemoveFlight $(p:Aircraft)$
ext wr *location* : $Aircraft \xrightarrow{m} Space$
pre $p \in \text{dom}\, location$
post $location = \{p\} \triangleleft \overleftarrow{location}$

Given a particular configuration of the ATC subsystem, it might be desirable to identify a particular set of airspaces from which it is permissible to leave the ATC region — such as parking bays and outgoing frontier airspaces — and to strengthen the precondition of this operation to only allow it to be invoked from those airspaces. This would mean making a change to the definition of *ATC* to incorporate such information, and is left to the reader as an exercise.

12.5 First refinement step

This section illustrates a possible first development step, in which the state is made more concrete and complex. This involves a change of emphasis, resulting in a model in which flight information is distributed across the system and the set of flights assigned to a controller is "implemented" as a queue. Amongst other things, this refinement illustrates how the structure of an implementation need not necessarily follow the structure of the original specification.

The change of emphasis results from taking a different view of airspaces. The abstract specification given in Section 12.3 models a more-or-less physical view of airspaces as things in which aircraft are located. In the refinement given, airspaces are seen more through the eyes of the controllers, so that *Space* now represents, say, the information which might be presented to the controller on a monitor, for example as shown in Fig. 12.6. In modern systems, such information is more likely to be presented to the controller on a radar screen. This case study talks in terms of monitors, however, to limit the complexity of the data structures involved. Such a change in perspective suggests, for example, a more distributed implementation of the ATC subsystem, whereby subcomponents such as monitors need only know about information which is relevant to them.

Airspace RA-1			
call sign	altitude	ground speed	emerg code
BA-1506	5,000	530	
KLM-74	20,000	770	H
Q-1	30,000	690	
system personalized for: *Stephanie*			

Figure 12.6: An airspace as its controller might see it via a monitor.

Section 12.5.1 below gives the specification for the new state space, and some aspects of its internal consistency are discussed in Section 12.5.2. In Section 12.5.3 the retrieve function relating the new state to the original one given in Section 12.3 is developed, and the associated well-formedness and adequacy proof obligations, which are necessary for the correctness of the refinement, are discussed in Section 12.5.4. To complete the refinement, it would then be necessary to give a counterpart for each of the operations specified in Section 12.4 and to prove, via the domain and result obligations, that each such operation implements its abstract counterpart correctly. This aspect of the refinement is dealt with in Section 12.5.5, but space permits only one operation to be discussed.

12.5.1 The new state definition

In this new view of the system, the position of an aircraft, recorded previously in the *location* field in the form of a map from *Aircraft* to *Space*, is instead stored in an *assignment map*. This associates with each airspace the queue of aircraft currently utilising it, and is specified as a new auxiliary data type *AssigMap* with an invariant to the effect that no aircraft can appear in two different queues:

$AssigMap = Space \xrightarrow{m} AircraftQueue$
inv $ass \triangleq \forall q_1, q_2 \in \text{rng } ass \cdot q_1 \neq q_2 \Rightarrow \text{elems } q_1 \cap \text{elems } q_2 = \{\}$

Here, *AircraftQueue* is an auxiliary data type modelling non-repeating sequences of aircraft (that is, sequences in which all aircraft are different):

$AircraftQueue = Aircraft^*$
inv $q \triangleq nonRptng[Aircraft](q)$

The function *nonRptng* is defined recursively: a sequence is non-repeating if it is empty or if its head does not occur in the elements of its tail and its tail is itself non-repeating. The function is also defined polymorphically (see Section 10.4.6) in terms of the type parameter @A. The specification is:

12.5 First refinement step

$$nonRptng\,[@A]: @A^* \to \mathbb{B}$$
$$nonRptng(s) \;\triangleq\; s = [\,] \lor hd\,s \notin elems\,tl\,s \land nonRptng[@A](tl\,s)$$

The new state definition then has an assignment map instead of the *location* field, the other three state components remaining unchanged:

state ATC_1 of
    $onduty_1$: *Controller*-set
    $control_1$: *Space* $\xleftrightarrow{m}$ *Controller*
    $capacity_1$: *Space* $\xrightarrow{m}$ $\mathbb{N}$
    $assigs_1$: *AssigMap*
inv $mk\text{-}ATC_1(cs, con, cap, ass)$ $\triangleq$
    rng $con \subseteq cs$
    $\land$ dom $con \subseteq$ dom cap
    $\land$ dom $ass =$ dom con
    $\land\, \forall s \in$ dom $ass \cdot$ len $ass(s) \leq cap(s)$
init $\sigma_1 \;\triangleq\; \sigma_1.onduty_1 = \{\,\} \land \sigma_1.capacity_1 = \{\mapsto\}$
end

The invariants on the state and the auxiliary data-types capture essentially the same subset of the requirements as before, but must additionally ensure that the restriction that an aircraft occupies a unique airspace (requirement **R7**) is maintained. (This came "free" in the original specification because the *location* field was specified to be a map from *Aircraft* to *Space*.)

The initialisation condition on the state makes all fields empty as before.

In fact the specification given above contains a subtle oversight, which might not become apparent until later in the development process, when it could be expensive to correct or have serious consequences. Fortunately, the error comes to light below in the course of attempting to discharge the proof obligations for the specification.

12.5.2 Internal consistency of the new state definition

The axioms, definitions and proof obligations for the new state ATC_1 closely parallel those for the abstract state *ATC* given in Section 12.3.2 so are not discussed here. The interested reader should have no difficulty writing them down. However, the auxiliary data-type *AssigMap* and the auxiliary function *nonRptng* are worth considering in some detail as they make use of VDM-SL constructs which have not so far featured in the examples treated in this case study.

The first of these represents a subtype, and is defined in exactly that way in the theory:

$$AssigMap \;\stackrel{\text{def}}{=}\; \ll m\colon Space \xrightarrow{m} AircraftQueue \mid inv\text{-}AssigMap(m) \gg$$

Another defined symbol is introduced to describe the invariant on *AssigMap*:

$$inv\text{-}AssigMap(m) \;\stackrel{\text{def}}{=}\; \forall q_1, q_2 \in \text{rng}\, m \cdot q_1 \neq q_2 \Rightarrow elems\, q_1 \cap elems\, q_2 = \{\,\}$$

and there is the usual well-formedness proof obligation to show that this invariant is boolean-valued:

$$\boxed{\textit{inv-AssigMap}\text{-form}} \; \frac{m\colon Space \xrightarrow{m} AircraftQueue}{\textit{inv-AssigMap}(m)\colon \mathbb{B}}$$

The axiom and proof obligation for the auxiliary function *nonRptng* are:

$$\boxed{\textit{nonRptng-defn}_0} \; \frac{s\colon A^*; \; (s=[\,] \lor \text{hd}\,s \notin \text{elems}\,\text{tl}\,s \land \textit{nonRptng}(\text{tl}\,s))\colon \mathbb{B}}{\textit{nonRptng}(s) = (s=[\,] \lor \text{hd}\,s \notin \text{elems}\,\text{tl}\,s \land \textit{nonRptng}(\text{tl}\,s))} \; \text{Ax}$$

$$\boxed{\textit{nonRptng}\text{-form}} \; \frac{s\colon A^*}{\textit{nonRptng}(s)\colon \mathbb{B}}$$

Note how the type parameter @A in the specification simply becomes a metavariable (A) in these axioms.

It is instructive to consider the proof of the well-formedness obligation as this illustrates how such proofs are tackled for recursively defined functions. The basic strategy for these proofs is the same as that for the non-recursive case illustrated above for the function *numOfAircraft* (see Section 12.3.2), namely to begin by proving a rule showing the well-formedness of the defining expression:

$$\boxed{\textit{nonRptng}\text{-wff}} \; \frac{s\colon A^*}{(s=[\,] \lor \text{hd}\,s \notin \text{elems}\,\text{tl}\,s \land \textit{nonRptng}(\text{tl}\,s))\colon \mathbb{B}}$$

However, it is clearly impossible to prove this using simply the formation rules for the operators comprising the expression which defines *nonRptng* as these include *nonRptng* itself. But the definition rule '*nonRptng*-defn$_0$' effectively implies that if *nonRptng* is well-formed for the tail of some sequence s then it is also well-formed for s itself because if *nonRptng*(tl s) is boolean-valued the second hypothesis of the definition rule is also boolean-valued and *nonRptng*(s) is equal to it. This suggests that the proof should employ sequence induction. Performing this as a first step yields the following partial proof:

from $s\colon A^*$
...
1    $([\,]=[\,] \lor \text{hd}\,[\,] \notin \text{elems}\,\text{tl}\,[\,] \land \textit{nonRptng}(\text{tl}\,[\,]))\colon \mathbb{B}$ ⟨?? justify ??⟩
2   from $h\colon A; \; t\colon A^*; \; (t=[\,] \lor \text{hd}\,t \notin \text{elems}\,\text{tl}\,t \land \textit{nonRptng}(\text{tl}\,t))\colon \mathbb{B}$
    ...
    infer $(\text{cons}(h,t)=[\,] \lor$
        $\text{hd}\,\text{cons}(h,t) \notin \text{elems}\,\text{tl}\,\text{cons}(h,t) \land \textit{nonRptng}(\text{tl}\,\text{cons}(h,t)))\colon \mathbb{B}$ ⟨?? justify ??⟩
infer $(s=[\,] \lor \text{hd}\,s \notin \text{elems}\,\text{tl}\,s \land \textit{nonRptng}(\text{tl}\,s))\colon \mathbb{B}$ seq-indn (h1, 1, 2)

An important point to note here is that, although it might seem reasonable to begin this proof by simplifying the conclusion immediately using the formation rule '∨-form-sqt' rather than by using sequence induction, this in fact does not lead to the simplest proof. The essential feature of the proof given above is that the second and third hypotheses of Subproof 2 match the hypotheses of the definition rule for *nonRptng* directly, and these can therefore be used to deduce

$$\textit{nonRptng}(t) = (t=[\,] \lor \text{hd}\,t \notin \text{elems}\,\text{tl}\,t \land \textit{nonRptng}(\text{tl}\,t))$$

and hence that *nonRptng*(t) is boolean-valued. Having done that, the rules 'hd-defn-cons'

12.5 First refinement step

and 'tl-defn-cons' can be used to rewrite the expressions hd cons(h, t) and tl cons(h, t) in the conclusion of Subproof 2, leading to:

from $s: A^*$
...
1   ([ ] = [ ] ∨ hd [ ] ∉ elems tl [ ] ∧ $nonRptng$(tl [ ])): $\mathbb{B}$ ⟨?? justify ??⟩
2   from $h: A$; $t: A^*$; (t = [ ] ∨ hd t ∉ elems tl t ∧ $nonRptng$(tl t)): $\mathbb{B}$
2.1 $nonRptng(t)$ =
                    (t = [ ] ∨ hd t ∉ elems tl t ∧ $nonRptng$(tl t)) $nonRptng$-defn$_0$ (2.h2, 2.h3)
2.2 $nonRptng(t)$: $\mathbb{B}$ =-type-inherit-left (2.h3, 2.1)
2.3   hd cons(h, t) = h hd-defn-cons (2.h1, 2.h2)
2.4   tl cons(h, t) = t tl-defn-cons (2.h1, 2.h2)
...
2.5   (cons(h, t) = [ ] ∨ h ∉ elems t ∧ $nonRptng(t)$): $\mathbb{B}$ ⟨?? justify ??⟩
2.6   (cons(h, t) = [ ] ∨
                 hd cons(h, t) ∉ elems t ∧ $nonRptng(t)$): $\mathbb{B}$ =-subs-right(b) (2.h1, 2.3, 2.5)
       infer (cons(h, t) = [ ] ∨ (hd cons(h, t) ∉ elems tl cons(h, t) ∧
                $nonRptng$(tl cons(h, t)))): $\mathbb{B}$ =-subs-right(b) (2.h2, 2.4, 2.6)
infer (s = [ ] ∨ hd s ∉ elems tl s ∧ $nonRptng$(tl s)): $\mathbb{B}$ seq-indn (h1, 1, 2)

from which point the proof can indeed be completed easily using standard formation rules.

It is worth noting that the fact that the proof of the well-formedness of *nonRptng* has been completed successfully indicates that the recursion in its definition is in fact sound. Conversely, failure to complete the well-formedness proof for a recursively-defined function is often a sign that the recursion itself is ill-formed.

The overall formation rule '*nonRptng*-form' is then proved from the above rule via the working version of the definition rule, just as for the non-recursive case.

12.5.3 Relating this specification to the original specification

In order to show that this new state ATC_1 is a valid refinement of the original state ATC, a retrieve function must be defined relating values of the new state to values of the old. In this case, the only change in the state definition is that the *location* field has been replaced by an assignment map, so defining the retrieve function essentially amounts to reconstructing the location map from the assignment map.

As a first step towards doing this, an auxiliary function is defined which returns all the aircraft known to the ATC system, corresponding in the top-level specification to the domain of the location map. This is simply given by the union of the elements of all the sequences in the range of the assignment map:

knownAircraft : *AssigMap* → *Aircraft*-set
knownAircraft(*ass*) ≜ ⋃{elems q | q ∈ rng *ass*}

Exercise 3 Write down the axiom(s) and proof obligation(s) for the auxiliary function *knownAircraft*. Construct the proof(s) of the proof obligation(s). □

A second auxiliary function is then used to determine the airspace utilised by a known aircraft. This function simply returns the airspace whose queue of aircraft contains the aircraft in question. Since the invariant on *AssigMap* ensures that a given aircraft cannot appear in two different queues, this should be unique:

$locOf : Aircraft \times AssigMap \to Space$
$locOf(p, ass) \triangleq \iota s \in \text{dom}\, ass \cdot p \in \text{elems}\, ass(s)$
pre $p \in knownAircraft(ass)$

Again, there are well-formedness proof obligations for the function as a whole and for its precondition:

$$\boxed{locOf\text{-form}}\ \frac{p: Aircraft;\ ass: AssigMap;\ pre\text{-}locOf(p, ass)}{locOf(p, ass): Space}$$

$$\boxed{pre\text{-}locOf\text{-form}}\ \frac{p: Aircraft;\ ass: AssigMap}{pre\text{-}locOf(p, ass): \mathbb{B}}$$

where *pre-locOf* is defined via:

$pre\text{-}locOf(p, ass) \stackrel{\text{def}}{=} p \in knownAircraft(ass)$

Following the procedure set out in the discussion of the proof of the well-formedness of *numOfAircraft* (see Section 12.3.3), the first step towards proving '*locOf*-form' is to prove the rule

$$\boxed{locOf\text{-wff}}\ \frac{p: Aircraft;\ ass: AssigMap;\ pre\text{-}locOf(p, ass)}{(\iota s \in \text{dom}\, ass \cdot p \in \text{elems}\, ass(s)): Space}$$

Here, the conclusion clearly has to be justified using the rule 'ι-form-set', which involves showing that there is a unique airspace in dom *ass* satisfying the given predicate. If the precondition of *locOf* is then expanded, the proof reduces to showing that every known aircraft occupies a unique airspace, which is simply **validation 3** restated in the context of the new specification. The rule for this validation is:

$$\boxed{\text{aircraft-in-unique-space}_1}\ \frac{p: Aircraft;\ ass: AssigMap;\ p \in knownAircraft(ass)}{\exists! s \in \text{dom}\, ass \cdot p \in \text{elems}\, ass(s)}$$

In terms of this, the proof of '*locOf*-wff' is:

from $p: Aircraft;\ ass: AssigMap;\ pre\text{-}locOf(p, ass)$
1 dom *ass*: *Space*-set   dom-form-*AssigMap* (h2)
2 $p \in knownAircraft(ass)$ unfolding (h3)
3 $\exists! s \in \text{dom}\, ass \cdot p \in \text{elems}\, ass(s)$ aircraft-in-unique-space$_1$ (h1, h2, 2)
infer $(\iota s \in \text{dom}\, ass \cdot p \in \text{elems}\, ass(s)): Space$ ι-form-set (1, 3)

Turning now to the proof of 'aircraft-in-unique-space$_1$', justifying a unique existential quantification over a set via the rule '∃!-I-set' involves both producing a witness value of

12.5 First refinement step

the correct type belonging to the set and showing that all possible witness values in the set are equal to it. However, at the start of the proof no objects of type *Space* are available to use as witnesses. This indicates that the way to approach the proof is to try to generate some appropriate object of type *Space* by working forwards from the hypotheses. Of these, only the last is not a simple typing assertion, so this clearly offers the only hope of progress.

Looking at the definition of *knownAircraft* and combining this with knowledge of the properties of distributed set union suggests a useful lemma (stated without proof) of the form:

$$\boxed{\in\text{-}knownAircraft\text{-}E} \quad \frac{p: Aircraft;\ ass: AssigMap;\ p \in knownAircraft(ass)}{\exists q \in \text{rng}\, ass \cdot p \in \text{elems}\, q}$$

Using this generates Line 2 of the proof below. Then application of '∃-E-set' is indicated, yielding Subproof 3 and Line 1, the latter being easy to justify using the rule 'rng-form-*AssigMap*'. Then the rule '∈-rng-E' can be used to deduce (Line 3.2) that there must be some airspace in the domain of the map *ass* which maps to the range value q. Again, the rule '∃-E-set' is used, generating Subproof 3.4. Then, substituting the equality from hypothesis 3.4.h3 into hypothesis 3.h3, thereby generating Line 3.4.1, leads to a state in which the airspace a can be used as the witness to the unique existential quantification.

At this stage, therefore, '∃!-I-set' is used, and it remains to be shown only that the witness value a is unique (Line 3.4.3). The appropriate rule here is '∀-I-set', yielding Subproof 3.4.2. Now the idea is to try to reach a point at which the invariant on *AssigMap*, the only piece of available information not used so far, can be brought into play. This requires producing two elements of rng *ass*, which is easy: the first, $ass(y)$, arises from the properties of map application (Line 3.4.2.3), the second, $ass(a)$, from simple substitution of equals (Line 3.4.2.4). Note that although q is already known to be in rng *ass* (hypothesis 3.h2) this step transforming it to $ass(a)$ is necessary because the required goal involves a and y and not q and y.

from $p: Aircraft;\ ass: AssigMap;\ p \in knownAircraft(ass)$
1   rng $ass: QueueOf(Aircraft)$-set   rng-form-*AssigMap* (h2)
2    $\exists q \in \text{rng}\, ass \cdot p \in \text{elems}\, q$ ∈-*knownAircraft*-E (h1, h2, h3)
3   from $q: QueueOf(Aircraft);\ q \in \text{rng}\, ass;\ p \in \text{elems}\, q$
3.1 $ass: Space \xrightarrow{m} QueueOf(Aircraft)$ *AssigMap*-supertype (h2)
3.2   dom $ass: Space$-set   dom-form-*AssigMap* (h2)
3.3 $\exists a \in \text{dom}\, ass \cdot ass(a) = q$ ∈-rng-E (3.h1, 3.1, 3.h2)
3.4   from $a: Space;\ a \in \text{dom}\, ass;\ ass(a) = q$
3.4.1 $p \in \text{elems}\, ass(a)$ =-subs-left(b) (3.h1, 3.4.h3, 3.h3)
3.4.2   from $y: Space;\ y \in \text{dom}\, ass$
3.4.2.1   inv-*AssigMap*(ass)   inv-*AssigMap*-I (h2)
3.4.2.2 $\forall q_1, q_2 \in \text{rng}\, ass \cdot q_1 \neq q_2 \Rightarrow$
                          elems $q_1 \cap$ elems $q_2 = \{\ \}$ unfolding (3.4.2.1)
3.4.2.3 $ass(y) \in \text{rng}\, ass$ ∈-rng-I-at (3.4.2.h1, 3.1, 3.4.2.h2)
                   ⋮

	⋮	
3.4.2.4	$ass(a) \in rng\, ass$	=-subs-left(b) (3.h1, 3.4.h3, 3.h2)
3.4.2.5	$\forall q_2 \in rng\, ass \cdot ass(y) \neq q_2 \Rightarrow$	
	elems $ass(y) \cap$ elems $q_2 = \{\,\}$	$\forall$-E-set (1, 3.4.2.3, 3.4.2.2)
3.4.2.6	$ass(y) \neq ass(a) \Rightarrow$	
	elems $ass(y) \cap$ elems $ass(a) = \{\,\}$	$\forall$-E-set (1, 3.4.2.4, 3.4.2.5)
	...	
3.4.2.7	$\delta(p \in$ elems $ass(y))$	⟨?? justify ??⟩
3.4.2.8	from $p \in$ elems $ass(y)$	
	...	
	infer $y = a$	⟨?? justify ??⟩
	infer $p \in$ elems $ass(y) \Rightarrow y = a$	$\Rightarrow$-I (3.4.2.7, 3.4.2.8)
3.4.3	$\forall y \in$ dom $ass \cdot p \in$ elems $ass(y) \Rightarrow y = a$	$\forall$-I-set (3.2, 3.4.2)
	infer $\exists ! s \in$ dom $ass \cdot p \in$ elems $ass(s)$	
		$\exists !$-I-set (3.4.h1, 3.2, 3.4.h2, 3.4.1, 3.4.3)
	infer $\exists ! s \in$ dom $ass \cdot p \in$ elems $ass(s)$	$\exists$-E-set (3.2, 3.3, 3.4)
infer $\exists ! s \in$ dom $ass \cdot p \in$ elems $ass(s)$		$\exists$-E-set (1, 2, 3)

At this point it is known that p is in both elems $ass(a)$ and elems $ass(y)$ (Line 3.4.1 and hypothesis 3.4.2.7.h1 respectively), from which it clearly follows that the intersection of these two sets cannot be empty. This, by the contraposition of Line 3.4.2.6, means that $ass(a) = ass(y)$. However, this is not sufficiently strong to ensure $y = a$ as required because the map ass is not known to be one-one. The proof therefore cannot be completed.

A moment's thought at this point should reveal that the invariant on *AssigMap* is not correct as it allows two different airspaces to contain exactly the same queue of aircraft. The specification must therefore be changed to rule out this possibility. The correct specification of *AssigMap* is:

$AssigMap = Space \xrightarrow{m} AircraftQueue$
inv $ass \triangleq \forall s_1, s_2 \in$ dom $ass \cdot s_1 \neq s_2 \Rightarrow$ elems $ass(s_1) \cap$ elems $ass(s_2) = \{\,\}$

Fortunately, this change to the specification does not mean that the work expended in the construction of the above failed proof is useless. Indeed, far from it – the vast majority of the proof survives and can be used as the starting point for the proof of the correctness of the revised specification. The only changes required are that the old definition of the invariant must be replaced by the new in Lines 3.4.2.2, 3.4.2.5 and 3.4.2.6 (with some minor modifications to the justifications of these lines) and that Lines 3.4.2.3 and 3.4.2.4 can be deleted (they have become redundant because the new invariant requires elements to be found from the domain of the map instead of the range). Other than this, discharging the new proof obligation simply requires completing those steps of the proof which were left unfinished in the original proof (Subproof 3.4.2). This is now very easy and is left as an exercise for the reader.

The reconstruction of the location map from the assignment map is completed with the help of another auxiliary function which simply constructs the map mapping each known aircraft to its location:

12.5 First refinement step

$extrLoc : AssigMap \rightarrow (Aircraft \xrightarrow{m} Space)$
$extrLoc(ass) \triangleq \{p \mapsto locOf(p, ass) \mid p \in knownAircraft(ass)\}$

This function is defined axiomatically via the following rule:

$$\boxed{extrLoc\text{-defn}_0} \quad \frac{\{p \mapsto locOf(p, ass) \mid \begin{array}{l} ass: AssigMap \\ p \in knownAircraft(ass)\}: Aircraft \xrightarrow{m} Space \end{array}}{extrLoc(ass) = \{p \mapsto locOf(p, ass) \mid p \in knownAircraft(ass)\}} \text{Ax}$$

and the corresponding proof obligation is:

$$\boxed{extrLoc\text{-form}} \quad \frac{ass: AssigMap}{extrLoc(ass): Aircraft \xrightarrow{m} Space}$$

Exercise 4 Prove the well-formedness rule '*extrLoc*-form'. □

The retrieve function $retr_1$ is now easy to define:

$retr_1 : ATC_1 \rightarrow ATC$
$retr_1(\sigma) \triangleq mk\text{-}ATC(\sigma.onduty_1, \sigma.control_1, \sigma.capacity_1, extrLoc(\sigma.assigs_1))$

Of course, the retrieve function is on the one hand simply another auxiliary function, so it has the appropriate defining axiom and well-formedness obligation (the latter being sometimes called the *totality* obligation):

$$\boxed{retr_1\text{-defn}_0} \quad \frac{\begin{array}{c} \sigma: ATC_1 \\ (mk\text{-}ATC(\sigma.onduty_1, \sigma.control_1, \\ \sigma.capacity_1, extrLoc(\sigma.assigs_1))): ATC \end{array}}{retr_1(\sigma) = mk\text{-}ATC(\sigma.onduty_1, \sigma.control_1, \sigma.capacity_1, extrLoc(\sigma.assigs_1))} \text{Ax}$$

$$\boxed{retr_1\text{-form}} \quad \frac{\sigma: ATC_1}{retr_1(\sigma): ATC}$$

In addition, however, it must generate all possible values of the abstract state ATC, a property which is embodied in the adequacy obligation:

$$\boxed{retr_1\text{-adeq}} \quad \frac{\sigma: ATC}{\exists \sigma_1: ATC_1 \cdot retr_1(\sigma_1) = \sigma}$$

The proofs of this and the formation rule are discussed in the next section.

12.5.4 The validity of the retrieve function

The strategy of proving the formation rule is exactly the same as that used to prove the formation rule for any other explicitly defined function. The first step is therefore to prove the rule stating the well-formedness of the defining expression:

$$\boxed{retr_1\text{-wff}} \quad \frac{\sigma: ATC_1}{(mk\text{-}ATC(\sigma.onduty_1, \sigma.control_1, \sigma.capacity_1, extrLoc(\sigma.assigs_1))): ATC}$$

Working backwards from the conclusion as usual, the formation rule '*mk-ATC*-form' requires that each of the arguments of the *mk*-function ($\sigma.onduty_1$, $\sigma.control_1$, $\sigma.capacity_1$ and $extrLoc(\sigma.assigs_1)$) should have the correct type and that together they should satisfy the invariant on *ATC*. The typing information follows directly from the formation rules for the selector functions, in the last case in conjunction with the formation rule for *extrLoc* proved above. For the invariant, the first two conjuncts follow immediately as they are identical to the first two conjuncts of the invariant on the concrete state ATC_1, so it remains to be shown only that:

- $\operatorname{rng} extrLoc(\sigma.assigs_1) \subseteq \operatorname{dom} \sigma.control_1$

- $\forall s \in \operatorname{rng} extrLoc(\sigma.assigs_1) \cdot$
  $numOfAircraft(s, extrLoc(\sigma.assigs_1)) \leq (\sigma.capacity_1)(s)$

This is best done with the help of a few lemmas (stated here without proof) giving properties of assignment maps and relating these to the auxiliary function *numOfAircraft* defined in the abstract specification. These are:

$$\boxed{\textit{rng-extrLoc}\text{-lemma}} \quad \frac{ass: AssigMap}{\operatorname{rng} extrLoc(ass) \subseteq \operatorname{dom} ass}$$

$$\boxed{\textit{dom-extrLoc}\text{-defn}} \quad \frac{ass: AssigMap}{\operatorname{dom} extrLoc(ass) = knownAircraft(ass)}$$

$$\boxed{\textit{numOfAircraft}\text{-elm-defn}} \quad \frac{s: Space;\ ass: AssigMap;\ s \in \operatorname{dom} ass}{numOfAircraft(s, extrLoc(ass)) = \operatorname{len} ass(s)}$$

which are relatively straightforward consequences of the definitions of the functions involved and the properties of map comprehension expressions.

Exercise 5 Construct the proof of '$retr_1$-wff' based on the above outline. □

At this stage one would normally proceed by proving the working version of the definition rule in the form

$$\boxed{retr_1\text{-defn}} \quad \frac{\sigma: ATC_1}{retr_1(\sigma) = \\ mk\text{-}ATC(\sigma.onduty_1, \sigma.control_1, \sigma.capacity_1, extrLoc(\sigma.assigs_1))}$$

and thence the formation rule, but the fact that the refinement (and hence the retrieve function) is essentially defined componentwise suggests that it is likely to be more useful to formulate a working version of the definition rule which makes the componentwise nature of the refinement more explicit. This is done using the *mk*-function instead of a metavariable to represent the state, and the appropriate rule is:

$$\boxed{retr_1\text{-defn-mk}} \quad \frac{mk\text{-}ATC_1(cs, con, cap, ass): ATC_1}{retr_1(mk\text{-}ATC_1(cs, con, cap, ass)) = \\ mk\text{-}ATC(cs, con, cap, extrLoc(ass))}$$

The proof of the formation rule either follows as before from '$retr_1$-defn' or can be done directly:

12.5 First refinement step

from $\sigma: ATC_1$
1 $(mk\text{-}ATC(\sigma.onduty_1, \sigma.control_1, \sigma.capacity_1, extrLoc(\sigma.assigs_1)))$: ATC
                           $retr_1$-wff (h1)
2 $retr_1(\sigma) =$
  $mk\text{-}ATC(\sigma.onduty_1, \sigma.control_1, \sigma.capacity_1, extrLoc(\sigma.assigs_1))$
                           $retr_1$-defn$_0$ (h1, 1)
infer $retr_1(\sigma): ATC$ =-type-inherit-left (1, 2)

Note that the above transformation relies on the fact that each element of the composite type has a unique representation in the form $mk\text{-}ATC(cs, con, cap, loc)$ (see Section 10.2.3).

Considerations of the specific form of a refinement can also be brought to bear when dealing with the adequacy obligation. The first step here is to make use of the componentwise nature of the refinement again to rewrite the obligation in terms of the mk-function:

$$\boxed{retr_1\text{-adeq-mk}} \quad \frac{mk\text{-}ATC(cs, con, cap, loc): ATC}{\exists \sigma_1: ATC_1 \cdot retr_1(\sigma_1) = mk\text{-}ATC(cs, con, cap, loc)}$$

The adequacy obligation '$retr_1$-adeq' is then proved from this simply by making use of the rule '$mk\text{-}ATC$-defn':

from $\sigma: ATC$
1 $mk\text{-}ATC(\sigma.onduty, \sigma.control, \sigma.capacity, \sigma.location) = \sigma$ $mk\text{-}ATC$-defn (h1)
2 $mk\text{-}ATC(\sigma.onduty, \sigma.control, \sigma.capacity, \sigma.location): ATC$
                           =-type-inherit-left (h1, 1)
3 $\exists \sigma_1: ATC_1 \cdot retr_1(\sigma_1) =$
  $mk\text{-}ATC(\sigma.onduty, \sigma.control, \sigma.capacity, \sigma.location)$ $retr_1$-adeq-mk (2)
infer $\exists \sigma_1: ATC_1 \cdot retr_1(\sigma_1) = \sigma$ =-subs-right(b) (h1, 1, 3)

Now the fact that the refinement leaves the first three components of the state unchanged and only affects the fourth indicates that the value of σ_1 chosen as the witness value to justify the existential quantification in the conclusion of the rule '$retr_1$-adeq-mk' must be of the form $mk\text{-}ATC_1(cs, con, cap, ass)$ for some assignment map ass. This suggests that the next step should be to formulate a simplification of the above rule involving only existential quantification over ass.

Of course the value of ass must be chosen so that it satisfies the invariant on ATC_1 and such that it retrieves to the given location map loc. By looking at the rule '$retr_1$-defn-mk' it is easy to see that the second of these two conditions will be satisfied if $loc = extrLoc(ass)$ so that the required simplification of the adequacy obligation is the rule

$$\boxed{retr_1\text{-adeq-assigs}} \quad \frac{mk\text{-}ATC(cs, con, cap, loc): ATC}{\exists ass: AssigMap \cdot} \\ inv\text{-}ATC_1(cs, con, cap, ass) \land loc = extrLoc(ass)$$

The claim now is that the rule '$retr_1$-adeq-mk' can be proved from this.

In fact the proof is not particularly difficult, as the rule '$retr_1$-adeq-$assigs$' directly asserts the existence of the assignment map required to construct the appropriate witness value for the existential quantification (as indeed it was intended to do). Of course, '∃-E' has to be applied before '∃-I' (see the discussion in Section 3.3.1) in order that the witness value be available. The full proof is:

from mk-$ATC(cs, con, cap, loc): ATC$
1   $\exists ass: AssigMap \cdot inv\text{-}ATC_1(cs, con, cap, ass) \land loc = extrLoc(ass)$
                                                                                                    $retr_1$-adeq-$assigs$ (h1)
2   from $ass: AssigMap$;
      $inv\text{-}ATC_1(cs, con, cap, ass) \land loc = extrLoc(ass)$
2.1 $cs: Controller$-set $onduty$-form-mk (h1)
2.2 $con: Space \xleftrightarrow{m} Controller$ $control$-form-mk (h1)
2.3 $cap: Space \xrightarrow{m} \mathbb{N}$ $capacity$-form-mk (h1)
2.4 $inv\text{-}ATC_1(cs, con, cap, ass)$ ∧-E-right (2.h2)
2.5 $mk\text{-}ATC_1(cs, con, cap, ass): ATC_1$ $mk\text{-}ATC_1$-form (2.1, 2.2, 2.3, 2.h1, 2.4)
2.6 $loc: Aircraft \xrightarrow{m} Space$ $location$-form-mk (h1)
2.7 $loc = extrLoc(ass)$ ∧-E-left (2.h2)
2.8 $retr_1(mk\text{-}ATC_1(cs, con, cap, ass)) =$
        $mk\text{-}ATC(cs, con, cap, extrLoc(ass))$ $retr_1$-defn-mk (2.5)
2.9 $retr_1(mk\text{-}ATC_1(cs, con, cap, ass)) =$
        $mk\text{-}ATC(cs, con, cap, loc)$ =-subs-left(a) (2.6, 2.7, 2.8)
  infer $\exists \sigma_1: ATC_1 \cdot retr_1(\sigma_1) = mk\text{-}ATC(cs, con, cap, loc)$ ∃-I (2.5, 2.9)
infer $\exists \sigma_1: ATC_1 \cdot retr_1(\sigma_1) = mk\text{-}ATC(cs, con, cap, loc)$ ∃-E (1, 2)

Now all that is required in order to complete the proof of the adequacy obligation is to prove the rule '$retr_1$-adeq-$assigs$'. Since this involves showing the existence of some value, there are again two potential strategies just as for the satisfiability proof obligations discussed earlier (see Section 12.4): either a witness value must be supplied or the existence must be shown by induction. In this particular case, the induction proof would involve induction over loc, but the proof would be complicated by the fact that, because loc appears in (two clauses of) the invariant on ATC, (those parts of) the invariant would have to be combined with the overall goal using '⇒-E-left' before the induction could be carried out. Thus the resulting proof is likely to be both long and cumbersome, and hence difficult to understand.

The other alternative, namely supplying a witness value for the existential quantification, essentially amounts to constructing an "inverse" of the retrieve function[2]. Such a function does not strictly have anything to do with the formalisation of the refinement, being introduced purely to assist with reasoning about it. One way of treating it, therefore, is to introduce it directly into the theory of the refinement by developing an axiomatisation of it using the standard techniques for axiomatisation described in earlier chapters. This is not always the most convenient approach, however, and sometimes it is simpler to specify the function as an auxiliary function and then to develop the axiomatisation from

---
[2]The indefinite article is chosen deliberately as the retrieve function only has a unique, well-defined inverse if it is one-one.

12.5 First refinement step

the specification as for any other auxiliary function (see Section 10.4). In this approach the specification is effectively being extended by some auxiliary "reasoning support" specification, which does not contribute to the description of the system being specified. This latter approach is adopted here simply because it provides a platform on which the discussion of two aspects of the verification and validation of specifications which have not so far been illustrated can be based: the fallibility of informal reasoning and the validation of implicitly specified functions.

One of the big problems with reasoning informally about a specification without using formal proof to support and verify the arguments is that some aspect of the problem which has been overlooked may not be revealed by an informal argument as this is based on intuition which is incomplete or incorrect if some detail has been overlooked. An informal argument may therefore appear to be entirely convincing even though it is fallacious, being based on unsound or incomplete premises. Consider, for example, the following informal argument supporting the validity of the rule '$retr_1$-adeq-$assigs$' by constructing an inverse of the retrieve function:

> Constructing an inverse of the retrieve function effectively amounts to defining a function *extrAss* (say) which builds an assignment map out of a location map, for the same reason (see Section 12.5.3) that constructing the retrieve function proceeded by defining the function *extrLoc* which built a location map out of an assignment map. Since the location map maps an aircraft to the airspace it currently occupies and the assignment map maps an airspace to the (queue of) aircraft currently occupying it, an assignment map can be constructed by mapping each airspace in the range of the location map to the set of aircraft in the domain of the location map which map to that airspace, this set being ordered arbitrarily to form a non-repeating queue. This ordering can be described by an auxiliary function *buildQueue*, specified implicitly via:
>
> *buildQueue* (s: *Aircraft*-set) q: *AircraftQueue*
> post elems $q = s$
>
> and the function *extrAss* can then be specified in terms of this using map comprehension:
>
> *extrAss* : (*Aircraft* $\xrightarrow{m}$ *Space*) → *AssigMap*
> *extrAss*(loc) $\triangleq$
> $\{s \mapsto buildQueue(\text{dom}(loc \triangleright \{s\})) \mid s \in \text{rng } loc\}$

The proof of the rule '$retr_1$-adeq-$assigs$' is then a consequence of the well-formedness of the function *extrAss*

$$\boxed{extrAss\text{-form}} \; \frac{loc: Aircraft \xrightarrow{m} Space}{extrAss(loc): AssigMap}$$

and a lemma stating that *extrAss* is an inverse of *extrLoc*:

$$\boxed{extrAss\text{-}extrLoc\text{-inverse}} \quad \frac{loc: Aircraft \xrightarrow{m} Space}{loc = extrLoc(extrAss(loc))}$$

by supplying *extrAss*(*loc*) as the witness value for the existential quantification.

Despite the fact that this argument probably sounds fairly plausible, it contains a mistake which the verifier may well not spot even on reviewing the argument. Moreover the argument could also convince some independent reviewer. An attempt to construct a formal proof based on the above skeleton would reveal the error, however, with the proof eventually breaking down. It should be pointed out that the error lies in the above argument and not in the rule it purports to prove – the rule $retr_1$-adeq-*assigs*' is valid, the informal "proof" of the rule given above is not.

Exercise 6 Find the mistake in the above argument and the correction required to make the argument sound by discovering the point at which the formal proof breaks down. **Hint:** The well-formedness of the function *buildQueue* is dealt with below and may be assumed, in the form of the rule

$$\boxed{buildQueue\text{-form}} \quad \frac{s: Aircraft\text{-set}}{buildQueue(s): AircraftQueue}$$

but the error may lie in any of the other three steps of the argument: the well-formedness of the function *extrAss*, the proof of the lemma '*extrAss*-*extrLoc*-inverse', and the proof of '$retr_1$-adeq-*assigs*' itself. □

Finally in this section, it is worth considering how the function *buildQueue* is treated as this is the first example of an implicitly defined function encountered in this case study. Following the template set out in Section 10.4.3, this function is described by two axioms:

$$\boxed{buildQueue\text{-defn}_0} \quad \frac{s: Aircraft\text{-set};\ \exists q: AircraftQueue \cdot \text{elems}\, q = s}{\text{elems}\, buildQueue(s) = s} \quad \text{Ax}$$

$$\boxed{buildQueue\text{-form}_0} \quad \frac{s: Aircraft\text{-set};\ \exists q: AircraftQueue \cdot \text{elems}\, q = s}{buildQueue(s): AircraftQueue} \quad \text{Ax}$$

and there are two associated proof obligations, one to show that the postcondition is boolean-valued, the other to show that the function is satisfiable:

$$\boxed{post\text{-}buildQueue\text{-form}} \quad \frac{s: Aircraft\text{-set};\ q: AircraftQueue}{post\text{-}buildQueue(s, q): \mathbb{B}}$$

$$\boxed{buildQueue\text{-sat}} \quad \frac{s: Aircraft\text{-set}}{\exists q: AircraftQueue \cdot post\text{-}buildQueue(s, q)}$$

Here, *post-buildQueue* is defined via:

$$post\text{-}buildQueue(s, q) \stackrel{\text{def}}{=} \text{elems}\, q = s$$

12.5 First refinement step

The first of these proofs is trivial and is left as an exercise for the reader. The second provides an example of a satisfiability proof which is perhaps best tackled by induction. Here, set induction is used, giving a base case in which it must be shown that

$$\exists q: AircraftQueue \cdot elems\, q = \{\,\}$$

and an induction step with hypothesis

$$\exists q_1: AircraftQueue \cdot elems\, q_1 = s_1$$

and goal

$$\exists q_2: AircraftQueue \cdot elems\, q_2 = add(a, s_1)$$

The base case follows trivially by supplying [ ] as the witness value for the existential quantification, the induction step by similarly supplying $cons(a, q_1)$. The complete proof is:

from $s: Aircraft$-set
1   [ ]: $AircraftQueue$ [ ]-form-queue
2    $elems\,[\,] = \{\,\}$ elems-defn-[ ]
3    $\exists q: AircraftQueue \cdot elems\, q = \{\,\}$ $\exists$-I (1, 2)
4   from $a: Aircraft$; $s_1: Aircraft$-set; $\exists q_1: AircraftQueue \cdot elems\, q_1 = s_1$; $a \notin s$
4.1   from $q_1: AircraftQueue$; $elems\, q_1 = s_1$
4.1.1 $a \notin elems\, q_1$ =-subs-left(b) (4.h2, 4.1.h2, 4.h4)
4.1.2 $cons(a, q_1): AircraftQueue$ cons-form-queue (4.h1, 4.1.h1, 4.1.1)
4.1.3 $elems\, cons(a, q_1) = add(a, elems\, q_1)$
       elems-defn-cons-queue (4.h1, 4.1.h1)
4.1.4 $elems\, cons(a, q_1) = add(a, s_1)$ =-subs-right(b) (4.h2, 4.1.h2, 4.1.3)
      infer $\exists q_2: AircraftQueue \cdot elems\, q_2 = add(a, s)$ $\exists$-I (4.1.2, 4.1.4)
   infer $\exists q_2: AircraftQueue \cdot elems\, q_2 = add(a, s)$ $\exists$-E (4.h3, 4.1)
5    $\exists q: AircraftQueue \cdot elems\, q = s$ set-indn (h1, 3, 4)
infer $\exists q: AircraftQueue \cdot post\text{-}buildQueue(s, q)$ folding (5)

The rules for queues used in this proof are:

$$\boxed{\text{[ ]-form-queue}}\ \frac{}{[\,]: AircraftQueue}$$

$$\boxed{\text{cons-form-queue}}\ \frac{a: Aircraft;\ q: AircraftQueue;\ a \notin elems\, q}{cons(a, q): AircraftQueue}$$

$$\boxed{\text{elems-defn-cons-queue}}\ \frac{a: Aircraft;\ q: AircraftQueue}{elems\, cons(a, q) = add(a, elems\, q)}$$

Working versions of the formation and definition rules

$$\boxed{buildQueue\text{-defn}}\ \frac{s: Aircraft\text{-set}}{elems\, buildQueue(s) = s}$$

$$\boxed{buildQueue\text{-form}} \quad \frac{s\colon Aircraft\text{-set}}{buildQueue(s)\colon AircraftQueue}$$

are then proved in the standard way.

12.5.5 Operations

The only operation considered in detail here is the one for adding a new flight to the ATC system. The concrete counterpart of the abstract operation *AddFlight* (see Section 12.4.9) is:

AddFlight$_1$ ($p\colon Aircraft, s\colon Space$)
  ext rd *control*$_1$: $Space \xleftrightarrow{m} Controller$
      rd *capacity*$_1$: $Space \xrightarrow{m} \mathbb{N}$
      wr *assigs*$_1$: $AssigMap$
  pre $s \in \mathrm{dom}\, control_1 \wedge p \notin knownAircraft(assigs_1) \wedge \mathrm{len}\, assigs_1(s) < capacity_1(s)$
  post $\overline{assigs_1} = \overline{assigs_1} \dagger \{s \mapsto \overline{assigs_1}(s) \frown [p]\}$

giving rise to definitions of *pre-AddFlight*$_1$ and *post-AddFlight*$_1$ of the form:

$$pre\text{-}AddFlight_1(p, s, con, cap, ass) \stackrel{\mathrm{def}}{=} s \in \mathrm{dom}\, con \wedge p \notin knownAircraft(ass) \wedge \\ \mathrm{len}\, ass(s) < cap(s)$$

$$post\text{-}AddFlight_1(p, s, \overline{ass}, ass) \stackrel{\mathrm{def}}{=} ass = \overline{ass} \dagger \{s \mapsto \overline{ass}(s) \frown [p]\}$$

There are the usual well-formedness obligations for these definitions, as well as the satisfiability obligation for the operation as a whole, but none of these are considered here. The purpose of this section is to consider the two additional proof obligations, the domain and result obligations, which arise by virtue of the fact that *AddFlight*$_1$ is intended as an "implementation" of *AddFlight*. These are stated as:

$$\boxed{AddFlight\text{-dom-obl}} \quad \frac{\begin{array}{c} p\colon Aircraft;\ s\colon Space \\ mk\text{-}ATC(cs, con, cap, loc)\colon ATC \\ mk\text{-}ATC_1(cs_1, con_1, cap_1, ass)\colon ATC_1 \\ mk\text{-}ATC(cs, con, cap, loc) = retr_1(mk\text{-}ATC_1(cs_1, con_1, cap_1, ass)) \\ pre\text{-}AddFlight(p, s, con, cap, loc) \end{array}}{pre\text{-}AddFlight_1(p, s, con_1, cap_1, ass)}$$

$$\boxed{AddFlight\text{-res-obl}} \quad \frac{\begin{array}{c} p\colon Aircraft;\ s\colon Space \\ mk\text{-}ATC(cs, con, cap, \overline{loc})\colon ATC \\ mk\text{-}ATC_1(cs_1, con_1, cap_1, \overline{ass})\colon ATC_1 \\ mk\text{-}ATC(cs, con, cap, \overline{loc}) = retr_1(mk\text{-}ATC_1(cs_1, con_1, cap_1, \overline{ass})) \\ mk\text{-}ATC(cs, con, cap, loc)\colon ATC \\ mk\text{-}ATC_1(cs_1, con_1, cap_1, ass)\colon ATC_1 \\ mk\text{-}ATC(cs, con, cap, loc) = retr_1(mk\text{-}ATC_1(cs_1, con_1, cap_1, ass)) \\ pre\text{-}AddFlight(p, s, con, cap, loc);\ post\text{-}AddFlight_1(p, s, \overline{ass}, ass) \end{array}}{post\text{-}AddFlight(p, s, \overline{loc}, loc)}$$

12.5 First refinement step

In this particular case, as with the adequacy obligation, these rules can be simplified by taking account of the componentwise nature of the refinement. This effectively entails making use of the rules:

$$\boxed{retr_1\text{-}E\text{-}onduty} \quad \frac{\begin{array}{c} mk\text{-}ATC(cs, con, cap, loc)\text{: }ATC \\ mk\text{-}ATC_1(cs_1, con_1, cap_1, ass)\text{: }ATC_1 \\ mk\text{-}ATC(cs, con, cap, loc) = retr_1(mk\text{-}ATC_1(cs_1, con_1, cap_1, ass)) \end{array}}{cs_1 = cs}$$

$$\boxed{retr_1\text{-}E\text{-}control} \quad \frac{\begin{array}{c} mk\text{-}ATC(cs, con, cap, loc)\text{: }ATC \\ mk\text{-}ATC_1(cs_1, con_1, cap_1, ass)\text{: }ATC_1 \\ mk\text{-}ATC(cs, con, cap, loc) = retr_1(mk\text{-}ATC_1(cs_1, con_1, cap_1, ass)) \end{array}}{con_1 = con}$$

$$\boxed{retr_1\text{-}E\text{-}capacity} \quad \frac{\begin{array}{c} mk\text{-}ATC(cs, con, cap, loc)\text{: }ATC \\ mk\text{-}ATC_1(cs_1, con_1, cap_1, ass)\text{: }ATC_1 \\ mk\text{-}ATC(cs, con, cap, loc) = retr_1(mk\text{-}ATC_1(cs_1, con_1, cap_1, ass)) \end{array}}{cap_1 = cap}$$

$$\boxed{retr_1\text{-}E\text{-}location} \quad \frac{\begin{array}{c} mk\text{-}ATC(cs, con, cap, loc)\text{: }ATC \\ mk\text{-}ATC_1(cs_1, con_1, cap_1, ass)\text{: }ATC_1 \\ mk\text{-}ATC(cs, con, cap, loc) = retr_1(mk\text{-}ATC_1(cs_1, con_1, cap_1, ass)) \end{array}}{extrLoc(ass) = loc}$$

as a basis for replacing cs_1 by cs, con_1 by con, cap_1 by cap, and loc by $extrLoc(ass)$.

Using these rules and substituting the equalities in their conclusions as the first steps in the proof of '*AddFlight*-dom-obl' leads to the following partial proof:

from p: *Aircraft*; s: *Space*; $mk\text{-}ATC(cs, con, cap, loc)$: *ATC*
    $mk\text{-}ATC_1(cs_1, con_1, cap_1, ass)$: *ATC*$_1$;
    $mk\text{-}ATC(cs, con, cap, loc) = retr_1(mk\text{-}ATC_1(cs_1, con_1, cap_1, ass))$
    pre-*AddFlight*(p, s, con, cap, loc)

1	cs: *Controller*-set	*onduty*-form-mk (h3)
2	con: *Space* $\xleftrightarrow{m}$ *Controller*	*control*-form-mk (h3)
3	cap: *Space* $\xrightarrow{m}$ **N**	*capacity*-form-mk (h3)
4	loc: *Aircraft* $\xrightarrow{m}$ *Space*	*location*-form-mk (h3)
5	$cs_1 = cs$	$retr_1$-E-*onduty* (h3, h4, h5)
6	$con_1 = con$	$retr_1$-E-*control* (h3, h4, h5)
7	$cap_1 = cap$	$retr_1$-E-*capacity* (h3, h4, h5)
8	$extrLoc(ass) = loc$	$retr_1$-E-*location* (h3, h4, h5)
9	pre-*AddFlight*$(p, s, con, cap, extrLoc(ass))$	=-subs-left(b) (4, 8, h6)
	...	
10	pre-*AddFlight*$_1(p, s, con, cap, ass)$	⟨?? justify ??⟩
11	pre-*AddFlight*$_1(p, s, con, cap_1, ass)$	=-subs-left(b) (3, 7, 10)
infer	pre-*AddFlight*$_1(p, s, con_1, cap_1, ass)$	=-subs-left(b) (2, 6, 11)

Note how Line 10 can now be proved using the lemma

$$
\text{AddFlight-dom-obl-simp} \; \dfrac{\begin{array}{c} p: Aircraft;\; s: Space \\ mk\text{-}ATC(cs, con, cap, extrLoc(ass)): ATC \\ mk\text{-}ATC_1(cs, con, cap, ass): ATC_1 \\ pre\text{-}AddFlight(p, s, con, cap, extrLoc(ass)) \end{array}}{pre\text{-}AddFlight_1(p, s, con, cap, ass)}
$$

which can be obtained more easily by making the substitutions for the components of the retrieval directly into the basic domain obligation '*AddFlight*-dom-obl'. Nor is the proof of this simplified version of the domain obligation difficult, as the lemmas 'dom-*extrLoc*-defn' and '*numOfAircraft*-elm-defn', which were used above to show the well-formedness of the retrieve function (see Section 12.5.4), together with a certain amount of substitution of equalities, are sufficient to complete the proof:

from $p: Aircraft;\; s: Space;\; mk\text{-}ATC(cs, con, cap, extrLoc(ass)): ATC;$
$\quad mk\text{-}ATC_1(cs, con, cap, ass): ATC_1;\; pre\text{-}AddFlight(p, s, con, cap, extrLoc(ass))$

1	$s \in \text{dom}\,con \wedge p \notin \text{dom}\,extrLoc(ass) \wedge$	
	$\quad numOfAircraft(s, extrLoc(ass)) < cap(s)$	unfolding (h5)
2	$ass: AssigMap$	$assigs_1$-form-mk (h4)
3	$\text{dom}\,extrLoc(ass) = knownAircraft(ass)$	dom-*extrLoc*-defn (3)
4	$s \in \text{dom}\,con$	$\wedge$-E-right (1)
5	$\text{dom}\,ass = \text{dom}\,con$	$inv\text{-}ATC_1$-I-mk-clause3 (h4)
6	$\text{dom}\,ass: Space\text{-set}$	dom-form-*AssigMap* (2)
7	$s \in \text{dom}\,ass$	=-subs-left(a) (6, 5, 4)
8	$numOfAircraft(s, extrLoc(ass)) = \text{len}\,ass(s)$	*numOfAircraft*-elm-defn (h2, 2, 7)
9	$extrLoc(ass): Aircraft \xrightarrow{m} Space$	*location*-form-mk (h3)
10	$numOfAircraft(s, extrLoc(ass)): \mathbb{N}$	*numOfAircraft*-form (h2, 9)
11	$s \in \text{dom}\,con \wedge p \notin \text{dom}\,extrLoc(ass) \wedge \text{len}\,ass(s) < cap(s)$	
		=-subs-right(a) (10, 8, 1)
12	$\text{dom}\,extrLoc(ass): Aircraft\text{-set}$	dom-form (9)
13	$s \in \text{dom}\,con \wedge p \notin knownAircraft(ass) \wedge \text{len}\,ass(s) < cap(s)$	
		=-subs-right(a) (12, 3, 11)
infer $pre\text{-}AddFlight_1(p, s, con, cap, ass)$		folding (13)

Turning now to the result obligation, this too can be simplified exactly as described above to:

$$
\text{AddFlight-res-obl-simp} \; \dfrac{\begin{array}{c} p: Aircraft;\; s: Space \\ mk\text{-}ATC(cs, con, cap, extrLoc(\overline{ass})): ATC \\ mk\text{-}ATC_1(cs, con, cap, \overline{ass}): ATC_1 \\ mk\text{-}ATC(cs, con, cap, extrLoc(ass)): ATC \\ mk\text{-}ATC_1(cs, con, cap, ass): ATC_1 \\ pre\text{-}AddFlight(p, s, con, cap, extrLoc(ass)) \\ post\text{-}AddFlight_1(p, s, \overline{ass}, ass) \end{array}}{post\text{-}AddFlight(p, s, extrLoc(\overline{ass}), extrLoc(ass))}
$$

12.5 First refinement step

Ignoring the first six hypotheses of this rule which essentially only give typing information and invariants, the meat of the proof is to show

$$extrLoc(ass) = extrLoc(\overleftarrow{ass}) \dagger \{p \mapsto s\}$$

under the following assumptions:

$$p \notin \mathrm{dom}\, extrLoc(\overleftarrow{ass}) \wedge s \in \mathrm{dom}\, con \wedge numOfAircraft(s, extrLoc(\overleftarrow{ass})) < cap(s)$$

$$ass = \overleftarrow{ass} \dagger \{s \mapsto \overleftarrow{ass}(s) \frown [p]\}$$

Using the rules 'dom-*extrLoc*-defn' and '*numOfAircraft*-elm-defn' together with the fact that $\mathrm{dom}\, con = \mathrm{dom}\, \overleftarrow{ass}$ (from the invariant on ATC_1), the first of these assumptions can be rewritten to

$$p \notin knownAircraft(\overleftarrow{ass}) \wedge s \in \mathrm{dom}\, \overleftarrow{ass} \wedge \mathrm{len}\, \overleftarrow{ass}(s) < cap(s)$$

Now the fact that the first two conjuncts of this expression are enough to ensure the invariant on *ass* suggests that a lemma of the form

$$\boxed{extrLoc\text{-}\dagger}\ \frac{p:Aircraft;\ s:Space;\ ass:AssigMap\quad p \notin knownAircraft(ass);\ s \in \mathrm{dom}\, ass}{extrLoc(ass \dagger \{s \mapsto ass(s) \frown [p]\}) = extrLoc(ass) \dagger \{p \mapsto s\}}$$

should be proved. However, the proof of this is rather long if attempted directly. A better strategy, therefore, is to develop a series of lemmas leading up to the proof of this one. This unfortunately requires more space than is available and does not really introduce any new proof techniques, so it is made the subject of the final exercise of this chapter.

Exercise 7 Prove the following lemmas:

$$\boxed{AssigMap\text{-form-}\dagger}\ \frac{p:Aircraft;\ s:Space;\ ass:AssigMap\quad p \notin knownAircraft(ass);\ s \in \mathrm{dom}\, ass}{ass \dagger \{s \mapsto ass(s) \frown [p]\} : AssigMap}$$

$$\boxed{knownAircraft\text{-}\dagger\text{-lemma}}\ \frac{p:Aircraft;\ s:Space;\ ass:AssigMap\quad p \notin knownAircraft(ass);\ s \in \mathrm{dom}\, ass}{knownAircraft(ass \dagger \{s \mapsto ass(s) \frown [p]\}) = add(p, knownAircraft(ass))}$$

$$\boxed{locOf\text{-}\dagger\text{-}\neq}\ \frac{p:Aircraft;\ s:Space;\ ass:AssigMap\quad a:Aircraft;\ p \notin knownAircraft(ass)\quad s \in \mathrm{dom}\, ass;\ a \in knownAircraft(ass)}{locOf(a, ass \dagger \{s \mapsto ass(s) \frown [p]\}) = locOf(a, ass)}$$

$$\boxed{locOf\text{-}\dagger\text{-}=}\ \frac{p:Aircraft;\ s:Space;\ ass:AssigMap\quad p \notin knownAircraft(ass);\ s \in \mathrm{dom}\, ass}{locOf(p, ass \dagger \{s \mapsto ass(s) \frown [p]\}) = s}$$

Use them, together with the rule 'map-comp-left-defn-*add*', to prove '*extrLoc*-†'. □

12.5.6 Adequacy of initialisation

As discussed in Section 11.2.2 there is a proof obligation concerned with showing that the possible initial states of the concrete specification have counterparts among the possible initial states of the abstract specification. This obligation, the adequacy of the initialisation condition, is very like the result obligation for an operation, though it is much simplified as there are no preconditions or previous states to be considered. This reinforces the notion introduced in Exercise 1 of Chapter 11 that the initialisation predicate could be viewed as an operation which has write access to all components of the state, no precondition, and postcondition which does not refer to the initial values of the state variables.

For the refinement step under consideration here the proof obligation has the form

$$\boxed{\textit{init-ATC}_1\textit{-adeq}} \quad \frac{\sigma: ATC;\ \sigma_1: ATC_1;\ \sigma = retr_1(\sigma_1);\ \textit{init-ATC}_1(\sigma_1)}{\textit{init-ATC}(\sigma)}$$

Its proof is straightforward because the only two state variables mentioned in the initialisation predicates do not change under the refinement.

12.6 Second refinement step

12.6.1 A database of controllers

The second development step introduces a database of information about controllers, recording whether or not they are currently on duty and, if so, which space they control:

$CInfo$ :: $onduty$: $\mathbb{B}$
$\qquad\qquad space$: $[Space]$
inv $mk\text{-}CInfo(d, s) \;\triangleq\; \neg d \Rightarrow s = \text{nil}$

It is easy to imagine $CInfo$ being extended to include other relevant information as well, such as .login files for customizing monitors to suit personal preferences.

The database is represented as a map from controllers to information in which no two controllers can control the same airspace:

$CDatabase = Controller \xrightarrow{m} CInfo$
inv $db \;\triangleq\; \forall c_1, c_2 \in \text{dom}\, db \cdot$
$\qquad$ let $s_i = db(c_i).space$ in
$\qquad c_1 \neq c_2 \Rightarrow s_1 = \text{nil} \vee s_2 = \text{nil} \vee s_1 \neq s_2$

12.6.2 The new state definition

The new state definition replaces the simple set of on-duty controllers with a database of information about controllers. The new state invariant says (amongst other things) that the database is consistent with the control map:

12.7 Concluding remarks

state ATC_2 **of**
    $info_2$: $CDatabase$
    $control_2$: $Space \xrightarrow{m} Controller$
    $capacity_2$: $Space \xrightarrow{m} \mathbb{N}$
    $assigs_2$: $AssigMap$
inv $mk\text{-}ATC_2(db, con, cap, ass) \triangleq \text{dom}\, con = activatedSpaces(db) \wedge$
    $\text{rng}\, con = assignedCtrls(db) \wedge$
    $\forall c \in assignedCtrls(db) \cdot con(db(c).space) = c \wedge$
    $activatedSpaces(db) \subseteq \text{dom}\, cap \wedge$
    $\forall s \in \text{dom}\, ass \cdot \text{len}\, ass(s) \leq cap(s)$
init $\sigma_2 \triangleq \sigma_2.capacity_2 = \{\mapsto\} \wedge ondutyCtrls(\sigma_2.info_2) = \{\}$
end

The auxiliary functions *activatedSpaces*, *assignedCtrls* and *ondutyCtrls*, returning respectively the set of activated airspaces, the set of assigned controllers, and the set of on-duty controllers for some given database, are specified as follows:

    $activatedSpaces : CDatabase \rightarrow Space\text{-set}$
    $activatedSpaces(db) \triangleq \{db(c).space \mid c \in assignedCtrls(db)\}$

    $assignedCtrls : CDatabase \rightarrow Controller\text{-set}$
    $assignedCtrls(db) \triangleq ondutyCtrls(db) \setminus availableCtrls(db)$

    $ondutyCtrls : CDatabase \rightarrow Controller\text{-set}$
    $ondutyCtrls(db) \triangleq \{c : Controller \mid c \in \text{dom}\, db \wedge db(c).onduty\}$

The second of these is defined in terms of another auxiliary function *availableCtrls* returning the set of controllers not already assigned:

    $availableCtrls : CDatabase \rightarrow Controller\text{-set}$
    $availableCtrls(db) \triangleq \{c : Controller \mid c \in ondutyCtrls(db) \wedge db(c).space = \text{nil}\}$

Note that $control_2$ is no longer explicitly required to be one-one (although it follows from the invariant). In fact, $control_2$ is redundant – but addition of redundancy is one of the most common refinement techniques.

The specification of the operations on the new state, the definition of the retrieve function, and all the associated proofs are left as exercises for the reader.

12.7 Concluding remarks

This case study has shown how the general means of interpreting components of specifications and reifications presented in Chapters 10 and 11 can be combined with the techniques for reasoning about the basic elements of the specification language discussed in Chapters 2 to 9 to provide a means of reasoning about the design and development of a specific system. In particular, it has illustrated how to construct a theory, in the form of a set of axioms, definitions and derived rules, from a specification and from a refinement step, and how the proof obligations can be stated as rules and proved in this theory. It has also discussed the use of validation conditions as a means of checking both that informal requirements on the system have been captured in the formal specification and that the operations specified on the formal model actually exhibit the expected and desired functionality.

Since this book is primarily concerned with proof rather than specification, the actual form of the specification given above has to some extent been influenced by the desire not only to include an example of how each of the different proof obligations discussed in Chapters 10 and 11 arises and is dealt with in practice but also to illustrate a wide range of different reasoning techniques. In addition, the specification is perhaps atypical because every operation has a postcondition which defines the new state components directly in terms of the old via some equality and because the refinement is defined component-wise rather than over the whole state. Both of these are the result of a deliberate attempt to make the examples complex enough to illustrate the points required whilst at the same time simple enough that those points do not get lost in extraneous detail.

Having said that, it cannot be stressed enough that the exact form of a specification can have a profound influence on the ease or otherwise with which reasoning about that specification can be carried out. First, since many proofs involve showing that some invariant holds, constructing the invariants out of some subset of the requirements and treating the other requirements as validation conditions can save an enormous amount of work. In that way the validation conditions are only proved once instead of every time the invariant has to be shown to hold. Although this point has not been illustrated explicitly above, looking at, for instance, the proof of '*Commission*-sat' given in Section 12.4.1, where something like two thirds of the proof is concerned with showing that the invariant on *ATC* is preserved, should be sufficient to convince the reader.

Second, introducing auxiliary data types and functions to represent concepts used in one's informal thinking about the specification generally simplifies both reasoning about the specification and the formulation of validation conditions. There are essentially two reasons for this. First, one is reasoning about objects of which one has some kind of mental picture, and second, the specification, and hence the proof obligations, is being divided up into smaller and more manageable units.

In a similar way, the whole reasoning process is made simpler if it too is divided into a series of small, easy to understand steps. Thus, whilst it would be perfectly possible to discharge all the proof obligations on a specification directly from the axioms and definitions describing that specification (assuming, of course, that the specification is sound), proofs constructed in this way tend to become so long and unmanageable that it is easy to lose track of how the proof is progressing. This is avoided by stating and proving lemmas embodying one's intuitive understanding of the various constructs involved in the reasoning. As an added bonus, this also saves work by reducing repetition in the proofs.

Finally, mention must be made of the magnitude of the task of formally verifying a "real" specification and design process. The case study presented here deals with a relatively small system and does not discuss the satisfiability of nine of the top-level operations, the internal consistency of the concrete specification, the satisfiability of any of the operations on the concrete state, or the operation modelling obligations for ten of the eleven operations. Moreover, some of the details of those proofs which are discussed have been omitted, either by leaving proofs incomplete or by leaving lemmas unproved. Despite all this, the case study runs to some fifty pages, so the reader is probably somewhat concerned (and rightly so) that a full formal development of even this example would be

12.7 Concluding remarks

prohibitively long.

The first point that should be noted here is that most of the proofs presented, although long, contain very few steps which are not routine. Indeed, some are entirely mechanical, for instance the well-formedness obligations which follow the pattern described in Section 9.4. Such proofs or parts of proofs could be discharged automatically by a proof tool instantiated with the appropriate inference rules. In this way, the task is split between the machine, capable of performing routine steps quickly and without error, and the human, whose intuition is essential in guiding the non-routine steps (for instance for determining an appropriate witness value to justify an existential quantifier).

The second, and far more important, point is that informal and formal reasoning and proof should be considered as something which can help with the development of a specification or a design step rather than some chore which has to be carried out after a formal specification or refinement has been written. Moreover, the reader should *not* feel that a proof of some proof obligations or validation condition is only of value if it has been completed fully formally (the term "proof obligation" is perhaps unfortunate in this respect). Indeed, as this case study has attempted to illustrate, planning a proof, sketching the main steps of a proof, or failing to formalise an argument can be at least as enlightening and informative as the finished proof.

It is important to remember that the main purpose of proof is to increase confidence in the quality of specifications and design decisions. Proof skills should be part of the system developer's normal toolkit. Applied judiciously and at an appropriate level of rigour, the techniques described above can make a significant contribution to the quality of the development process.

Chapter 13

Advanced Topics

13.1 Introduction

As stated at the outset, the aim of this book is not to provide a complete description of the whole of the VDM specification language. Rather, it uses VDM-SL as an example to introduce and explain, in as natural and intuitive a way as possible, the techniques necessary to enable the reader to confidently tackle not only proofs about specifications but also the axiomatisation of theories. The data types and constructs discussed in Chapters 2 to 9 do not therefore represent all the available features of VDM-SL, although they are generally adequate for most applications.

The features of the language which have not been covered fall broadly into two categories. The first of these contains constructs like the familiar arithmetic operators (for example −, /, ↑) which would be treated entirely analogously to constructs already discussed. The reader should have no difficulty applying the lessons learned so far to determine a reasonable set of axioms and derived rules for such operators.

Constructs in the second category, on the other hand, have been omitted from the preceding discussion either because they do not fit easily into the simple logical framework presented here (for example "loose" let statements; see Section 13.7.1) or because they complicate the basic theories presented above in such a way that the axioms and rules for familiar data types become hopelessly unintuitive and cumbersome (for example function types; see Section 13.2). This chapter briefly discusses some of these constructs and indicates possible ways in which they might be treated. Indications are also given of the repercussions these have on the material presented in earlier chapters.

The chapter also discusses how to generate formal descriptions of constructs with variable arity such as quote types and enumerated sets, maps and sequences (see Sections 13.8 and 13.5 respectively), as well as extensions to some of the topics covered in the main body of the book. These include an indication of how the treatment of equality can be generalised to allow the comparison of values of different types (Section 13.3) and a discussion of how to deal with recursively-defined types in a specification and how to formulate induction rules for them (Section 13.4).

13.2 Functions as a data type

As discussed in Chapter 7, when constructing maps using map comprehension, care must be taken to ensure amongst other things that the resulting expression only contains a finite number of associations. Thus, for example, the expression

$$\{n \mapsto n^2 \mid n: \mathbb{N}\}$$

which associates with each natural number n its square n^2, does not represent a map because its domain (all the natural numbers) is infinite. This notion can, however, be expressed in VDM using *lambda expressions* as

$$\lambda n: \mathbb{N} \cdot n^2$$

the type of which is the *function type* $\mathbb{N} \to \mathbb{N}$.

More generally, the function type $A \to B$ represents all (total) functions from the type A to the type B, that is those functions which, given an object of type A, return an object of type B. An element f of the function type $A \to B$ therefore differs from an element g of the map type $A \xrightarrow{m} B$ when A is an infinite type because $f(a)$ is defined for all elements a belonging to the type A whereas $g(a)$ is only defined if a belongs to the (finite) domain of the map g.

It is not particularly difficult to write down axioms which describe the properties of functions as outlined above. These might be:

$$\frac{x: A \vdash_x P(x): B}{(\lambda x: A \cdot P(x)): A \to B}\text{-Ax} \qquad \frac{a: A; \quad \lambda x: A \cdot P(x): A \to B}{(\lambda x: A \cdot P(x)) \cdot (a) = P(a)}\text{-Ax}$$

$$\frac{a: A; \quad f: A \to B}{f \cdot (a): B}\text{-Ax}$$

One might also consider defining axioms describing the equality of functions, such as

$$\frac{x: A \vdash_x P(x) = Q(x)}{\lambda x: A \cdot P(x) = \lambda x: A \cdot Q(x)}\text{-Ax} \qquad \frac{f: A \to B}{\lambda x: A \cdot (f \cdot (x)) = f}\text{-Ax}$$

though it is somewhat debatable whether this notion ought be supported.

The main problem with function types is not the axiomatisation, however, but the fact that VDM does not allow them to be combined with the other basic type constructors arbitrarily. Instead, it introduces a notion of *flatness* of a type and considers the function type and certain types constructed from a combination of function types and the other type constructors as *non-flat*. It then imposes restrictions on the use of non-flat types.

One example of these restrictions is that it is illegal to construct a set of functions in VDM (more generally, it is illegal to construct a set of objects of any non-flat type). This means that the rules given above in Chapter 6 for building sets are not valid when the sets are of non-flat type. In particular, rules such as the formation rule for the empty set '{ }-form' require an additional hypothesis in the presence of non-flat types to ensure that only legal sets are constructed. This rule would thus have the form

$$\frac{\textit{is-flat}(A)}{\{\,\}: A\text{-set}}\text{-Ax}$$

13.3 Comparing elements of disjoint types

where the predicate *is-flat* (not defined here) represents the notion of a flat type.

Fully supporting a description of function types, therefore, would require not only an axiomatisation of the concept of flatness but also significant changes, similar to that to the formation rule for the empty set shown above, to many of the formation rules already presented. Whilst these changes could certainly be made, it was felt that the corresponding loss of intuition and clarity in the axiomatisation of sets, maps, etc. presented above which would thereby result was prohibitive. It is, however, worth keeping in mind that not all the rules for sets, maps, etc. presented above are valid in the presence of function types. They are all valid when no function types are present, though, as all types constructed using only the set, map, sequence and record constructors are automatically flat.

13.3 Comparing elements of disjoint types

Using the axiomatisation of equality given in Section 3.4 above, it is possible to deduce (using the rule 'δ-=-I') that any two elements of the same type are either equal or unequal, but at this level there is nothing to determine which of these alternatives is actually true. This is perfectly adequate when it comes to comparing arbitrary variables of some type, and the rule 'δ-=-I' is therefore used primarily in proofs to set up a case distinction on the equality or otherwise of arbitrary elements of a given type, but is not sufficient for comparing specific elements of a type. This extra information comes from rules for equality on the specific type in question, so that, for example, the rule '=-set-defn' defining equality on sets makes it possible to show that the empty set is different from the singleton set $\{a\}$ for arbitrary (but denoting) a:

$$\{\} \neq \{a\}$$

Between them, therefore, the general axioms of equality and the rules defining equality for the specific types and type constructors give all the information necessary for comparing any two elements of any given type. But what about comparing elements from two different types?

Some progress towards this can be made with the help of union types: it has already been shown in Section 4.2 how they can be used to prove a generalisation of the rule 'δ-=-I':

$$\boxed{\delta\text{-=-I-gen}} \; \frac{a:A; \; b:B}{\delta(a = b)}$$

stating that two arbitrary elements of two arbitrary (i.e. possibly different) types are either equal or unequal, and a similar technique can be used to construct generalisations of the specific equality rules for the data types so as to allow some level of comparison between constructed objects of different types, for instance between an object of type A-set and one of type B-set. However, the most that can be deduced using these generalisations is that expressions like

$$7 = \text{true} \qquad \{7\} = \{\text{true}\}$$

are either true or false, even though the first of these possibilities appears to be ridiculous. One can also prove relationships between some expressions of this kind, for instance that the two expressions given above must have the same value, that is that $7 = \text{true}$ $\Leftrightarrow \{7\} = \{\text{true}\}$.

The extra information required in order to rule out these unwanted cases would have to be supplied as additional axioms explicitly stating that elements of distinct types are unequal. Thus, for example, the case 7 = true might be excluded by an axiom of the form:

$$\frac{a:\mathbb{B};\ b:\mathbb{R}}{a \neq b}\text{Ax}$$

The problem with this approach is that it rapidly gets out of hand because axioms of this form are not only required for other pairs of distinct basic types, they are also required for each possible combination of a basic type and a type constructor and for different combinations of type constructors. Furthermore, axioms are also needed which state that an element of some type introduced in a specification is different from an element of any basic type, from an element of a basic type constructor, and from an element of any other type introduced in a specification.

Another possible approach is to formalise the notion of types being disjoint, say through some predicate *are-disjoint*, and to introduce one set of axioms describing its general properties, for example:

$$\frac{a:A;\ b:B;\ are\text{-}disjoint(A,B)}{a \neq b}\text{Ax} \qquad \frac{}{are\text{-}disjoint(A\text{-set},B^*)}\text{Ax}$$

and another set defining which specific types are disjoint, for example:

$$\frac{}{are\text{-}disjoint(\mathbb{B},\mathbb{R})}\text{Ax}$$

This approach has the advantage that fewer axioms are needed because some of the information has been included by the parameterisation inherent in the first of its sets of axioms, but it still requires an axiom in the second set for each possible pair of types taken from the basic types and the types introduced via specification. In particular, the practical upshot is that every time a new type is specified a new set of axioms is required to say both that it is disjoint from each of the basic types and that it is disjoint from all the types so far specified.

Experience shows that these axioms are not widely needed when reasoning about specifications (although there is some indication that they can be important when specifying abstract syntax), and the high level of unmanageability has led to the omission of a formulation of disjoint types from this book. However, the generation of the axioms for the second of the two approaches described above is straightforward, and it is easy to see how mechanical support could be used to take the burden out of this by generating the appropriate axioms for *are-disjoint* automatically whenever a new type is added to a specification.

13.4 Recursive type definitions

This section gives some indicative examples of how one can define and reason about recursive type definitions.

A simple example of a recursive type definition is the following definition of binary trees with numerical leaves:

13.4 Recursive type definitions

$$NTree = \mathbb{N} \mid NTree \times NTree$$

It can be seen that the definition of *NTree* is well-founded, because the name of the type being defined does not occur in one of the branches of the union type construction that is used in the definition. In effect, there is a "terminating clause" (by analogy with recursive function definitions).

Treating this as a definition in the logical frame:

$$NTree \stackrel{\text{def}}{=} \mathbb{N} \mid NTree \times NTree$$

the following two formation rules can be proven from the typing rules for Cartesian products and union types:

$$\boxed{NTree\text{-leaf-form}} \quad \frac{n:\mathbb{N}}{n:NTree}$$

$$\boxed{NTree\text{-node-form}} \quad \frac{t_1, t_2: NTree}{mk\text{-}(t_1, t_2): NTree}$$

From the definition and the axiom '|-E' the following rule is obtained:

$$\boxed{NTree\text{-E}} \quad \frac{t:NT \qquad n:\mathbb{N} \vdash_n P(n) \qquad t_1:NTree,\ t_2:NTree \vdash_{t_1,t_2} P(mk\text{-}(t_1, t_2))}{P(t)}$$

Unfortunately, this rule is useless in general! To see why, consider the following function definition:

sumNTree : *NTree* → $\mathbb{N}$
sumNTree(*t*) $\triangleq$ cases *t* :
        mk-(t_1, t_2) → *sumNTree*(t_1) + *sumNTree*(t_2),
        others → *t*
   end

An attempt to prove the formation rule for this function:

$$\boxed{sumNTree\text{-form}} \quad \frac{t:NTree}{sumNTree(t):\mathbb{N}}$$

using the above rules will fail. At some stage in the proof, it will be necessary to show that:

$$sumNTree(t_1) + sumNTree(t_2):\mathbb{N}$$

for the case where there are some t_1, t_2 (both of type *NTree*) such that $t = mk\text{-}(t_1, t_2)$. However, it is not possible to show that $sumNTree(t_1):\mathbb{N}$ given only that $t_1:NTree$ — this is the same problem that the present proof is trying to solve!

In order to reason about values of a recursive type definition, some form of induction axiom must be supplied. This can be constructed by analysis of induction rules (or similar "property-propagating" rules) for the type constructors used in the definition. This leads to the following induction scheme for *NTree*:

$$\text{NTree-indn} \quad \frac{t: NTree \qquad n: \mathbf{N} \vdash_n P(n) \qquad t_1: NTree,\ t_2: NTree,\ P(t_1),\ P(t_2) \vdash_{t_1, t_2} P(mk\text{-}(t_1, t_2))}{P(t)} \text{Ax}$$

Notice that 'all' this has done is to strengthen the sequent hypothesis of '*NTree*-E' by assuming additionally that P holds for all sequent variables of type *NTree*.

This induction scheme can be used to derive properties that are true for all trees and also to give properties of function that are defined recursively by structural induction. Using this axiom to prove '*sumNTree*-form', when the point is reached where '*sumNTree*(t_1): $\mathbf{N}$' is required, it will be present already as a hypothesis of the 'step' case of the induction:

from $t: NTree$
1   from $n: \mathbf{N}$
     ...
     infer $sumNTree(n): \mathbf{N}$ ⟨?? justify ??⟩
2   from $t_1: NTree$; $t_2: NTree$; $sumNTree(t_1): \mathbf{N}$; $sumNTree(t_2): \mathbf{N}$
2.1 $sumNTree(t_1) + sumNTree(t_2): \mathbf{N}$ +-form (2.h1, 2.h2)
     ...
2.2 $sumNTree(mk\text{-}(t_1, t_2)) = sumNTree(t_1) + sumNTree(t_2)$ ⟨?? justify ??⟩
     infer $sumNTree(mk\text{-}(t_1, t_2)): \mathbf{N}$ =-type-inherit-left (2.1, 2.2)
infer $sumNTree(t): \mathbf{N}$ *NTree*-indn (h1, 1, 2)

13.4.1 Mutual recursion

Mutually recursive type definitions are permitted in VDM. For example, a definition of binary trees with numerical labels at each node is:

$NTptr = [NT]$

$NT = NTptr \times \mathbf{N} \times NTptr$

(This definition is somewhat artificial, but does bear similarities to more realistic constructions.)

Converting this into definitions, the following formation rules can be proven from typing rules for optional types and Cartesian products:

$$\text{NTptr-nil} \quad \frac{}{nil: NTptr}$$

$$\text{NTptr-form} \quad \frac{nt: NT}{nt: NTptr}$$

$$\text{NTptr-E} \quad \frac{ntp: NTptr;\ P(nil);\ nt: NT \vdash_{nt} P(nt)}{P(ntp)}$$

13.4 Recursive type definitions

$$\boxed{NT\text{-form}} \quad \frac{nt_1: NTptr;\ n: \mathbb{N};\ nt_2: NTptr}{mk\text{-}(nt_1, n, nt_2): NT}$$

As before, these rules are not sufficient to allow proof by induction on *NT*, and an additional induction scheme axiom must be supplied. One form of induction scheme for *NT* is:

$$\boxed{NT\text{-indn}} \quad \frac{\begin{array}{l} ntp_1: NTptr,\ ntp_2: NTptr,\ n: \mathbb{N}, \\ ntp_1 = \text{nil} \lor P(ntp_1), \\ ntp_2 = \text{nil} \lor P(ntp_2) \end{array} \bigg|\!\!\!-\!\!\!\frac{}{ntp_1,n,ntp_2} P(mk\text{-}(ntp_1, n, ntp_2)) \\ t: NT}{P(t)} \quad \text{Ax}$$

In the above, the "propagation" of the property *P* through the optional type constructor has been incorporated into the single sequent hypothesis. This has the visually unfortunate consequence that the base and step cases of the induction are not separated, but with some manipulation of the sequent hypothesis, quantifiers and disjunctions, it can be re-expressed as:

$$\boxed{NT\text{-indn}} \quad \frac{\begin{array}{l} n: \mathbb{N} \vdash_n P(mk\text{-}(\text{nil}, n, \text{nil})) \\ nt: NT,\ n: \mathbb{N},\ P(nt) \vdash_{nt,n} P(mk\text{-}(nt, n, \text{nil})) \\ nt: NT,\ n: \mathbb{N},\ P(nt) \vdash_{nt,n} P(mk\text{-}(\text{nil}, n, nt)) \\ nt_1: NT,\ n: \mathbb{N},\ nt_2: NT, \\ P(nt_1),\ P(nt_2) \end{array} \bigg|\!\!\!-\!\!\!\frac{}{ntp_1,n,ntp_2} P(mk\text{-}(nt_1, n, nt_2)) \\ t: NT}{P(t)} \quad \text{Ax}$$

In the case of any recursive type definition, care must be taken to ensure that the definition is meaningful. The following are examples of meaningless definitions:

$X = X \times X$

$A = A\text{-set}$

In each case, the definitions are ill-formed because there is no "base case" type expression upon which the definition can be founded. It is still possible to generate rules for these definitions as done above, and a similar approach to developing the induction scheme leads to schemes such as:

$$\frac{x: X,\ y: X,\ P(x),\ P(y) \vdash_{x,y} P(mk\text{-}(x, y))}{v: X} \\ \frac{}{P(v)}$$

which has no base case. This might appear to be dangerous, as it describes how to prove properties for a type definition that is not well-formed, but in fact it is not possible to satisfy the hypothesis $v: X$. To see this, note that the only way to construct an object of type *X* will be via a formation rule of the form:

$$\frac{x: X;\ y: X}{mk\text{-}(x, y): X}$$

so that there is no way to construct a "base" *X* value.

13.5 Enumerated sets, maps and sequences

The treatment of sets, maps and sequences in Chapters 6, 7 and 8 concentrated mainly on reasoning about general elements of these data types, this manifesting in the fact that most of the axioms and rules given both in the chapters themselves and in the relevant sections of the directory (Chapter 14) are couched in terms of metavariables. Indeed, the only specific elements of the data types which were discussed were the empty collections ({ }, $\{\mapsto\}$ and [ ]) and the singleton or unit collections ($\{a\}$, $\{a \mapsto b\}$ and $[a]$). Sometimes, however, more complex specific elements of these data types are useful, for instance:

$$\{1, 3, 4, 7\} \qquad \{a \mapsto \text{true}, b \mapsto \text{true}\} \qquad [e_1, e_2, e_3]$$

Intuitively these constructs are very easy to interpret: the first represents the set containing the four numbers 1, 3, 4 and 7; the second, the map which maps both a and b to true; and the third, the sequence containing the elements e_1, e_2 and e_3, in that order. Their properties are also simple to determine. For example, the number 4 is clearly an element of the set $\{1, 3, 4, 7\}$ whereas the number 5 is not:

$$4 \in \{1, 3, 4, 7\} \qquad 5 \notin \{1, 3, 4, 7\}$$

and the union of the set $\{1, 3, 4, 7\}$ with the set $\{3, 7, 11\}$ is the set $\{1, 3, 4, 7, 11\}$:

$$\{1, 3, 4, 7\} \cup \{3, 7, 11\} = \{1, 3, 4, 7, 11\}$$

Unfortunately, the fact that these *enumerated* collections do not have a fixed arity (so that they can contain any number of elements) means that it is impossible to describe the general form of these expressions within the logical framework used in this book. Any given enumerated collection can be described, however, and two possible methods are suggested.

The first method relies on the fact that any enumerated collection having two or more elements can be expressed in terms of the appropriate singleton collection and standard operators on the data types. Thus, enumerated sets can be expressed in terms of singleton sets and set union or *add*, for example:

$$\{a, b, c\} = \{a\} \cup \{b\} \cup \{c\} = add(a, add(b, \{c\}))$$

enumerated maps in terms of singleton maps and map override or *addm*, for example:

$$\{a \mapsto b, c \mapsto d\} = \{a \mapsto b\} \dagger \{c \mapsto d\} = addm(a \mapsto b, \{c \mapsto d\})$$

and enumerated sequences in terms of singleton sequences and sequence concatenation or cons, for example:

$$[a, b, c] = [a] \frown [b] \frown [c] = cons(a, cons(b, [c]))$$

One could thus envisage some sort of automatic "pre-processor" which could be applied to a specification before any reasoning was carried out and which would "translate" all

13.5 Enumerated sets, maps and sequences

enumerated collections having two or more elements into one or other of the appropriate equivalent forms given above. Reasoning about the specification would then be performed at the level of the singleton collections and the appropriate operators chosen as the basis for the translation, for which general definitions, axioms and rules are available.

The alternative approach is to introduce a new defined symbol for each enumerated collection of *fixed* size in just the same way as the singleton collections are defined in terms of the empty collections, then to develop a series of derived rules for these. In this way, an arbitrary set containing two elements $\{\_,\_\}$ would be defined via:

$$\{a,b\} \stackrel{\text{def}}{=} add(a, \{b\})$$

then sets containing three elements would be defined in terms of this via:

$$\{a,b,c\} \stackrel{\text{def}}{=} add(a, \{b,c\})$$

and so on. Enumerated maps and sequences would be defined analogously using *addm* and cons respectively.

Rules describing these constructs would also be developed in a similar recursive manner, so that rules such as:

$$\frac{a:A;\ b:A}{b \in \{a,b\}}$$

$$\frac{a:A}{\{a,a\} = \{a\}}$$

$$\frac{a:A;\ b:A}{\{a,b\} = \{b,a\}}$$

would be proved using the definition of $\{a,b\}$ together with the derived rules for $\{a\}$, then rules describing $\{a,b,c\}$ would be derived from its definition together with the derived rules for $\{a,b\}$, and so on. In this way, definitions and rules describing any given enumerated collection can be developed.

The main advantage of the first ("translation") approach is that it is generally applicable and does not require the introduction of a whole slew of new definitions and the development of rules to describe them (though it is likely that additional rules dealing, for instance, with expressions involving multiple set union will be required). On the other hand, it suffers from the big disadvantage that one has to reason about constructs which bear only a tenuous relationship to what was actually written in the specification, whereas the second method retains the form of the expression written in the specification in the theory. Given that it is generally rare for enumerated collections having more than a few elements to be used in specifications, this faithfulness of the theory to the original specification probably outweighs the disadvantage of genericity, which argues for preferring the second treatment.

13.6 Patterns

The notion of *patterns* is pervasive throughout VDM-SL, and though they have been used earlier (for example in Chapter 10) they merit further consideration here.

A pattern is an expression that contains variables that are to be bound as a result of *matching* the pattern against some value. Patterns can be used in many places where simple variables are used, for example:

in function/operation arguments:

$f : T \times Tree \to U$
$f(mk\text{-}T(x,y), mk\text{-}Tree(d, [mk\text{-}Tree(d, tl)])) \triangleq x + y + d + g(tl)$

in quantifiers:

$\forall mk\text{-}T(\_, w, s): T \cdot \neg(w \wedge s)$

in set comprehensions:

$\{x + y \mid mk\text{-}T(x,y) \in aTSet \cdot x > y\}$

in let expressions:

let $mk\text{-}T(x,y) = f(z)$ in $x + y$

and, of course, in cases expressions:

cases e :
   $mk\text{-}T(x,y) \to x + y,$
   $mk\text{-}U(v,\_,x) \to v \times x$
end

Patterns play two roles in VDM-SL: to limit the realm of discourse and to associate variables with subexpressions. The first role is most obvious in cases expressions, but can also apply to quantified expressions. For example:

$\forall mk\text{-}T(x,x): T \cdot P(x)$

could be considered to be true if $P(x)$ holds for any T whose two components are equal.

Such quantified patterns have not been introduced into the logical framework presented thus far. Though the quantification above may appear "obvious", there are some subtle points to be made.

If T is defined as:

$T :: a : C$
     $b : C$

then it is tempting to treat the above quantification as "syntactic sugar" for:

$\forall t: T \cdot P(t.a).$

However, this is incorrect. The original formula "ignores" values of T whose fields are different, whereas the formula above does not. (Suppose for example that there are some

13.6 Patterns

$x, y: C$ with $x \neq y$, such that $P(mk\text{-}T(x, y))$ is false.)

It is also tempting to "remove" T from the quantification, and treat the formula as:

$\forall x: X \cdot P(x)$.

This *is* equivalent to the original formula, because $mk\text{-}T$ is total on $C \times C$; however, if T had an invariant, then the latter formula would be overstrict (consider some $y: C$ such that both $inv\text{-}T(y, y)$ and $P(y)$ are false.)

The subtle point of quantified patterns is that it is necessary to consider what the quantification means for values that do not match the pattern (an issue that does not arise for simple variables). In the case of the universal quantification, only values of T that match the pattern should have components that satisfy the predicate. This suggests the use of a predicate "matches" as a guard in the quantification; then:

$\forall mk\text{-}T(x, x): T \cdot P(x)$

could be treated as a shorthand for:

$\forall t: T \cdot t \text{ matches } mk\text{-}T(x, x) \Rightarrow P(x)$

However, this is not satisfactory as the variable x is now free (and cannot be bound by the "matches" predicate and subsequently used in a distinct subformula). The solution is two-fold: firstly, define:

$t \text{ matches } mk\text{-}T(x, x)$

using the existential quantification:

$\exists x: C \cdot t = mk\text{-}T(x, x)$

and secondly, replace the x in $P(x)$ with a selector expression in t; in this case either $P(t.a)$ or $P(t.b)$ will do. Consequently, the original formula can be considered as a shorthand for:

$\forall t: T \cdot (\exists x: C \cdot t = mk\text{-}T(x, x)) \Rightarrow P(t.a)$

Thus, $\forall mk\text{-}T(x, x): T \cdot P(x)$ is not as obvious as it first appears! The shorthand version can be used, but it should be noted that its translation into the definition is not a simple syntactic process: it requires knowledge about the composite type definition T (the types of its components, the names of its selectors, and their relationship to the arguments to the constructor.)

The corresponding approach for:

$\exists mk\text{-}T(x, x): T \cdot P(x)$

gives:

$\exists t: T \cdot (\exists x: C \cdot t = mk\text{-}T(x, x)) \land P(t.a)$.

Note the use of conjunction instead of implication. As a simple exercise, derive the universal quantifier form from the existential form and the definition of $\forall$ in terms of $\exists$ given in Chapter 3.

Where patterns are used as function arguments, it is possible to reproduce them in the corresponding axioms and obligations. For example, given:

$sum\_T : T \to \mathbb{N}$
$sum\_T(mk\text{-}T(x,y)) \triangleq x+y$

then the corresponding definition axiom can be given as:

$$\boxed{sum\_T\text{-defn}_0} \; \frac{mk\text{-}T(x,y):T;\; x+y:\mathbb{N}}{sum\_T(mk\text{-}T(x,y)) = x+y} \; \text{Ax}$$

where the metavariables of the rule are x and y. Note that to replace an application of sum_T to an arbitrary expression e of type T by the body expression, it is necessary to rewrite e to the form $mk\text{-}T(e_1, e_2)$, so that x and y can be matched to e_1, e_2 respectively.

Patterns can contain *wildcards*, which represent "don't care" patterns, for example:

$diff\_W : W \to \mathbb{N}$
$diff\_W(mk\text{-}W(x, \_, y)) \triangleq x-y$

There is no notion of "don't care" value in the logical framework; however, these can be replaced by "throwaway" metavariables in the corresponding axioms and rules, for example:

$$\boxed{diff\_W\text{-defn}_0} \; \frac{mk\text{-}W(x,dc,y):W\;;\; x-y:\mathbb{N}}{diff\_W(mk\text{-}W(x,dc,y)) = x-y} \; \text{Ax}$$

Note that when a pattern contains several wildcards, a separate "don't care" metavariable is required for each.

The above discussion has centred upon composite (record) patterns. Similar techniques can be used for other forms of patterns (set enumerations, set unions, sequence enumerations and concatenations).

Patterns of the forms $A \cup B$ and $s_1 \frown s_2$ (where A, B, s_1 and s_2 can be pattern variables or compound patterns) can introduce problems with determinacy. For example, the pattern $A \cup B$ (with A, B as pattern variables) can be matched against the set $\{1,2,3\}$ in several ways, such as $A = \{1\}, B = \{2,3\}$, or $A = \{1,3\}, B = \{2\}$.

13.7 Other expressions

13.7.1 Let expressions

The simplest use of a let expression is to introduce a shorthand notation, in the form of a new variable, to stand for some complicated expression. Thus, for example, one might "factor out" the common expression $n^2 + 7n + 13$ appearing in the formula

$$(n^2 + 7n + 13)^3 + 3(n^2 + 7n + 13) + 5$$

by writing instead

$$\text{let } x = n^2 + 7n + 13 \text{ in } x^3 + 3x + 5$$

Here, the let expression can be interpreted as the instruction "replace x by the expression $n^2 + 7n + 13$ everywhere it occurs in the expression $x^3 + 3x + 5$".

13.7 Other expressions

The most general form of such an expression is then

$$\text{let } x = y \text{ in } P(x)$$

with the implicit instruction being to replace every occurrence of the variable x in the expression $P(x)$ by the expression y. Clearly, one would expect this general let expression to be shorthand for $P(y)$, though care is needed to ensure that the substitution actually produces a sensible expression. For example, one would not expect the expression

$$\text{let } x = n^2 + 1 \text{ in } y \in \text{dom}\, x$$

to be meaningful as $n^2 + 1$ is not a map, and therefore does not have a domain. Some guard is therefore needed to ensure that the expression $P(y)$ represents a valid expression. This takes the form of a typing hypothesis, and leads to an axiom describing this form of let statements of the form

$$\frac{P(y):A}{(\text{let } x = y \text{ in } P(x)) = P(y)} \text{Ax}$$

This form of let expression is straightforward to describe axiomatically because, provided it denotes a value at all, that value is uniquely determined. However, VDM-SL also admits a form of let expression, sometimes called a "loose" let expression, where a range of different values are all possible. Here, the variable x is defined implicitly by giving a predicate $P(x)$ which it satisfies instead of explicitly via some equation (analogous to defining a function in a specification by means of a postcondition instead of an explicit definition). The most general form of this kind of let expression is

$$\text{let } x:A \text{ be s.t. } P(x) \text{ in } Q(x)$$

with the looseness arising because there is no guarantee in general that there will be only one value of x of the correct type A satisfying the predicate $P(x)$.

When the typing information and the predicate do uniquely determine the value of the variable, this kind of let expression is no more difficult to describe axiomatically than the simpler equational let expression introduced above. For example, it is clear that the value of the expression

$$\text{let } x:\mathbf{N} \text{ be s.t. } x^2 + 3x = 4 \text{ in } x^2 + 5x + 7$$

must be 13 because the typing information and the predicate together mean that x must be 1. More generally, the case with arbitrary predicates can be described axiomatically via the rule:

$$\frac{\exists!\, x:A \cdot P(x);\ Q(\iota x:A \cdot P(x)):B}{(\text{let } x:A \text{ be s.t. } P(x) \text{ in } Q(x)) = Q(\iota x:A \cdot P(x))} \text{Ax}$$

Here, the unique existential operator $\exists!$ and the unique choice operator ι (see Sections 3.5.2 and 3.5.3) are used respectively to ensure that there is a unique value of the variable x and to determine that value. The second hypothesis then ensures that the predicate $Q(x)$ is well-formed for that particular value of x.

Consider, however, what happens when the predicate and the typing information do not uniquely determine the value of the variable x, as in

$$\text{let } x:\mathbf{Z} \text{ be s.t. } x^2 + 3x = 4 \text{ in } x^2 + 5x + 7$$

In this example, there are two possible values of x, namely 1 and -4, and since these give rise to two different values of the overall expression it is no longer quite so clear what that value should be: should it be 3 or 13? In fact, according to the semantics of VDM-SL, it can be either of these. More generally, when a set of possible values exists, the value can be any value in that set.

This sort of arbitrariness could be captured using the non-unique choice operator ε, analogous to the unique choice operator ι but returning simply *some* element from a possible set of elements satisfying the appropriate predicate $P(x)$. This operator could be described by axioms analogous to those given for ι in Section 3.5.3, obtained simply by replacing ι by ε and $\exists!$ by $\exists$:

$$\boxed{\varepsilon\text{-form}}\ \dfrac{\exists x : A \cdot P(x)}{(\varepsilon\, x : A \cdot P(x)) : A}\ \text{Ax} \qquad \boxed{\varepsilon\text{-I}}\ \dfrac{\exists x : A \cdot P(x)}{P(\varepsilon\, x : A \cdot P(x))}\ \text{Ax}$$

and it is tempting to try to apply the same transformation to generalise the axiom describing the form of let expression where the variable is uniquely determined to the case where it is not:

$$\dfrac{\exists x : A \cdot P(x);\ Q(\varepsilon x : A \cdot P(x)) : B}{(\text{let } x : A \text{ be s.t. } P(x) \text{ in } Q(x)) = Q(\varepsilon x : A \cdot P(x))}\ \text{Ax}$$

The difficulty here is that the above axioms mean that the choice operator ε is under-determined but deterministic, that is that the expression $\varepsilon\, x : A \cdot P(x)$ denotes an arbitrary element x satisfying $P(x)$ but that every occurrence of this expression denotes the *same* element (because the rule '=-self-I' means that any expression that can be assigned a type is equal to itself). This in turn means that the let expression described in terms of ε is also under-determined but deterministic, that is that it will take any value of the range of possible values but it will always take the same value. Unfortunately, this contradicts the semantics of VDM-SL which allows the same let expression to take different values in different contexts within the same specification. For example, if two auxiliary functions are specified via:

$f : \mathbf{Z} \to \mathbf{Z}$
$f(z)\ \triangleq\ z + \text{let } x : \mathbf{Z} \text{ be s.t. } x^2 + 3x = 4 \text{ in } x^2 + 5x + 7$

$g : \mathbf{Z} \to \mathbf{Z}$
$g(z)\ \triangleq\ z + \text{let } x : \mathbf{Z} \text{ be s.t. } x^2 + 3x = 4 \text{ in } x^2 + 5x + 7$

then $f(z)$ and $g(z)$ are not necessarily equal because the let expression does not necessarily have the same value in both contexts. Thus, the formulation in terms of $\exists$ and ε does not work.

In fact, it is impossible to capture the balance of determinism and under-determinedness required by the VDM-SL semantics with the machinery available so far. One might try to solve the problem by introducing some non-deterministic analogue of the choice operator ε, as this automatically ensures that in the example given above the two functions f and g will not necessarily return the same value when applied to the same value z. However, this freeness has the unfortunate side-effect that $f(z)$ then does not necessarily always represent the same value in different contexts within a specification (i.e. $f(z)$ is not necessarily equal to $f(z)$), contrary to the semantics of VDM-SL which constrains

13.7 Other expressions

functions to be deterministic. Thus the problem has simply been inverted – instead of having to find some way of describing non-determinism with a deterministic operator it is now necessary to try to incorporate the required determinism into a description based on a non-deterministic operator.

Another possible solution might be to introduce some form of parameterized let expression, with the parameters recording the details of the context in which the expression occurred within the specification. This seems a more promising line of approach and its investigation has been taken up by Larsen ([Lar93]), but preliminary indications are that a large amount of contextual information is needed, making the manipulation of the parameterized let expressions exceedingly cumbersome. Loose let expressions are therefore considered to be outside the scope of this book.

13.7.2 Cases expressions

The cases expression of VDM-SL is a powerful tool; unfortunately it is also difficult to handle in a proof-theoretic manner. In this section, some possible approaches to reasoning about cases expressions are presented, though none of these is wholly satisfactory.

The general form of a cases expression is:

```
cases E :
    Pat₁,₁, Pat₁,₂, ... → E₁,
    Pat₂,₁, Pat₂,₂, ... → E₂,
    ...
    Patₙ,₁, Patₙ,₂, ... → Eₙ,
    others → E₀
end
```

where E, E_i and E_o are expressions, and $Pat_{i,j}$ are patterns. Naturally, the patterns can contain variables to be matched, and E_i can mention the variables in $Pat_{i,j}$.

The value of such a cases expression is the value of the right hand expression of the first case containing a pattern that matches E. Thus, evaluating a cases expression involves checking whether or not E matches each $Pat_{i,j}$ in turn; if a match is found, then the result is the corresponding E_i (with variables in the expression replaced by their matched values)[1]. If none of the patterns match, then the result is the value of the others clause.

One approach to a proof theory for cases expressions is to give a set of "evaluation rules" whereby a cases expression can be simplified. Consider a cases expression of the form:

```
cases s :
    []        → 0,
    [a] ⌢ tls → 1 + length(tls)
end
```

then the following rules could be used to simplify occurrences of this cases expression in proofs:

---

[1] If more than one pattern matches for the same case, then it would seem natural to use the bindings from the first pattern; however, the semantic interpretation in VDM-SL implies a non-deterministic choice.

$$\boxed{\text{nil-case}} \quad \frac{s:X^*;\ s = [\,]}{\left(\begin{array}{l}\text{cases } s\ :\\ \quad [\,] \to 0,\\ \quad [a]\,\widehat{}\ tls \to 1 + length(tls)\\ \text{end}\end{array}\right) = 0}$$

$$\boxed{\text{conc-case}} \quad \frac{s:X^*;\ a:X;\ tls:X^*;\ s = [a]\,\widehat{}\ tls;\ 1 + length(tls):\mathbb{N}}{\left(\begin{array}{l}\text{cases } s\ :\\ \quad [\,] \to 0,\\ \quad [a]\,\widehat{}\ tls \to 1 + length(tls)\\ \text{end}\end{array}\right) = 1 + length(tls)}$$

This relies on being able to treat variables in patterns as metavariables in rules. The hypothesis $1 + length(tls):\mathbb{N}$ is needed to ensure that the equality in the conclusion is well-formed.

The above rules are reasonably straightforward, because this is a special form of cases expression, where the patterns are both mutually exclusive and exhaustive (every sequence will match precisely one of the patterns). If the patterns were not mutually exclusive, then the second rule would require an additional hypothesis stating that s did *not* match [ ]. The rule for the third pattern of such a cases statement would need two such hypotheses, and so on.

An alternative approach would be to give rules that "destruct" the cases expression in a list-processing manner. An informal statement of such rules might be:

$$\boxed{\text{eval-case-match}} \quad \frac{e:X;\ e \text{ matches } pat_1;\ e_1:A}{\left(\begin{array}{l}\text{cases } e\ :\\ \quad pat_1 \to e_1,\\ \quad \ldots\\ \text{end}\end{array}\right) = e_1}$$

and:

$$\boxed{\text{eval-case-next}} \quad \frac{e:X;\ \neg e \text{ matches } pat_1}{\left(\begin{array}{l}\text{cases } e\ :\\ \quad pat_1 \to e_1,\\ \quad pat_2 \to e_2,\\ \quad \ldots\\ \text{end}\end{array}\right) = \left(\begin{array}{l}\text{cases } e\ :\\ \quad pat_2 \to e_2,\\ \quad \ldots\\ \text{end}\end{array}\right)}$$

$$\boxed{\text{eval-case-others}} \quad \frac{e:X;\ e_0:A}{\left(\begin{array}{l}\text{cases } e\ :\\ \quad \text{others} \to e_0\\ \text{end}\end{array}\right) = e_0}$$

It is important to note that 'eval-case-next' is incorrect as stated above. It is incorrect to assert the equality in the conclusion without guaranteeing that either side is well-formed. Consequently, 'eval-case-next' should have a hypothesis stating that the right-hand cases expression is well-formed (has a type). There should be a corresponding set of formation rules for cases expressions, which work by a similar process of reducing the cases

13.7 Other expressions

expression.

In the logical frame presented, it is not possible to state evaluation rules (and corresponding formation rules) in a sufficiently generic form to cover all cases expressions, because there is no way to say "*e* matches *pat*" generically. To make this approach more general, it would be necessary to make matching of patterns against expressions, and the resulting bindings of pattern variables to expressions, "first-class citizens" in the logical frame, that can be manipulated in inference rules.

Note that these rules say nothing about a cases expression which has no matching patterns and no others clause.

A third, less direct, approach would be to translate a cases expression into a conditional, whose conditions include "match" tests (as introduced in Section 13.6); the body expressions would have instances of pattern variables replaced by appropriate access expressions. So, for example, given:

$T :: a : \mathbf{N}$
$ b : \mathbf{N}$

$U :: c : \mathbf{N}$

cases e :
  $mk\text{-}T(x,y) \rightarrow x+y,$
  $mk\text{-}U(v) \rightarrow 2 \times v,$
  others $\rightarrow 0$
end

would become:

if $\exists x: \mathbf{N}, y: \mathbf{N} \cdot e = mk\text{-}T(x,y)$ then $e.a + e.b$ else
if $\exists v: \mathbf{N} \cdot e = mk\text{-}U(v)$ then $2 \times e.c$
else 0

For the sequence example, the corresponding condition is:

if $s = [\,]$ then 0 else
if $\exists a: X, tls: X^* \cdot s = [a] \frown tls$ then $1 + length(\text{tl}\,s)$

though the second conditional is redundant (at least, when s is a sequence expression).

Such translation only makes sense when the original cases expression is well-formed. When there is no others clause, for example in:

cases e :
  $mk\text{-}T(x,y) \rightarrow x+y,$
  $mk\text{-}U(v) \rightarrow 2 \times v$
end

then the supplied patterns must be exhaustive for (all possible values of) the expression e:

$(\exists x: \mathbf{N}, y: \mathbf{N} \cdot e = mk\text{-}T(x,y)) \vee (\exists v: \mathbf{N} \cdot e = mk\text{-}U(v))$

13.7.3 μ expressions

The VDM-SL μ operator provides a mechanism for describing modifications to the fields of an element of a composite type by explicitly listing the fields which are to change together with their new values. For example, taking the data-type *ATC* from the case study (see Section 12.3) as a representative composite type, the expression

$$\mu(\sigma, onduty \mapsto cs')$$

where σ: *ATC* represents the result of replacing the *onduty* field of σ with the value cs'. Another way of putting this is that, if σ is of the form $mk\text{-}ATC(cs, con, cap, loc)$ then $\mu(\sigma, onduty \mapsto cs')$ represents the expression $mk\text{-}ATC(cs', con, cap, loc)$, provided that this value satisfies the invariant on *ATC*. This condition can easily be accommodated by incorporating it into the hypotheses of a rule describing the above replacement axiomatically, for example via:

$$\frac{\sigma: ATC;\ mk\text{-}ATC(cs, \sigma.control, \sigma.capacity, \sigma.location): ATC}{\mu(\sigma, onduty \mapsto cs) = mk\text{-}ATC(cs, \sigma.control, \sigma.capacity, \sigma.location)}\text{Ax}$$

but this is far from a general solution – not only does it only describe the μ operator for the specific composite type *ATC*, it also only deals with modification to the *onduty* field of that type.

A completely general treatment of μ would have to be parameterized over an arbitrary composite type having an arbitrary number of fields, which would mean that the μ operator would have to have variable arity and that the notion of being the *mk*-function or a selector function of a composite type would have to be formalised. Both of these fall outside the logical framework used here. The best bet, therefore is to treat each μ expression used in a specification separately.

Two approaches would seem to be possible here. First, a different μ symbol could be introduced into the theory for each different combination of composite type and those fields which are modified appearing in the specification. In this way, the expression $\mu(\sigma, onduty \mapsto cs)$ considered above might be described in the theory by a symbol $\mu_{ATC,1}$, representing general modification to the first field of the composite type *ATC* and described by an axiom, analogous to the one given above, of the form:

$$\frac{\sigma: ATC;\ mk\text{-}ATC(cs, \sigma.control, \sigma.capacity, \sigma.location): ATC}{\mu_{ATC,1}(\sigma, cs) = mk\text{-}ATC(cs, \sigma.control, \sigma.capacity, \sigma.location)}\text{Ax}$$

Expressions involving μ applied to different components of an object of type *ATC* would then be described by different μ operators. For example, the expression $\mu(\sigma, control \mapsto con, capacity \mapsto cap)$ would be described by the expression $\mu_{ATC,2,3}(\sigma, con, cap)$ in this scheme, with the symbol $\mu_{ATC,2,3}$ being defined axiomatically via:

$$\frac{\sigma: ATC;\ mk\text{-}ATC(\sigma.onduty, con, cap, \sigma.location): ATC}{\mu_{ATC,2,3}(\sigma, con, cap) = mk\text{-}ATC(\sigma.onduty, con, cap.\sigma.location)}\text{Ax}$$

The advantage of this approach is that one axiom is sufficient to describe each of the different μ symbols introduced. The corresponding disadvantage is that the number of axioms proliferates annoyingly if the specification contains a large number of different μ expressions.

The other possible approach is to "translate out" all the μ expressions in the specification before attempting to reason about them, replacing them with the appropriate *mk*-function applied to the appropriate fields constructed exactly as described above for the other possible treatment. The fact that the invariant has to hold for this replacement to make sense would then appear as a proof obligation to show that the expression replacing the μ expression is of the correct type. The advantage of this approach is that no extension of the theory is required. The disadvantage is that any proofs involving the "expanded out" μ expressions no longer explicitly depend on these expansions being well-formed. The effect of this is that, even though a proof might have been completed successfully, it is only valid if the well-formedness proof obligations on which it implicitly depends have all been discharged. Although this is a subtle distinction, it runs counter to the tenet assumed throughout this book that any result that has been proved from axioms alone is valid. For this reason the strategy of representing each different μ expression by a different symbol in the theory is preferred.

13.8 Other types

13.8.1 Tokens

The distinguished type token in VDM-SL is a source of countably many structureless values on which the only defined comparator is equality. It is used in the definition of types for which the specifier does not (yet) want to give a representation. For example, in giving an abstract specification of a programming language, it may not be of any importance what the representation of procedure names is, or one may wish to defer this detail to a later refinement stage:

Proc_Name = token

The type definition above results in a single type constant *Proc_Name* being added to the theory of the specification. This allows one to deduce that equality is defined on *Proc_Name* by 'δ-=-I'. The fact that the class of tokens is infinite could be captured by an axiom of the form:

$$\boxed{\textit{Proc\_Name}\text{-infinite}} \; \dfrac{\textit{pns}: \textit{Proc\_Name}\text{-set}}{\exists p: \textit{Proc\_Name} \cdot p \notin \textit{pns}} \; \textbf{Ax}$$

A specification may contain definitions of a number of token types, for example:

$T1$ = token

$T2$ = token

This does not mean that $T1$ and $T2$ are the same type, nor does it mean they are distinct types: they are each infinite classes of structureless values. In the theory of the specification, elements of the types are denoting, and therefore equality is defined on them, but it is not possible to tell whether the types are the same or not.

13.8.2 Quote types

A *quote type* consists of just one value denoted by the same character string as the type itself. In a specification, quote types are distinguished by a special character set. Such types are used to represent constants. An enumerated type is a union of quote types. For example, a specification of part of an operating system might contain a definition:

Component = KEYBOARD | MOUSE | SCREEN

This introduces three quote types: KEYBOARD, MOUSE and SCREEN. Each of these has just one element of the same name as the type. Thus:

$$\boxed{\text{MOUSE-form}} \; \frac{}{\text{MOUSE: MOUSE}} \; \textbf{Ax}$$

$$\boxed{\text{MOUSE-singleton}} \; \frac{m: \text{MOUSE}}{m = \text{MOUSE}} \; \textbf{Ax}$$

Quote types of different names are distinct, so that it is necessary to give axioms differentiating the types, for example

$$\boxed{\text{KEYBOARD-MOUSE-disjoint}} \; \frac{}{\text{KEYBOARD} \neq \text{MOUSE}} \; \textbf{Ax}$$

for each possible combination of quote types introduced in a specification.

Quote types are usually introduced in the context of a union type, as shown in the example above. The intention here is to achieve the effect of an enumerated type. The rules for type union allow one to prove that

$$\frac{d: Component}{d = \text{KEYBOARD} \lor d = \text{MOUSE} \lor d = \text{SCREEN}}$$

13.8.3 Characters

The type char consists of the VDM-SL character set. Values of the type are distinguished by the use of quote marks. The type is completely described by a set of axioms stating that each element of the character set is of type char. These include:

$$\frac{}{\text{`}\alpha\text{': char}} \textbf{Ax} \qquad \frac{}{\text{`a': char}} \textbf{Ax} \qquad \frac{}{\text{`+': char}} \textbf{Ax}$$

Text strings, shown in specifications between speech marks ("..."), represent sequences of characters (elements of the type char*).

Part III

Directory of Theorems

Chapter 14

Directory of Theorems

This final chapter forms a "reference manual", aimed at readers who wish to apply the proof techniques described in the earlier chapters to their own examples. Sections 14.1 to 14.8 correspond in turn to Chapters 2 to 9. Each consists of separate listings of: the axioms of the theory, arranged in logical order (that is so that axioms defining a particular concept appear before those using that concept to define some other concept); the defined symbols of the theory, arranged in the same order; and a collection of useful derived rules, arranged in "alphabetical" order.

These listings include all axioms, definitions and rules mentioned or used in the main body of the text, and in addition include extra "useful" derived rules. However, these lists cannot be exhaustive, so the reader should always be ready to invent and prove new rules as the need arises.

Sections 14.9 and 14.10 summarise the templates for the axioms, definitions and proof obligations for the various components of specifications and reifications which were given in Chapters 10 and 11 respectively. Generic examples are used as the basis for these templates.

The final two sections of this chapter contain the specific axioms, definitions and proof obligations for the ATC system discussed in the case study (Chapter 12). These sections also include subsections listing the validation conditions which were discussed therein and a selection of lemmas which are useful in discharging the proof obligations and the validation conditions. The first of these two sections deals with the abstract ATC specification discussed in Sections 12.3 and 12.4; the second deals with the concrete specification and the refinement, discussed in Section 12.5.

14.1 Propositonal LPF

Axioms

$$\boxed{\text{true-I}}\ \frac{}{\text{true}}\ \textbf{Ax}$$

$$\boxed{\vee\text{-E}}\ \frac{e_1 \vee e_2;\ e_1 \vdash e;\ e_2 \vdash e}{e}\ \textbf{Ax}$$

$$\boxed{\vee\text{-I-left}}\ \frac{e_2}{e_1 \vee e_2}\ \text{Ax}$$

$$\boxed{\vee\text{-I-right}}\ \frac{e_1}{e_1 \vee e_2}\ \text{Ax}$$

$$\boxed{\neg\neg\text{-E}}\ \frac{\neg\neg e}{e}\ \text{Ax}$$

$$\boxed{\neg\neg\text{-I}}\ \frac{e}{\neg\neg e}\ \text{Ax}$$

$$\boxed{\text{contradiction}}\ \frac{e_1;\ \neg e_1}{e_2}\ \text{Ax}$$

$$\boxed{\neg\text{-}\vee\text{-E-left}}\ \frac{\neg(e_1 \vee e_2)}{\neg e_2}\ \text{Ax}$$

$$\boxed{\neg\text{-}\vee\text{-E-right}}\ \frac{\neg(e_1 \vee e_2)}{\neg e_1}\ \text{Ax}$$

$$\boxed{\neg\text{-}\vee\text{-I}}\ \frac{\neg e_1;\ \neg e_2}{\neg(e_1 \vee e_2)}\ \text{Ax}$$

Definitions

$$e_1 \wedge e_2 \stackrel{\text{def}}{=} \neg(\neg e_1 \vee \neg e_2)$$

$$\text{false} \stackrel{\text{def}}{=} \neg\text{true}$$

$$e_1 \Rightarrow e_2 \stackrel{\text{def}}{=} \neg e_1 \vee e_2$$

$$e_1 \Leftrightarrow e_2 \stackrel{\text{def}}{=} (e_1 \Rightarrow e_2) \wedge (e_2 \Rightarrow e_1)$$

$$\delta e \stackrel{\text{def}}{=} e \vee \neg e$$

Derived rules

$$\boxed{\wedge\text{-}\vee\text{-dist-contract}}\ \frac{(e_1 \wedge e_2) \vee (e_1 \wedge e_3)}{e_1 \wedge (e_2 \vee e_3)}$$

$$\boxed{\wedge\text{-}\vee\text{-dist-expand}}\ \frac{e_1 \wedge (e_2 \vee e_3)}{(e_1 \wedge e_2) \vee (e_1 \wedge e_3)}$$

14.1 Propositional LPF

$$\boxed{\wedge\text{-ass-left}}\ \frac{(e_1 \wedge e_2) \wedge e_3}{e_1 \wedge (e_2 \wedge e_3)}$$

$$\boxed{\wedge\text{-ass-right}}\ \frac{e_1 \wedge (e_2 \wedge e_3)}{(e_1 \wedge e_2) \wedge e_3}$$

$$\boxed{\wedge\text{-comm}}\ \frac{e_1 \wedge e_2}{e_2 \wedge e_1}$$

$$\boxed{\wedge\text{-E-left}}\ \frac{e_1 \wedge e_2}{e_2}$$

$$\boxed{\wedge\text{-E-right}}\ \frac{e_1 \wedge e_2}{e_1}$$

$$\boxed{\wedge\text{-I}}\ \frac{e_1;\ e_2}{e_1 \wedge e_2}$$

$$\boxed{\wedge\text{-subs-left}}\ \frac{e_1 \wedge e_2;\ e_1 \vdash e}{e \wedge e_2}$$

$$\boxed{\wedge\text{-subs-right}}\ \frac{e_1 \wedge e_2;\ e_2 \vdash e}{e_1 \wedge e}$$

$$\boxed{\delta\text{-}\wedge\text{-inherit}}\ \frac{\delta e_1;\ \delta e_2}{\delta(e_1 \wedge e_2)}$$

$$\boxed{\delta\text{-}\wedge\text{-inherit-sqt}}\ \frac{\delta e_1;\ e_1 \vdash \delta e_2}{\delta(e_1 \wedge e_2)}$$

$$\boxed{\delta\text{-}\Leftrightarrow\text{-inherit}}\ \frac{\delta e_1;\ \delta e_2}{\delta(e_1 \Leftrightarrow e_2)}$$

$$\boxed{\delta\text{-}\Rightarrow\text{-inherit}}\ \frac{\delta e_1;\ \delta e_2}{\delta(e_1 \Rightarrow e_2)}$$

$$\boxed{\delta\text{-}\Rightarrow\text{-inherit-sqt}}\ \frac{\delta e_1;\ e_1 \vdash \delta e_2}{\delta(e_1 \Rightarrow e_2)}$$

$$\boxed{\delta\text{-}\neg\text{-inherit}}\ \frac{\delta e}{\delta(\neg e)}$$

$$\boxed{\delta\text{-}\vee\text{-I-left}}\ \frac{e_2}{\delta(e_1 \vee e_2)}$$

$$\boxed{\delta\text{-}\vee\text{-I-right}}\ \frac{e_1}{\delta(e_1 \vee e_2)}$$

$$\boxed{\delta\text{-}\vee\text{-inherit}}\ \frac{\delta e_1;\ \delta e_2}{\delta(e_1 \vee e_2)}$$

$$\boxed{\delta\text{-}\vee\text{-inherit-sqt}}\ \frac{\delta e_1;\ \neg e_1 \vdash \delta e_2}{\delta(e_1 \vee e_2)}$$

$$\boxed{\delta\text{-E}}\ \frac{\delta e_1;\ e_1 \vdash e_2;\ \neg e_1 \vdash e_2}{e_2}$$

$$\boxed{\delta\text{-I}}\ \frac{e}{\delta e}$$

$$\boxed{\delta\text{-I-}\neg}\ \frac{\neg e}{\delta e}$$

$$\boxed{\Leftrightarrow\text{-}\neg\text{-I}}\ \frac{e_1 \Leftrightarrow e_2}{\neg e_1 \Leftrightarrow \neg e_2}$$

$$\boxed{\Leftrightarrow\text{-comm}}\ \frac{e_1 \Leftrightarrow e_2}{e_2 \Leftrightarrow e_1}$$

$$\boxed{\Leftrightarrow\text{-E-full}}\ \frac{e_1 \Leftrightarrow e_2}{e_1 \wedge e_2 \vee \neg e_1 \wedge \neg e_2}$$

$$\boxed{\Leftrightarrow\text{-E-left}}\ \frac{e_1 \Leftrightarrow e_2;\ e_1}{e_2}$$

$$\boxed{\Leftrightarrow\text{-E-left-}\delta}\ \frac{e_1 \Leftrightarrow e_2}{\delta e_2}$$

$$\boxed{\Leftrightarrow\text{-E-left-}\neg}\ \frac{e_1 \Leftrightarrow e_2;\ \neg e_1}{\neg e_2}$$

$$\boxed{\Leftrightarrow\text{-E-right}}\ \frac{e_1 \Leftrightarrow e_2;\ e_2}{e_1}$$

$$\boxed{\Leftrightarrow\text{-E-right-}\delta}\ \frac{e_1 \Leftrightarrow e_2}{\delta e_1}$$

$$\boxed{\Leftrightarrow\text{-E-right-}\neg}\ \frac{e_1 \Leftrightarrow e_2;\ \neg e_2}{\neg e_1}$$

$$\boxed{\Leftrightarrow\text{-I}}\ \frac{e_1;\ e_2}{e_1 \Leftrightarrow e_2}$$

$$\boxed{\Leftrightarrow\text{-I-}\wedge}\ \frac{e_1 \wedge e_2}{e_1 \Leftrightarrow e_2}$$

14.1 Propositional LPF

$$\boxed{\Leftrightarrow\text{-I-}\wedge\text{-}\neg}\ \frac{\neg e_1 \wedge \neg e_2}{e_1 \Leftrightarrow e_2}$$

$$\boxed{\Leftrightarrow\text{-I-}\neg}\ \frac{\neg e_1;\ \neg e_2}{e_1 \Leftrightarrow e_2}$$

$$\boxed{\Leftrightarrow\text{-self-I}}\ \frac{\delta e}{e \Leftrightarrow e}$$

$$\boxed{\Rightarrow\text{-}\wedge\text{-left-E}}\ \frac{e_1;\ e_1 \wedge e_2 \Rightarrow e_3}{e_2 \Rightarrow e_3}$$

$$\boxed{\Rightarrow\text{-}\neg\text{-conseq}}\ \frac{e_1 \Rightarrow e_3;\ \neg e_1 \vdash \neg e_2}{e_2 \Rightarrow e_3}$$

$$\boxed{\Rightarrow\text{-conseq}}\ \frac{e_1 \Rightarrow e_2;\ e_2 \vdash e_3}{e_1 \Rightarrow e_3}$$

$$\boxed{\Rightarrow\text{-contrp}}\ \frac{e_1 \Rightarrow e_2}{\neg e_2 \Rightarrow \neg e_1}$$

$$\boxed{\Rightarrow\text{-E-left}}\ \frac{e_1 \Rightarrow e_2;\ e_1}{e_2}$$

$$\boxed{\Rightarrow\text{-E-right}}\ \frac{e_1 \Rightarrow e_2;\ \neg e_2}{\neg e_1}$$

$$\boxed{\Rightarrow\text{-I}}\ \frac{\delta e_1;\ e_1 \vdash e_2}{e_1 \Rightarrow e_2}$$

$$\boxed{\Rightarrow\text{-I-left-vac}}\ \frac{e_2}{e_1 \Rightarrow e_2}$$

$$\boxed{\Rightarrow\text{-I-right-vac}}\ \frac{\neg e_1}{e_1 \Rightarrow e_2}$$

$$\boxed{\Rightarrow\text{-self-I}}\ \frac{\delta e}{e \Rightarrow e}$$

$$\boxed{\Rightarrow\text{-trans}}\ \frac{e_1 \Rightarrow e_2;\ e_2 \Rightarrow e_3}{e_1 \Rightarrow e_3}$$

$$\boxed{\neg\text{-}\wedge\text{-E-deM}}\ \frac{\neg(e_1 \wedge e_2)}{\neg e_1 \vee \neg e_2}$$

$$\boxed{\neg\text{-}\wedge\text{-E-left}}\ \frac{e_1;\ \neg(e_1 \wedge e_2)}{\neg e_2}$$

$\boxed{\neg\text{-}\wedge\text{-E-right}}\ \dfrac{e_2;\ \neg(e_1 \wedge e_2)}{\neg e_1}$

$\boxed{\neg\text{-}\wedge\text{-I-deM}}\ \dfrac{\neg e_1 \vee \neg e_2}{\neg(e_1 \wedge e_2)}$

$\boxed{\neg\text{-}\wedge\text{-I-left}}\ \dfrac{\neg e_2}{\neg(e_1 \wedge e_2)}$

$\boxed{\neg\text{-}\wedge\text{-I-right}}\ \dfrac{\neg e_1}{\neg(e_1 \wedge e_2)}$

$\boxed{\neg\text{-}\wedge\text{-I-sqt}}\ \dfrac{\delta e_1;\ e_1 \vdash \neg e_2}{\neg(e_1 \wedge e_2)}$

$\boxed{\neg\text{-}\Rightarrow\text{-E}}\ \dfrac{\neg(e_1 \Rightarrow e_2)}{e_1 \wedge \neg e_2}$

$\boxed{\neg\text{-}\Rightarrow\text{-E-left}}\ \dfrac{\neg(e_1 \Rightarrow e_2)}{\neg e_2}$

$\boxed{\neg\text{-}\Rightarrow\text{-E-right}}\ \dfrac{\neg(e_1 \Rightarrow e_2)}{e_1}$

$\boxed{\neg\text{-}\Rightarrow\text{-I}}\ \dfrac{e_1;\ \neg e_2}{\neg(e_1 \Rightarrow e_2)}$

$\boxed{\neg\text{-}\vee\text{-E-deM}}\ \dfrac{\neg(e_1 \vee e_2)}{\neg e_1 \wedge \neg e_2}$

$\boxed{\neg\text{-}\vee\text{-I-deM}}\ \dfrac{\neg e_1 \wedge \neg e_2}{\neg(e_1 \vee e_2)}$

$\boxed{\neg\text{-false-I}}\ \dfrac{}{\neg\text{false}}$

$\boxed{\vee\text{-}\wedge\text{-dist-contract}}\ \dfrac{(e_1 \vee e_2) \wedge (e_1 \vee e_3)}{e_1 \vee (e_2 \wedge e_3)}$

$\boxed{\vee\text{-}\wedge\text{-dist-expand}}\ \dfrac{e_1 \vee (e_2 \wedge e_3)}{(e_1 \vee e_2) \wedge (e_1 \vee e_3)}$

$\boxed{\vee\text{-ass-left}}\ \dfrac{(e_1 \vee e_2) \vee e_3}{e_1 \vee (e_2 \vee e_3)}$

$\boxed{\vee\text{-ass-right}}\ \dfrac{e_1 \vee (e_2 \vee e_3)}{(e_1 \vee e_2) \vee e_3}$

14.2 Predicate LPF with equality

$$\boxed{\vee\text{-comm}} \ \frac{e_1 \vee e_2}{e_2 \vee e_1}$$

$$\boxed{\vee\text{-E-left-}\neg} \ \frac{e_1 \vee e_2; \ \neg e_1}{e_2}$$

$$\boxed{\vee\text{-E-right-}\neg} \ \frac{e_1 \vee e_2; \ \neg e_2}{e_1}$$

$$\boxed{\vee\text{-subs-left}} \ \frac{e_1 \vee e_2; \ e_1 \vdash e}{e \vee e_2}$$

$$\boxed{\vee\text{-subs-right}} \ \frac{e_1 \vee e_2; \ e_2 \vdash e}{e_1 \vee e}$$

$$\boxed{\text{false-contr}} \ \frac{\delta e; \ e \vdash \text{false}}{\neg e}$$

$$\boxed{\text{false-E}} \ \frac{\text{false}}{e}$$

14.2 Predicate LPF with equality

14.2.1 Predicate LPF

Axioms

$$\boxed{\exists\text{-E}} \ \frac{\exists x \colon A \cdot P(x) \quad y \colon A, \ P(y) \vdash_y e}{e} \ \text{Ax}$$

$$\boxed{\exists\text{-I}} \ \frac{a \colon A; \ P(a)}{\exists x \colon A \cdot P(x)} \ \text{Ax}$$

$$\boxed{\neg\text{-}\exists\text{-E}} \ \frac{a \colon A; \ \neg(\exists x \colon A \cdot P(x))}{\neg P(a)} \ \text{Ax}$$

$$\boxed{\neg\text{-}\exists\text{-I}} \ \frac{x \colon A \vdash_x \neg P(x)}{\neg(\exists y \colon A \cdot P(y))} \ \text{Ax}$$

$$\boxed{\delta\text{-}\exists\text{-inherit}} \ \frac{x \colon A \vdash_x \delta P(x)}{\delta(\exists x \colon A \cdot P(x))} \ \text{Ax}$$

Definitions

$$\forall x : A \cdot P(x) \overset{\text{def}}{=} \neg \exists x : A \cdot \neg P(x)$$

$$inhabited(A) \overset{\text{def}}{=} \exists x : A \cdot \text{true}$$

Derived rules

$$\boxed{\forall\text{-}\forall\text{-comm}} \quad \frac{\forall x : A \cdot \forall y : B \cdot P(x, y)}{\forall y : B \cdot \forall x : A \cdot P(x, y)}$$

$$\boxed{\forall\forall\text{-E}} \quad \frac{a : A; \ b : B; \ \forall x : A \cdot \forall y : B \cdot P(x, y)}{P(a, b)}$$

$$\boxed{\forall\forall\text{-I}} \quad \frac{x : A, \ y : B \vdash_{x,y} P(x, y)}{\forall x : A \cdot \forall y : B \cdot P(x, y)}$$

$$\boxed{\forall\forall\text{-subs}} \quad \frac{\forall x : A \cdot \forall y : B \cdot P(x, y) \quad x : A, \ y : B, \ P(x, y) \vdash_{x,y} Q(x, y)}{\forall x : A \cdot \forall y : B \cdot Q(x, y)}$$

$$\boxed{\forall\text{-}\wedge\text{-dist-contract}} \quad \frac{(\forall x : A \cdot P(x)) \wedge (\forall x : A \cdot Q(x))}{\forall x : A \cdot P(x) \wedge Q(x)}$$

$$\boxed{\forall\text{-}\wedge\text{-dist-expand}} \quad \frac{\forall x : A \cdot P(x) \wedge Q(x)}{(\forall x : A \cdot P(x)) \wedge (\forall x : A \cdot Q(x))}$$

$$\boxed{\forall\text{-}\delta\text{-}\vee\text{-inherit}} \quad \frac{\forall x : A \cdot \delta P(x); \ \forall y : A \cdot \delta Q(y)}{\forall z : A \cdot \delta(P(z) \vee Q(z))}$$

$$\boxed{\forall\text{-}\delta\text{-I-}\neg} \quad \frac{\forall x : A \cdot \neg P(x)}{\forall x : A \cdot \delta P(x)}$$

$$\boxed{\forall\text{-}\Leftrightarrow\text{-E-left-}\delta} \quad \frac{\forall x : A \cdot P(x) \Leftrightarrow Q(x)}{\forall x : A \cdot \delta Q(x)}$$

$$\boxed{\forall\text{-}\Leftrightarrow\text{-E-right-}\delta} \quad \frac{\forall x : A \cdot P(x) \Leftrightarrow Q(x)}{\forall x : A \cdot \delta P(x)}$$

$$\boxed{\forall\text{-}\Leftrightarrow\text{-subs}} \quad \frac{\forall x : A \cdot P(x) \quad x : A \vdash_x P(x) \Leftrightarrow Q(x)}{\forall x : A \cdot Q(x)}$$

$$\boxed{\forall\text{-}\Leftrightarrow\text{-subs-}\delta} \quad \frac{\forall x : A \cdot \delta P(x) \quad \forall x : A \cdot P(x) \Leftrightarrow Q(x)}{\forall x : A \cdot \delta Q(x)}$$

14.2 Predicate LPF with equality

$$\boxed{\forall\text{-}{\Rightarrow}\text{-subs}}\ \frac{\forall x{:}A \cdot P(x)\quad x{:}A \vdash_x P(x) \Rightarrow Q(x)}{\forall x{:}A \cdot Q(x)}$$

$$\boxed{\forall\text{-}\vee\text{-dist-contract}}\ \frac{(\forall x{:}A \cdot P(x)) \vee (\forall x{:}A \cdot Q(x))}{\forall x{:}A \cdot P(x) \vee Q(x)}$$

$$\boxed{\forall\text{-}\vee\text{-I-left}}\ \frac{\forall x{:}A \cdot Q(x)}{\forall x{:}A \cdot P(x) \vee Q(x)}$$

$$\boxed{\forall\text{-}\vee\text{-I-right}}\ \frac{\forall x{:}A \cdot P(x)}{\forall x{:}A \cdot P(x) \vee Q(x)}$$

$$\boxed{\forall \to \exists}\ \frac{\forall x{:}A \cdot P(x);\ \mathit{inhabited}(A)}{\exists x{:}A \cdot P(x)}$$

$$\boxed{\forall \to \neg\text{-}\exists\text{-deM}}\ \frac{\forall x{:}A \cdot \neg P(x)}{\neg(\exists x{:}A \cdot P(x))}$$

$$\boxed{\forall\text{-E}}\ \frac{a{:}A;\ \forall x{:}A \cdot P(x)}{P(a)}$$

$$\boxed{\forall\text{-fix}}\ \frac{\forall x{:}A \cdot \forall y{:}A \cdot P(x,y)}{\forall x{:}A \cdot P(x,x)}$$

$$\boxed{\forall\text{-I}}\ \frac{y{:}A \vdash_y P(y)}{\forall x{:}A \cdot P(x)}$$

$$\boxed{\forall\text{-subs}}\ \frac{\forall y{:}A \cdot P(y)\quad x{:}A,\ P(x) \vdash_x Q(x)}{\forall y{:}A \cdot Q(y)}$$

$$\boxed{\delta\text{-}\forall\forall\text{-I}}\ \frac{x{:}A,\ y{:}B \vdash_{x,y} \delta P(x,y)}{\delta(\forall x{:}A \cdot \forall y{:}B \cdot P(x,y))}$$

$$\boxed{\delta\text{-}\forall\text{-inherit}}\ \frac{y{:}A \vdash_y \delta P(y)}{\delta(\forall x{:}A \cdot P(x))}$$

$$\boxed{\exists\text{-}\forall \to \forall\text{-}\exists}\ \frac{\exists x{:}A \cdot \forall y{:}B \cdot P(x,y)}{\forall y{:}B \cdot \exists x{:}A \cdot P(x,y)}$$

$$\boxed{\exists\forall\text{-subs}}\ \frac{\exists x{:}A \cdot \forall y{:}B \cdot P(x,y)\quad x{:}A,\ y{:}B,\ P(x,y) \vdash_{x,y} Q(x,y)}{\exists x{:}A \cdot \forall y{:}B \cdot Q(x,y)}$$

$$\boxed{\exists\text{-}\wedge\text{-dist-expand}}\ \frac{\exists x{:}A \cdot P(x) \wedge Q(x)}{(\exists y{:}A \cdot P(y)) \wedge (\exists z{:}A \cdot Q(z))}$$

$$\boxed{\exists\text{-}\wedge\text{-E-left}} \quad \frac{\exists x\colon A \cdot P(x) \wedge Q(x)}{\exists x\colon A \cdot Q(x)}$$

$$\boxed{\exists\text{-}\wedge\text{-E-right}} \quad \frac{\exists x\colon A \cdot P(x) \wedge Q(x)}{\exists x\colon A \cdot P(x)}$$

$$\boxed{\exists\text{-}\exists\text{-comm}} \quad \frac{\exists x\colon A \cdot \exists y\colon B \cdot P(x,y)}{\exists y\colon B \cdot \exists x\colon A \cdot P(x,y)}$$

$$\boxed{\exists\exists\text{-E}} \quad \frac{\exists x\colon A \cdot \exists y\colon B \cdot P(x,y) \quad x\colon A,\; y\colon B,\; P(x,y) \vdash_{x,y} e}{e}$$

$$\boxed{\exists\exists\text{-I}} \quad \frac{a\colon A;\; b\colon B;\; P(a,b)}{\exists x\colon A \cdot \exists y\colon B \cdot P(x,y)}$$

$$\boxed{\exists\exists\text{-subs}} \quad \frac{\exists x\colon A \cdot \exists y\colon B \cdot P(x,y) \quad x\colon A,\; y\colon B,\; P(x,y) \vdash_{x,y} Q(x,y)}{\exists x\colon A \cdot \exists y\colon B \cdot Q(x,y)}$$

$$\boxed{\exists\text{-}\Leftrightarrow\text{-subs}} \quad \frac{\exists x\colon A \cdot P(x) \quad x\colon A \vdash_x P(x) \Leftrightarrow Q(x)}{\exists x\colon A \cdot Q(x)}$$

$$\boxed{\exists\text{-}\Rightarrow\text{-subs}} \quad \frac{\exists x\colon A \cdot P(x) \quad x\colon A \vdash_x (P(x) \Rightarrow Q(x))}{\exists x\colon A \cdot Q(x)}$$

$$\boxed{\exists\text{-}\vee\text{-dist-contract}} \quad \frac{(\exists x\colon A \cdot P(x)) \vee (\exists x\colon A \cdot Q(x))}{\exists x\colon A \cdot P(x) \vee Q(x)}$$

$$\boxed{\exists\text{-}\vee\text{-dist-expand}} \quad \frac{\exists x\colon A \cdot P(x) \vee Q(x)}{(\exists x\colon A \cdot P(x)) \vee (\exists x\colon A \cdot Q(x))}$$

$$\boxed{\exists \to \neg\text{-}\forall\text{-deM}} \quad \frac{\exists x\colon A \cdot \neg P(x)}{\neg (\forall x\colon A \cdot P(x))}$$

$$\boxed{\exists\text{-I-1pt}} \quad \frac{a\colon A;\; P(a)}{\exists x\colon A \cdot x = a \wedge P(x)}$$

$$\boxed{\exists\text{-split}} \quad \frac{\exists x\colon A \cdot P(x,x)}{\exists x\colon A \cdot \exists y\colon A \cdot P(x,y)}$$

$$\boxed{\exists\text{-subs}} \quad \frac{\exists y\colon A \cdot P(y) \quad x\colon A,\; P(x) \vdash_x Q(x)}{\exists y\colon A \cdot Q(y)}$$

14.2 Predicate LPF with equality

$$\boxed{\neg\text{-}\forall \to \exists\text{-deM}} \quad \frac{\neg(\forall x\colon A \cdot P(x))}{\exists x\colon A \cdot \neg P(x)}$$

$$\boxed{\neg\text{-}\forall\text{-E}} \quad \frac{\neg(\forall x\colon A \cdot P(x)) \qquad y\colon A,\ \neg P(y) \vdash_y e}{e}$$

$$\boxed{\neg\text{-}\forall\text{-I}} \quad \frac{a\colon A;\ P(a)}{\neg(\forall x\colon A \cdot \neg P(x))}$$

$$\boxed{\neg\text{-}\forall\text{-I-}\neg} \quad \frac{a\colon A;\ \neg P(a)}{\neg(\forall x\colon A \cdot P(x))}$$

$$\boxed{\neg\text{-}\exists \to \forall\text{-deM}} \quad \frac{\neg(\exists x\colon A \cdot P(x))}{\forall x\colon A \cdot \neg P(x)}$$

14.2.2 Equality

Axioms

$$\boxed{=\text{-self-I}} \quad \frac{a\colon A}{a = a} \ \mathbf{Ax}$$

$$\boxed{=\text{-subs-left(b)}} \quad \frac{b\colon A;\ a = b;\ P(b)}{P(a)} \ \mathbf{Ax}$$

$$\boxed{=\text{-subs-right(a)}} \quad \frac{a\colon A;\ a = b;\ P(a)}{P(b)} \ \mathbf{Ax}$$

$$\boxed{\delta\text{-=-I}} \quad \frac{a\colon A;\ b\colon A}{\delta(a = b)} \ \mathbf{Ax}$$

Definitions

$$e_1 \neq e_2 \ \stackrel{\text{def}}{=} \ \neg(e_1 = e_2)$$

Derived rules

$$\boxed{\delta\text{-}\neq\text{-I}} \quad \frac{a\colon A;\ b\colon A}{\delta(a \neq b)}$$

$$\boxed{=\text{-}\vee\text{-}\neq} \quad \frac{a\colon A;\ b\colon A}{a = b \vee a \neq b}$$

| =-cases | $\dfrac{a:A;\ b:A;\ a=b \vdash e;\ a \neq b \vdash e}{e}$ |

| =-extend(a) | $\dfrac{a:A;\ a=b;\ E(a):B}{E(a)=E(b)}$ |

| =-extend(b) | $\dfrac{a:A;\ a=b;\ E(b):B}{E(a)=E(b)}$ |

| =-subs-left(a) | $\dfrac{a:A;\ a=b;\ P(b)}{P(a)}$ |

| =-subs-right(b) | $\dfrac{b:A;\ a=b;\ P(a)}{P(b)}$ |

| =-symm(a) | $\dfrac{a:A;\ a=b}{b=a}$ |

| =-symm(b) | $\dfrac{b:A;\ a=b}{b=a}$ |

| =-trans(a) | $\dfrac{a:A;\ a=b;\ b=c}{a=c}$ |

| =-trans(b) | $\dfrac{b:A;\ a=b;\ b=c}{a=c}$ |

| =-trans(c) | $\dfrac{c:A;\ a=b;\ b=c}{a=c}$ |

| =-trans-left(a) | $\dfrac{a:A;\ a=b;\ a=c}{b=c}$ |

| =-trans-left(b) | $\dfrac{b:A;\ a=b;\ a=c}{b=c}$ |

| =-trans-left(c) | $\dfrac{c:A;\ a=b;\ a=c}{b=c}$ |

| =-trans-right(a) | $\dfrac{a:A;\ a=c;\ b=c}{a=b}$ |

| =-trans-right(b) | $\dfrac{b:A;\ a=c;\ b=c}{a=b}$ |

| =-trans-right(c) | $\dfrac{c:A;\ a=c;\ b=c}{a=b}$ |

14.2 Predicate LPF with equality

$$\boxed{\text{=-type-inherit-left}} \quad \frac{a:A; \ b = a}{b:A}$$

$$\boxed{\text{=-type-inherit-right}} \quad \frac{b:A; \ b = a}{a:A}$$

$$\boxed{\neg\text{-}\neq\text{-self-I}} \quad \frac{a:A}{\neg(a \neq a)}$$

$$\boxed{\neq\text{-comm}} \quad \frac{a:A; \ b:A; \ a \neq b}{b \neq a}$$

14.2.3 Other quantifiers

Axioms

$$\boxed{\iota\text{-form}} \quad \frac{\exists! x:A \cdot P(x)}{(\iota y:A \cdot P(y)):A} \ \text{Ax}$$

$$\boxed{\iota\text{-I}} \quad \frac{\exists! x:A \cdot P(x)}{P(\iota y:A \cdot P(y))} \ \text{Ax}$$

Definitions

$$\exists! x:A \cdot P(x) \ \stackrel{\text{def}}{=} \ \exists x:A \cdot P(x) \land \forall y:A \cdot P(y) \Rightarrow y = x$$

Derived rules

$$\boxed{\exists! \forall \to \forall \exists} \quad \frac{\exists! x:A \cdot \forall y:B \cdot P(x,y)}{\forall y:B \cdot \exists x:A \cdot P(x,y)}$$

$$\boxed{\exists!\text{-=-I}} \quad \frac{a:A}{\exists! b:A \cdot b = a}$$

$$\boxed{\exists!\text{-}\lor\text{-dist-expand}} \quad \frac{\exists! x:A \cdot P(x) \lor Q(x)}{(\exists! x:A \cdot P(x)) \lor (\exists! x:A \cdot Q(x))}$$

$$\boxed{\exists! \to \exists} \quad \frac{\exists! x:A \cdot P(x)}{\exists x:A \cdot P(x)}$$

$$\boxed{\exists!\text{-E}} \quad \frac{\exists! x:A \cdot P(x) \quad y:A, \ P(y), \ \forall z:A \cdot P(z) \Rightarrow z = y \vdash_y e}{e}$$

$$\boxed{\exists!\text{-I}}\ \frac{a\colon A;\ P(a);\ \forall y\colon A\cdot P(y)\Rightarrow y=a}{\exists!\,x\colon A\cdot P(x)}$$

$$\boxed{\exists!\text{-same}}\ \frac{a\colon A;\ b\colon A;\ P(a);\ P(b);\ \exists!\,x\colon A\cdot P(x)}{a=b}$$

$$\boxed{\exists!\text{-subs}}\ \frac{\exists!\,y\colon A\cdot P(y)\quad x\colon A,\ P(x)\vdash Q(x)}{\exists y\colon A\cdot Q(y)}$$

$$\boxed{\iota\text{-defn}}\ \frac{a\colon A;\ P(a);\ \exists!\,x\colon A\cdot P(x)}{(\iota x\colon A\cdot P(x))=a}$$

$$\boxed{\neg\text{-}\exists!\text{-E}}\ \frac{a\colon A;\ \neg(\exists!\,x\colon A\cdot P(x))}{\neg P(a)\vee \exists z\colon A\cdot P(z)\wedge\neg(z=a)}$$

$$\boxed{\neg\text{-}\exists!\text{-I}}\ \frac{a\colon A;\ b\colon A;\ P(a);\ P(b);\ a\neq b}{\neg(\exists!\,x\colon A\cdot P(x))}$$

$$\boxed{\neg\text{-}\exists!\text{-I-vac}}\ \frac{\neg(\exists x\colon A\cdot P(x))}{\neg(\exists!\,x\colon A\cdot P(x))}$$

14.2.4 Conditionals

Axioms

$$\boxed{\text{condition-false}}\ \frac{c\colon A;\ \neg a}{(\text{if }a\text{ then }b\text{ else }c)=c}\ \textbf{Ax}$$

$$\boxed{\text{condition-true}}\ \frac{b\colon A;\ a}{(\text{if }a\text{ then }b\text{ else }c)=b}\ \textbf{Ax}$$

Derived rules

$$\boxed{\text{condition-true-ident}}\ \frac{a\colon A;\ b\colon A}{(\text{if }a=a\text{ then }b\text{ else }c)=b}$$

$$\boxed{\text{ITE-form}}\ \frac{\delta a;\ b\colon A;\ c\colon A}{(\text{if }a\text{ then }b\text{ else }c)\colon A}$$

$$\boxed{\text{ITE-form-sqt}}\ \frac{\delta a\quad a\vdash b\colon A\quad \neg a\vdash c\colon A}{(\text{if }a\text{ then }b\text{ else }c)\colon A}$$

14.3 Basic type constructors

14.3.1 Union types

Axioms

$$\boxed{\text{|-E}} \;\; \dfrac{\begin{array}{c} u:(A\mid B) \\ a:A \vdash_a P(a) \\ b:B \vdash_b P(b) \end{array}}{P(u)} \;\; \mathbf{Ax}$$

$$\boxed{\text{|-I-left}} \;\; \dfrac{b:B}{b:(A\mid B)} \;\; \mathbf{Ax}$$

$$\boxed{\text{|-I-right}} \;\; \dfrac{a:A}{a:(A\mid B)} \;\; \mathbf{Ax}$$

Derived rules

$$\boxed{\delta\text{-=-I-gen}} \;\; \dfrac{a:A;\ b:B}{\delta(a=b)}$$

$$\boxed{\text{|-ass-left}} \;\; \dfrac{a:(A\mid B)\mid C}{a:A\mid (B\mid C)}$$

$$\boxed{\text{|-ass-right}} \;\; \dfrac{a:A\mid (B\mid C)}{a:(A\mid B)\mid C}$$

$$\boxed{\text{|-comm}} \;\; \dfrac{a:(A\mid B)}{a:(B\mid A)}$$

14.3.2 Cartesian product types

Axioms

$$\boxed{\text{fst-defn}} \;\; \dfrac{(a,b):A\times B}{\text{fst}\,(a,b)=a} \;\; \mathbf{Ax}$$

$$\boxed{\text{fst-form}} \;\; \dfrac{p:A\times B}{\text{fst}\,p:A} \;\; \mathbf{Ax}$$

$$\boxed{\text{pair-defn}} \;\; \dfrac{p:A\times B}{(\text{fst}\,p,\text{snd}\,p)=p} \;\; \mathbf{Ax}$$

$$\boxed{\text{pair-form}} \;\; \dfrac{a:A;\ b:B}{(a,b):A\times B} \;\; \mathbf{Ax}$$

$$\boxed{\text{snd-defn}}\ \frac{(a,b):A\times B}{\text{snd}\ (a,b)=b}\ \textbf{Ax}$$

$$\boxed{\text{snd-form}}\ \frac{p:A\times B}{\text{snd}\ p:B}\ \textbf{Ax}$$

Derived rules

$$\boxed{\text{pair-=-merge}}\ \frac{p_1:A\times B;\ p_2:A\times B;\ \text{fst}\ p_1 = \text{fst}\ p_2 \wedge \text{snd}\ p_1 = \text{snd}\ p_2}{p_1 = p_2}$$

$$\boxed{\text{pair-=-split}}\ \frac{p_1:A\times B;\ p_1 = p_2}{\text{fst}\ p_1 = \text{fst}\ p_2 \wedge \text{snd}\ p_1 = \text{snd}\ p_2}$$

$$\boxed{\text{pair-|-extend-left}}\ \frac{p:A\times B}{p:(A\mid C)\times B}$$

$$\boxed{\text{pair-|-extend-right}}\ \frac{p:A\times B}{p:A\times (B\mid C)}$$

14.3.3 Optional types

Axioms

$$\boxed{\text{nil-form}}\ \frac{}{\text{nil}:[A]}\ \textbf{Ax}$$

$$\boxed{\text{opt-E}}\ \frac{a:[A];\ P(\text{nil});\ b:A \vdash_b P(b)}{P(a)}\ \textbf{Ax}$$

$$\boxed{\text{opt-I}}\ \frac{a:A}{a:[A]}\ \textbf{Ax}$$

Derived rules

$$\boxed{\text{opt-|-extend-left}}\ \frac{a:[A]}{a:[B\mid A]}$$

$$\boxed{\text{opt-|-extend-right}}\ \frac{a:[A]}{a:[A\mid B]}$$

$$\boxed{\text{opt-E-}\neq\text{-nil}}\ \frac{a:[A];\ a\neq\text{nil}}{a:A}$$

14.3.4 Subtypes

Axioms

$$\boxed{\text{subtype-E}} \quad \frac{a: \ll x{:}A \mid P(x) \gg}{P(a)} \quad \textbf{Ax}$$

$$\boxed{\text{subtype-I}} \quad \frac{a{:}A; \ P(a)}{a: \ll x{:}A \mid P(x) \gg} \quad \textbf{Ax}$$

$$\boxed{\text{supertype}} \quad \frac{a: \ll x{:}A \mid P(x) \gg}{a{:}A} \quad \textbf{Ax}$$

Derived rules

$$\boxed{\text{sequent-E-basic}} \quad \frac{a{:}A; \ x{:}A \vdash_x P(x)}{P(a)}$$

$$\boxed{\text{sequent-E-basic-2}} \quad \frac{\begin{array}{c} a{:}A; \ b{:}B \\ x{:}A, \ y{:}B \vdash_{x,y} P(x,y) \end{array}}{P(a,b)}$$

$$\boxed{\text{sequent-E-gen}} \quad \frac{a{:}A; \ P(a); \ x{:}A, \ P(x) \vdash_x Q(x)}{Q(a)}$$

$$\boxed{\text{sequent-E-gen-2}} \quad \frac{\begin{array}{c} a{:}A; \ b{:}B; \ P(a); \ Q(b) \\ x{:}A, \ y{:}B, \ P(x), \ Q(y) \vdash_{x,y} R(x,y) \end{array}}{R(a,b)}$$

$$\boxed{\text{subtype-}|\text{-extend-left}} \quad \frac{a: \ll x{:}A \mid P(x) \gg}{a: \ll x{:}(B \mid A) \mid P(x) \gg}$$

$$\boxed{\text{subtype-}|\text{-extend-right}} \quad \frac{a: \ll x{:}A \mid P(x) \gg}{a: \ll x{:}(A \mid B) \mid P(x) \gg}$$

$$\boxed{\text{subtype-subs}} \quad \frac{\begin{array}{c} a: \ll x{:}A \mid P(x) \gg \\ y{:}A, \ P(y) \vdash_y Q(y) \end{array}}{a: \ll x{:}A \mid Q(x) \gg}$$

14.4 Natural numbers

Axioms

$$\boxed{\text{0-form}} \ \dfrac{}{0:\mathsf{N}} \ \text{Ax}$$

$$\boxed{\text{succ-form}} \ \dfrac{n:\mathsf{N}}{\text{succ}(n):\mathsf{N}} \ \text{Ax}$$

$$\boxed{\text{N-indn}} \ \dfrac{n:\mathsf{N}; \ P(0) \\ k:\mathsf{N}, \ P(k) \vdash_k P(\text{succ}(k))}{P(n)} \ \text{Ax}$$

$$\boxed{\text{succ} \neq 0} \ \dfrac{n:\mathsf{N}}{\text{succ}(n) \neq 0} \ \text{Ax}$$

$$\boxed{\text{succ-1-1}} \ \dfrac{n_1:\mathsf{N}; \ n_2:\mathsf{N}; \ \text{succ}(n_1) = \text{succ}(n_2)}{n_1 = n_2} \ \text{Ax}$$

$$\boxed{\text{+-defn-0-left}} \ \dfrac{n:\mathsf{N}}{0 + n = n} \ \text{Ax}$$

$$\boxed{\text{+-defn-succ-left}} \ \dfrac{n_1:\mathsf{N}; \ n_2:\mathsf{N}}{\text{succ}(n_1) + n_2 = \text{succ}(n_1 + n_2)} \ \text{Ax}$$

$$\boxed{\text{×-defn-0-left}} \ \dfrac{n:\mathsf{N}}{0 \times n = 0} \ \text{Ax}$$

$$\boxed{\text{×-defn-succ-left}} \ \dfrac{n_1:\mathsf{N}; \ n_2:\mathsf{N}}{\text{succ}(n_1) \times n_2 = n_1 \times n_2 + n_2} \ \text{Ax}$$

$$\boxed{\leq\text{-}\leq\text{-defn}} \ \dfrac{i:\mathsf{N}; \ j:\mathsf{N}; \ k:\mathsf{N}}{i \leq j \leq k \Leftrightarrow i \leq j \wedge j \leq k} \ \text{Ax}$$

Definitions

$\mathsf{N}_1 \stackrel{\text{def}}{=} \ll n:\mathsf{N} \mid n \neq 0 \gg$

$n > m \stackrel{\text{def}}{=} \exists k:\mathsf{N}_1 \cdot m + k = n$

$n \geq m \stackrel{\text{def}}{=} \exists k:\mathsf{N} \cdot m + k = n$

14.4 Natural numbers

$$n < m \overset{\text{def}}{=} m > n$$

$$n \leq m \overset{\text{def}}{=} m \geq n$$

Derived rules

$$\boxed{\delta\text{->}} \quad \frac{n_1:\mathsf{N};\ n_2:\mathsf{N}}{\delta(n_1 > n_2)}$$

$$\boxed{\delta\text{-<}} \quad \frac{n_1:\mathsf{N};\ n_2:\mathsf{N}}{\delta(n_1 < n_2)}$$

$$\boxed{\delta\text{-}\leq\text{-}\leq} \quad \frac{i:\mathsf{N};\ j:\mathsf{N};\ k:\mathsf{N}}{\delta(i \leq j \leq k)}$$

$$\boxed{\text{>-irreflexive}} \quad \frac{n:\mathsf{N}}{\neg(n > n)}$$

$$\boxed{\text{>-total-order}} \quad \frac{n_1:\mathsf{N};\ n_2:\mathsf{N}}{n_1 > n_2 \lor n_1 = n_2 \lor n_2 > n_1}$$

$$\boxed{\text{>-trans}} \quad \frac{n_1:\mathsf{N};\ n_2:\mathsf{N};\ n_3:\mathsf{N};\ n_1 > n_2;\ n_2 > n_3}{n_1 > n_3}$$

$$\boxed{\geq\text{-0-I}} \quad \frac{n:\mathsf{N}}{n = 0 \lor n > 0}$$

$$\boxed{\geq\text{-succ-I}} \quad \frac{m:\mathsf{N};\ n:\mathsf{N};\ n > m}{n > \mathrm{succ}(m) \lor n = \mathrm{succ}(m)}$$

$$\boxed{<\vdash \neq} \quad \frac{n_1:\mathsf{N};\ n_2:\mathsf{N};\ n_1 < n_2}{n_1 \neq n_2}$$

$$\boxed{\text{<-irreflexive}} \quad \frac{n:\mathsf{N}}{\neg(n < n)}$$

$$\boxed{\text{<-total-order}} \quad \frac{n_1:\mathsf{N};\ n_2:\mathsf{N}}{n_1 < n_2 \lor n_1 = n_2 \lor n_2 < n_1}$$

$$\boxed{\text{<-trans}} \quad \frac{n_1:\mathsf{N};\ n_2:\mathsf{N};\ n_3:\mathsf{N};\ n_1 < n_2;\ n_2 < n_3}{n_1 < n_3}$$

$$\boxed{\leq\text{-succ-defn}} \quad \frac{n_1:\mathsf{N};\ n_2:\mathsf{N}}{n_1 = \mathrm{succ}(n_2) \lor n_1 \leq n_2 \Leftrightarrow n_1 \leq \mathrm{succ}(n_2)}$$

N-cases $\dfrac{n:\mathsf{N};\ P(0)\quad k:\mathsf{N}\vdash_k P(\mathrm{succ}(k))}{P(n)}$

N_1-E $\dfrac{n:\mathsf{N}_1}{n\neq 0}$

N_1-I $\dfrac{n:\mathsf{N};\ n\neq 0}{n:\mathsf{N}_1}$

N_1-indn $\dfrac{n:\mathsf{N}_1;\ P(\mathrm{succ}(0))\quad k:\mathsf{N}_1,\ P(k)\vdash_k P(\mathrm{succ}(k))}{P(n)}$

N_1-supertype $\dfrac{n:\mathsf{N}_1}{n:\mathsf{N}}$

$\neg$-<-0 $\dfrac{n:\mathsf{N}}{\neg(n<0)}$

+=0-E $\dfrac{n_1:\mathsf{N};\ n_2:\mathsf{N};\ n_1+n_2=0}{n_1=0\wedge n_2=0}$

+-ass $\dfrac{n_1:\mathsf{N};\ n_2:\mathsf{N};\ n_3:\mathsf{N}}{(n_1+n_2)+n_3=n_1+(n_2+n_3)}$

+-comm $\dfrac{n_1:\mathsf{N};\ n_2:\mathsf{N}}{n_1+n_2=n_2+n_1}$

+-defn-0-right $\dfrac{n:\mathsf{N}}{n+0=n}$

+-defn-succ-left-comm $\dfrac{n_1:\mathsf{N};\ n_2:\mathsf{N}}{\mathrm{succ}(n_1+n_2)=\mathrm{succ}(n_1)+n_2}$

+-defn-succ-right $\dfrac{n_1:\mathsf{N};\ n_2:\mathsf{N}}{n_1+\mathrm{succ}(n_2)=\mathrm{succ}(n_1+n_2)}$

+-form $\dfrac{n_1:\mathsf{N};\ n_2:\mathsf{N}}{(n_1+n_2):\mathsf{N}}$

×-ass $\dfrac{n_1:\mathsf{N};\ n_2:\mathsf{N};\ n_3:\mathsf{N}}{(n_1\times n_2)\times n_3=n_1\times(n_2\times n_3)}$

×-comm $\dfrac{n_1:\mathsf{N};\ n_2:\mathsf{N}}{n_1\times n_2=n_2\times n_1}$

14.5 Finite sets

$$\boxed{\times\text{-form}} \quad \frac{n_1\colon \mathsf{N};\ n_2\colon \mathsf{N}}{n_1 \times n_2\colon \mathsf{N}}$$

$$\boxed{0 < n(\mathsf{N}_1)} \quad \frac{n\colon \mathsf{N}_1}{0 < n}$$

$$\boxed{n{=}0 \Leftrightarrow n{\leq}0} \quad \frac{n\colon \mathsf{N}}{n = 0 \Leftrightarrow n \leq 0}$$

$$\boxed{n < \text{succ}(n)} \quad \frac{n\colon \mathsf{N}}{n < \text{succ}(n)}$$

$$\boxed{n_2 < n_1 \vdash 0 < n_1} \quad \frac{n_1\colon \mathsf{N};\ n_2\colon \mathsf{N};\ n_2 < n_1}{0 < n_1}$$

$$\boxed{\text{succ-}{>}\text{-inherit}} \quad \frac{n_1\colon \mathsf{N};\ n_2\colon \mathsf{N};\ n_1 > n_2}{\text{succ}(n_1) > \text{succ}(n_2)}$$

$$\boxed{\text{succ-1-1-}\neq} \quad \frac{n_1\colon \mathsf{N};\ n_2\colon \mathsf{N};\ n_1 \neq n_2}{\text{succ}(n_1) \neq \text{succ}(n_2)} \ \text{Ax}$$

14.5 Finite sets

Axioms

$$\boxed{\{\,\}\text{-form}} \quad \frac{}{\{\,\}\colon A\text{-set}} \ \text{Ax}$$

$$\boxed{\{\,\}\text{-is-empty}} \quad \frac{a\colon A}{a \notin \{\,\}} \ \text{Ax}$$

$$\boxed{\text{add-form}} \quad \frac{a\colon A;\ s\colon A\text{-set}}{\text{add}(a,s)\colon A\text{-set}} \ \text{Ax}$$

$$\boxed{\in\text{-add-defn}} \quad \frac{a\colon A;\ b\colon A;\ s\colon A\text{-set}}{a \in \text{add}(b,s) \Leftrightarrow a = b \vee a \in s} \ \text{Ax}$$

$$\boxed{\text{set-indn}} \quad \frac{s\colon A\text{-set};\ P(\{\,\})\quad a\colon A,\ s'\colon A\text{-set},\ P(s'),\ a \notin s' \vdash_{a,s'} P(\text{add}(a,s'))}{P(s)} \ \text{Ax}$$

$$\boxed{\exists\text{-E-set}} \quad \frac{s\colon A\text{-set};\ \exists x \in s \cdot P(x)\quad y\colon A,\ y \in s,\ P(y) \vdash_y e}{e} \ \text{Ax}$$

$$\boxed{\exists\text{-I-set}}\ \frac{a\colon A;\ s\colon A\text{-set};\ a\in s;\ P(a)}{\exists x\in s\cdot P(x)}\ \mathbf{Ax}$$

$$\boxed{\neg\text{-}\exists\text{-E-set}}\ \frac{a\colon A;\ s\colon A\text{-set};\ a\in s;\ \neg(\exists x\in s\cdot P(x))}{\neg P(a)}\ \mathbf{Ax}$$

$$\boxed{\neg\text{-}\exists\text{-I-set}}\ \frac{s\colon A\text{-set};\ x\colon A,\ x\in s\vdash_x \neg P(x)}{\neg(\exists y\in s\cdot P(y))}\ \mathbf{Ax}$$

$$\boxed{\iota\text{-form-set}}\ \frac{s\colon A\text{-set};\ \exists!\,x\in s\cdot P(x)}{(\iota y\in s\cdot P(y))\colon A}\ \mathbf{Ax}$$

$$\boxed{\iota\text{-I-set}}\ \frac{s\colon A\text{-set};\ \exists!\,x\in s\cdot P(x)}{P(\iota y\in s\cdot P(y))}\ \mathbf{Ax}$$

$$\boxed{\subseteq\text{-defn}}\ \frac{s_1\colon A\text{-set};\ s_2\colon A\text{-set}}{s_1\subseteq s_2\Leftrightarrow \forall a\in s_1\cdot a\in s_2}\ \mathbf{Ax}$$

$$\boxed{\subset\text{-defn}}\ \frac{s_1\colon A\text{-set};\ s_2\colon A\text{-set}}{s_1\subset s_2\Leftrightarrow s_1\subseteq s_2\wedge s_1\neq s_2}\ \mathbf{Ax}$$

$$\boxed{=\text{-set-defn}}\ \frac{s_1\colon A\text{-set};\ s_2\colon A\text{-set}}{s_1=s_2\Leftrightarrow s_1\subseteq s_2\wedge s_2\subseteq s_1}\ \mathbf{Ax}$$

$$\boxed{\text{card-defn-}\{\,\}}\ \frac{}{\operatorname{card}\{\,\}=0}\ \mathbf{Ax}$$

$$\boxed{\text{card-defn-add}}\ \frac{a\colon A;\ s\colon A\text{-set};\ a\notin s}{\operatorname{card}\,add(a,s)=\operatorname{succ}(\operatorname{card} s)}\ \mathbf{Ax}$$

$$\boxed{\cup\text{-form}}\ \frac{s_1\colon A\text{-set};\ s_2\colon A\text{-set}}{s_1\cup s_2\colon A\text{-set}}\ \mathbf{Ax}$$

$$\boxed{\in\text{-}\cup\text{-defn}}\ \frac{a\colon A;\ s_1\colon A\text{-set};\ s_2\colon A\text{-set}}{a\in s_1\cup s_2\Leftrightarrow a\in s_1\vee a\in s_2}\ \mathbf{Ax}$$

$$\boxed{\cap\text{-form}}\ \frac{s_1\colon A\text{-set};\ s_2\colon A\text{-set}}{s_1\cap s_2\colon A\text{-set}}\ \mathbf{Ax}$$

$$\boxed{\in\text{-}\cap\text{-defn}}\ \frac{a\colon A;\ s_1\colon A\text{-set};\ s_2\colon A\text{-set}}{a\in s_1\cap s_2\Leftrightarrow a\in s_1\wedge a\in s_2}\ \mathbf{Ax}$$

$$\boxed{\text{diff-form}}\ \frac{s_1\colon A\text{-set};\ s_2\colon A\text{-set}}{s_1\setminus s_2\colon A\text{-set}}\ \mathbf{Ax}$$

$$\boxed{\in\text{-diff-defn}}\ \frac{a\colon A;\ s_1\colon A\text{-set};\ s_2\colon A\text{-set}}{a\in s_1\setminus s_2\Leftrightarrow a\in s_1\wedge a\notin s_2}\ \mathbf{Ax}$$

14.5 Finite sets

$$\boxed{\bigcup\text{-form}}\ \frac{s:A\text{-set-set}}{\bigcup s:A\text{-set}}\ \text{Ax}$$

$$\boxed{\in\text{-}\bigcup\text{-defn}}\ \frac{a:A;\ s:A\text{-set-set}}{a\in\bigcup s\Leftrightarrow \exists t\in s\cdot a\in t}\ \text{Ax}$$

$$\boxed{\bigcap\text{-form}}\ \frac{s:A\text{-set-set};\ s\neq\{\}}{\bigcap s:A\text{-set}}\ \text{Ax}$$

$$\boxed{\in\text{-}\bigcap\text{-defn}}\ \frac{a:A;\ s:A\text{-set-set};\ s\neq\{\}}{a\in\bigcap s\Leftrightarrow \forall t\in s\cdot a\in t}\ \text{Ax}$$

$$\boxed{\text{pow-form}}\ \frac{s:A\text{-set}}{\mathcal{F}s:A\text{-set-set}}\ \text{Ax}$$

$$\boxed{\in\text{-pow-defn}}\ \frac{s_1:A\text{-set};\ s_2:A\text{-set}}{s_1\in\mathcal{F}s_2\Leftrightarrow s_1\subseteq s_2}\ \text{Ax}$$

$$\boxed{\text{set-comp-form}}\ \frac{\begin{array}{c}\forall x:A\cdot \delta P(x)\\ x:A,\ P(x)\vdash_x f(x):B\\ \exists s:B\text{-set}\cdot \forall y:A\cdot P(y)\Rightarrow f(y)\in s\end{array}}{\{f(x)\mid x:A\cdot P(x)\}:B\text{-set}}\ \text{Ax}$$

$$\boxed{\in\text{-set-comp-defn}}\ \frac{\begin{array}{c}b:B\\ \forall x:A\cdot \delta P(x)\\ x:A,\ P(x)\vdash_x f(x):B\\ \exists s:B\text{-set}\cdot \forall y:A\cdot P(y)\Rightarrow f(y)\in s\end{array}}{b\in\{f(x)\mid x:A\cdot P(x)\}\Leftrightarrow \exists a:A\cdot P(a)\wedge b=f(a)}\ \text{Ax}$$

$$\boxed{\text{set-comp-defn-set}}\ \frac{\begin{array}{c}s:A\text{-set}\\ \forall x\in s\cdot \delta P(x)\\ x:A,\ x\in s,\ P(x)\vdash_x f(x):B\\ \exists t:B\text{-set}\cdot \forall y\in s\cdot P(y)\Rightarrow f(y)\in t\end{array}}{\{f(x)\mid x\in s\cdot P(x)\}=\{f(x)\mid x:A\cdot x\in s\wedge P(x)\}}\ \text{Ax}$$

Definitions

$a\notin s\ \stackrel{\text{def}}{=}\ \neg(a\in s)$

$\forall x\in s\cdot P(x)\ \stackrel{\text{def}}{=}\ \neg\exists x\in s\cdot \neg P(x)$

$\exists!x\in s\cdot P(x)\ \stackrel{\text{def}}{=}\ \exists x\in s\cdot P(x)\wedge \forall y\in s\cdot P(y)\Rightarrow y=x$

$\{a\}\ \stackrel{\text{def}}{=}\ add(a,\{\})$

$$\{x{:}A \mid P(x)\} \stackrel{\text{def}}{=} \{x \mid x{:}A \cdot P(x)\}$$

$$\{f(x) \mid x \in s\} \stackrel{\text{def}}{=} \{f(x) \mid x \in s \cdot \text{true}\}$$

$$\{f(x) \mid x{:}A\} \stackrel{\text{def}}{=} \{f(x) \mid x{:}A \cdot \text{true}\}$$

$$\{i,\ldots,j\} \stackrel{\text{def}}{=} \{n{:}\mathbb{N} \mid i \leq n \leq j\}$$

Derived Rules

$$\boxed{\{\}\text{-is-subset}} \quad \frac{s{:}A\text{-set}}{\{\} \subseteq s}$$

$$\boxed{\{a\}\text{-comp}} \quad \frac{a{:}A}{\{a\} = \{x{:}A \mid x = a\}}$$

$$\boxed{\{a\}\text{-form}} \quad \frac{a{:}A}{\{a\}{:}A\text{-set}}$$

$$\boxed{\forall \to \forall\text{-set}} \quad \frac{s{:}A\text{-set};\ \forall x{:}A \cdot x \in s \Rightarrow P(x)}{\forall x \in s \cdot P(x)}$$

$$\boxed{\forall\text{-E-set}} \quad \frac{a{:}A;\ s{:}A\text{-set};\ a \in s;\ \forall x \in s \cdot P(x)}{P(a)}$$

$$\boxed{\forall\text{-I-set}} \quad \frac{s{:}A\text{-set};\ y{:}A,\ y \in s \vdash_y P(y)}{\forall x \in s \cdot P(x)}$$

$$\boxed{\forall\text{-set} \to \forall} \quad \frac{s{:}A\text{-set};\ \forall x \in s \cdot P(x)}{\forall x{:}A \cdot x \in s \Rightarrow P(x)}$$

$$\boxed{\delta\text{-}\forall\text{-inherit-set}} \quad \frac{s{:}A\text{-set};\ y{:}A,\ y \in s \vdash_y \delta P(y)}{\delta(\forall x \in s \cdot P(x))}$$

$$\boxed{\delta\text{-}\exists\text{-inherit-set}} \quad \frac{s{:}A\text{-set};\ x{:}A,\ x \in s \vdash_x \delta P(x)}{\delta(\exists x \in s \cdot P(x))}$$

$$\boxed{\delta\text{-}\in} \quad \frac{a{:}A;\ s{:}A\text{-set}}{\delta(a \in s)}$$

$$\boxed{\delta\text{-}\cap\text{-empty}} \quad \frac{s_1{:}A\text{-set};\ s_2{:}A\text{-set}}{\delta(s_1 \cap s_2 = \{\})}$$

$$\boxed{\delta\text{-}\subseteq} \quad \frac{s_1{:}A\text{-set};\ s_2{:}A\text{-set}}{\delta(s_1 \subseteq s_2)}$$

14.5 Finite sets

$$\boxed{\delta\text{-empty}} \quad \frac{s : A\text{-set}}{\delta(s = \{\,\})}$$

$$\boxed{=\text{-}\{\,\}\text{-I}} \quad \frac{s : A\text{-set} \\ a : A \vdash_a a \notin s}{s = \{\,\}}$$

$$\boxed{=\text{-set-E}} \quad \frac{s_1 : A\text{-set};\ s_1 = s_2}{(s_1 \subseteq s_2) \land (s_2 \subseteq s_1)}$$

$$\boxed{=\text{-set-I-}\subseteq} \quad \frac{s_1 : A\text{-set};\ s_2 : A\text{-set};\ s_1 \subseteq s_2;\ s_2 \subseteq s_1}{s_1 = s_2}$$

$$\boxed{=\text{-set-I-sqt}} \quad \frac{\begin{array}{c} s_1 : A\text{-set};\ s_2 : A\text{-set} \\ a : A,\ a \in s_1 \vdash_a a \in s_2 \\ b : A,\ b \in s_2 \vdash_b b \in s_1 \end{array}}{s_1 = s_2}$$

$$\boxed{\exists \to \exists\text{-set}} \quad \frac{s : A\text{-set};\ \exists x : A \cdot x \in s \land P(x)}{\exists x \in s \cdot P(x)}$$

$$\boxed{\exists\text{-set} \to \exists} \quad \frac{s : A\text{-set};\ \exists x \in s \cdot P(x)}{\exists x : A \cdot x \in s \land P(x)}$$

$$\boxed{\exists!\text{-E-set}} \quad \frac{\begin{array}{c} s : A\text{-set};\ \exists! x \in s \cdot P(x) \\ y : A,\ y \in s,\ P(y),\ \forall x \in s \cdot P(x) \Rightarrow x = y \vdash_y e \end{array}}{e}$$

$$\boxed{\exists!\text{-I-set}} \quad \frac{a : A;\ s : A\text{-set};\ a \in s;\ P(a);\ \forall y \in s \cdot P(y) \Rightarrow y = a}{\exists! x \in s \cdot P(x)}$$

$$\boxed{\in\text{-}\{a\}\text{-E}} \quad \frac{a : A;\ b : A;\ b \in \{a\}}{b = a}$$

$$\boxed{\in\text{-}\{a\}\text{-I}} \quad \frac{a : A}{a \in \{a\}}$$

$$\boxed{\in\text{-}\{a\}\text{-I-=}} \quad \frac{a : A;\ b = a}{b \in \{a\}}$$

$$\boxed{\in\text{-}\cap\text{-E}} \quad \frac{a : A;\ s_1 : A\text{-set};\ s_2 : A\text{-set};\ a \in s_1 \cap s_2}{a \in s_1 \land a \in s_2}$$

$$\boxed{\in\text{-}\cap\text{-E-left}} \quad \frac{a : A;\ s_1 : A\text{-set};\ s_2 : A\text{-set};\ a \in s_1 \cap s_2}{a \in s_2}$$

$\in\text{-}\cap\text{-E-right}$ $\dfrac{a:A;\ s_1:A\text{-set};\ s_2:A\text{-set};\ a \in s_1 \cap s_2}{a \in s_1}$

$\in\text{-}\cap\text{-I}$ $\dfrac{a:A;\ s_1:A\text{-set};\ s_2:A\text{-set};\ a \in s_1;\ a \in s_2}{a \in s_1 \cap s_2}$

$\in\text{-}\notin\text{-contr}$ $\dfrac{a:A;\ b:A;\ s:A\text{-set};\ a \in s;\ b \notin s}{a \neq b}$

$\in\text{-}\vee\text{-}\notin$ $\dfrac{a:A;\ s:A\text{-set}}{a \in s \vee a \notin s}$

$\in\text{-}\cup\text{-E}$ $\dfrac{a:A;\ s_1:A\text{-set};\ s_2:A\text{-set};\ a \in s_1 \cup s_2}{a \in s_1 \vee a \in s_2}$

$\in\text{-}\cup\text{-I}$ $\dfrac{a:A;\ s_1:A\text{-set};\ s_2:A\text{-set};\ a \in s_1 \vee a \in s_2}{a \in s_1 \cup s_2}$

$\in\text{-}\cup\text{-I-left}$ $\dfrac{a:A;\ s_1:A\text{-set};\ s_2:A\text{-set};\ a \in s_2}{a \in s_1 \cup s_2}$

$\in\text{-}\cup\text{-I-right}$ $\dfrac{a:A;\ s_1:A\text{-set};\ s_2:A\text{-set};\ a \in s_1}{a \in s_1 \cup s_2}$

$\in\text{-}\bigcup\text{-E}$ $\dfrac{a:A;\ s:A\text{-set-set};\ a \in \bigcup s}{\exists t \in s \cdot a \in t}$

$\in\text{-}\bigcup\text{-I}$ $\dfrac{a:A;\ s:A\text{-set-set};\ \exists t \in s \cdot a \in t}{a \in \bigcup s}$

$\in\text{-add-E}$ $\dfrac{a:A;\ b:A;\ s:A\text{-set};\ a \in add(b,s)}{a = b \vee a \in s}$

$\in\text{-add-I}$ $\dfrac{a:A;\ b:A;\ s:A\text{-set};\ a = b \vee a \in s}{a \in add(b,s)}$

$\in\text{-add-I-elem}$ $\dfrac{a:A;\ s:A\text{-set}}{a \in add(a,s)}$

$\in\text{-add-I-elem-=}$ $\dfrac{a:A;\ s:A\text{-set};\ a = b}{a \in add(b,s)}$

$\in\text{-add-I-set}$ $\dfrac{a:A;\ b:A;\ s:A\text{-set};\ a \in s}{a \in add(b,s)}$

$\in\text{-cases}$ $\dfrac{a:A;\ s:A\text{-set};\ a \in s \vdash e;\ a \notin s \vdash e}{e}$

14.5 Finite sets

$$\boxed{\in\text{-diff-E}}\ \frac{a\colon A;\ s_1\colon A\text{-set};\ s_2\colon A\text{-set};\ a\in s_1\setminus s_2}{a\in s_1 \wedge a\notin s_2}$$

$$\boxed{\in\text{-diff-E-left}}\ \frac{a\colon A;\ s_1\colon A\text{-set};\ s_2\colon A\text{-set};\ a\in s_1\setminus s_2}{a\notin s_2}$$

$$\boxed{\in\text{-diff-E-right}}\ \frac{a\colon A;\ s_1\colon A\text{-set};\ s_2\colon A\text{-set};\ a\in s_1\setminus s_2}{a\in s_1}$$

$$\boxed{\in\text{-diff-I}}\ \frac{a\colon A;\ s_1\colon A\text{-set};\ s_2\colon A\text{-set};\ a\in s_1;\ a\notin s_2}{a\in s_1\setminus s_2}$$

$$\boxed{\in\text{-set-comp-E}}\ \frac{\begin{array}{c} b\colon B;\ \forall x\colon A\cdot \delta P(x) \\ x\colon A,\ P(x) \vdash_{\!\!x} f(x)\colon B \\ \exists s\colon B\text{-set}\cdot \forall y\colon A\cdot P(y) \Rightarrow f(y)\in s \\ b\in \{f(x)\mid x\colon A\cdot P(x)\} \end{array}}{\exists a\colon A\cdot P(a) \wedge b = f(a)}$$

$$\boxed{\in\text{-set-comp-I}}\ \frac{\begin{array}{c} b\colon B;\ \forall x\colon A\cdot \delta P(x) \\ x\colon A,\ P(x) \vdash_{\!\!x} f(x)\colon B \\ \exists s\colon B\text{-set}\cdot \forall y\colon A\cdot P(y) \Rightarrow f(y)\in s \\ \exists a\colon A\cdot P(a) \wedge b = f(a) \end{array}}{b\in \{f(x)\mid x\colon A\cdot P(x)\}}$$

$$\boxed{\in\text{-set-comp-I-}f(a)}\ \frac{\begin{array}{c} a\colon A;\ P(a) \\ \forall x\colon A\cdot \delta P(x) \\ x\colon A,\ P(x)\vdash_{\!\!x} f(x)\colon B \\ \exists s\colon B\text{-set}\cdot \forall y\colon A\cdot P(y)\Rightarrow f(y)\in s \end{array}}{f(a)\in \{f(x)\mid x\colon A\cdot P(x)\}}$$

$$\boxed{\in\text{-interval-defn}}\ \frac{i\colon \mathbb{N};\ j\colon \mathbb{N};\ k\colon \mathbb{N}}{k\in \{i,\ldots,j\} \Leftrightarrow i\le k\le j}$$

$$\boxed{\in\text{-those-defn}}\ \frac{\begin{array}{c} a\colon A \\ \forall x\colon A\cdot \delta P(x) \\ \exists s\colon A\text{-set}\cdot \forall y\colon A\cdot P(y)\Rightarrow y\in s \end{array}}{a\in \{y\colon A\mid P(y)\} \Leftrightarrow P(a)}$$

$$\boxed{\in\text{-those-E}}\ \frac{\begin{array}{c} a\colon A;\ \forall x\colon A\cdot \delta P(x) \\ \exists s\colon A\text{-set}\cdot \forall y\colon A\cdot P(y)\Rightarrow y\in s \\ a\in \{x\colon A\mid P(x)\} \end{array}}{P(a)}$$

$$\boxed{\in\text{-those-I}}\ \frac{\begin{array}{c} a\colon A;\ P(a);\ \forall x\colon A\cdot \delta P(x) \\ \exists s\colon A\text{-set}\cdot \forall y\colon A\cdot P(y)\Rightarrow y\in s \end{array}}{a\in \{x\colon A\mid P(x)\}}$$

$\boxed{\cap\text{-}\{a\}\text{-defn-}\in}\ \dfrac{a\colon A;\ s\colon A\text{-set};\ a\in s}{\{a\}\cap s=\{a\}}$

$\boxed{\cap\text{-}\{a\}\text{-empty-E}}\ \dfrac{a\colon A;\ s\colon A\text{-set};\ \{a\}\cap s=\{\,\}}{a\notin s}$

$\boxed{\cap\text{-}\cup\text{-dist-left}}\ \dfrac{s_1\colon A\text{-set};\ s_2\colon A\text{-set};\ s_3\colon A\text{-set}}{s_1\cap(s_2\cup s_3)=(s_1\cap s_2)\cup(s_1\cap s_3)}$

$\boxed{\cap\text{-}\cup\text{-dist-right}}\ \dfrac{s_1\colon A\text{-set};\ s_2\colon A\text{-set};\ s_3\colon A\text{-set}}{(s_1\cup s_2)\cap s_3=(s_1\cap s_3)\cup(s_2\cap s_3)}$

$\boxed{\cap\text{-}\cup\text{-empty-E-left}}\ \dfrac{s_1\colon A\text{-set};\ s_2\colon A\text{-set};\ s_3\colon A\text{-set};\ (s_1\cup s_2)\cap s_3=\{\,\}}{s_2\cap s_3=\{\,\}}$

$\boxed{\cap\text{-}\cup\text{-empty-E-right}}\ \dfrac{s_1\colon A\text{-set};\ s_2\colon A\text{-set};\ s_3\colon A\text{-set};\ (s_1\cup s_2)\cap s_3=\{\,\}}{s_1\cap s_3=\{\,\}}$

$\boxed{\cap\text{-}\cup\text{-left-empty-I}}\ \dfrac{s_1\colon A\text{-set};\ s_2\colon A\text{-set};\ s_3\colon A\text{-set};\ s_1\cap s_3=\{\,\};\ s_2\cap s_3=\{\,\}}{(s_1\cup s_2)\cap s_3=\{\,\}}$

$\boxed{\cap\text{-}\cup\text{-right-empty-I}}\ \dfrac{s_1\colon A\text{-set};\ s_2\colon A\text{-set};\ s_3\colon A\text{-set};\ s_1\cap s_2=\{\,\};\ s_1\cap s_3=\{\,\}}{s_1\cap(s_2\cup s_3)=\{\,\}}$

$\boxed{\cap\text{-ass}}\ \dfrac{s_1\colon A\text{-set};\ s_2\colon A\text{-set};\ s_3\colon A\text{-set}}{(s_1\cap s_2)\cap s_3=s_1\cap(s_2\cap s_3)}$

$\boxed{\cap\text{-comm}}\ \dfrac{s_1\colon A\text{-set};\ s_2\colon A\text{-set}}{s_1\cap s_2=s_2\cap s_1}$

$\boxed{\cap\text{-comp}}\ \dfrac{s_1\colon A\text{-set};\ s_2\colon A\text{-set}}{s_1\cap s_2=\{x\colon A\mid x\in s_1\wedge x\in s_2\}}$

$\boxed{\cap\text{-defn-}\{\,\}\text{-left}}\ \dfrac{s\colon A\text{-set}}{\{\,\}\cap s=\{\,\}}$

$\boxed{\cap\text{-defn-}\{\,\}\text{-right}}\ \dfrac{s\colon A\text{-set}}{s\cap\{\,\}=\{\,\}}$

$\boxed{\cap\text{-add-I-}\in}\ \dfrac{a\colon A;\ s_1\colon A\text{-set};\ s_2\colon A\text{-set};\ a\in s_2}{add(a,s_1)\cap s_2=add(a,s_1\cap s_2)}$

$\boxed{\cap\text{-add-I-}\notin}\ \dfrac{a\colon A;\ s_1\colon A\text{-set};\ s_2\colon A\text{-set};\ a\notin s_2}{add(a,s_1)\cap s_2=s_1\cap s_2}$

$\boxed{\cap\text{-I-right-}\subseteq}\ \dfrac{s_1\colon A\text{-set};\ s_2\colon A\text{-set};\ s_1\subseteq s_2}{s_1\cap s_2=s_1}$

14.5 Finite sets

$$\boxed{\cap\text{-self}}\ \frac{s\colon A\text{-set}}{s\cap s=s}$$

$$\boxed{\neg\text{-add-}\subseteq\text{-I-elem}}\ \frac{a\colon A;\ s_1\colon A\text{-set};\ s_2\colon A\text{-set};\ a\notin s_2}{\neg(add(a,s_1)\subseteq s_2)}$$

$$\boxed{\neg\text{-add-}\subseteq\text{-I-set}}\ \frac{a\colon A;\ s_1\colon A\text{-set};\ s_2\colon A\text{-set};\ \neg(s_1\subseteq s_2)}{\neg(add(a,s_1)\subseteq s_2)}$$

$$\boxed{\notin\text{-}\{a\}\text{-I}}\ \frac{a\colon A;\ b\colon B;\ a\neq b}{a\notin\{b\}}$$

$$\boxed{\notin\text{-}\cap\text{-E}}\ \frac{a\colon A;\ s_1\colon A\text{-set};\ s_2\colon A\text{-set};\ a\notin s_1\cap s_2}{a\notin s_1\vee a\notin s_2}$$

$$\boxed{\notin\text{-}\cap\text{-I-left}}\ \frac{a\colon A;\ s_1\colon A\text{-set};\ s_2\colon A\text{-set};\ a\notin s_2}{a\notin s_1\cap s_2}$$

$$\boxed{\notin\text{-}\cap\text{-I-right}}\ \frac{a\colon A;\ s_1\colon A\text{-set};\ s_2\colon A\text{-set};\ a\notin s_1}{a\notin s_1\cap s_2}$$

$$\boxed{\notin\text{-}\cup\text{-E}}\ \frac{a\colon A;\ si\colon A\text{-set};\ s_2\colon A\text{-set};\ a\notin s_1\cup s_2}{a\notin s_1\wedge a\notin s_2}$$

$$\boxed{\notin\text{-}\cup\text{-E-left}}\ \frac{a\colon A;\ s_1\colon A\text{-set};\ s_2\colon A\text{-set};\ a\notin s_1\cup s_2}{a\notin s_2}$$

$$\boxed{\notin\text{-}\cup\text{-E-right}}\ \frac{a\colon A;\ s_1\colon A\text{-set};\ s_2\colon A\text{-set};\ a\notin s_1\cup s_2}{a\notin s_1}$$

$$\boxed{\notin\text{-}\cup\text{-I}}\ \frac{a\colon A;\ s_1\colon A\text{-set};\ s_2\colon A\text{-set};\ a\notin s_1;\ a\notin s_2}{a\notin s_1\cup s_2}$$

$$\boxed{\notin\text{-add-E}}\ \frac{a\colon A;\ b\colon A;\ s\colon A\text{-set};\ a\notin add(b,s)}{a\neq b\wedge a\notin s}$$

$$\boxed{\notin\text{-add-E-left}}\ \frac{a\colon A;\ b\colon A;\ s\colon A\text{-set};\ a\notin add(b,s)}{a\notin s}$$

$$\boxed{\notin\text{-add-E-right}}\ \frac{a\colon A;\ b\colon A;\ s\colon A\text{-set};\ a\notin add(b,s)}{a\neq b}$$

$$\boxed{\notin\text{-add-I}}\ \frac{a\colon A;\ b\colon A;\ s\colon A\text{-set};\ a\neq b;\ a\notin s}{a\notin add(b,s)}$$

$$\boxed{\notin\text{-diff-E}}\ \frac{a\colon A;\ s_1\colon A\text{-set};\ s_2\colon A\text{-set};\ a\notin s_1\setminus s_2}{a\notin s_1\vee a\in s_2}$$

$\notin$-diff-I-left $\dfrac{a:A;\ s_1:A\text{-set};\ s_2:A\text{-set};\ a\in s_2}{a\notin s_1\setminus s_2}$

$\notin$-diff-I-right $\dfrac{a:A;\ s_1:A\text{-set};\ s_2:A\text{-set};\ a\notin s_1}{a\notin s_1\setminus s_2}$

$\notin$-subset-I $\dfrac{a:A;\ s_1:A\text{-set};\ s_2:A\text{-set};\ s_1\subseteq s_2;\ a\notin s_2}{a\notin s_1}$

$\notin$-those-E $\dfrac{\begin{array}{c}a:A;\ \forall x:A\cdot \delta P(x)\\ \exists s:A\text{-set}\cdot \forall y:A\cdot P(y)\Rightarrow y\in s\\ a\notin \{x:A\mid P(x)\}\end{array}}{\neg P(a)}$

$\notin$-those-I $\dfrac{\begin{array}{c}a:A;\ \neg P(a);\ \forall x:A\cdot \delta P(x)\\ \exists s:A\text{-set}\cdot \forall y:A\cdot P(y)\Rightarrow y\in s\end{array}}{a\notin \{x:A\mid P(x)\}}$

$\subseteq$-add-add-I $\dfrac{a:A;\ b:A;\ s:A\text{-set}}{add(a,add(b,s))\subseteq add(b,add(a,s))}$

$\subseteq$-E $\dfrac{a:A;\ s_1:A\text{-set};\ s_2:A\text{-set};\ a\in s_1;\ s_1\subseteq s_2}{a\in s_2}$

$\subseteq$-I $\dfrac{\begin{array}{c}s_1:A\text{-set};\ s_2:A\text{-set}\\ a:A,\ a\in s_1\vdash_a a\in s_2\end{array}}{s_1\subseteq s_2}$

$\subseteq$-self $\dfrac{s:A\text{-set}}{s\subseteq s}$

$\subseteq$-trans $\dfrac{s_1:A\text{-set};\ s_2:A\text{-set};\ s_3:A\text{-set};\ s_1\subseteq s_2;\ s_2\subseteq s_3}{s_1\subseteq s_3}$

$\cup\text{-}\cap$-dist-left $\dfrac{s_1:A\text{-set};\ s_2:A\text{-set};\ s_3:A\text{-set}}{s_1\cup(s_2\cap s_3)=(s_1\cup s_2)\cap(s_1\cup s_3)}$

$\cup\text{-}\cap$-dist-right $\dfrac{s_1:A\text{-set};\ s_2:A\text{-set};\ s_3:A\text{-set}}{(s_1\cap s_2)\cup s_3=(s_1\cup s_3)\cap(s_2\cup s_3)}$

$\cup$-add-left-I $\dfrac{a:A;\ s_1:A\text{-set};\ s_2:A\text{-set}}{add(a,s_1)\cup s_2=add(a,s_1\cup s_2)}$

$\cup$-add-right-I $\dfrac{a:A;\ s_1:A\text{-set};\ s_2:A\text{-set}}{s_1\cup add(a,s_2)=add(a,s_1\cup s_2)}$

$\cup$-ass $\dfrac{s_1:A\text{-set};\ s_2:A\text{-set};\ s_3:A\text{-set}}{(s_1\cup s_2)\cup s_3=s_1\cup(s_2\cup s_3)}$

14.5 Finite sets

$$\boxed{\cup\text{-comm}}\ \frac{s_1: A\text{-set};\ s_2: A\text{-set}}{s_1 \cup s_2 = s_2 \cup s_1}$$

$$\boxed{\cup\text{-comp}}\ \frac{s_1: A\text{-set};\ s_2: A\text{-set}}{s_1 \cup s_2 = \{x:A \mid x \in s_1 \vee x \in s_2\}}$$

$$\boxed{\cup\text{-defn-}\{\}\text{-left}}\ \frac{s: A\text{-set}}{\{\} \cup s = s}$$

$$\boxed{\cup\text{-defn-}\{\}\text{-left-rev}}\ \frac{s: A\text{-set}}{s = \{\} \cup s}$$

$$\boxed{\cup\text{-defn-}\{\}\text{-right}}\ \frac{s: A\text{-set}}{s \cup \{\} = s}$$

$$\boxed{\cup\text{-defn-}\{\}\text{-right-rev}}\ \frac{s: A\text{-set}}{s = s \cup \{\}}$$

$$\boxed{\cup\text{-defn-those}}\ \frac{\begin{array}{c}\forall x: A \cdot \delta P(x) \\ \forall w: A \cdot \delta Q(w) \\ \exists s: A\text{-set} \cdot \forall y: A \cdot P(y) \Rightarrow y \in s \\ \exists t: A\text{-set} \cdot \forall z: A \cdot Q(z) \Rightarrow z \in t \end{array}}{\{z:A \mid P(z) \vee Q(z)\} = \{x:A \mid P(x)\} \cup \{y:A \mid Q(y)\}}$$

$$\boxed{\cup\text{-I-left-}\subseteq}\ \frac{s_1: A\text{-set};\ s_2: A\text{-set};\ s_1 \subseteq s_2}{s_1 \cup s_2 = s_2}$$

$$\boxed{\cup\text{ of subsets is subset}}\ \frac{s_1: A\text{-set};\ s_2: A\text{-set};\ s_3: A\text{-set};\ s_1 \subseteq s_3;\ s_2 \subseteq s_3}{(s_1 \cup s_2) \subseteq s_3}$$

$$\boxed{\cup\text{-self}}\ \frac{s: A\text{-set}}{s \cup s = s}$$

$$\boxed{\bigcup\text{-}\cup\text{-dist}}\ \frac{s_1: A\text{-set-set};\ s_2: A\text{-set-set}}{\bigcup(s_1 \cup s_2) = (\bigcup s_1) \cup (\bigcup s_2)}$$

$$\boxed{\bigcup\text{-comp}}\ \frac{s: A\text{-set-set}}{\bigcup s = \{x:A \mid \exists xs \in s \cdot x \in xs\}}$$

$$\boxed{\bigcup\text{-defn-}\{\}}\ \frac{}{\bigcup\{\} = \{\}}$$

$$\boxed{\bigcup\text{-defn-}\{a\}}\ \frac{s: A\text{-set}}{\bigcup\{s\} = s}$$

$$\boxed{\bigcup\text{-defn-add}}\ \frac{s_1: A\text{-set};\ s_2: A\text{-set-set}}{\bigcup add(s_1, s_2) = s_1 \cup \bigcup s_2}$$

$\boxed{\text{add-}\subseteq\text{-E-left}}\ \dfrac{a\!:\!A;\ s_1\!:\!A\text{-set};\ s_2\!:\!A\text{-set};\ add(a,s_1) \subseteq s_2}{s_1 \subseteq s_2}$

$\boxed{\text{add-}\subseteq\text{-E-right}}\ \dfrac{a\!:\!A;\ s_1\!:\!A\text{-set};\ s_2\!:\!A\text{-set};\ add(a,s_1) \subseteq s_2}{a \in s_2}$

$\boxed{\text{add-}\subseteq\text{-I}}\ \dfrac{a\!:\!A;\ s_1\!:\!A\text{-set};\ s_2\!:\!A\text{-set};\ a \in s_2;\ s_1 \subseteq s_2}{add(a,s_1) \subseteq s_2}$

$\boxed{\text{add}\to\cup}\ \dfrac{a\!:\!A;\ s\!:\!A\text{-set}}{add(a,s) = \{a\} \cup s}$

$\boxed{\text{add-abs}}\ \dfrac{a\!:\!A;\ s\!:\!A\text{-set}}{add(a, add(a,s)) = add(a,s)}$

$\boxed{\text{add-add-form}}\ \dfrac{a\!:\!A;\ b\!:\!A;\ s\!:\!A\text{-set}}{add(a, add(b,s))\!:\!A\text{-set}}$

$\boxed{\text{add-comm}}\ \dfrac{a\!:\!A;\ b\!:\!A;\ s\!:\!A\text{-set}}{add(a, add(b,s)) = add(b, add(a,s))}$

$\boxed{\text{add-comp}}\ \dfrac{a\!:\!A;\ s\!:\!A\text{-set}}{add(a,s) = \{x\!:\!A \mid x = a \vee x \in s\}}$

$\boxed{\text{add-diff-}\subseteq\text{-I}}\ \dfrac{a\!:\!A;\ s_1\!:\!A\text{-set};\ s_2\!:\!A\text{-set}}{(add(a,s_1) \setminus s_2) \subseteq add(a, (s_1 \setminus s_2))}$

$\boxed{\text{add-reduction}}\ \dfrac{a\!:\!A;\ s\!:\!A\text{-set};\ a \in s}{add(a,s) = s}$

$\boxed{\text{card=0-I}}\ \dfrac{s = \{\,\}}{\text{card}\,s = 0}$

$\boxed{\text{card}\neq\text{0-E}}\ \dfrac{s\!:\!A\text{-set};\ \text{card}\,s \neq 0}{s \neq \{\,\}}$

$\boxed{\text{card-defn-}\cup}\ \dfrac{s_1\!:\!A\text{-set};\ s_2\!:\!A\text{-set}}{\text{card}\,(s_1 \cup s_2) = (\text{card}\,s_1 + \text{card}\,s_2) - \text{card}\,(s_1 \cap s_2)}$

$\boxed{\text{card-form}}\ \dfrac{s\!:\!A\text{-set}}{\text{card}\,s\ :\ \mathbf{N}}$

$\boxed{\text{diff-=-}\{\,\}\text{-defn}}\ \dfrac{s_1\!:\!A\text{-set};\ s_2\!:\!A\text{-set}}{(s_1 \setminus s_2 = \{\,\}) \Leftrightarrow (s_1 \subseteq s_2)}$

$\boxed{\text{diff-}\cap\text{-deM}}\ \dfrac{s_1\!:\!A\text{-set};\ s_2\!:\!A\text{-set};\ s_3\!:\!A\text{-set}}{s_1 \setminus (s_2 \cap s_3) = (s_1 \setminus s_2) \cup (s_1 \setminus s_3)}$

14.5 Finite sets

$$\boxed{\text{diff-}\cap\text{-I}}\ \frac{s_1\colon A\text{-set};\ s_2\colon A\text{-set};\ s_3\colon A\text{-set}}{(s_1 \setminus s_2) \cap s_3 = (s_1 \cap s_3) \setminus s_2}$$

$$\boxed{\text{diff-}\subseteq\text{-I}}\ \frac{s_1\colon A\text{-set};\ s_2\colon A\text{-set}}{(s_1 \setminus s_2) \subseteq s_1}$$

$$\boxed{\text{diff-}\cup\text{-deM}}\ \frac{s_1\colon A\text{-set};\ s_2\colon A\text{-set};\ s_3\colon A\text{-set}}{s_1 \setminus (s_2 \cup s_3) = (s_1 \setminus s_2) \cap (s_1 \setminus s_3)}$$

$$\boxed{\text{diff-add-I-}\in}\ \frac{a\colon A;\ s_1\colon A\text{-set};\ s_2\colon A\text{-set};\ a \in s_2}{add(a, s_1) \setminus s_2 = s_1 \setminus s_2}$$

$$\boxed{\text{diff-add-I-}\notin}\ \frac{a\colon A;\ s_1\colon A\text{-set};\ s_2\colon A\text{-set};\ a \notin s_2}{add(a, s_1) \setminus s_2 = add(a, s_1 \setminus s_2)}$$

$$\boxed{\text{diff-comp}}\ \frac{s_1\colon A\text{-set};\ s_2\colon A\text{-set}}{s_1 \setminus s_2 = \{x\colon A \mid x \in s_1 \land x \notin s_2\}}$$

$$\boxed{\text{diff-defn-}\{\ \}\text{-left}}\ \frac{s\colon A\text{-set}}{\{\ \} \setminus s = \{\ \}}$$

$$\boxed{\text{diff-defn-}\{\ \}\text{-right}}\ \frac{s\colon A\text{-set}}{s \setminus \{\ \} = s}$$

$$\boxed{\text{diff-I-}\subseteq}\ \frac{s_1\colon A\text{-set};\ s_2\colon A\text{-set};\ s_1 \subseteq s_2}{s_1 \setminus s_2 = \{\ \}}$$

$$\boxed{\text{diff-self}}\ \frac{s\colon A\text{-set}}{s \setminus s = \{\ \}}$$

$$\boxed{\text{finite-set-image}}\ \frac{s\colon A\text{-set};\ x\colon A \vdash_x f(x)\colon B}{\exists t\colon B\text{-set} \cdot \forall x \in s \cdot f(x) \in t}$$

$$\boxed{\text{inhabited}\Rightarrow\text{non-empty}}\ \frac{a\colon A;\ s\colon A\text{-set};\ a \in s}{s \neq \{\ \}}$$

$$\boxed{\text{initial-interval-1-form}}\ \frac{n\colon \mathbb{N}}{\{1, \ldots, n\}\colon \mathbb{N}_1\text{-set}}$$

$$\boxed{\text{initial-interval-form}}\ \frac{n\colon \mathbb{N}}{\{0, \ldots, n\}\colon \mathbb{N}\text{-set}}$$

$$\boxed{\text{interval-diff-defn}}\ \frac{i\colon \mathbb{N};\ j\colon \mathbb{N}}{\{i+1, \ldots, j\} = \{0, \ldots, j\} \setminus \{0, \ldots, i\}}$$

$$\boxed{\text{interval-empty}}\ \frac{i\colon \mathbb{N};\ j\colon \mathbb{N};\ j < i}{\{i, \ldots, j\} = \{\ \}}$$

$$\boxed{\text{interval-finite}}\ \frac{i:\mathbb{N};\ j:\mathbb{N}}{\exists s:\mathbb{N}\text{-set}\cdot \forall y:\mathbb{N}\cdot i\le y\le j \Rightarrow y\in s}$$

$$\boxed{\text{interval-form}}\ \frac{i:\mathbb{N};\ j:\mathbb{N}}{\{i,\ldots,j\}:\mathbb{N}\text{-set}}$$

$$\boxed{\text{non-empty-set-inhabited}}\ \frac{s:A\text{-set};\ s\ne\{\,\}}{\exists a:A\cdot a\in s}$$

$$\boxed{\text{pow-comp}}\ \frac{s:A\text{-set}}{\mathcal{F}s=\{t:A\text{-set}\mid t\subseteq s\}}$$

$$\boxed{\text{set-|-extend-left}}\ \frac{s:A\text{-set}}{s:(B\mid A)\text{-set}}$$

$$\boxed{\text{set-|-extend-right}}\ \frac{s:A\text{-set}}{s:(A\mid B)\text{-set}}$$

$$\boxed{\text{set-comp-form-set-ident}}\ \frac{\begin{array}{c}s:A\text{-set}\\ x:A,\ x\in s\vdash_x f(x):B\\ \exists t:B\text{-set}\cdot \forall y\in s\cdot f(y)\in t\end{array}}{\{f(x)\mid x\in s\}:B\text{-set}}$$

$$\boxed{\text{set-comp-form-set-ident-global}}\ \frac{\begin{array}{c}s:A\text{-set}\\ x:A\vdash_x f(x):B\end{array}}{\{f(x)\mid x\in s\}:B\text{-set}}$$

$$\boxed{\text{set-comp-rewrite}}\ \frac{\begin{array}{c}\forall x:A\cdot P(x)\Leftrightarrow Q(x)\\ x:A,\ P(x)\vdash_x f(x):B\\ \exists s:B\text{-set}\cdot \forall y:A\cdot P(y)\Rightarrow f(y)\in s\end{array}}{\{f(x)\mid x:A\cdot P(x)\}=\{f(x)\mid x:A\cdot Q(x)\}}$$

$$\boxed{\text{set-image-form}}\ \frac{s:A\text{-set};\ x:A\vdash_x f(x):B}{\{f(x)\mid x\in s\}:B\text{-set}}$$

$$\boxed{\text{those-=-form}}\ \frac{a:A}{\{x:A\mid x=a\}:A\text{-set}}$$

$$\boxed{\text{those-}\in\text{-form}}\ \frac{s:A\text{-set}}{\{e:A\mid e\in s\}:A\text{-set}}$$

$$\boxed{\text{those-}\vee\text{-form}}\ \frac{\begin{array}{c}\forall x:A\cdot \delta P(x)\\ \forall w:A\cdot \delta Q(w)\\ \exists s:A\text{-set}\cdot \forall y:A\cdot P(y)\Rightarrow y\in s\\ \exists t:A\text{-set}\cdot \forall z:A\cdot Q(z)\Rightarrow z\in t\end{array}}{\{x:A\mid P(x)\vee Q(x)\}:A\text{-set}}$$

14.5 Finite sets

$$\boxed{\text{those}\to\{\,\}}\ \frac{\forall x{:}A\cdot \neg P(x)}{\{y{:}A\mid P(y)\} = \{\,\}}$$

$$\boxed{\text{those-form}}\ \frac{\forall x{:}A\cdot \delta P(x) \quad \exists s{:}A\text{-set}\cdot \forall y{:}A\cdot P(y)\Rightarrow y\in s}{\{x{:}A\mid P(x)\}{:}A\text{-set}}$$

$$\boxed{\text{those-form-}\in\text{-}\notin}\ \frac{s_1{:}A\text{-set};\ s_2{:}A\text{-set}}{\{x{:}A\mid x\in s_1\wedge x\notin s_2\}{:}A\text{-set}}$$

$$\boxed{\text{those-form-rewrite}}\ \frac{\forall y{:}A\cdot P(y)\Leftrightarrow Q(y) \quad \exists s{:}A\text{-set}\cdot \forall y{:}A\cdot P(y)\Rightarrow y\in s}{\{x{:}A\mid Q(x)\}{:}A\text{-set}}$$

$$\boxed{\text{those-I}}\ \frac{s{:}A\text{-set}}{s = \{e{:}A\mid e\in s\}}$$

$$\boxed{\text{those-rewrite}}\ \frac{\forall x{:}A\cdot P(x)\Leftrightarrow Q(x) \quad \exists s{:}A\text{-set}\cdot \forall y{:}A\cdot P(y)\Rightarrow y\in s}{\{x{:}A\mid P(x)\} = \{z{:}A\mid Q(z)\}}$$

$$\boxed{\text{those-weaken}}\ \frac{\begin{array}{c}\forall x{:}A\cdot \delta P(x)\\ \forall w{:}A\cdot \delta Q(w)\\ \exists s{:}A\text{-set}\cdot \forall y{:}A\cdot P(y)\Rightarrow y\in s\\ \exists t{:}A\text{-set}\cdot \forall z{:}A\cdot Q(z)\Rightarrow z\in t\\ x{:}A,\ P(x)\vdash_x Q(x)\end{array}}{\{a{:}A\mid P(a)\}\subseteq \{b{:}A\mid Q(b)\}}$$

$$\boxed{(s_1\cap s_2)\subseteq s_1}\ \frac{s_1{:}A\text{-set};\ s_2{:}A\text{-set}}{s_1\cap s_2\subseteq s_1}$$

$$\boxed{(s_1\cap s_2)\subseteq s_2}\ \frac{s_1{:}A\text{-set};\ s_2{:}A\text{-set}}{s_1\cap s_2\subseteq s_2}$$

$$\boxed{s_1\cap(s_1\setminus s_2)=s_1\setminus s_2}\ \frac{s_1{:}A\text{-set};\ s_2{:}A\text{-set}}{s_1\cap(s_1\setminus s_2)=s_1\setminus s_2}$$

$$\boxed{s_1\cap(s_2\setminus s_1)=\{\,\}}\ \frac{s_1{:}A\text{-set};\ s_2{:}A\text{-set}}{s_1\cap(s_2\setminus s_1)=\{\,\}}$$

$$\boxed{s_1\subseteq(s_1\cup s_2)}\ \frac{s_1{:}A\text{-set};\ s_2{:}A\text{-set}}{s_1\subseteq(s_1\cup s_2)}$$

$$\boxed{s_2\subseteq(s_1\cup s_2)}\ \frac{s_1{:}A\text{-set};\ s_2{:}A\text{-set}}{s_2\subseteq(s_1\cup s_2)}$$

$$\boxed{s_1\cup(s_1\setminus s_2)=s_1}\ \frac{s_1{:}A\text{-set};\ s_2{:}A\text{-set}}{s_1\cup(s_1\setminus s_2)=s_1}$$

$$\boxed{s_1 \cup (s_2 \setminus s_1) = s_1 \cup s_2} \quad \frac{s_1: A\text{-set};\ s_2: A\text{-set}}{s_1 \cup (s_2 \setminus s_1) = s_1 \cup s_2}$$

$$\boxed{s_1 \setminus (s_1 \setminus s_2) = s_1 \cap s_2} \quad \frac{s_1: A\text{-set};\ s_2: A\text{-set}}{s_1 \setminus (s_1 \setminus s_2) = s_1 \cap s_2}$$

14.6 Finite maps

Axioms

$$\boxed{\{\mapsto\}\text{-form}} \quad \frac{}{\{\mapsto\}: A \xrightarrow{m} B} \ \textbf{Ax}$$

$$\boxed{\text{addm-form}} \quad \frac{a: A;\ b: B;\ m: A \xrightarrow{m} B}{addm(a \mapsto b, m): A \xrightarrow{m} B} \ \textbf{Ax}$$

$$\boxed{\text{addm-overwrite}} \quad \frac{a: A;\ b_1: B;\ b_2: B;\ m: A \xrightarrow{m} B}{addm(a \mapsto b_1, addm(a \mapsto b_2, m)) = addm(a \mapsto b_1, m)} \ \textbf{Ax}$$

$$\boxed{\text{addm-comm}} \quad \frac{a: A;\ b: B;\ c: A;\ d: B;\ m: A \xrightarrow{m} B;\ a \neq c}{addm(a \mapsto b, addm(c \mapsto d, m)) = addm(c \mapsto d, addm(a \mapsto b, m))} \ \textbf{Ax}$$

$$\boxed{\text{map-indn}} \quad \frac{\begin{array}{c} m_0: A \xrightarrow{m} B;\ P(\{\mapsto\}) \\ a: A,\ b: B,\ m: A \xrightarrow{m} B,\ P(m),\ a \notin \mathrm{dom}\, m \vdash_{a,b,m} P(addm(a \mapsto b, m)) \end{array}}{P(m_0)} \ \textbf{Ax}$$

$$\boxed{\text{dom-defn-}\{\mapsto\}} \quad \frac{}{\mathrm{dom}\,\{\mapsto\} = \{\}} \ \textbf{Ax}$$

$$\boxed{\text{dom-defn-addm}} \quad \frac{a: A;\ b: B;\ m: A \xrightarrow{m} B}{\mathrm{dom}\,addm(a \mapsto b, m) = add(a, \mathrm{dom}\,m)} \ \textbf{Ax}$$

$$\boxed{\text{rng-defn-}\{\mapsto\}} \quad \frac{}{\mathrm{rng}\,\{\mapsto\} = \{\}} \ \textbf{Ax}$$

$$\boxed{\text{rng-defn-addm-}\notin} \quad \frac{a: A;\ b: B;\ m: A \xrightarrow{m} B;\ a \notin \mathrm{dom}\,m}{\mathrm{rng}\,addm(a \mapsto b, m) = add(b, \mathrm{rng}\,m)} \ \textbf{Ax}$$

$$\boxed{\triangleleft\text{-defn-}\{\mapsto\}} \quad \frac{s: A\text{-set}}{s \triangleleft \{\mapsto\} = \{\mapsto\}} \ \textbf{Ax}$$

$$\boxed{\triangleleft\text{-defn-addm-}\in} \quad \frac{a: A;\ b: B;\ m: A \xrightarrow{m} B;\ s: A\text{-set};\ a \in s}{s \triangleleft addm(a \mapsto b, m) = s \triangleleft m} \ \textbf{Ax}$$

$$\boxed{\triangleleft\text{-defn-addm-}\notin} \quad \frac{a: A;\ b: B;\ m: A \xrightarrow{m} B;\ s: A\text{-set};\ a \notin s}{s \triangleleft addm(a \mapsto b, m) = addm(a \mapsto b, s \triangleleft m)} \ \textbf{Ax}$$

14.6 Finite maps

$$\boxed{\text{◁-defn-}\{\mapsto\}} \quad \frac{s: A\text{-set}}{s \triangleleft \{\mapsto\} = \{\mapsto\}} \text{ Ax}$$

$$\boxed{\text{◁-defn-addm-}\in} \quad \frac{a:A;\ b:B;\ m:A \xrightarrow{m} B;\ s:A\text{-set};\ a \in s}{s \triangleleft addm(a \mapsto b, m) = addm(a \mapsto b, s \triangleleft m)} \text{ Ax}$$

$$\boxed{\text{◁-defn-addm-}\notin} \quad \frac{a:A;\ b:B;\ m:A \xrightarrow{m} B;\ s:A\text{-set};\ a \notin s}{s \triangleleft addm(a \mapsto b, m) = s \triangleleft m} \text{ Ax}$$

$$\boxed{\text{▷-defn-}\{\mapsto\}} \quad \frac{s: B\text{-set}}{\{\mapsto\} \triangleright s = \{\mapsto\}} \text{ Ax}$$

$$\boxed{\text{▷-defn-addm-}\in} \quad \frac{a:A;\ b:B;\ m:A \xrightarrow{m} B;\ s:B\text{-set};\ b \in s}{addm(a \mapsto b, m) \triangleright s = \{a\} \triangleleft (m \triangleright s)} \text{ Ax}$$

$$\boxed{\text{▷-defn-addm-}\notin} \quad \frac{a:A;\ b:B;\ m:A \xrightarrow{m} B;\ s:B\text{-set};\ b \notin s}{addm(a \mapsto b, m) \triangleright s = addm(a \mapsto b, m \triangleright s)} \text{ Ax}$$

$$\boxed{\text{▶-defn-}\{\mapsto\}} \quad \frac{s: B\text{-set}}{\{\mapsto\} \triangleright s = \{\mapsto\}} \text{ Ax}$$

$$\boxed{\text{▶-defn-addm-}\in} \quad \frac{a:A;\ b:B;\ m:A \xrightarrow{m} B;\ s:B\text{-set};\ b \in s}{addm(a \mapsto b, m) \triangleright s = addm(a \mapsto b, m \triangleright s)} \text{ Ax}$$

$$\boxed{\text{▶-defn-addm-}\notin} \quad \frac{a:A;\ b:B;\ m:A \xrightarrow{m} B;\ s:B\text{-set};\ b \notin s}{addm(a \mapsto b, m) \triangleright s = \{a\} \triangleleft (m \triangleright s)} \text{ Ax}$$

$$\boxed{\text{at-defn-addm-=}} \quad \frac{a:A;\ b:B;\ m:A \xrightarrow{m} B}{addm(a \mapsto b, m)(a) = b} \text{ Ax}$$

$$\boxed{\text{at-defn-addm-}\neq} \quad \frac{a:A;\ b:B;\ c:A;\ m:A \xrightarrow{m} B;\ c \neq a;\ c \in \text{dom}\, m}{addm(a \mapsto b, m)(c) = m(c)} \text{ Ax}$$

$$\boxed{\text{=-map-defn}} \quad \frac{m_1:A \xrightarrow{m} B;\ m_2:A \xrightarrow{m} B \\ \text{dom}\, m_1 = \text{dom}\, m_2;\ \forall a \in \text{dom}\, m_1 \cdot m_1(a) = m_2(a)}{m_1 = m_2} \text{ Ax}$$

$$\boxed{\text{†-defn-}\{\mapsto\}\text{-right}} \quad \frac{m:A \xrightarrow{m} B}{m \dagger \{\mapsto\} = m} \text{ Ax}$$

$$\boxed{\text{†-defn-addm}} \quad \frac{a:A;\ b:B;\ m_1:A \xrightarrow{m} B;\ m_2:A \xrightarrow{m} B}{m_1 \dagger addm(a \mapsto b, m_2) = addm(a \mapsto b, m_1 \dagger m_2)} \text{ Ax}$$

$$\boxed{\text{compatible-defn}} \quad \frac{m_1:A \xrightarrow{m} B;\ m_2:A \xrightarrow{m} B}{compatible(m_1, m_2) \Leftrightarrow \forall a \in \text{dom}\, m_1 \cap \text{dom}\, m_2 \cdot m_1(a) = m_2(a)} \text{ Ax}$$

$$\boxed{\text{is-1-1-defn}}\ \frac{m\colon A \xrightarrow{m} B}{\textit{is-1-1}(m) \Leftrightarrow \forall x, y \in \text{dom}\,m \cdot m(x) = m(y) \Rightarrow x = y}\ \textbf{Ax}$$

$$\boxed{\uplus\text{-defn}}\ \frac{m_1\colon A \xrightarrow{m} B;\ m_2\colon A \xrightarrow{m} B;\ \textit{compatible}(m_1, m_2)}{m_1 \uplus m_2 = m_1 \dagger m_2}\ \textbf{Ax}$$

$$\boxed{\circ\text{-defn-}\{\mapsto\}}\ \frac{m\colon A \xrightarrow{m} B}{m \circ \{\mapsto\} = \{\mapsto\}}\ \textbf{Ax}$$

$$\boxed{\circ\text{-defn-addm}}\ \frac{\begin{array}{c}a\colon A;\ b\colon B;\ m_1\colon B \xrightarrow{m} C;\ m_2\colon A \xrightarrow{m} B\\ \text{rng}\,m_2 \subseteq \text{dom}\,m_1;\ a \notin \text{dom}\,m_2;\ b \in \text{dom}\,m_1\end{array}}{m_1 \circ \textit{addm}(a \mapsto b, m_2) = \textit{addm}(a \mapsto m_1(b), m_1 \circ m_2)}\ \textbf{Ax}$$

$$\boxed{\text{merge-defn-}\{\mapsto\}}\ \frac{}{\text{merge}\ \{\,\} = \{\mapsto\}}\ \textbf{Ax}$$

$$\boxed{\text{merge-defn-add}}\ \frac{\begin{array}{c}m\colon A \xrightarrow{m} B;\ s\colon (A \xrightarrow{m} B)\text{-set}\\ \forall m_1, m_2 \in \textit{add}(m, s) \cdot \textit{compatible}(m_1, m_2)\end{array}}{\text{merge}\ \textit{add}(m, s) = m \dagger (\text{merge}\ s)}\ \textbf{Ax}$$

$$\boxed{\text{inv-defn}}\ \frac{m\colon A \xleftrightarrow{m} B}{m^{-1} = \{m(a) \mapsto a \mid a \in \text{dom}\,m\}}\ \textbf{Ax}$$

$$\boxed{\text{map-comp-form}}\ \frac{\begin{array}{c}\forall x\colon A \cdot \delta P(x)\\ x\colon A,\ P(x) \vdash_x f(x)\colon B\\ x\colon A,\ P(x) \vdash_x g(x)\colon C\\ \exists s\colon B\text{-set} \cdot \forall y\colon A \cdot P(y) \Rightarrow f(y) \in s\\ \forall a_1, a_2\colon A \cdot P(a_1) \wedge P(a_2) \wedge f(a_1) = f(a_2) \Rightarrow g(a_1) = g(a_2)\end{array}}{\{f(x) \mapsto g(x) \mid x\colon A \cdot P(x)\}\colon B \xrightarrow{m} C}\ \textbf{Ax}$$

$$\boxed{\text{dom-defn-map-comp}}\ \frac{\begin{array}{c}\forall x\colon A \cdot \delta P(x)\\ x\colon A,\ P(x) \vdash_x f(x)\colon B\\ x\colon A,\ P(x) \vdash_x g(x)\colon C\\ \exists s\colon B\text{-set} \cdot \forall y\colon A \cdot P(y) \Rightarrow f(y) \in s\\ \forall a_1, a_2\colon A \cdot P(a_1) \wedge P(a_2) \wedge f(a_1) = f(a_2) \Rightarrow g(a_1) = g(a_2)\end{array}}{\text{dom}\ \{f(x) \mapsto g(x) \mid x\colon A \cdot P(x)\} = \{f(x) \mid x\colon A \cdot P(x)\}}\ \textbf{Ax}$$

$$\boxed{\text{at-defn-map-comp}}\ \frac{\begin{array}{c}b\colon B\\ \forall x\colon A \cdot \delta P(x)\\ x\colon A,\ P(x) \vdash_x f(x)\colon B\\ x\colon A,\ P(x) \vdash_x g(x)\colon C\\ \exists s\colon B\text{-set} \cdot \forall y\colon A \cdot P(y) \Rightarrow f(y) \in s\\ \forall a_1, a_2\colon A \cdot P(a_1) \wedge P(a_2) \wedge f(a_1) = f(a_2) \Rightarrow g(a_1) = g(a_2)\\ b \in \text{dom}\ \{f(x) \mapsto g(x) \mid x\colon A \cdot P(x)\}\end{array}}{\begin{array}{c}\{f(x) \mapsto g(x) \mid x\colon A \cdot P(x)\}(b) =\\ \iota c\colon C \cdot \forall x\colon A \cdot P(x) \wedge b = f(x) \Rightarrow c = g(x)\end{array}}\ \textbf{Ax}$$

14.6 Finite maps

$$\boxed{\text{map-comp-defn-set}} \quad \frac{\begin{array}{c} s: A\text{-set} \\ \forall x \in s \cdot \delta P(x) \\ x: A, \ x \in s, \ P(x) \vdash_{\overline{x}} f(x): B \\ x: A, \ x \in s, \ P(x) \vdash_{\overline{x}} g(x): C \\ \exists t: B\text{-set} \cdot \forall y \in s \cdot P(y) \Rightarrow f(y) \in t \\ \forall a_1, a_2 \in s \cdot P(a_1) \land P(a_2) \land f(a_1) = f(a_2) \Rightarrow g(a_1) = g(a_2) \end{array}}{\{f(x) \mapsto g(x) \mid x \in s \cdot P(x)\} = \{f(x) \mapsto g(x) \mid x: A \cdot x \in s \land P(x)\}} \quad \text{Ax}$$

Definitions

$$A \xleftrightarrow{m} B \stackrel{\text{def}}{=} \ll m: A \xrightarrow{m} B \mid \text{is-1-1}(m) \gg$$

$$\{a \mapsto b\} \stackrel{\text{def}}{=} addm(a \mapsto b, \{\mapsto\})$$

$$\{f(x) \mapsto g(x) \mid x \in s\} \stackrel{\text{def}}{=} \{f(x) \mapsto g(x) \mid x \in s \cdot \text{true}\}$$

$$\{f(x) \mapsto g(x) \mid x: A\} \stackrel{\text{def}}{=} \{f(x) \mapsto g(x) \mid x: A \cdot \text{true}\}$$

Derived Rules

$$\boxed{\{\mapsto\}\text{-is-1-1}} \quad \overline{\text{is-1-1}(\{\mapsto\})}$$

$$\boxed{\{\mapsto\}\text{-dom-disjoint}} \quad \frac{m: A \xrightarrow{m} B}{\text{dom}\{\mapsto\} \cap \text{dom}\, m = \{\}}$$

$$\boxed{\{\mapsto\}\text{-form-bimap}} \quad \overline{\{\mapsto\}: A \xleftrightarrow{m} B}$$

$$\boxed{\{a \mapsto b\}\text{-form}} \quad \frac{a: A; \ b: B}{\{a \mapsto b\}: A \xrightarrow{m} B}$$

$$\boxed{\circ\text{-form}} \quad \frac{m_1: B \xrightarrow{m} C; \ m_2: A \xrightarrow{m} B; \ \text{rng}\, m_2 \subseteq \text{dom}\, m_1}{m_1 \circ m_2: A \xrightarrow{m} C}$$

$$\boxed{\delta\text{-}\{\mapsto\}} \quad \frac{m: A \xrightarrow{m} B}{\delta(m = \{\mapsto\})}$$

$$\boxed{\delta\text{-}\in\text{-dom-addm-I}} \quad \frac{a_1: A; \ a_2: A; \ b: B; \ m: A \xrightarrow{m} B}{\delta(a_1 \in \text{dom}\, addm(a_2 \mapsto b, m))}$$

$$\boxed{\delta\text{-}\in\text{-dom-I}} \quad \frac{a: A; \ m: A \xrightarrow{m} B}{\delta(a \in \text{dom}\, m)}$$

$$\boxed{\delta\text{-}\in\text{-rng-I}}\ \frac{b\colon B;\ m\colon A\xrightarrow{m} B}{\delta(b\in\text{rng}\,m)}$$

$$\boxed{\delta\text{-compatible}}\ \frac{m_1\colon A\xrightarrow{m} B;\ m_2\colon A\xrightarrow{m} B}{\delta(\text{compatible}(m_1,m_2))}$$

$$\boxed{\delta\text{-is-1-1}}\ \frac{m\colon A\xrightarrow{m} B}{\delta(\text{is-1-1}(m))}$$

$$\boxed{\delta\text{-is-1-1-pred}}\ \frac{a\colon A;\ b\colon A;\ m\colon A\xrightarrow{m} B}{\delta((a\in\text{dom}\,m\wedge b\in\text{dom}\,m)\wedge m(a)=m(b))}$$

$$\boxed{\triangleleft\text{-form}}\ \frac{m\colon A\xrightarrow{m} B;\ s\colon A\text{-set}}{s\triangleleft m\colon A\xrightarrow{m} B}$$

$$\boxed{\triangleleft\text{-defn-}\{\ \}}\ \frac{m\colon A\xrightarrow{m} B}{\{\ \}\triangleleft m=m}$$

$$\boxed{\triangleleft\text{-defn-}\{a\}\text{-}\notin}\ \frac{a\colon A;\ m\colon A\xrightarrow{m} B;\ a\notin\text{dom}\,m}{\{a\}\triangleleft m=m}$$

$$\boxed{\triangleleft\text{-defn-addm-}\{a\}\text{-}=}\ \frac{a\colon A;\ b\colon B;\ m\colon A\xrightarrow{m} B}{\{a\}\triangleleft\text{addm}(a\mapsto b,m)=\{a\}\triangleleft m}$$

$$\boxed{\triangleleft\text{-defn-addm-}\{a\}\text{-}\neq}\ \frac{a_1\colon A;\ a_2\colon A;\ b\colon B;\ m\colon A\xrightarrow{m} B;\ a_1\neq a_2}{\{a_1\}\triangleleft\text{addm}(a_2\mapsto b,m)=\text{addm}(a_2\mapsto b,\{a_1\}\triangleleft m)}$$

$$\boxed{\triangleleft\text{-form}}\ \frac{m\colon A\xrightarrow{m} B;\ s\colon A\text{-set}}{s\triangleleft m\colon A\xrightarrow{m} B}$$

$$\boxed{\in\text{-dom-addm-E}}\ \frac{a_1\colon A;\ a_2\colon A;\ b\colon B;\ m\colon A\xrightarrow{m} B;\ a_1\in\text{dom}\,\text{addm}(a_2\mapsto b,m)}{a_1=a_2\vee a_1\in\text{dom}\,m}$$

$$\boxed{\in\text{-dom-addm-E-}\notin}\ \frac{\begin{array}{c}a_1\colon A;\ a_2\colon A;\ b\colon B;\ m\colon A\xrightarrow{m} B\\ a_1\in\text{dom}\,\text{addm}(a_2\mapsto b,m);\ a_2\notin\text{dom}\,m\end{array}}{a_1=a_2\vee a_1\in\text{dom}\,m\wedge a_2\neq a_1}$$

$$\boxed{\in\text{-dom-addm-I-elem}}\ \frac{a\colon A;\ b\colon B;\ m\colon A\xrightarrow{m} B}{a\in\text{dom}\,\text{addm}(a\mapsto b,m)}$$

$$\boxed{\in\text{-dom-addm-I-map}}\ \frac{a_1\colon A;\ a_2\colon A;\ b\colon B;\ m\colon A\xrightarrow{m} B;\ a_1\in\text{dom}\,m}{a_1\in\text{dom}\,\text{addm}(a_2\mapsto b,m)}$$

14.6 Finite maps

$$\boxed{\in\text{-dom-map-comp-I-}f(a)} \quad \frac{\begin{array}{c} a:A;\ P(a) \\ \forall x:A \cdot \delta P(x) \\ x:A,\ P(x) \vdash_{\overline{x}} f(x):B \\ x:A,\ P(x) \vdash_{\overline{x}} g(x):C \\ \exists s:B\text{-set} \cdot \forall y:A \cdot P(y) \Rightarrow f(y) \in s \\ \forall a_1, a_2:A \cdot P(a_1) \wedge P(a_2) \wedge f(a_1)=f(a_2) \Rightarrow g(a_1)=g(a_2) \end{array}}{f(a) \in \text{dom}\,\{f(x) \mapsto g(x) \mid x:A \cdot P(x)\}}$$

$$\boxed{\in\text{-rng-addm-I-elem}} \quad \frac{a:A;\ b:B;\ m:A \xrightarrow{m} B}{b \in \text{rng}\,m \dagger \{a \mapsto b\}}$$

$$\boxed{\in\text{-rng-}\dagger\text{-}\{a \mapsto b\}\text{-I-elem}} \quad \frac{a:A;\ b:B;\ m:A \xrightarrow{m} B}{b \in \text{rng}\,addm(a \mapsto b, m)}$$

$$\boxed{\in\text{-rng-addm-I-map}} \quad \frac{a:A;\ b_1:B;\ b_2:B;\ m:A \xrightarrow{m} B;\ b_2 \in \text{rng}\,m;\ a \notin \text{dom}\,m}{b_2 \in \text{rng}\,addm(a \mapsto b_1, m)}$$

$$\boxed{\in\text{-rng-E}} \quad \frac{b:B;\ m:A \xrightarrow{m} B;\ b \in \text{rng}\,m}{\exists a \in \text{dom}\,m \cdot m(a)=b}$$

$$\boxed{\in\text{-rng-I-}\exists} \quad \frac{b:B;\ m:A \xrightarrow{m} B;\ \exists a \in \text{dom}\,m \cdot b=m(a)}{b \in \text{rng}\,m}$$

$$\boxed{\in\text{-rng-I-at}} \quad \frac{a:A;\ m:A \xrightarrow{m} B;\ a \in \text{dom}\,m}{m(a) \in \text{rng}\,m}$$

$$\boxed{\in\text{-rng-I-at-bimap}} \quad \frac{a:A;\ m:A \xleftrightarrow{m} B;\ a \in \text{dom}\,m}{m(a) \in \text{rng}\,m}$$

$$\boxed{\neg\text{-}\in\text{-dom-}\{\mapsto\}\text{-I}} \quad \frac{a:A}{\neg(a \in \text{dom}\,\{\mapsto\})}$$

$$\boxed{\neg\text{-}\in\text{-rng-}\{\mapsto\}\text{-I}} \quad \frac{b:B}{\neg(b \in \text{rng}\,\{\mapsto\})}$$

$$\boxed{\notin\text{-dom-}\triangleleft\text{-I-}\{a\}} \quad \frac{a:A;\ m:A \xrightarrow{m} B}{a \notin \text{dom}(\{a\} \triangleleft m)}$$

$$\boxed{\notin\text{-dom-addm-E}} \quad \frac{a_1:A;\ a_2:A;\ b:B;\ m:A \xrightarrow{m} B;\ a_1 \notin \text{dom}\,addm(a_2 \mapsto b, m)}{a_1 \neq a_2 \wedge a_1 \notin \text{dom}\,m}$$

$$\boxed{\notin\text{-dom-addm-E-left}} \quad \frac{a_1:A;\ a_2:A;\ b:B;\ m:A \xrightarrow{m} B;\ a_1 \notin \text{dom}\,addm(a_2 \mapsto b, m)}{a_1 \notin \text{dom}\,m}$$

$$\boxed{\notin\text{-dom-addm-E-right}} \quad \frac{a_1:A;\ a_2:A;\ b:B;\ m:A \xrightarrow{m} B;\ a_1 \notin \text{dom}\,addm(a_2 \mapsto b, m)}{a_1 \neq a_2}$$

$\boxed{\notin\text{-dom-inv-I}}\ \dfrac{b:B;\ m:A \xleftrightarrow{m} B;\ b \notin \operatorname{rng} m}{b \notin \operatorname{dom}(m^{-1})}$

$\boxed{\notin\text{-rng-addm-E}}\ \dfrac{a:A;\ b_1:B;\ b_2:B;\ m:A \xrightarrow{m} B;\ b_1 \notin \operatorname{rng} addm(a \mapsto b_2, m);\ a \notin \operatorname{dom} m}{b_1 \neq b_2 \land b_1 \notin \operatorname{rng} m}$

$\boxed{\notin\text{-rng-addm-E-left}}\ \dfrac{a:A;\ b_1:B;\ b_2:B;\ m:A \xrightarrow{m} B;\ b_1 \notin \operatorname{rng} addm(a \mapsto b_2, m);\ a \notin \operatorname{dom} m}{b_1 \notin \operatorname{rng} m}$

$\boxed{\notin\text{-rng-addm-E-right}}\ \dfrac{a:A;\ b_1:B;\ b_2:B;\ m:A \xrightarrow{m} B;\ b_1 \notin \operatorname{rng} addm(a \mapsto b_2, m)}{b_2 \neq b_1}$

$\boxed{\notin\text{-rng-inv-I}}\ \dfrac{a:A;\ m:A \xleftrightarrow{m} B;\ a \notin \operatorname{dom} m}{a \notin \operatorname{rng}(m^{-1})}$

$\boxed{\dagger\text{-ass}}\ \dfrac{m_1:A \xrightarrow{m} B;\ m_2:A \xrightarrow{m} B;\ m_3:A \xrightarrow{m} B}{(m_1 \dagger m_2) \dagger m_3 = m_1 \dagger (m_2 \dagger m_3)}$

$\boxed{\dagger\text{-comm}}\ \dfrac{m_1:A \xrightarrow{m} B;\ m_2:A \xrightarrow{m} B;\ compatible(m_1, m_2)}{m_1 \dagger m_2 = m_2 \dagger m_1}$

$\boxed{\dagger\text{-defn-}\{\mapsto\}\text{-left}}\ \dfrac{m:A \xrightarrow{m} B}{\{\mapsto\} \dagger m = m}$

$\boxed{\dagger\text{-form}}\ \dfrac{m_1:A \xrightarrow{m} B;\ m_2:A \xrightarrow{m} B}{m_1 \dagger m_2:A \xrightarrow{m} B}$

$\boxed{\dagger\text{-preserves-dom-}\subseteq}\ \dfrac{m_1:A \xrightarrow{m} B;\ m_2:A \xrightarrow{m} C;\ m_3:A \xrightarrow{m} C;\ \operatorname{dom} m_1 \subseteq \operatorname{dom} m_2}{\operatorname{dom} m_1 \subseteq \operatorname{dom}(m_2 \dagger m_3)}$

$\boxed{\dagger\text{-self}}\ \dfrac{m:A \xrightarrow{m} B}{m \dagger m = m}$

$\boxed{\triangleright\text{-}\{a\}\text{-not-empty-E}}\ \dfrac{b:B;\ m:A \xrightarrow{m} B;\ m \triangleright \{b\} \neq \{\mapsto\}}{b \in \operatorname{rng} m}$

$\boxed{\triangleright\text{-defn-}\{a\}\text{-}\notin}\ \dfrac{b:B;\ m:A \xrightarrow{m} B;\ b \notin \operatorname{rng} m}{m \triangleright \{b\} = \{\mapsto\}}$

$\boxed{\triangleright\text{-form}}\ \dfrac{m:A \xrightarrow{m} B;\ s:B\text{-set}}{m \triangleright s:A \xrightarrow{m} B}$

$\boxed{\blacktriangleright\text{-form}}\ \dfrac{m:A \xrightarrow{m} B;\ s:B\text{-set}}{m \blacktriangleright s:A \xrightarrow{m} B}$

14.6 Finite maps

$$\boxed{\subseteq\text{-dom-}\dagger\text{-I}}\ \frac{m_1: A \xrightarrow{m} B;\ m_2: A \xrightarrow{m} B}{\operatorname{dom} m_1 \subseteq \operatorname{dom}(m_1 \dagger m_2)}$$

$$\boxed{\uplus\text{-ass}}\ \frac{\begin{array}{c}m_1: A \xrightarrow{m} B;\ m_2: A \xrightarrow{m} B;\ m_3: A \xrightarrow{m} B\\ \textit{compatible}(m_1,m_2);\ \textit{compatible}(m_2,m_3);\ \textit{compatible}(m_1,m_3)\end{array}}{(m_1 \uplus m_2) \uplus m_3 = m_1 \uplus (m_2 \uplus m_3)}$$

$$\boxed{\uplus\text{-comm}}\ \frac{m_1: A \xrightarrow{m} B;\ m_2: A \xrightarrow{m} B;\ \textit{compatible}(m_1,m_2)}{m_1 \uplus m_2 = m_2 \uplus m_1}$$

$$\boxed{\uplus\text{-defn-}\{\mapsto\}\text{-left}}\ \frac{m: A \xrightarrow{m} B}{\{\mapsto\} \uplus m = m}$$

$$\boxed{\uplus\text{-defn-}\{\mapsto\}\text{-right}}\ \frac{m: A \xrightarrow{m} B}{m \uplus \{\mapsto\} = m}$$

$$\boxed{\uplus\text{-form}}\ \frac{m_1: A \xrightarrow{m} B;\ m_2: A \xrightarrow{m} B;\ \textit{compatible}(m_1,m_2)}{m_1 \uplus m_2: A \xrightarrow{m} B}$$

$$\boxed{\textit{addm}\text{-}\dagger\text{-defn-}\in}\ \frac{a:A;\ b:B;\ m_1: A \xrightarrow{m} B;\ m_2: A \xrightarrow{m} B;\ a \in \operatorname{dom} m_2}{\textit{addm}(a \mapsto b, m_1) \dagger m_2 = m_1 \dagger m_2}$$

$$\boxed{\textit{addm}\text{-}\dagger\text{-defn-}\notin}\ \frac{a:A;\ b:B;\ m_1: A \xrightarrow{m} B;\ m_2: A \xrightarrow{m} B;\ a \notin \operatorname{dom} m_2}{\textit{addm}(a \mapsto b, m_1) \dagger m_2 = \textit{addm}(a \mapsto b, m_1 \dagger m_2)}$$

$$\boxed{\textit{addm}\text{-}\dagger\text{-defn-compatible}}\ \frac{\begin{array}{c}a:A;\ b:B;\ m_1: A \xrightarrow{m} B;\ m_2: A \xrightarrow{m} B\\ \textit{compatible}(\textit{addm}(a \mapsto b, m_1), m_2)\end{array}}{\textit{addm}(a \mapsto b, m_1) \dagger m_2 = \textit{addm}(a \mapsto b, (m_1 \dagger m_2))}$$

$$\boxed{\textit{addm}\text{-}\dagger\text{-ident}}\ \frac{a:A;\ b:B;\ m: A \xrightarrow{m} B;\ a \in \operatorname{dom} m;\ m(a) = b}{\textit{addm}(a \mapsto b, m) = m}$$

$$\boxed{\textit{addm} \to \dagger}\ \frac{a:A;\ b:B;\ m: A \xrightarrow{m} B}{m \dagger \{a \mapsto b\} = \textit{addm}(a \mapsto b, m)}$$

$$\boxed{\textit{addm}\text{-defn-}\triangleleft\text{-}\{a\}\text{-=}}\ \frac{a:A;\ b:B;\ m: A \xrightarrow{m} B}{\textit{addm}(a \mapsto b, m) = \textit{addm}(a \mapsto b, \{a\} \triangleleft m)}$$

$$\boxed{\textit{addm}\text{-extract}}\ \frac{a:A;\ m: A \xrightarrow{m} B;\ a \in \operatorname{dom} m}{m = \textit{addm}(a \mapsto m(a), \{a\} \triangleleft m)}$$

$$\boxed{\textit{addm}\text{-form-bimap}}\ \frac{a:A;\ b:B;\ m: A \xleftrightarrow{m} B;\ a \notin \operatorname{dom} m;\ b \notin \operatorname{rng} m}{\textit{addm}(a \mapsto b, m): A \xleftrightarrow{m} B}$$

$$\boxed{\textit{at}\text{-defn-}\dagger\text{-}\{a \mapsto b\}\text{-=}}\ \frac{a:A;\ b:B;\ m: A \xrightarrow{m} B}{(m \dagger \{a \mapsto b\})(a) = b}$$

14 Directory of Theorems

$$\text{at-defn-†-}\{a \mapsto b\}\text{-}\neq \quad \frac{a_1:A;\ b:B;\ a_2:A;\ m:A \xrightarrow{m} B;\ a_2 \in \text{dom}\, m;\ a_2 \neq a_1}{(m \dagger \{a_1 \mapsto b\})(a_2) = m(a_2)}$$

$$\text{at-defn-†-addm-=} \quad \frac{a:A;\ b:B;\ m_1:A \xrightarrow{m} B;\ m_2:A \xrightarrow{m} B}{(m_1 \dagger \text{addm}(a \mapsto b, m_2))(a) = b}$$

$$\text{at-defn-†-left} \quad \frac{a:A;\ m_1:A \xrightarrow{m} B;\ m_2:A \xrightarrow{m} B;\ a \notin \text{dom}\, m_2;\ a \in \text{dom}\, m_1}{(m_1 \dagger m_2)(a) = m_1(a)}$$

$$\text{at-defn-†-right} \quad \frac{a:A;\ m_1:A \xrightarrow{m} B;\ m_2:A \xrightarrow{m} B;\ a \in \text{dom}\, m_2}{(m_1 \dagger m_2)(a) = m_2(a)}$$

$$\text{at-defn-map-comp-}f(a) \quad \frac{\begin{array}{c} a:A;\ P(a) \\ \forall x:A \cdot \delta P(x) \\ x:A,\ P(x) \vdash_{\overline{x}} f(x):B \\ x:A,\ P(x) \vdash_{\overline{x}} g(x):C \\ \exists s:B\text{-set} \cdot \forall y:A \cdot P(y) \Rightarrow f(y) \in s \\ \forall a_1, a_2:A \cdot P(a_1) \wedge P(a_2) \wedge f(a_1) = f(a_2) \Rightarrow g(a_1) = g(a_2) \end{array}}{\{f(x) \mapsto g(x) \mid x:A \cdot P(x)\}(f(a)) = g(a)}$$

$$\text{at-defn-map-comp-left-set} \quad \frac{\begin{array}{c} a:A;\ s:A\text{-set};\ a \in s \\ x:A,\ x \in s \vdash_{\overline{x}} f(x):B \end{array}}{\{x \mapsto f(x) \mid x \in s\}(a) = f(a)}$$

$$\text{at-form} \quad \frac{a:A;\ m:A \xrightarrow{m} B;\ a \in \text{dom}\, m}{m(a):B}$$

$$\text{at-form-bimap} \quad \frac{a:A;\ m:A \xleftrightarrow{m} B;\ a \in \text{dom}\, m}{m(a):B}$$

$$\text{bimap-1-1} \quad \frac{a_1:A;\ a_2:A;\ m:A \xleftrightarrow{m} B;\ a_1 \in \text{dom}\, m;\ a_2 \in \text{dom}\, m;\ m(a_1) = m(a_2)}{a_1 = a_2}$$

$$\text{bimap-1-1-}\neg \quad \frac{a_1:A;\ a_2:A;\ m:A \xleftrightarrow{m} B;\ a_1 \in \text{dom}\, m;\ a_2 \in \text{dom}\, m;\ a_1 \neq a_2}{m(a_1) \neq m(a_2)}$$

$$\text{bimap-E} \quad \frac{m:A \xleftrightarrow{m} B}{\text{is-1-1}(m)}$$

$$\text{bimap-form} \quad \frac{m:A \xrightarrow{m} B;\ \text{is-1-1}(m)}{m:A \xleftrightarrow{m} B}$$

$$\text{bimap-indn} \quad \frac{\begin{array}{c} m_0:A \xleftrightarrow{m} B;\ P(\{\mapsto\}) \\ a:A,\ b:B,\ m:A \xleftrightarrow{m} B, \\ P(m),\ a \notin \text{dom}\, m,\ b \notin \text{rng}\, m \;\vdash_{a,b,m} P(\text{addm}(a \mapsto b, m)) \end{array}}{P(m_0)}$$

14.6 Finite maps

$$\boxed{\text{bimap-supertype}}\ \dfrac{m\colon A \xleftrightarrow{m} B}{m\colon A \xrightarrow{m} B}$$

$$\boxed{\text{bimap-unique-rng-elem}}\ \dfrac{a\colon A;\ m\colon A \xleftrightarrow{m} B;\ a \in \operatorname{dom} m}{\exists!\, b\colon B \cdot b = m(a)}$$

$$\boxed{\text{compatible-}\dagger\text{-I-left}}\ \dfrac{\begin{array}{c} m_1\colon A \xrightarrow{m} B;\ m_2\colon A \xrightarrow{m} B;\ m_3\colon A \xrightarrow{m} B \\ compatible(m_1, m_3);\ compatible(m_2, m_3) \end{array}}{compatible(m_1 \dagger m_2, m_3)}$$

$$\boxed{\text{compatible-}\dagger\text{-I-right}}\ \dfrac{\begin{array}{c} m_1\colon A \xrightarrow{m} B;\ m_2\colon A \xrightarrow{m} B;\ m_3\colon A \xrightarrow{m} B \\ compatible(m_1, m_2);\ compatible(m_1, m_3) \end{array}}{compatible(m_1, m_2 \dagger m_3)}$$

$$\boxed{\text{compatible-addm-E-left-}\notin}\ \dfrac{\begin{array}{c} a\colon A;\ b\colon B;\ m_1\colon A \xrightarrow{m} B;\ m_2\colon A \xrightarrow{m} B \\ a \notin \operatorname{dom} m_1;\ compatible(addm(a \mapsto b, m_1), m_2) \end{array}}{compatible(m_1, m_2)}$$

$$\boxed{\text{compatible-addm-E-right}}\ \dfrac{\begin{array}{c} a\colon A;\ b\colon B;\ m_1\colon A \xrightarrow{m} B;\ m_2\colon A \xrightarrow{m} B \\ a \in \operatorname{dom} m_2;\ compatible(addm(a \mapsto b, m_1), m_2) \end{array}}{m_2(a) = b}$$

$$\boxed{\text{compatible-comm}}\ \dfrac{m_1\colon A \xrightarrow{m} B;\ m_2\colon A \xrightarrow{m} B;\ compatible(m_1, m_2)}{compatible(m_2, m_1)}$$

$$\boxed{\text{compatible-defn-}\{\mapsto\}\text{-left}}\ \dfrac{m\colon A \xrightarrow{m} B}{compatible(\{\mapsto\}, m)}$$

$$\boxed{\text{compatible-defn-}\{\mapsto\}\text{-right}}\ \dfrac{m\colon A \xrightarrow{m} B}{compatible(m, \{\mapsto\})}$$

$$\boxed{\text{compatible-E}}\ \dfrac{m_1\colon A \xrightarrow{m} B;\ m_2\colon A \xrightarrow{m} B;\ compatible(m_1, m_2)}{\forall a \in \operatorname{dom} m_1 \cap \operatorname{dom} m_2 \cdot m_1(a) = m_2(a)}$$

$$\boxed{\text{compatible-I}}\ \dfrac{\begin{array}{c} m_1\colon A \xrightarrow{m} B;\ m_2\colon A \xrightarrow{m} B \\ \forall a \in \operatorname{dom} m_1 \cap \operatorname{dom} m_2 \cdot m_1(a) = m_2(a) \end{array}}{compatible(m_1, m_2)}$$

$$\boxed{\text{dom-}\{\mapsto\}\text{-I}}\ \dfrac{m = \{\mapsto\}}{\operatorname{dom} m = \{\,\}}$$

$$\boxed{\text{dom-}\triangleleft\text{-defn}}\ \dfrac{m\colon A \xrightarrow{m} B;\ s\colon A\text{-set}}{\operatorname{dom}(s \triangleleft m) = \operatorname{dom} m \setminus s}$$

$$\boxed{\text{dom-}\neq\text{-}\{\,\}\text{-E}}\ \dfrac{m\colon A \xrightarrow{m} B;\ \operatorname{dom} m \neq \{\,\}}{m \neq \{\mapsto\}}$$

$$\text{dom-addm-}\cap\text{-E-left} \quad \frac{a\colon A;\ b\colon B;\ m_1\colon A \xrightarrow{m} B;\ m_2\colon A \xrightarrow{m} B \quad \operatorname{dom} addm(a \mapsto b, m_1) \cap \operatorname{dom} m_2 = \{\,\}}{\operatorname{dom} m_1 \cap \operatorname{dom} m_2 = \{\,\}}$$

$$\text{dom-addm-}\cap\text{-E-right} \quad \frac{a\colon A;\ b\colon B;\ m_1\colon A \xrightarrow{m} B;\ m_2\colon A \xrightarrow{m} B \quad \operatorname{dom} addm(a \mapsto b, m_1) \cap \operatorname{dom} m_2 = \{\,\}}{a \notin \operatorname{dom} m_2}$$

$$\text{dom-defn-}\dagger \quad \frac{m_1\colon A \xrightarrow{m} B;\ m_2\colon A \xrightarrow{m} B}{\operatorname{dom}(m_1 \dagger m_2) = \operatorname{dom} m_1 \cup \operatorname{dom} m_2}$$

$$\text{dom-defn-addm-}\in \quad \frac{a\colon A;\ b\colon B;\ m\colon A \xrightarrow{m} B;\ a \in \operatorname{dom} m}{\operatorname{dom} addm(a \mapsto b, m) = \operatorname{dom} m}$$

$$\text{dom-defn-inv} \quad \frac{m\colon A \xleftrightarrow{m} B}{\operatorname{dom}(m^{-1}) = \operatorname{rng} m}$$

$$\text{dom-defn-map-comp-left-set} \quad \frac{s\colon A\text{-set} \quad x\colon A,\ x \in s \vdash_x f(x)\colon B}{\operatorname{dom}\{x \mapsto f(x) \mid x \in s\} = s}$$

$$\text{dom-finite}\Rightarrow\text{rng-finite} \quad \frac{\begin{array}{c}\forall x\colon A \cdot \delta P(x) \\ x\colon A,\ P(x) \vdash_x f(x)\colon B \\ x\colon A,\ P(x) \vdash_x g(x)\colon C \\ \exists s\colon B\text{-set} \cdot \forall y\colon A \cdot P(y) \Rightarrow f(y) \in s \\ \forall a_1, a_2\colon A \cdot P(a_1) \wedge P(a_2) \wedge f(a_1)=f(a_2) \Rightarrow g(a_1)=g(a_2)\end{array}}{\exists t\colon C\text{-set} \cdot \forall a\colon A \cdot P(a) \Rightarrow g(a) \in t}$$

$$\text{dom-form} \quad \frac{m\colon A \xrightarrow{m} B}{\operatorname{dom} m\colon A\text{-set}}$$

$$\text{dom-form-bimap} \quad \frac{m\colon A \xleftrightarrow{m} B}{\operatorname{dom} m\colon A\text{-set}}$$

$$\text{inv-form} \quad \frac{m\colon A \xleftrightarrow{m} B}{m^{-1}\colon B \xleftrightarrow{m} A}$$

$$\text{is-1-1-}\dagger\text{-}\{a \mapsto b\}\text{-E-}\notin\text{-rng} \quad \frac{a\colon A;\ b\colon B;\ m\colon A \xrightarrow{m} B \quad \textit{is-1-1}(m \dagger \{a \mapsto b\});\ a \notin \operatorname{dom} m}{b \notin \operatorname{rng} m}$$

$$\text{is-1-1-addm-E-}\notin\text{-map} \quad \frac{a\colon A;\ b\colon B;\ m\colon A \xrightarrow{m} B \quad \textit{is-1-1}(addm(a \mapsto b, m));\ a \notin \operatorname{dom} m}{\textit{is-1-1}(m)}$$

14.6 Finite maps

$$\boxed{\text{is-1-1-addm-E-}\notin\text{-rng}}\quad \frac{a\!:\!A;\ b\!:\!B;\ m\!:\!A \xrightarrow{m} B}{\text{is-1-1}(addm(a \mapsto b, m));\ a \notin \mathrm{dom}\,m}$$

$$\boxed{\text{is-1-1-E}}\quad \frac{m\!:\!A \xrightarrow{m} B;\ \text{is-1-1}(m)}{\forall x, y \in \mathrm{dom}\,m \cdot m(x) = m(y) \Rightarrow x = y}$$

$$\boxed{\text{is-1-1-I}}\quad \frac{m\!:\!A \xrightarrow{m} B \qquad \forall x, y \in \mathrm{dom}\,m \cdot m(x) = m(y) \Rightarrow x = y}{\text{is-1-1}(m)}$$

$$\boxed{\text{map-}\vert\text{-extend-dom-left}}\quad \frac{s\!:\!A \xrightarrow{m} B}{s\!:\!(C \mid A) \xrightarrow{m} B}$$

$$\boxed{\text{map-}\vert\text{-extend-dom-right}}\quad \frac{s\!:\!A \xrightarrow{m} B}{s\!:\!(A \mid C) \xrightarrow{m} B}$$

$$\boxed{\text{map-}\vert\text{-extend-rng-left}}\quad \frac{s\!:\!A \xrightarrow{m} B}{s\!:\!A \xrightarrow{m} (C \mid B)}$$

$$\boxed{\text{map-}\vert\text{-extend-rng-right}}\quad \frac{s\!:\!A \xrightarrow{m} B}{s\!:\!A \xrightarrow{m} (B \mid C)}$$

$$\boxed{\text{map-comp-form-left}}\quad \frac{\begin{array}{c}\forall x\!:\!A \cdot \delta P(x) \\ x\!:\!A,\ P(x) \vdash_{\!\!x} f(x)\!:\!B \\ \exists s\!:\!A\text{-set} \cdot \forall y\!:\!A \cdot P(y) \Rightarrow y \in s\end{array}}{\{x \mapsto f(x) \mid x\!:\!A \cdot P(x)\}\!:\!A \xrightarrow{m} B}$$

$$\boxed{\text{map-comp-form-left-set}}\quad \frac{\begin{array}{c}s\!:\!A\text{-set} \\ x\!:\!A,\ x \in s \vdash_{\!\!x} f(x)\!:\!B\end{array}}{\{x \mapsto f(x) \mid x \in s\}\!:\!A \xrightarrow{m} B}$$

$$\boxed{\text{map-comp-form-set-ident}}\quad \frac{\begin{array}{c}s\!:\!A\text{-set} \\ x\!:\!A \vdash_{\!\!x} f(x)\!:\!B \\ x\!:\!A,\ x \in s \vdash_{\!\!x} g(x)\!:\!C \\ \forall a_1, a_2 \in s \cdot f(a_1) = f(a_2) \Rightarrow g(a_1) = g(a_2)\end{array}}{\{f(x) \mapsto g(x) \mid x \in s\}\!:\!B \xrightarrow{m} C}$$

$$\boxed{\text{map-comp-left-defn-}add}\quad \frac{\begin{array}{c}a\!:\!A;\ s\!:\!A\text{-set};\ f(a)\!:\!B \\ x\!:\!A,\ x \in s \vdash_{\!\!x} f(x)\!:\!B\end{array}}{\begin{array}{c}\{x \mapsto f(x) \mid x \in add(a, s)\} = \\ \{x \mapsto f(x) \mid x \in s\} \dagger \{a \mapsto f(a)\}\end{array}}$$

$$\boxed{\text{merge-form}}\quad \frac{\begin{array}{c}s\!:\!(A \xrightarrow{m} B)\text{-set} \\ \forall m_1, m_2 \in s \cdot compatible(m_1, m_2)\end{array}}{\text{merge } s\!:\!A \xrightarrow{m} B}$$

$$\boxed{\text{rng-defn}}\ \dfrac{m: A \xrightarrow{m} B}{\operatorname{rng} m = \{m(a) \mid a \in \operatorname{dom} m\}}$$

$$\boxed{\text{rng-defn-addm}}\ \dfrac{a: A;\ b: B;\ m: A \xrightarrow{m} B}{\operatorname{rng} addm(a \mapsto b, m) = add(b, \operatorname{rng}(\{a\} \triangleleft m))}$$

$$\boxed{\text{rng-defn-addm-}\in}\ \dfrac{a: A;\ b: B;\ m: A \xrightarrow{m} B;\ a \in \operatorname{dom} m}{\operatorname{rng} addm(a \mapsto b, m) = add(b, \operatorname{rng}(\{a\} \triangleleft m))}$$

$$\boxed{\text{rng-defn-inv}}\ \dfrac{m: A \xleftrightarrow{m} B}{\operatorname{rng}(m^{-1}) = \operatorname{dom} m}$$

$$\boxed{\text{rng-defn-map-comp}}\ \dfrac{\begin{array}{c}\forall x: A \cdot \delta P(x) \\ x: A,\ P(x) \vdash_{x} f(x): B \\ x: A,\ P(x) \vdash_{x} g(x): C \\ \exists s: B\text{-set} \cdot \forall y: A \cdot P(y) \Rightarrow f(y) \in s \\ \forall a_1, a_2: A \cdot P(a_1) \wedge P(a_2) \wedge f(a_1) = f(a_2) \Rightarrow g(a_1) = g(a_2)\end{array}}{\operatorname{rng}\{f(x) \mapsto g(x) \mid x: A \cdot P(x)\} = \{g(x) \mid x: A \cdot P(x)\}}$$

$$\boxed{\text{rng-form}}\ \dfrac{m: A \xrightarrow{m} B}{\operatorname{rng} m: B\text{-set}}$$

$$\boxed{\text{rng-form-bimap}}\ \dfrac{m: A \xleftrightarrow{m} B}{\operatorname{rng} m: B\text{-set}}$$

14.7 Finite sequences

Axioms

$$\boxed{\text{[]-form}}\ \dfrac{}{[\,]: A^*}\ \mathbf{Ax}$$

$$\boxed{\text{cons-form-seq+}}\ \dfrac{a: A;\ s: A^*}{\operatorname{cons}(a, s): A^+}\ \mathbf{Ax}$$

$$\boxed{\text{seq-indn}}\ \dfrac{\begin{array}{c}s: A^*;\ P([\,]) \\ h: A,\ t: A^*,\ P(t) \vdash_{h,t} P(\operatorname{cons}(h, t))\end{array}}{P(s)}\ \mathbf{Ax}$$

$$\boxed{\text{hd-defn-cons}}\ \dfrac{a: A;\ s: A^*}{\operatorname{hd}\operatorname{cons}(a, s) = a}\ \mathbf{Ax}$$

$$\boxed{\text{tl-defn-cons}}\ \dfrac{a: A;\ s: A^*}{\operatorname{tl}\operatorname{cons}(a, s) = s}\ \mathbf{Ax}$$

14.7 Finite sequences

$$\boxed{\text{$\sim$-defn-[ ]-left}} \quad \dfrac{s:A^*}{[\,]\,\widetilde{}\,s = s} \; \textbf{Ax}$$

$$\boxed{\text{$\sim$-defn-cons-left}} \quad \dfrac{a:A;\; s_1:A^*;\; s_2:A^*}{\text{cons}(a,s_1)\,\widetilde{}\,s_2 = \text{cons}(a, s_1\,\widetilde{}\,s_2)} \; \textbf{Ax}$$

$$\boxed{\text{appl-defn-hd}} \quad \dfrac{s:A^+}{s(1) = \text{hd}\,s} \; \textbf{Ax}$$

$$\boxed{\text{appl-defn-tl}} \quad \dfrac{s:A^+;\; i:\mathbb{N}_1;\; i\neq 1;\; i \leq \text{len}\,s}{s(i) = (\text{tl}\,s)(i-1)} \; \textbf{Ax}$$

Definitions

$A^+ \overset{\text{def}}{=} \ll s:A^* \mid s \neq [\,] \gg$

$[a] \overset{\text{def}}{=} \text{cons}(a,[\,])$

$\text{len}\,s \overset{\text{def}}{=}$ if $s = [\,]$ then 0 else $\text{succ}(\text{len}(\text{tl}\,s))$

$\text{elems}\,s \overset{\text{def}}{=}$ if $s = [\,]$ then $\{\,\}$ else $add(\text{hd}\,s, \text{elems}(\text{tl}\,s))$

$\text{conc}\,s \overset{\text{def}}{=}$ if $s = [\,]$ then $[\,]$ else $(\text{hd}\,s)\,\widetilde{}\,\text{conc}(\text{tl}\,s)$

$\text{inds}\,s \overset{\text{def}}{=} \{1,\ldots,\text{len}\,s\}$

Derived rules

$$\boxed{\delta\text{-[ ]-I}} \quad \dfrac{s:A^*}{\delta(s = [\,])}$$

$$\boxed{\text{=-seq-defn-cons}} \quad \dfrac{a_1:A;\; a_2:A;\; s_1:A^*;\; s_2:A^*}{\text{cons}(a_1,s_1) = \text{cons}(a_2,s_2) \Leftrightarrow a_1 = a_2 \wedge s_1 = s_2}$$

$$\boxed{\text{=-seq+-defn}} \quad \dfrac{s_1:A^+;\; s_2:A^+}{s_1 = s_2 \Leftrightarrow \text{hd}\,s_1 = \text{hd}\,s_2 \wedge \text{tl}\,s_1 = \text{tl}\,s_2}$$

$$\boxed{\in\text{-elems-cons-E}} \quad \dfrac{a:A;\; b:A;\; s:A^*;\; a \in \text{elems}\,\text{cons}(b,s)}{a = b \vee a \in \text{elems}\,s}$$

$$\boxed{\in\text{-inds-E}} \quad \dfrac{s:A^+;\; n:\mathbb{N}_1;\; n \in \text{inds}\,s}{n \leq \text{len}\,s}$$

$$\boxed{\notin\text{-elems-[\,]-I}}\quad \frac{a:A}{a\notin\text{elems}[\,]}$$

$$\boxed{\notin\text{-inds-[\,]-I}}\quad \frac{a:A}{a\notin\text{inds}[\,]}$$

$$\boxed{\frown\text{-ass}}\quad \frac{s_1:A^*;\ s_2:A^*;\ s_3:A^*}{(s_1\frown s_2)\frown s_3 = s_1\frown(s_2\frown s_3)}$$

$$\boxed{\frown\text{-defn-[\,]-right}}\quad \frac{s:A^*}{s\frown[\,]=s}$$

$$\boxed{\frown\text{-form}}\quad \frac{s_1:A^*;\ s_2:A^*}{s_1\frown s_2:A^*}$$

$$\boxed{[a]\text{-}\neq\text{-}[\,]}\quad \frac{a:A}{[a]\neq[\,]}$$

$$\boxed{[a]\text{-form}}\quad \frac{a:A}{[a]:A^*}$$

$$\boxed{\text{appl-form}}\quad \frac{s:A^+;\ i:\mathbb{N}_1;\ i\leq\text{len}\,s}{s(i):A}$$

$$\boxed{\text{conc-defn-[\,]}}\quad \frac{}{\text{conc}\,[\,]=[\,]}$$

$$\boxed{\text{conc-defn-cons}}\quad \frac{s_1:A^*;\ s_2:A^{**}}{\text{conc}\,\text{cons}(s_1,s_2)=s_1\frown\text{conc}\,s_2}$$

$$\boxed{\text{conc-form}}\quad \frac{s:A^{**}}{\text{conc}\,s:A^*}$$

$$\boxed{\text{cons-}\neq\text{-[\,]}}\quad \frac{a:A;\ s:A^*}{\text{cons}(a,s)\neq[\,]}$$

$$\boxed{\text{cons}\to\frown}\quad \frac{a:A;\ s:A^*}{[a]\frown s=\text{cons}(a,s)}$$

$$\boxed{\text{cons-form}}\quad \frac{a:A;\ s:A^*}{\text{cons}(a,s):A^*}$$

$$\boxed{\text{cons-I}}\quad \frac{s:A^+}{\text{cons}(\text{hd}\,s,\text{tl}\,s)=s}$$

$$\boxed{\text{elems}\to\text{those}}\quad \frac{s:A^*}{\text{elems}\,s=\{s(i)\mid i\in\text{inds}\,s\}}$$

14.7 Finite sequences

$$\boxed{\text{elems-defn-[ ]}} \quad \overline{\text{elems}\,[\,] = \{\,\}}$$

$$\boxed{\text{elems-defn-}\frown} \quad \frac{s_1\colon A^*;\ s_2\colon A^*}{\text{elems}\,(s_1 \frown s_2) = \text{elems}\,s_1 \cup \text{elems}\,s_2}$$

$$\boxed{\text{elems-defn-}\frown\text{-cons}} \quad \frac{a\colon A;\ s_1\colon A^*;\ s_2\colon A^*}{\text{elems}\,(\text{cons}(a,s_1) \frown s_2) = add(a, \text{elems}\,(s_1 \frown s_2))}$$

$$\boxed{\text{elems-defn-cons}} \quad \frac{a\colon A;\ s\colon A^*}{\text{elems}\,\text{cons}(a,s) = add(a, \text{elems}\,s)}$$

$$\boxed{\text{elems-defn-cons-}\{a\}} \quad \frac{a\colon A;\ s\colon A^*}{\text{elems}\,\text{cons}(a,s) = \{a\} \cup \text{elems}\,s}$$

$$\boxed{\text{elems-form}} \quad \frac{s\colon A^*}{\text{elems}\,s\colon A\text{-set}}$$

$$\boxed{\text{elems-form-seq+}} \quad \frac{s\colon A^+}{\text{elems}\,s\colon A\text{-set}}$$

$$\boxed{\text{hd-defn-[a]}} \quad \frac{a\colon A}{\text{hd}\,[a] = a}$$

$$\boxed{\text{hd-form}} \quad \frac{s\colon A^+}{\text{hd}\,s\colon A}$$

$$\boxed{\text{inds-defn-[ ]}} \quad \overline{\text{inds}\,[\,] = \{\,\}}$$

$$\boxed{\text{inds-form}} \quad \frac{s\colon A^*}{\text{inds}\,s\colon \mathbf{N}_1\text{-set}}$$

$$\boxed{\text{len-defn-[ ]}} \quad \overline{\text{len}\,[\,] = 0}$$

$$\boxed{\text{len-defn-}\frown} \quad \frac{s_1\colon A^*;\ s_2\colon A^*}{\text{len}\,(s_1 \frown s_2) = \text{len}\,s_1 + \text{len}\,s_2}$$

$$\boxed{\text{len-defn-[a]}} \quad \frac{a\colon A}{\text{len}\,[a] = 1}$$

$$\boxed{\text{len-defn-cons}} \quad \frac{a\colon A;\ s\colon A^*}{\text{len}\,\text{cons}(a,s) = \text{succ}\,\text{len}\,s}$$

$$\boxed{\text{len-defn-seq+}} \quad \frac{s\colon A^+}{\text{len}\,s = \text{succ}\,\text{len}\,\text{tl}\,s}$$

$$\boxed{\text{len-form}} \quad \frac{s:A^*}{\operatorname{len} s:\mathbb{N}}$$

$$\boxed{\text{len-form-seq+}} \quad \frac{s:A^+}{\operatorname{len} s:\mathbb{N}_1}$$

$$\boxed{\text{seq+-E}} \quad \frac{s:A^+}{s \neq [\,]}$$

$$\boxed{\text{seq+-I}} \quad \frac{s:A^*;\ s \neq [\,]}{s:A^+}$$

$$\boxed{\text{seq+-hnf}} \quad \frac{s:A^+ \qquad h:A,\ t:A^* \vdash_{h,t} P(\operatorname{cons}(h,t))}{P(s)}$$

$$\boxed{\text{seq+-indn}} \quad \frac{\begin{array}{c} s:A^+ \\ a:A \vdash_a P([a]) \\ h:A,\ t:A^+,\ P(t) \vdash_{h,t} P(\operatorname{cons}(h,t)) \end{array}}{P(s)}$$

$$\boxed{\text{seq+-supertype}} \quad \frac{s:A^+}{s:A^*}$$

$$\boxed{\text{seq-}\frown\text{-indn}} \quad \frac{\begin{array}{c} s:A^*;\ P([\,]) \\ a:A \vdash_a P([a]) \\ s_1:A^*,\ s_2:A^*,\ P(s_1),\ P(s_2) \vdash_{s_1,s_2} P(s_1 \frown s_2) \end{array}}{P(s)}$$

$$\boxed{\text{seq-|-extend-right}} \quad \frac{s:A^*}{s:A \mid B^*}$$

$$\boxed{\text{seq-|-extend-left}} \quad \frac{s:A^*}{s:B \mid A^*}$$

$$\boxed{\text{seq-sep}} \quad \frac{s:A^*}{s = [\,] \vee \exists h:A \cdot \exists t:A^* \cdot s = \operatorname{cons}(h,t)}$$

$$\boxed{\text{tl-defn-[a]}} \quad \frac{a:A}{\operatorname{tl}[a] = [\,]}$$

$$\boxed{\text{tl-form}} \quad \frac{s:A^+}{\operatorname{tl} s:A^*}$$

14.8 Booleans

Axioms

$$\boxed{\delta \to \mathbb{B}} \; \frac{\delta a}{a : \mathbb{B}} \; \text{Ax}$$

$$\boxed{\mathbb{B} \to \delta} \; \frac{a : \mathbb{B}}{\delta a} \; \text{Ax}$$

$$\boxed{\Leftrightarrow \to =} \; \frac{a \Leftrightarrow b}{a = b} \; \text{Ax}$$

Derived rules

$$\boxed{\forall\text{-form}} \; \frac{y : A \vdash_y P(y) : \mathbb{B}}{(\forall x : A \cdot P(x)) : \mathbb{B}}$$

$$\boxed{\forall\text{-form-set}} \; \frac{\begin{array}{c} s : A\text{-set} \\ y : A, \, y \in s \vdash_y P(y) : \mathbb{B} \end{array}}{(\forall x \in s \cdot P(x)) : \mathbb{B}}$$

$$\boxed{\wedge\text{-form}} \; \frac{e_1 : \mathbb{B}; \; e_2 : \mathbb{B}}{(e_1 \wedge e_2) : \mathbb{B}}$$

$$\boxed{\wedge\text{-form-sqt}} \; \frac{e_1 : \mathbb{B}; \; e_1 \vdash e_2 : \mathbb{B}}{(e_1 \wedge e_2) : \mathbb{B}}$$

$$\boxed{\mathbb{B}\text{-eval}} \; \frac{a : \mathbb{B}}{a = \text{true} \vee a = \text{false}}$$

$$\boxed{= \to \Leftrightarrow} \; \frac{a : \mathbb{B}; \; a = b}{a \Leftrightarrow b}$$

$$\boxed{=\text{-form}} \; \frac{a : A; \; b : A}{(a = b) : \mathbb{B}}$$

$$\boxed{\exists\text{-form}} \; \frac{y : A \vdash_y P(y) : \mathbb{B}}{(\exists x : A \cdot P(x)) : \mathbb{B}}$$

$$\boxed{\exists\text{-form-set}} \; \frac{\begin{array}{c} s : A\text{-set} \\ y : A, \, y \in s \vdash_y P(y) : \mathbb{B} \end{array}}{(\exists x \in s \cdot P(x)) : \mathbb{B}}$$

$$\boxed{\exists!\text{-form}} \; \frac{y : A \vdash_y P(y) : \mathbb{B}}{(\exists! x : A \cdot P(x)) : \mathbb{B}}$$

$\boxed{\exists!\text{-form-set}}\ \dfrac{s:A\text{-set}\quad y:A,\ y\in s\vdash_y P(y):\mathbb{B}}{(\exists!\,x\in s\cdot P(x)):\mathbb{B}}$

$\boxed{\Leftrightarrow\text{-form}}\ \dfrac{e_1:\mathbb{B};\ e_2:\mathbb{B}}{(e_1\Leftrightarrow e_2):\mathbb{B}}$

$\boxed{\Leftrightarrow\text{-subs-left}}\ \dfrac{a\Leftrightarrow b;\ P(b)}{P(a)}$

$\boxed{\Leftrightarrow\text{-subs-right}}\ \dfrac{a\Leftrightarrow b;\ P(a)}{P(b)}$

$\boxed{\Rightarrow\text{-form}}\ \dfrac{e_1:\mathbb{B};\ e_2:\mathbb{B}}{(e_1\Rightarrow e_2):\mathbb{B}}$

$\boxed{\Rightarrow\text{-form-sqt}}\ \dfrac{e_1:\mathbb{B};\ e_1\vdash e_2:\mathbb{B}}{(e_1\Rightarrow e_2):\mathbb{B}}$

$\boxed{\in\text{-form}}\ \dfrac{a:A;\ s:A\text{-set}}{(a\in s):\mathbb{B}}$

$\boxed{<\text{-form}}\ \dfrac{n_1:\mathbb{N};\ n_2:\mathbb{N}}{(n_1<n_2):\mathbb{B}}$

$\boxed{\leq\text{-form}}\ \dfrac{n_1:\mathbb{N};\ n_2:\mathbb{N}}{(n_1\leq n_2):\mathbb{B}}$

$\boxed{\neg\text{-form}}\ \dfrac{a:\mathbb{B}}{(\neg a):\mathbb{B}}$

$\boxed{\neq\text{-form}}\ \dfrac{a:A;\ b:A}{(a\neq b):\mathbb{B}}$

$\boxed{\notin\text{-form}}\ \dfrac{a:A;\ s:A\text{-set}}{(a\notin s):\mathbb{B}}$

$\boxed{\vee\text{-form}}\ \dfrac{e_1:\mathbb{B};\ e_2:\mathbb{B}}{(e_1\vee e_2):\mathbb{B}}$

$\boxed{\vee\text{-form-sqt}}\ \dfrac{e_1:\mathbb{B};\ \neg e_1\vdash e_2:\mathbb{B}}{(e_1\vee e_2):\mathbb{B}}$

$\boxed{\subseteq\text{-form}}\ \dfrac{s_1:A\text{-set};\ s_2:A\text{-set}}{(s_1\subseteq s_2):\mathbb{B}}$

14.9 Specifications

$$\boxed{\text{false-form}}\ \dfrac{}{\textit{false}:\mathbb{B}}$$

$$\boxed{\text{true-form}}\ \dfrac{}{\textit{true}:\mathbb{B}}$$

14.9 Specifications

For each construct definitions and rules are given in terms of a typical example.

14.9.1 Simple type definitions

$T = \textit{Texp}$
inv $e \;\triangleq\; P(e)$

Definitions

$\textit{inv-T}(e) \stackrel{\text{def}}{=} P(e)$

$T \stackrel{\text{def}}{=} \ll e\!:\!\textit{Texp} \mid \textit{inv-T}(e) \gg$

Derived rules

$$\boxed{\textit{T-form}}\ \dfrac{e\!:\!\textit{Texp};\ \textit{inv-T}(e)}{e\!:\!T}$$

$$\boxed{\textit{T-supertype}}\ \dfrac{e\!:\!T}{e\!:\!\textit{Texp}}$$

$$\boxed{\textit{T-E}}\ \dfrac{e\!:\!T}{\textit{inv-T}(e)}$$

Obligation

$$\boxed{\textit{inv-T-form}}\ \dfrac{e\!:\!\textit{Texp}}{\textit{inv-T}(e)\!:\!\mathbb{B}}$$

Validation

$$\boxed{\textit{T-inhab}}\ \dfrac{}{\textit{inhabited}(T)}$$

14.9.2 Composite type definitions

$T :: a : A$
$ b : B$
inv $\textit{mk-T}(a,b) \;\triangleq\; P(a,b)$

Definition

$$inv\text{-}T(a,b) \stackrel{\text{def}}{=} P(a,b)$$

Axioms

$$\boxed{mk\text{-}T\text{-form}} \quad \frac{x:A;\ y:B;\ inv\text{-}T(x,y)}{mk\text{-}T(x,y):T} \text{ Ax}$$

$$\boxed{a\text{-form}} \quad \frac{t:T}{t.a:A} \text{ Ax}$$

$$\boxed{b\text{-form}} \quad \frac{t:T}{t.b:B} \text{ Ax}$$

$$\boxed{a\text{-defn}} \quad \frac{mk\text{-}T(x,y):T}{mk\text{-}T(x,y).a = x} \text{ Ax}$$

$$\boxed{b\text{-defn}} \quad \frac{mk\text{-}T(x,y):T}{mk\text{-}T(x,y).b = y} \text{ Ax}$$

$$\boxed{mk\text{-}T\text{-defn}} \quad \frac{t:T}{mk\text{-}T(t.a,t.b) = t} \text{ Ax}$$

$$\boxed{inv\text{-}T\text{-I}} \quad \frac{mk\text{-}T(x,y):T}{inv\text{-}T(x,y)} \text{ Ax}$$

Obligation

$$\boxed{inv\text{-}T\text{-form}} \quad \frac{x:A;\ y:B}{inv\text{-}T(x,y):\mathbb{B}}$$

Validation

$$\boxed{T\text{-inhab}} \quad \frac{}{inhabited(T)}$$

14.9.3 The state

state S of
    $a : A$
    $b : B$
inv $mk\text{-}S(a,b) \;\underline{\triangle}\; P(a,b)$
init $mk\text{-}S(a,b) \;\underline{\triangle}\; Q(a,b)$
end

The same definitions and rules that appear for composite types apply to the state and the invariant, together with a definition and obligations for the initialisation condition.

14.9 Specifications

Definition

$$\text{init-}S(s) \stackrel{\text{def}}{=} Q(s.a, s.b)$$

(Note that unlike *inv-S* which is defined on the components of the state, *init-S* is treated as a predicate in the whole state type S.)

Obligations

$$\boxed{\text{init-}S\text{-form}} \quad \frac{s:S}{\text{init-}S(s):\mathbb{B}}$$

$$\boxed{\text{init-}S\text{-sat}} \quad \frac{}{\exists s:S \cdot \text{init-}S(s)}$$

14.9.4 Functions

Explicit function definitions

$$f : A \times B \to C$$
$$f(a, b) \triangleq E(a, b)$$
$$\text{pre } P(a, b)$$

Definition

$$\text{pre-}f(a, b) \stackrel{\text{def}}{=} P(a, b)$$

Obligation

$$\boxed{\text{pre-}f\text{-form}} \quad \frac{a:A;\ b:B}{\text{pre-}f(a,b):\mathbb{B}}$$

If a parameter of f is not mentioned in the precondition expression, the definition takes fewer parameters.

Axiom

$$\boxed{f\text{-defn}_0} \quad \frac{a:A;\ b:B;\ E(a,b):C;\ \text{pre-}f(a,b)}{f(a,b) = E(a,b)} \text{ Ax}$$

If a parameter is not mentioned, it is still necessary to keep the typing hypothesis for that argument.

Obligation

$$\boxed{f\text{-wff}}\ \frac{a{:}A;\ b{:}B;\ pre\text{-}f(a,b)}{E(a,b){:}C}$$

Working rule (for use once the obligation has been discharged)

$$\boxed{f\text{-defn}}\ \frac{a{:}A;\ b{:}B;\ pre\text{-}f(a,b)}{f(a,b) = E(a,b)}$$

Implicit function definitions

$f\ (a{:}A, b{:}B)\ c{:}C$
pre $Pr(a,b)$
post $Po(a,b,c)$

Definitions

$pre\text{-}f(a,b) \stackrel{\text{def}}{=} Pr(a,b)$

$post\text{-}f(a,b,c) \stackrel{\text{def}}{=} Po(a,b,c)$

If a parameter is not mentioned, the definitions take fewer parameters.

Axioms

$$\boxed{f\text{-form}_0}\ \frac{a{:}A;\ b{:}B;\ pre\text{-}f(a,b);\ \exists c{:}C \cdot post\text{-}f(a,b,c)}{f(a,b){:}C}\ \mathbf{Ax}$$

$$\boxed{f\text{-defn}_0}\ \frac{a{:}A;\ b{:}B;\ pre\text{-}f(a,b);\ \exists c{:}C \cdot post\text{-}f(a,b,c)}{post\text{-}f(a,b,f(a,b))}\ \mathbf{Ax}$$

Obligations

$$\boxed{pre\text{-}f\text{-form}}\ \frac{a{:}A;\ b{:}B}{pre\text{-}f(a,b){:}\mathbb{B}}$$

$$\boxed{post\text{-}f\text{-form}}\ \frac{a{:}A;\ b{:}B;\ c{:}C;\ pre\text{-}f(a,b)}{post\text{-}f(a,b,c){:}\mathbb{B}}$$

$$\boxed{f\text{-sat}}\ \frac{a{:}A;\ b{:}B;\ pre\text{-}f(a,b)}{\exists c{:}C \cdot post\text{-}f(a,b,c)}$$

Working rules (for use once the proof obligations have been discharged)

$$\boxed{f\text{-form}}\ \frac{a{:}A;\ b{:}B;\ pre\text{-}f(a,b)}{f(a,b){:}C}$$

14.9 Specifications

$$\boxed{f\text{-defn}} \; \frac{a:A; \; b:B; \; pre\text{-}f(a,b)}{post\text{-}f(a,b,f(a,b))}$$

14.9.5 Value expressions

$v:T \;\; \triangleq \;\; E$

Axiom

$$\boxed{v\text{-defn}_0} \; \frac{E:T}{v=E} \; \text{Ax}$$

Obligation

$$\boxed{v\text{-form}} \; \frac{}{E:T}$$

Working rule (for use once the proof obligation has been discharged)

$$\boxed{v\text{-defn}} \; \frac{}{v=E}$$

14.9.6 Operations

The definitions and obligation for operations are given for the following state model and implicit operation:

```
state Σ of                          OP (i:I) o:O
    r : R                               ext rd r : R
    w : W                                   wr w : W
    u : U                               pre Pr(i, r, w)
inv mk-Σ(r, w, u)   ≜   ...         post Po(i, o, r, ⃖w, w)
init mk-Σ(r, w, u)  ≜   ...
end
```

Definitions

$pre\text{-}OP(i, r, w) \;\stackrel{\text{def}}{=}\; Pr(i, r, w)$

$post\text{-}OP(i, o, r, \overleftarrow{w}, w) \;\stackrel{\text{def}}{=}\; Po(i, o, r, \overleftarrow{w}, w)$

Obligation

$$\boxed{OP\text{-sat}} \; \frac{i:I; \; mk\text{-}\Sigma(\overleftarrow{r}, \overleftarrow{w}, \overleftarrow{u}):\Sigma; \; pre\text{-}OP(i, \overleftarrow{r}, \overleftarrow{w})}{\exists o:O, mk\text{-}\Sigma(r, w, u):\Sigma \cdot \\ post\text{-}OP(i, o, r, \overleftarrow{w}, w) \wedge r = \overleftarrow{r} \wedge u = \overleftarrow{u}}$$

14.10 Reifications

Rules are given in terms of a typical example:

<table>
<tr><td>Abstract state</td><td>Concrete state</td></tr>
<tr><td>

state S_a of
  r_a : R_a
  w_a : W_a
  u_a : U_a
inv $mk\text{-}S_a(r_a, w_a, u_a) \triangleq inv_a(r_a, w_a, u_a)$
init $mk\text{-}S_a(r_a, w_a, u_a) \triangleq init_a(r_a, w_a, u_a)$
end

</td><td>

state S_c of
  r_c : R_c
  w_c : W_c
  u_c : U_c
inv $mk\text{-}S_c(r_c, w_c, u_c) \triangleq inv_c(r_c, w_c, u_c)$
init $mk\text{-}S_c(r_c, w_c, u_c) \triangleq init_c(r_c, w_c, u_c)$
end

</td></tr>
</table>

Although the two states have corresponding components, this does not imply that retrieval is component-wise.

14.10.1 Retrieve functions

Retrieval is defined between the whole states S_c and S_a.

$retr\text{-}S : S_c \to S_a$
$retr\text{-}S(s_c: S_c) \triangleq body\text{-}expression$

Definitions, axioms and obligations for explicit functions apply (Section 14.9.4). Totality is formalised by the lack of a precondition.

Obligations

$$\boxed{retr\text{-}S\text{-}adeq} \quad \frac{s_a: S_a}{\exists s_c: S_c \cdot retr\text{-}S(s_c) = s_a}$$

$$\boxed{init\text{-}adeq} \quad \frac{\begin{array}{c} s_a: S_a; \ s_c: S_c \\ s_a = retr\text{-}S(s_c) \\ init\text{-}S_c(s_c) \end{array}}{init\text{-}S_a(s_a)}$$

14.10.2 Operation modelling

<table>
<tr><td>Abstract operation</td><td>Concrete operation</td></tr>
<tr><td>

OP_a $(a: A)$ $t: T$
ext rd r_a : R_a
    wr w_a : W_a
pre $P_a(a, r_a, w_a)$
post $Q_a(a, t, r_a, \overleftarrow{w_a}, w_a)$

</td><td>

OP_c $(a: A)$ $t: T$
ext rd r_c : R_c
    wr w_c : W_c
pre $P_c(a, r_c, w_c)$
post $Q_c(a, t, r_c, \overleftarrow{w_c}, w_c)$

</td></tr>
</table>

Operations have corresponding names and the same argument and result types.

14.11 Case study I: abstract specification

Obligations

$$\boxed{\text{OP-dom-obl}}\ \frac{\begin{array}{c}a{:}A;\ s_c{:}S_c;\ s_a{:}S_a\\ s_a = \text{retr-}S(s_c)\\ \text{pre-}OP_a(a, s_a.r_a, s_a.w_a)\end{array}}{\text{pre-}OP_c(a, s_c.r_c, s_c.w_c)}$$

$$\boxed{\text{OP-res-obl}}\ \frac{\begin{array}{c}a{:}A;\ t{:}T\\ s_a{:}S_a;\ s_c{:}S_c;\ s_a = \text{retr-}S(s_c)\\ \overleftarrow{s_a}{:}S_a;\ \overleftarrow{s_c}{:}S_c;\ \overleftarrow{s_a} = \text{retr-}S(\overleftarrow{s_c})\\ \text{pre-}OP_a(a, \overleftarrow{s_a}.r_a, \overleftarrow{s_a}.w_a)\\ \text{post-}OP_c(a, t, s_c.r_c, \overleftarrow{s_c}.w_c, s_c.w_c)\\ \wedge\ s_c.r_c = \overleftarrow{s_c}.r_c\ \wedge\ s_c.u_c = \overleftarrow{s_c}.u_c\end{array}}{\begin{array}{c}\text{post-}OP_a(a, t, s_a.r_a, \overleftarrow{s_a}.w_a, s_a.w_a)\\ \wedge\ s_a.r_a = \overleftarrow{s_a}.r_a\ \wedge\ s_a.u_a = \overleftarrow{s_a}.u_a\end{array}}$$

14.10.3 Implementing functions

Implicit function	*Explicit function*
$f_i\ (a{:}A)\ r{:}R$	$f_e : A \to R$
pre $P_i(a)$	$f_e(a) \triangleq h(a)$
post $Q_i(a, r)$	pre $P_e(a)$

The definitions, axioms and obligations for implicit and explicit functions apply (Section 14.9.4), in addition to the obligations listed below.

Obligations

$$\boxed{f_i\text{-}f_e\text{-dom-obl}}\ \frac{a{:}A;\ \text{pre-}f_i(a)}{\text{pre-}f_e(a)}$$

$$\boxed{f_i\text{-}f_e\text{-satn}}\ \frac{a{:}A;\ \text{pre-}f_i(a)}{\text{post-}f_i(a, f_e(a))}$$

14.11 Case study I: abstract specification

Axioms

$$\boxed{\text{mk-ATC-form}}\ \frac{\begin{array}{c}cs{:}\text{Controller-set};\ con{:}\text{Space} \overset{m}{\longleftrightarrow} \text{Controller}\\ cap{:}\text{Space} \overset{m}{\longrightarrow} \mathbb{N};\ loc{:}\text{Aircraft} \overset{m}{\longrightarrow} \text{Space}\\ \text{inv-ATC}(cs, con, cap, loc)\end{array}}{\text{mk-ATC}(cs, con, cap, loc){:}\text{ATC}}\ \textbf{Ax}$$

$$\boxed{\text{mk-ATC-defn}}\ \frac{\sigma{:}\text{ATC}}{\text{mk-ATC}(\sigma.\textit{onduty}, \sigma.\textit{control}, \sigma.\textit{capacity}, \sigma.\textit{location}) = \sigma}\ \textbf{Ax}$$

$$\boxed{\textit{inv-ATC-I}}\ \frac{mk\text{-}ATC(cs, con, cap, loc): ATC}{inv\text{-}ATC(cs, con, cap, loc)}\ \textbf{Ax}$$

$$\boxed{\textit{capacity-defn}}\ \frac{mk\text{-}ATC(cs, con, cap, loc): ATC}{mk\text{-}ATC(cs, con, cap, loc).capacity = cap}\ \textbf{Ax}$$

$$\boxed{\textit{capacity-form}}\ \frac{\sigma: ATC}{\sigma.capacity: Space \xrightarrow{m} \mathbb{N}}\ \textbf{Ax}$$

$$\boxed{\textit{control-defn}}\ \frac{mk\text{-}ATC(cs, con, cap, loc): ATC}{mk\text{-}ATC(cs, con, cap, loc).control = con}\ \textbf{Ax}$$

$$\boxed{\textit{control-form}}\ \frac{\sigma: ATC}{\sigma.control: Space \xleftarrow{m} Controller}\ \textbf{Ax}$$

$$\boxed{\textit{location-defn}}\ \frac{mk\text{-}ATC(cs, con, cap, loc): ATC}{mk\text{-}ATC(cs, con, cap, loc).location = loc}\ \textbf{Ax}$$

$$\boxed{\textit{location-form}}\ \frac{\sigma: ATC}{\sigma.location: Aircraft \xrightarrow{m} Space}\ \textbf{Ax}$$

$$\boxed{\textit{onduty-defn}}\ \frac{mk\text{-}ATC(cs, con, cap, loc): ATC}{mk\text{-}ATC(cs, con, cap, loc).onduty = cs}\ \textbf{Ax}$$

$$\boxed{\textit{onduty-form}}\ \frac{\sigma: ATC}{\sigma.onduty: Controller\text{-set}}\ \textbf{Ax}$$

$$\boxed{\textit{controllerOf-defn}_0}\ \frac{p: Aircraft;\ \sigma: ATC;\ pre\text{-}controllerOf(p, \sigma)}{(\sigma.control(\sigma.location(p))): Controller}\ \textbf{Ax}$$
$$controllerOf(p, \sigma) = \sigma.control(\sigma.location(p))$$

$$\boxed{\textit{is-activated-defn}_0}\ \frac{s: Space;\ \sigma: ATC;\ (s \in \text{dom}(\sigma.control)): \mathbb{B}}{is\text{-}activated(s, \sigma) = (s \in \text{dom}(\sigma.control))}\ \textbf{Ax}$$

$$\boxed{\textit{is-known-defn}_0}\ \frac{p: Aircraft;\ \sigma: ATC;\ (p \in \text{dom}(\sigma.location)): \mathbb{B}}{is\text{-}known(p, \sigma) = (p \in \text{dom}(\sigma.location))}\ \textbf{Ax}$$

$$\boxed{\textit{numOfAircraft-defn}_0}\ \frac{s: Space;\ loc: Aircraft \xrightarrow{m} Space}{\text{card}(\text{dom}(loc \triangleright \{s\})): \mathbb{N}}\ \textbf{Ax}$$
$$numOfAircraft(s, loc) = \text{card}(\text{dom}(loc \triangleright \{s\}))$$

Definitions

$inv\text{-}ATC(cs, con, cap, loc) \stackrel{\text{def}}{=} \text{rng}\,con \subseteq cs \land \text{dom}\,con \subseteq \text{dom}\,cap \land$
$\qquad \text{rng}\,loc \subseteq \text{dom}\,con \land \forall s \in \text{rng}\,loc \cdot numOfAircraft(s, loc) \leq cap(s)$

$init\text{-}ATC(\sigma) \stackrel{\text{def}}{=} \sigma.onduty = \{\,\} \land \sigma.capacity = \{\mapsto\}$

14.11 Case study I: abstract specification

$pre\text{-}Activate(s, cs, con, cap) \stackrel{\text{def}}{=} s \in (\text{dom}\, cap \setminus \text{dom}\, con) \land \text{rng}\, con \neq cs$

$pre\text{-}Commission(s, cap) \stackrel{\text{def}}{=} s \notin \text{dom}\, cap$

$pre\text{-}controllerOf(p, \sigma) \stackrel{\text{def}}{=} is\text{-}known(p, \sigma)$

$pre\text{-}Decommission(s, con, cap) \stackrel{\text{def}}{=} s \in (\text{dom}\, cap \setminus \text{dom}\, con)$

$pre\text{-}ResetCapacity(s, n, cap, loc) \stackrel{\text{def}}{=} s \in \text{dom}\, cap \land numOfAircraft(s, loc) \leq n$

$post\text{-}Activate(s, c, \overleftarrow{con}, con) \stackrel{\text{def}}{=} c \in cs \land c \notin \text{rng}\, \overleftarrow{con} \land con = \overleftarrow{con} \dagger \{s \mapsto c\}$

$post\text{-}Commission(s, n, \overleftarrow{cap}, cap) \stackrel{\text{def}}{=} cap = \overleftarrow{cap} \dagger \{s \mapsto n\}$

$post\text{-}Decommission(s, \overleftarrow{cap}, cap) \stackrel{\text{def}}{=} cap = \{s\} \triangleleft \overleftarrow{cap}$

$post\text{-}ResetCapacity(s, n, \overleftarrow{cap}, cap) \stackrel{\text{def}}{=} cap = \overleftarrow{cap} \dagger \{s \mapsto n\}$

Proof obligations

$\boxed{Commission\text{-}sat}\ \dfrac{\begin{array}{c} s\text{:}\,Space;\ n\text{:}\,\mathbb{N};\ cs\text{:}\,Controller\text{-}set \\ con\text{:}\,Space \stackrel{m}{\leftrightarrow} Controller;\ \overleftarrow{cap}\text{:}\,Space \stackrel{m}{\to} \mathbb{N} \\ loc\text{:}\,Aircraft \stackrel{m}{\to} Space;\ inv\text{-}ATC(cs, con, \overleftarrow{cap}, loc) \\ pre\text{-}Commission(s, \overleftarrow{cap}) \end{array}}{\exists cap\text{:}\,Space \stackrel{m}{\to} \mathbb{N} \cdot \\ post\text{-}Commission(s, n, \overleftarrow{cap}, cap) \land inv\text{-}ATC(cs, con, cap, loc)}$

$\boxed{controllerOf\text{-}form}\ \dfrac{p\text{:}\,Aircraft;\ \sigma\text{:}\,ATC;\ pre\text{-}controllerOf(p, \sigma)}{controllerOf(p, \sigma)\text{:}\,Controller}$

$\boxed{init\text{-}ATC\text{-}form}\ \dfrac{\sigma\text{:}\,ATC}{init\text{-}ATC(\sigma)\text{:}\,\mathbb{B}}$

$\boxed{init\text{-}ATC\text{-}sat}\ \dfrac{}{\exists \sigma\text{:}\,ATC \cdot init\text{-}ATC(\sigma)}$

$\boxed{inv\text{-}ATC\text{-}form}\ \dfrac{\begin{array}{c} cs\text{:}\,Controller\text{-}set;\ con\text{:}\,Space \stackrel{m}{\leftrightarrow} Controller \\ cap\text{:}\,Space \stackrel{m}{\to} \mathbb{N};\ loc\text{:}\,Aircraft \stackrel{m}{\to} Space \end{array}}{inv\text{-}ATC(cs, con, cap, loc)\text{:}\,\mathbb{B}}$

$\boxed{is\text{-}activated\text{-}form}\ \dfrac{s\text{:}\,Space;\ \sigma\text{:}\,ATC}{is\text{-}activated(s, \sigma)\text{:}\,\mathbb{B}}$

$$\boxed{\textit{is-known}\text{-form}}\ \frac{p:\textit{Aircraft};\ \sigma:\textit{ATC}}{\textit{is-known}(p,\sigma):\mathbb{B}}$$

$$\boxed{\textit{numOfAircraft}\text{-form}}\ \frac{s:\textit{Space};\ \textit{loc}:\textit{Aircraft} \xrightarrow{m} \textit{Space}}{\textit{numOfAircraft}(s,\textit{loc}):\mathbb{N}}$$

$$\boxed{\textit{post-Commission}\text{-form}}\ \frac{\begin{array}{c}s:\textit{Space};\ n:\mathbb{N};\ cs:\textit{Controller}\text{-set}\\ \textit{con}:\textit{Space} \xleftrightarrow{m} \textit{Controller};\ \overleftarrow{\textit{cap}}:\textit{Space} \xrightarrow{m} \mathbb{N}\\ \textit{cap}:\textit{Space} \xrightarrow{m} \mathbb{N};\ \textit{loc}:\textit{Aircraft} \xrightarrow{m} \textit{Space}\\ \textit{inv-ATC}(cs,\textit{con},\overleftarrow{\textit{cap}},\textit{loc});\ \textit{pre-Commission}(s,\overleftarrow{\textit{cap}})\end{array}}{\textit{post-Commission}(s,n,\overleftarrow{\textit{cap}},\textit{cap}):\mathbb{B}}$$

$$\boxed{\textit{post-ResetCapacity}\text{-form}}\ \frac{\begin{array}{c}s:\textit{Space};\ n:\mathbb{N};\ cs:\textit{Controller}\text{-set}\\ \textit{con}:\textit{Space} \xleftrightarrow{m} \textit{Controller};\ \overleftarrow{\textit{cap}}:\textit{Space} \xrightarrow{m} \mathbb{N}\\ \textit{cap}:\textit{Space} \xrightarrow{m} \mathbb{N};\ \textit{loc}:\textit{Aircraft} \xrightarrow{m} \textit{Space}\\ \textit{inv-ATC}(cs,\textit{con},\overleftarrow{\textit{cap}},\textit{loc})\\ \textit{pre-ResetCapacity}(s,n,\overleftarrow{\textit{cap}},\textit{loc})\end{array}}{\textit{post-ResetCapacity}(s,n,\overleftarrow{\textit{cap}},\textit{cap}):\mathbb{B}}$$

$$\boxed{\textit{pre-Commission}\text{-form}}\ \frac{\begin{array}{c}s:\textit{Space};\ n:\mathbb{N};\ cs:\textit{Controller}\text{-set}\\ \textit{con}:\textit{Space} \xleftrightarrow{m} \textit{Controller};\ \textit{cap}:\textit{Space} \xrightarrow{m} \mathbb{N}\\ \textit{loc}:\textit{Aircraft} \xrightarrow{m} \textit{Space};\ \textit{inv-ATC}(cs,\textit{con},\textit{cap},\textit{loc})\end{array}}{\textit{pre-Commission}(s,\textit{cap}):\mathbb{B}}$$

$$\boxed{\textit{pre-controllerOf}\text{-form}}\ \frac{p:\textit{Aircraft};\ \sigma:\textit{ATC}}{\textit{pre-controllerOf}(p,\sigma):\mathbb{B}}$$

$$\boxed{\textit{pre-ResetCapacity}\text{-form}}\ \frac{\begin{array}{c}s:\textit{Space};\ n:\mathbb{N};\ cs:\textit{Controller}\text{-set}\\ \textit{con}:\textit{Space} \xleftrightarrow{m} \textit{Controller};\ \textit{cap}:\textit{Space} \xrightarrow{m} \mathbb{N}\\ \textit{loc}:\textit{Aircraft} \xrightarrow{m} \textit{Space};\ \textit{inv-ATC}(cs,\textit{con},\textit{cap},\textit{loc})\end{array}}{\textit{pre-ResetCapacity}(s,n,\textit{cap},\textit{loc}):\mathbb{B}}$$

$$\boxed{\textit{ResetCapacity}\text{-sat}}\ \frac{\begin{array}{c}s:\textit{Space};\ n:\mathbb{N};\ cs:\textit{Controller}\text{-set}\\ \textit{con}:\textit{Space} \xleftrightarrow{m} \textit{Controller};\ \overleftarrow{\textit{cap}}:\textit{Space} \xrightarrow{m} \mathbb{N}\\ \textit{loc}:\textit{Aircraft} \xrightarrow{m} \textit{Space};\ \textit{inv-ATC}(cs,\textit{con},\overleftarrow{\textit{cap}},\textit{loc})\\ \textit{pre-ResetCapacity}(s,n,\overleftarrow{\textit{cap}},\textit{loc})\end{array}}{\exists \textit{cap}:\textit{Space} \xrightarrow{m} \mathbb{N}\cdot\\ \textit{post-ResetCapacity}(s,n,\overleftarrow{\textit{cap}},\textit{cap}) \wedge \textit{inv-ATC}(cs,\textit{con},\textit{cap},\textit{loc})}$$

14.11 Case study I: abstract specification

Validation conditions

$$\textit{Activate-lemma} \; \frac{\begin{array}{c} s\colon Space;\; c\colon Controller \\ \textit{mk-ATC}(cs, \overleftarrow{con}, cap, loc)\colon ATC;\; \textit{mk-ATC}(cs, con, cap, loc)\colon ATC \\ \textit{pre-Activate}(s, cs, \overleftarrow{con}, cap);\; \textit{post-Activate}(s, c, \overleftarrow{con}, con) \end{array}}{c \in (cs \setminus \textrm{rng}\,\overleftarrow{con})}$$

$$\textit{aircraft-controller-unique} \; \frac{p\colon Aircraft;\; \sigma\colon ATC;\; \textit{is-known}(p, \sigma)}{\exists!\, c\colon Controller \cdot c = \textit{controllerOf}(p, \sigma)}$$

$$\textit{aircraft-in-unique-space} \; \frac{p\colon Aircraft;\; \sigma\colon ATC;\; \textit{is-known}(p, \sigma)}{\exists!\, s\colon Space \cdot s = \sigma.\textit{location}(p)}$$

$$\textit{airspace-controller-unique} \; \frac{s\colon Space;\; \sigma\colon ATC;\; \textit{is-activated}(s, \sigma)}{\exists!\, c\colon Controller \cdot c = \sigma.\textit{control}(s)}$$

$$\textit{controllerOf-onduty} \; \frac{p\colon Aircraft;\; \sigma\colon ATC;\; \textit{is-known}(p, \sigma)}{\textit{controllerOf}(p, \sigma) \in \sigma.\textit{onduty}}$$

$$\textit{Decommission-lemma} \; \frac{s\colon Space;\; \textit{mk-ATC}(cs, con, cap, loc)\colon ATC;\; s \in \textrm{rng}\, loc}{\neg\, \textit{pre-Decommission}(s, con, cap)}$$

$$\textit{no-double-assignment} \; \frac{\begin{array}{c} s_1\colon Space;\; s_2\colon Space;\; \sigma\colon ATC;\; \textit{is-activated}(s_1, \sigma) \\ \textit{is-activated}(s_2, \sigma);\; \sigma.\textit{control}(s_1) = \sigma.\textit{control}(s_2) \end{array}}{s_1 = s_2}$$

$$\textit{not activated} \Rightarrow \textit{empty} \; \frac{s\colon Space;\; \sigma\colon ATC;\; \neg\, (\textit{is-activated}(s, \sigma))}{\textit{numOfAircraft}(s, \sigma.\textit{location}) = 0}$$

Useful lemmas

$$\neg\textit{-is-activated-E} \; \frac{s\colon Space;\; \sigma\colon ATC;\; \neg\, (\textit{is-activated}(s, \sigma))}{s \notin \textrm{dom}(\sigma.\textit{control})}$$

$$\textit{capacity-form-mk} \; \frac{\textit{mk-ATC}(cs, con, cap, loc)\colon ATC}{cap\colon Space \xrightarrow{m} \mathbb{N}}$$

$$\textit{control-form-mk} \; \frac{\textit{mk-ATC}(cs, con, cap, loc)\colon ATC}{con\colon Space \xleftrightarrow{m} Controller}$$

$$\textit{controllerOf-defn} \; \frac{p\colon Aircraft;\; \sigma\colon ATC;\; \textit{is-known}(p, \sigma)}{\textit{controllerOf}(p, \sigma) = \sigma.\textit{control}(\sigma.\textit{location}(p))}$$

$$\textit{controllerOf-wff} \; \frac{p\colon Aircraft;\; \sigma\colon ATC;\; \textit{pre-controllerOf}(p, \sigma)}{(\sigma.\textit{control}(\sigma.\textit{location}(p)))\colon Controller}$$

$\boxed{\textit{inv-ATC}\text{-E-clause1}} \quad \dfrac{cs\colon \textit{Controller}\text{-set};\ con\colon \textit{Space} \xleftrightarrow{m} \textit{Controller} \\ cap\colon \textit{Space} \xrightarrow{m} \mathbf{N};\ loc\colon \textit{Aircraft} \xrightarrow{m} \textit{Space} \\ \textit{inv-ATC}(cs, con, cap, loc)}{\operatorname{rng} con \subseteq cs}$

$\boxed{\textit{inv-ATC}\text{-E-clause2}} \quad \dfrac{cs\colon \textit{Controller}\text{-set};\ con\colon \textit{Space} \xleftrightarrow{m} \textit{Controller} \\ cap\colon \textit{Space} \xrightarrow{m} \mathbf{N};\ loc\colon \textit{Aircraft} \xrightarrow{m} \textit{Space} \\ \textit{inv-ATC}(cs, con, cap, loc)}{\operatorname{dom} con \subseteq \operatorname{dom} cap}$

$\boxed{\textit{inv-ATC}\text{-E-clause3}} \quad \dfrac{cs\colon \textit{Controller}\text{-set};\ con\colon \textit{Space} \xleftrightarrow{m} \textit{Controller} \\ cap\colon \textit{Space} \xrightarrow{m} \mathbf{N};\ loc\colon \textit{Aircraft} \xrightarrow{m} \textit{Space} \\ \textit{inv-ATC}(cs, con, cap, loc)}{\operatorname{rng} loc \subseteq \operatorname{dom} con}$

$\boxed{\textit{inv-ATC}\text{-E-clause4}} \quad \dfrac{cs\colon \textit{Controller}\text{-set};\ con\colon \textit{Space} \xleftrightarrow{m} \textit{Controller} \\ cap\colon \textit{Space} \xrightarrow{m} \mathbf{N};\ loc\colon \textit{Aircraft} \xrightarrow{m} \textit{Space} \\ \textit{inv-ATC}(cs, con, cap, loc)}{\forall s \in \operatorname{rng} loc \cdot \textit{numOfAircraft}(s, loc) \leq cap(s)}$

$\boxed{\textit{inv-ATC}\text{-I-clause1}} \quad \dfrac{\sigma\colon \textit{ATC}}{\operatorname{rng} \sigma.\textit{control} \subseteq \sigma.\textit{onduty}}$

$\boxed{\textit{inv-ATC}\text{-I-clause3}} \quad \dfrac{\sigma\colon \textit{ATC}}{\operatorname{rng} \sigma.\textit{location} \subseteq \operatorname{dom} \sigma.\textit{control}}$

$\boxed{\textit{inv-ATC}\text{-I-mk-clause1}} \quad \dfrac{\textit{mk-ATC}(cs, con, cap, loc)\colon \textit{ATC}}{\operatorname{rng} con \subseteq cs}$

$\boxed{\textit{inv-ATC}\text{-I-mk-clause2}} \quad \dfrac{\textit{mk-ATC}(cs, con, cap, loc)\colon \textit{ATC}}{\operatorname{dom} con \subseteq \operatorname{dom} cap}$

$\boxed{\textit{inv-ATC}\text{-I-mk-clause3}} \quad \dfrac{\textit{mk-ATC}(cs, con, cap, loc)\colon \textit{ATC}}{\operatorname{rng} loc \subseteq \operatorname{dom} con}$

$\boxed{\textit{inv-ATC}\text{-I-mk-clause4}} \quad \dfrac{\textit{mk-ATC}(cs, con, cap, loc)\colon \textit{ATC}}{\forall s \in \operatorname{rng} loc \cdot \textit{numOfAircraft}(s, loc) \leq cap(s)}$

$\boxed{\textit{inv-ATC}\text{-I-separate}} \quad \dfrac{cs\colon \textit{Controller}\text{-set};\ con\colon \textit{Space} \xleftrightarrow{m} \textit{Controller} \\ cap\colon \textit{Space} \xrightarrow{m} \mathbf{N};\ loc\colon \textit{Aircraft} \xrightarrow{m} \textit{Space} \\ \operatorname{rng} con \subseteq cs;\ \operatorname{dom} con \subseteq \operatorname{dom} cap;\ \operatorname{rng} loc \subseteq \operatorname{dom} con \\ \forall s \in \operatorname{rng} loc \cdot \textit{numOfAircraft}(s, loc) \leq cap(s)}{\textit{inv-ATC}(cs, con, cap, loc)}$

$\boxed{\textit{is-activated}\text{-defn}} \quad \dfrac{s\colon \textit{Space};\ \sigma\colon \textit{ATC}}{\textit{is-activated}(s, \sigma) = (s \in \operatorname{dom} \sigma.\textit{control})}$

14.12 Case study II: refinement

$$\boxed{\text{is-activated-E}} \; \frac{s \colon Space; \;\; \sigma \colon ATC; \;\; is\text{-}activated(s, \sigma)}{s \in \mathrm{dom}\,(\sigma.control)}$$

$$\boxed{\text{is-activated-I}} \; \frac{s \colon Space; \;\; \sigma \colon ATC; \;\; s \in \mathrm{dom}\,(\sigma.control)}{is\text{-}activated(s, \sigma)}$$

$$\boxed{\text{is-activated-wff}} \; \frac{s \colon Space; \;\; \sigma \colon ATC}{(s \in \mathrm{dom}\,(\sigma.control)) \colon \mathbb{B}}$$

$$\boxed{\text{is-known-defn}} \; \frac{p \colon Aircraft; \;\; \sigma \colon ATC}{is\text{-}known(p, \sigma) = (p \in \mathrm{dom}\,(\sigma.location))}$$

$$\boxed{\text{is-known-E}} \; \frac{p \colon Aircraft; \;\; \sigma \colon ATC; \;\; is\text{-}known(p, \sigma)}{p \in \mathrm{dom}\,(\sigma.location)}$$

$$\boxed{\text{is-known-wff}} \; \frac{p \colon Aircraft; \;\; \sigma \colon ATC}{(p \in \mathrm{dom}\,(\sigma.location)) \colon \mathbb{B}}$$

$$\boxed{\text{location-form-mk}} \; \frac{mk\text{-}ATC(cs, con, cap, loc) \colon ATC}{loc \colon Aircraft \xrightarrow{m} Space}$$

$$\boxed{\text{numOfAircraft-defn}} \; \frac{s \colon Space; \;\; loc \colon Aircraft \xrightarrow{m} Space}{numOfAircraft(s, loc) = \mathrm{card}\,(\mathrm{dom}\,(loc \triangleright \{s\}))}$$

$$\boxed{\text{numOfAircraft-wff}} \; \frac{s \colon Space; \;\; loc \colon Aircraft \xrightarrow{m} Space}{\mathrm{card}\,(\mathrm{dom}\,(loc \triangleright \{s\})) \colon \mathbb{N}}$$

$$\boxed{\text{onduty-form-mk}} \; \frac{mk\text{-}ATC(cs, con, cap, loc) \colon ATC}{cs \colon Controller\text{-set}}$$

14.12 Case study II: refinement

Axioms

$$\boxed{mk\text{-}ATC_1\text{-form}} \; \frac{\begin{array}{c} cs \colon Controller\text{-set}; \;\; con \colon Space \xleftrightarrow{m} Controller \\ cap \colon Space \xrightarrow{m} \mathbb{N}; \;\; ass \colon AssigMap \\ inv\text{-}ATC_1(cs, con, cap, ass) \end{array}}{mk\text{-}ATC_1(cs, con, cap, ass) \colon ATC_1} \; \mathbf{Ax}$$

$$\boxed{mk\text{-}ATC_1\text{-defn}} \; \frac{\sigma \colon ATC_1}{mk\text{-}ATC_1(\sigma.onduty_1, \sigma.control_1, \sigma.capacity_1, \sigma.assigs_1) = \sigma} \; \mathbf{Ax}$$

$$\boxed{inv\text{-}ATC_1\text{-I}} \; \frac{mk\text{-}ATC_1(cs, con, cap, ass) \colon ATC_1}{inv\text{-}ATC_1(cs, con, cap, ass)} \; \mathbf{Ax}$$

$\boxed{assigs_1\text{-defn}} \quad \dfrac{mk\text{-}ATC_1(cs, con, cap, ass): ATC_1}{mk\text{-}ATC_1(cs, con, cap, ass).assigs_1 = ass} \quad \textbf{Ax}$

$\boxed{assigs_1\text{-form}} \quad \dfrac{\sigma: ATC_1}{\sigma.assigs_1: AssigMap} \quad \textbf{Ax}$

$\boxed{capacity_1\text{-defn}} \quad \dfrac{mk\text{-}ATC_1(cs, con, cap, ass): ATC_1}{mk\text{-}ATC_1(cs, con, cap, ass).capacity_1 = cap} \quad \textbf{Ax}$

$\boxed{capacity_1\text{-form}} \quad \dfrac{\sigma: ATC_1}{\sigma.capacity_1: Space \xrightarrow{m} \mathbb{N}} \quad \textbf{Ax}$

$\boxed{control_1\text{-defn}} \quad \dfrac{mk\text{-}ATC_1(cs, con, cap, ass): ATC_1}{mk\text{-}ATC_1(cs, con, cap, ass).control_1 = con} \quad \textbf{Ax}$

$\boxed{control_1\text{-form}} \quad \dfrac{\sigma: ATC_1}{\sigma.control_1: Space \xleftrightarrow{m} Controller} \quad \textbf{Ax}$

$\boxed{onduty_1\text{-defn}} \quad \dfrac{mk\text{-}ATC_1(cs, con, cap, ass): ATC_1}{mk\text{-}ATC_1(cs, con, cap, ass).onduty_1 = cs} \quad \textbf{Ax}$

$\boxed{onduty_1\text{-form}} \quad \dfrac{\sigma: ATC_1}{\sigma.onduty_1: Controller\text{-set}} \quad \textbf{Ax}$

$\boxed{nonRptng\text{-defn}_0} \quad \dfrac{s: A^*;\ (s = [\,]\ \vee\ \mathrm{hd}\,s \notin \mathrm{elems}\,\mathrm{tl}\,s \wedge nonRptng(\mathrm{tl}\,s)): \mathbb{B}}{nonRptng(s) = (s = [\,]\ \vee\ \mathrm{hd}\,s \notin \mathrm{elems}\,\mathrm{tl}\,s \wedge nonRptng(\mathrm{tl}\,s))} \quad \textbf{Ax}$

$\boxed{knownAircraft\text{-defn}_0} \quad \dfrac{\begin{array}{c} ass: AssigMap \\ \bigcup\{\mathrm{elems}\,q \mid q \in \mathrm{rng}\,ass\}: Aircraft\text{-set} \end{array}}{knownAircraft(ass) = \bigcup\{\mathrm{elems}\,q \mid q \in \mathrm{rng}\,ass\}} \quad \textbf{Ax}$

$\boxed{locOf\text{-defn}_0} \quad \dfrac{\begin{array}{c} p: Aircraft;\ ass: AssigMap;\ \mathrm{pre\text{-}}locOf(p, ass) \\ (\iota s \in \mathrm{dom}\,ass \cdot p \in \mathrm{elems}\,ass(s)): Space \end{array}}{locOf(p, ass) = \iota s \in \mathrm{dom}\,ass \cdot p \in \mathrm{elems}\,ass(s)} \quad \textbf{Ax}$

$\boxed{extrLoc\text{-defn}_0} \quad \dfrac{\begin{array}{c} ass: AssigMap \\ \{p \mapsto locOf(p, ass) \mid \\ p \in knownAircraft(ass)\}: Aircraft \xrightarrow{m} Space \end{array}}{\begin{array}{c} extrLoc(ass) = \\ \{p \mapsto locOf(p, ass) \mid p \in knownAircraft(ass)\} \end{array}} \quad \textbf{Ax}$

$\boxed{retr_1\text{-defn}_0} \quad \dfrac{\begin{array}{c} \sigma: ATC_1 \\ (mk\text{-}ATC(\sigma.onduty_1, \sigma.control_1, \\ \sigma.capacity_1, extrLoc(\sigma.assigs_1))): ATC \end{array}}{\begin{array}{c} retr_1(\sigma) = mk\text{-}ATC(\sigma.onduty_1, \sigma.control_1, \\ \sigma.capacity_1, extrLoc(\sigma.assigs_1)) \end{array}} \quad \textbf{Ax}$

14.12 Case study II: refinement

$$\boxed{\textit{buildQueue-defn}_0} \quad \frac{s\colon \textit{Aircraft-set};\ \exists q\colon \textit{AircraftQueue} \cdot \textsf{elems}\, q = s}{\textsf{elems}\, \textit{buildQueue}(s) = s} \quad \mathbf{Ax}$$

$$\boxed{\textit{buildQueue-form}_0} \quad \frac{s\colon \textit{Aircraft-set};\ \exists q\colon \textit{AircraftQueue} \cdot \textsf{elems}\, q = s}{\textit{buildQueue}(s)\colon \textit{AircraftQueue}} \quad \mathbf{Ax}$$

$$\boxed{\textit{extrAss-defn}_0} \quad \frac{\textit{loc}\colon \textit{Aircraft} \xrightarrow{m} \textit{Space}}{\{s \mapsto \textit{buildQueue}(\textsf{dom}(\textit{loc} \triangleright \{s\}))\mid s \in \textsf{rng}\, \textit{loc}\}\colon \textit{AssigMap}} \quad \mathbf{Ax}$$
$$\textit{extrAss}(\textit{loc}) = \{s \mapsto \textit{buildQueue}(\textsf{dom}(\textit{loc} \triangleright \{s\})) \mid s \in \textsf{rng}\, \textit{loc}\}$$

Definitions

$\textit{inv-ATC}_1(cs, con, cap, ass) \stackrel{\text{def}}{=}\ \textsf{rng}\, con \subseteq cs \wedge \textsf{dom}\, con \subseteq \textsf{dom}\, cap\ \wedge$
$\qquad\qquad\qquad\qquad\qquad\qquad \textsf{dom}\, ass = \textsf{dom}\, con \wedge \forall s \in \textsf{dom}\, ass \cdot \textsf{len}\, ass(s) \leq cap(s)$

$\textit{init-ATC}_1(\sigma) \stackrel{\text{def}}{=}\ \sigma.\textit{onduty}_1 = \{\,\} \wedge \sigma.\textit{capacity}_1 = \{\mapsto\}$

$\textit{AssigMap} \stackrel{\text{def}}{=}\ \ll m\colon \textit{Space} \xrightarrow{m} \textit{AircraftQueue} \mid \textit{inv-AssigMap}(m) \gg$

$\textit{inv-AssigMap}(m) \stackrel{\text{def}}{=}\ \forall s_1, s_2 \in \textsf{dom}\, ass \cdot s_1 \neq s_2 \Rightarrow$
$\qquad\qquad\qquad\qquad\qquad\qquad \textsf{elems}\, ass(s_1) \cap \textsf{elems}\, ass(s_2) = \{\,\}$

$\textit{AircraftQueue} \stackrel{\text{def}}{=}\ \ll s\colon \textit{Aircraft}^* \mid \textit{inv-AircraftQueue}(s) \gg$

$\textit{inv-AircraftQueue}(s) \stackrel{\text{def}}{=}\ \textit{nonRptng}(s)$

$\textit{pre-locOf}(p, ass) \stackrel{\text{def}}{=}\ p \in \textit{knownAircraft}(ass)$

$\textit{post-buildQueue}(s, q) \stackrel{\text{def}}{=}\ \textsf{elems}\, q = s$

$\textit{pre-AddFlight}_1(p, s, con, cap, ass) \stackrel{\text{def}}{=}\ s \in \textsf{dom}\, con \wedge p \notin \textit{knownAircraft}(ass)\ \wedge$
$\qquad\qquad\qquad\qquad\qquad\qquad\qquad \textsf{len}\, ass(s) < cap(s)$

$\textit{post-AddFlight}_1(p, s, \overleftarrow{ass}, ass) \stackrel{\text{def}}{=}\ ass = \overleftarrow{ass} \dagger \{s \mapsto \overleftarrow{ass}(s) \frown [p]\}$

Proof obligations

$$\boxed{\textit{AddFlight-dom-obl}} \quad \frac{\begin{array}{c} p\colon \textit{Aircraft};\ s\colon \textit{Space} \\ \textit{mk-ATC}(cs, con, cap, loc)\colon \textit{ATC} \\ \textit{mk-ATC}_1(cs_1, con_1, cap_1, ass)\colon \textit{ATC}_1 \\ \textit{mk-ATC}(cs, con, cap, loc) = \textit{retr}_1(\textit{mk-ATC}_1(cs_1, con_1, cap_1, ass)) \\ \textit{pre-AddFlight}(p, s, con, cap, loc) \end{array}}{\textit{pre-AddFlight}_1(p, s, con_1, cap_1, ass)}$$

AddFlight-res-obl
$$\frac{\begin{array}{c}p: Aircraft;\ s: Space\\ mk\text{-}ATC(cs, con, cap, \overleftarrow{loc}): ATC\\ mk\text{-}ATC_1(cs_1, con_1, cap_1, \overleftarrow{ass}): ATC_1\\ mk\text{-}ATC(cs, con, cap, \overleftarrow{loc}) = retr_1(mk\text{-}ATC_1(cs_1, con_1, cap_1, \overleftarrow{ass}))\\ mk\text{-}ATC(cs, con, cap, loc): ATC\\ mk\text{-}ATC_1(cs_1, con_1, cap_1, ass): ATC_1\\ mk\text{-}ATC(cs, con, cap, loc) = retr_1(mk\text{-}ATC_1(cs_1, con_1, cap_1, ass))\\ pre\text{-}AddFlight(p, s, con, cap, loc);\ post\text{-}AddFlight_1(p, s, \overleftarrow{ass}, ass)\end{array}}{post\text{-}AddFlight(p, s, \overleftarrow{loc}, loc)}$$

AddFlight$_1$-sat
$$\frac{\begin{array}{c}p: Aircraft;\ s: Space;\ cs: Controller\text{-}set\\ con: Space \xleftarrow{m} Controller;\ cap: Space \xrightarrow{m} \mathbb{N}\\ \overline{ass}: AssigMap;\ inv\text{-}ATC_1(cs, con, cap, \overline{ass})\\ pre\text{-}AddFlight_1(p, s, con, cap, \overline{ass})\end{array}}{\exists ass: AssigMap \cdot post\text{-}AddFlight_1(p, s, \overline{ass}, ass) \wedge inv\text{-}ATC(cs, con, cap, ass)}$$

buildQueue-sat
$$\frac{s: Aircraft\text{-}set}{\exists q: AircraftQueue \cdot post\text{-}buildQueue(s, q)}$$

extrAss-form
$$\frac{loc: Aircraft \xrightarrow{m} Space}{extrAss(loc): AssigMap}$$

extrLoc-form
$$\frac{ass: AssigMap}{extrLoc(ass): Aircraft \xrightarrow{m} Space}$$

init-ATC$_1$-adeq
$$\frac{\sigma: ATC;\ \sigma_1: ATC_1;\ \sigma = retr_1(\sigma_1);\ init\text{-}ATC_1(\sigma_1)}{init\text{-}ATC(\sigma)}$$

init-ATC$_1$-form
$$\frac{\sigma: ATC_1}{init\text{-}ATC_1(\sigma): \mathbb{B}}$$

init-ATC$_1$-sat
$$\overline{\exists \sigma: ATC_1 \cdot init\text{-}ATC_1(\sigma)}$$

inv-AssigMap-form
$$\frac{m: Space \xrightarrow{m} AircraftQueue}{inv\text{-}AssigMap(m): \mathbb{B}}$$

inv-ATC$_1$-form
$$\frac{\begin{array}{c}cs: Controller\text{-}set;\ con: Space \xleftarrow{m} Controller\\ cap: Space \xrightarrow{m} \mathbb{N};\ ass: AssigMap\end{array}}{inv\text{-}ATC_1(cs, con, cap, ass): \mathbb{B}}$$

inv-queue-form
$$\frac{s: Aircraft^*}{inv\text{-}AircraftQueue(s): \mathbb{B}}$$

14.12 Case study II: refinement

$$\boxed{knownAircraft\text{-form}} \ \frac{ass\colon AssigMap}{knownAircraft(ass)\colon Aircraft\text{-set}}$$

$$\boxed{locOf\text{-form}} \ \frac{p\colon Aircraft;\ ass\colon AssigMap;\ pre\text{-}locOf(p, ass)}{locOf(p, ass)\colon Space}$$

$$\boxed{nonRptng\text{-form}} \ \frac{s\colon A^*}{nonRptng(s)\colon \mathbb{B}}$$

$$\boxed{post\text{-}AddFlight_1\text{-form}} \ \frac{\begin{array}{c} p\colon Aircraft;\ s\colon Space;\ cs\colon Controller\text{-set} \\ con\colon Space \xleftarrow{m} Controller;\ cap\colon Space \xrightarrow{m} \mathbb{N} \\ \overleftarrow{ass}\colon AssigMap;\ ass\colon AssigMap \\ inv\text{-}ATC_1(cs, con, cap, \overleftarrow{ass});\ pre\text{-}AddFlight_1(p, s, con, cap, \overleftarrow{ass}) \end{array}}{post\text{-}AddFlight_1(p, s, \overleftarrow{ass}, ass)\colon \mathbb{B}}$$

$$\boxed{post\text{-}buildQueue\text{-form}} \ \frac{s\colon Aircraft\text{-set};\ q\colon AircraftQueue}{post\text{-}buildQueue(s, q)\colon \mathbb{B}}$$

$$\boxed{pre\text{-}AddFlight_1\text{-form}} \ \frac{\begin{array}{c} p\colon Aircraft;\ s\colon Space;\ cs\colon Controller\text{-set} \\ con\colon Space \xleftarrow{m} Controller;\ cap\colon Space \xrightarrow{m} \mathbb{N} \\ ass\colon AssigMap;\ inv\text{-}ATC_1(cs, con, cap, ass) \end{array}}{pre\text{-}AddFlight_1(p, s, con, cap, ass)\colon \mathbb{B}}$$

$$\boxed{pre\text{-}locOf\text{-form}} \ \frac{p\colon Aircraft;\ ass\colon AssigMap}{pre\text{-}locOf(p, ass)\colon \mathbb{B}}$$

$$\boxed{retr_1\text{-adeq}} \ \frac{\sigma\colon ATC}{\exists \sigma_1\colon ATC_1 \cdot retr_1(\sigma_1) = \sigma}$$

$$\boxed{retr_1\text{-form}} \ \frac{\sigma\colon ATC_1}{retr_1(\sigma)\colon ATC}$$

Useful lemmas

$$\boxed{[\,]\text{-form-queue}} \ \frac{}{[\,]\colon AircraftQueue}$$

$$\boxed{\in\text{-}knownAircraft\text{-E}} \ \frac{p\colon Aircraft;\ ass\colon AssigMap;\ p \in knownAircraft(ass)}{\exists q \in \mathsf{rng}\,ass \cdot p \in \mathsf{elems}\,q}$$

$$\boxed{\notin\text{-}knownAircraft\text{-E}} \ \frac{p\colon Aircraft;\ ass\colon AssigMap;\ p \notin knownAircraft(ass)}{\forall q \in \mathsf{rng}\,ass \cdot p \notin \mathsf{elems}\,q}$$

14 Directory of Theorems

$$\boxed{AddFlight\text{-dom-obl-simp}} \quad \frac{\begin{array}{c} p\colon Aircraft;\ s\colon Space \\ mk\text{-}ATC(cs, con, cap, extrLoc(ass))\colon ATC \\ mk\text{-}ATC_1(cs, con, cap, ass)\colon ATC_1 \\ pre\text{-}AddFlight(p, s, con, cap, extrLoc(ass)) \end{array}}{pre\text{-}AddFlight_1(p, s, con, cap, ass)}$$

$$\boxed{AddFlight\text{-res-obl-simp}} \quad \frac{\begin{array}{c} p\colon Aircraft;\ s\colon Space \\ mk\text{-}ATC(cs, con, cap, extrLoc(\overleftarrow{ass}))\colon ATC \\ mk\text{-}ATC_1(cs, con, cap, \overleftarrow{ass})\colon ATC_1 \\ mk\text{-}ATC(cs, con, cap, extrLoc(ass))\colon ATC \\ mk\text{-}ATC_1(cs, con, cap, ass)\colon ATC_1 \\ pre\text{-}AddFlight(p, s, con, cap, extrLoc(ass)) \\ post\text{-}AddFlight_1(p, s, \overleftarrow{ass}, ass) \end{array}}{post\text{-}AddFlight(p, s, extrLoc(\overleftarrow{ass}), extrLoc(ass))}$$

$$\boxed{aircraft\text{-in-unique-space}_1} \quad \frac{p\colon Aircraft;\ ass\colon AssigMap;\ p \in knownAircraft(ass)}{\exists!\, s \in \operatorname{dom} ass \cdot p \in \operatorname{elems} ass(s)}$$

$$\boxed{AssigMap\text{-form-}\dagger} \quad \frac{\begin{array}{c} p\colon Aircraft;\ s\colon Space;\ ass\colon AssigMap \\ p \notin knownAircraft(ass);\ s \in \operatorname{dom} ass \end{array}}{ass \dagger \{s \mapsto ass(s) \smallfrown [p]\}\colon AssigMap}$$

$$\boxed{AssigMap\text{-supertype}} \quad \frac{ass\colon AssigMap}{ass\colon Space \xrightarrow{m} AircraftQueue}$$

$$\boxed{AssigMap\text{-form}} \quad \frac{m\colon Space \xrightarrow{m} AircraftQueue;\ inv\text{-}AssigMap(m)}{m\colon AssigMap}$$

$$\boxed{assigs_1\text{-form-mk}} \quad \frac{mk\text{-}ATC_1(cs, con, cap, ass)\colon ATC_1}{ass\colon AssigMap}$$

$$\boxed{buildQueue\text{-defn}} \quad \frac{s\colon Aircraft\text{-set}}{\operatorname{elems} buildQueue(s) = s}$$

$$\boxed{buildQueue\text{-form}} \quad \frac{s\colon Aircraft\text{-set}}{buildQueue(s)\colon AircraftQueue}$$

$$\boxed{capacity_1\text{-form-mk}} \quad \frac{mk\text{-}ATC_1(cs, con, cap, ass)\colon ATC_1}{cap\colon Space \xrightarrow{m} \mathbf{N}}$$

$$\boxed{cons\text{-form-queue}} \quad \frac{a\colon Aircraft;\ q\colon AircraftQueue;\ a \notin \operatorname{elems} q}{cons(a, q)\colon AircraftQueue}$$

$$\boxed{control_1\text{-form-mk}} \quad \frac{mk\text{-}ATC_1(cs, con, cap, ass)\colon ATC_1}{con\colon Space \xleftrightarrow{m} Controller}$$

14.12 Case study II: refinement

$$\text{dom-}extrAss\text{-defn} \quad \frac{loc: Aircraft \xrightarrow{m} Space}{\text{dom}\, extrAss(loc) = \text{rng}\, loc}$$

$$\text{dom-}extrLoc\text{-defn} \quad \frac{ass: AssigMap}{\text{dom}\, extrLoc(ass) = knownAircraft(ass)}$$

$$\text{dom-form-}AssigMap \quad \frac{ass: AssigMap}{\text{dom}\, ass: Space\text{-set}}$$

$$\text{elems-defn-cons-queue} \quad \frac{a: Aircraft;\; q: AircraftQueue}{\text{elems}\, \text{cons}(a, q) = \text{add}(a, \text{elems}\, q)}$$

$$\text{elems-form-queue} \quad \frac{q: AircraftQueue}{\text{elems}\, q: Aircraft\text{-set}}$$

$$extrAss\text{-}extrLoc\text{-inverse} \quad \frac{loc: Aircraft \xrightarrow{m} Space}{loc = extrLoc(extrAss(loc))}$$

$$extrLoc\text{-}\dagger \quad \frac{p: Aircraft;\; s: Space;\; ass: AssigMap \\ p \notin knownAircraft(ass);\; s \in \text{dom}\, ass}{extrLoc(ass \dagger \{s \mapsto ass(s) \curvearrowright [p]\}) = extrLoc(ass) \dagger \{p \mapsto s\}}$$

$$extrLoc\text{-defn} \quad \frac{ass: AssigMap}{extrLoc(ass) = \{p \mapsto locOf(p, ass) \mid p \in knownAircraft(ass)\}}$$

$$extrLoc\text{-wff} \quad \frac{ass: AssigMap}{\{p \mapsto locOf(p, ass) \mid p \in knownAircraft(ass)\}: Aircraft \xrightarrow{m} Space}$$

$$inv\text{-}AssigMap\text{-I} \quad \frac{ass: AssigMap}{inv\text{-}AssigMap(ass)}$$

$$inv\text{-}ATC_1\text{-I-clause1} \quad \frac{\sigma: ATC_1}{\text{rng}\, \sigma.control_1 \subseteq \sigma.onduty_1}$$

$$inv\text{-}ATC_1\text{-I-clause2} \quad \frac{\sigma: ATC_1}{\text{dom}\, \sigma.control_1 \subseteq \text{dom}\, \sigma.capacity_1}$$

$$inv\text{-}ATC_1\text{-I-clause3} \quad \frac{\sigma: ATC_1}{\text{dom}\, \sigma.assigs_1 = \text{dom}\, \sigma.control_1}$$

$$inv\text{-}ATC_1\text{-I-clause4} \quad \frac{\sigma: ATC_1}{\forall s \in \text{dom}\, \sigma.assigs_1 \cdot \text{len}\,(\sigma.assigs_1)(s) \leq (\sigma.capacity_1)(s)}$$

$$inv\text{-}ATC_1\text{-I-mk-clause3} \quad \frac{mk\text{-}ATC_1(cs, con, cap, ass): ATC_1}{\text{dom}\, ass = \text{dom}\, con}$$

inv-ATC_1-I-separate	cs: $Controller$-set; con: $Space \xleftrightarrow{m} Controller$ cap: $Space \xrightarrow{m} \mathbb{N}$; ass: $AssigMap$ $\text{rng } con \subseteq cs$; $\text{dom } con \subseteq \text{dom } cap$; $\text{dom } ass = \text{dom } con$ $\forall s \in \text{dom } ass \cdot \text{len } ass(s) \leq cap(s)$
	$inv\text{-}ATC_1(cs, con, cap, ass)$

knownAircraft-†-lemma	p: $Aircraft$; s: $Space$; ass: $AssigMap$ $p \notin knownAircraft(ass)$; $s \in \text{dom } ass$
	$knownAircraft(ass \dagger \{s \mapsto ass(s) \frown [p]\}) =$ $add(p, knownAircraft(ass))$

knownAircraft-defn	ass: $AssigMap$
	$knownAircraft(ass) = \bigcup \{\text{elems } q \mid q \in \text{rng } ass\}$

knownAircraft-wff	ass: $AssigMap$
	$\bigcup \{\text{elems } q \mid q \in \text{rng } ass\}$: $Aircraft$-set

locOf-†-=	p: $Aircraft$; s: $Space$; ass: $AssigMap$ $p \notin knownAircraft(ass)$; $s \in \text{dom } ass$
	$locOf(p, ass \dagger \{s \mapsto ass(s) \frown [p]\}) = s$

locOf-†-≠	p: $Aircraft$; s: $Space$; ass: $AssigMap$ a: $Aircraft$; $p \notin knownAircraft(ass)$ $s \in \text{dom } ass$; $a \in knownAircraft(ass)$
	$locOf(a, ass \dagger \{s \mapsto ass(s) \frown [p]\}) = locOf(a, ass)$

locOf-defn	p: $Aircraft$; ass: $AssigMap$; $pre\text{-}locOf(p, ass)$
	$locOf(p, ass) = \iota s \in \text{dom } ass \cdot p \in \text{elems } ass(s)$

locOf-wff	p: $Aircraft$; ass: $AssigMap$; $pre\text{-}locOf(p, ass)$
	$(\iota s \in \text{dom } ass \cdot p \in \text{elems } ass(s))$: $Space$

nonRptng-defn	s: A^*
	$nonRptng(s) = (s = [\,] \lor \text{hd } s \notin \text{elems tl } s \land nonRptng(\text{tl } s))$

nonRptng-wff	s: A^*
	$(s = [\,] \lor \text{hd } s \notin \text{elems tl } s \land nonRptng(\text{tl } s))$: $\mathbb{B}$

numOfAircraft-elm-defn	s: $Space$; ass: $AssigMap$; $s \in \text{dom } ass$
	$numOfAircraft(s, extrLoc(ass)) = \text{len } ass(s)$

onduty$_1$-form-mk	$mk\text{-}ATC_1(cs, con, cap, ass)$: ATC_1
	cs: $Controller$-set

retr$_1$-adeq-assigs	$mk\text{-}ATC(cs, con, cap, loc)$: ATC
	$\exists ass$: $AssigMap \cdot$ $inv\text{-}ATC_1(cs, con, cap, ass) \land loc = extrLoc(ass)$

14.12 Case study II: refinement

$$\boxed{retr_1\text{-adeq-mk}} \; \frac{mk\text{-}ATC(cs, con, cap, loc): ATC}{\exists \sigma_1: ATC_1 \cdot retr_1(\sigma_1) = mk\text{-}ATC(cs, con, cap, loc)}$$

$$\boxed{retr_1\text{-defn}} \; \frac{\sigma: ATC_1}{retr_1(\sigma) = \\ mk\text{-}ATC(\sigma.onduty_1, \sigma.control_1, \sigma.capacity_1, extrLoc(\sigma.assigs_1))}$$

$$\boxed{retr_1\text{-defn-mk}} \; \frac{mk\text{-}ATC_1(cs, con, cap, ass): ATC_1}{retr_1(mk\text{-}ATC_1(cs, con, cap, ass)) = \\ mk\text{-}ATC(cs, con, cap, extrLoc(ass))}$$

$$\boxed{retr_1\text{-E-capacity}} \; \frac{\begin{array}{c} mk\text{-}ATC(cs, con, cap, loc): ATC \\ mk\text{-}ATC_1(cs_1, con_1, cap_1, ass): ATC_1 \\ mk\text{-}ATC(cs, con, cap, loc) = retr_1(mk\text{-}ATC_1(cs_1, con_1, cap_1, ass)) \end{array}}{cap_1 = cap}$$

$$\boxed{retr_1\text{-E-control}} \; \frac{\begin{array}{c} mk\text{-}ATC(cs, con, cap, loc): ATC \\ mk\text{-}ATC_1(cs_1, con_1, cap_1, ass): ATC_1 \\ mk\text{-}ATC(cs, con, cap, loc) = retr_1(mk\text{-}ATC_1(cs_1, con_1, cap_1, ass)) \end{array}}{con_1 = con}$$

$$\boxed{retr_1\text{-E-location}} \; \frac{\begin{array}{c} mk\text{-}ATC(cs, con, cap, loc): ATC \\ mk\text{-}ATC_1(cs_1, con_1, cap_1, ass): ATC_1 \\ mk\text{-}ATC(cs, con, cap, loc) = retr_1(mk\text{-}ATC_1(cs_1, con_1, cap_1, ass)) \end{array}}{extrLoc(ass) = loc}$$

$$\boxed{retr_1\text{-E-onduty}} \; \frac{\begin{array}{c} mk\text{-}ATC(cs, con, cap, loc): ATC \\ mk\text{-}ATC_1(cs_1, con_1, cap_1, ass): ATC_1 \\ mk\text{-}ATC(cs, con, cap, loc) = retr_1(mk\text{-}ATC_1(cs_1, con_1, cap_1, ass)) \end{array}}{cs_1 = cs}$$

$$\boxed{retr_1\text{-wff}} \; \frac{\sigma: ATC_1}{(mk\text{-}ATC(\sigma.onduty_1, \sigma.control_1, \sigma.capacity_1, extrLoc(\sigma.assigs_1))): ATC}$$

$$\boxed{\text{rng-}extrLoc\text{-lemma}} \; \frac{ass: AssigMap}{rng \, extrLoc(ass) \subseteq \mathbf{dom} \, ass}$$

$$\boxed{\text{rng-form-}AssigMap} \; \frac{ass: AssigMap}{rng \, ass: AircraftQueue\text{-set}}$$

Bibliography

[AI91] Derek Andrews and Darrell Ince. *Practical formal methods with VDM*. McGraw-Hill, 1991. ISBN 0-07-707214-6.

[BCJ84] H. Barringer, J.H. Cheng, and C.B. Jones. A Logic Covering Undefinedness in Program Proofs. *Acta Informatica*, 21:251–269, 1984.

[Bic93] J. C. Bicarregui. Algorithm refinement with read and write frames. In *FME'93: Industrial-Strength Formal Methods*, pages 148–161. Springer-Verlag, Berlin, 1993. (LNCS 670).

[BN92] S. M. Brien and J. E. Nicholls. Z Base Standard version 1.0. Technical Report PRG–107, Programming Research Group, Oxford University Computing Laboratory, Oxford, UK, November 1992. ISBN 0-902928-84-8.

[BSI92] British Standards Institute, Working Group IST/5/19. *VDM Specification Language Proto-Standard: Draft*, 1992. Document N231 I-9, 8 August.

[Cha81] D. Charlwood. *Take-off to Touchdown: The Story of Air Traffic Control*. Australian Government Publishing Service, Canberra, 1981.

[Che86] Jen Huan Cheng. *A Logic for Partial Functions*. PhD thesis, Dept. of Computer Science, University of Manchester, UK, January 1986. Technical Report No. UMCS-86-7-1.

[Cho88] F.K. Chorley. Electronics and communications in air traffic control. *J Instit Electronic and Radio Engineers*, 58(1):1–11, 1988.

[Cle93] T. Clement. A tutorial on data reification. Technical Report UMCS-93-8-2, Dept. of Computer Science, University of Manchester, August 1993.

[Daw91] John Dawes. *The VDM-SL Reference Guide*. Pitman Publishing, 1991. ISBN 0-273-03151-1.

[DKRS91] Roger Duke, Paul King, Gordon Rose, and Graeme Smith. The Object-Z Specification Language Version 1. Technical Report 91-1, Software Verification Research Centre, University of Queensland, May 1991.

[End72] H.B. Enderton. *A Mathematical Introduction to Logic*. Academic Press, 1972.

[GLT89] J.-Y. Girard, Y. Lafont, and P. Taylor. *Proofs and Types*. Cambridge Tracts in Theoretical Computer Science. Cambridge University Press, 1989.

[HHP87]   R. Harper, F. Honsell, and G. Plotkin. A framework for defining logics. In *Proceedings of Second Symposium on Logic in Computer Science*, pages 194–204, 1987.

[Hoa85]   C. A. R. Hoare. *Communicating Sequential Processes*. Prentice-Hall, 1985. ISBN 0-13-153289-8 Pbk.

[IEE]   Special issue devoted to Air Traffic Control in the USA. Proceedings of the IEEE Vol. 77 No. 11, November 1989.

[JJLM91]   C.B. Jones, K.D. Jones, P.A. Lindsay, and R. Moore. *mural: A Formal Development Support System*. Springer-Verlag, London, 1991.

[Jon90]   C. B. Jones. *Systematic Software Development Using VDM*. Prentice Hall International(UK), second edition, 1990.

[Lar93]   Peter Gorm Larsen. Towards Proof Rules for Looseness in Explicit Definitions from VDM-SL. In *Proceedings of the International Workshop on Semantics of Specification Languages, Utrecht, October 1993*, Workshops in Computing. Springer-Verlag, 1993. To appear.

[Mid90]   C.A. Middelburg. *Syntax and Semantics of VVSL: A Language for Structured VDM Specifications*. PhD thesis, University of Amsterdam, 1990.

[Mor90]   C. Morgan. *Programming from Specifications*. Prentice-Hall, 1990.

[Nip86]   T. N. Nipkow. *Behavioural Implementation Concepts for Nondeterministic Data Types*. PhD thesis, Dept. of Computer Science, University of Manchester, December 1986. Technical Report UMCS-87-5-3.

[Ost92]   J. Ostroff. Formal Methods for the Specification and Design of Real-Time Safety Critical Systems. *Journal of Systems and Software*, 18, 1992.

[Pra65]   D. Prawitz. *Natural Deduction*. Almqvist and Wiskell, 1965.

[Rob89]   Robin Milner. *Communication and Concurrency*. Prentice-Hall, 1989. ISBN 0-13-115007-3 Pbk.

[RSL92]   RAISE Language Group. *The RAISE Specification Language*, 1992. Prentice Hall, BCS Practitioners Series.

[Sch86]   O. Schoett. *Data Abstraction and the Correctness of Modular Programming*. PhD thesis, Dept. of Computer Science, University of Edinburgh, 1986. Technical Report CST-42-87 or ECS-LFCS-87-19.

[Vyt92]   J. Vytopil, editor. *Proceedings of the Symposium in Formal Techniques in Real-Time and Fault-Tolerant Systems*. Springer-Verlag, 1992. Lecture Notes in Computer Science Vol. 571.

[WH93]   Mark Woodman and Benedict Heal. *Introduction to VDM*. McGraw-Hill, 1993. ISBN 0-07-707434-3.

[WL93]　　J. C. P. Woodcock and P. G. Larsen, editors. *FME'93: Industrial-Strength Formal Methods*. Springer-Verlag, 1993. Lecture Notes in Computer Science Vol. 670, ISBN 3-540-56662-7.

Index

∀-I/∀-E, 46, 48
∃-E/∃-I, 44, 48, 58

adequacy obligation, 183, 229, 231, 232
    of initialisation, 183, 240
assumption, local, 15
auxiliary function, 167, 200
axiom, 9
axiomatisation
    development of, 41, 72–75, 86, 108, 133, 134, 262
    of composite types, 68, 164–166, 262
    of explicit functions, 167–169, 200, 201, 229
    of implicit functions, 170–171, 201
    of initialisation, 166, 200
    of operations, 175–177, 212
    of polymorphic functions, 174–175, 224
    of recursive functions, 171–173, 224
    of recursive type definitions, 248–251
    of state, 166–167, 199
    of type definitions, 162–166, 223
    of value definitions, 175

binder, 10, 56, 57

case distinction, 26, 27, 34, 56
cases expression, 259–262
character type, 264
choice
    non-unique, 258
    unique, 57, 257
comprehension
    axiomatisation of, 126
    definedness of, *see* definedness, of comprehension expressions, 100, 126
    finiteness of, 99, 101, 126
    map, 126
    set, 99, 100
conclusion, 11
    local, 15

conditional, 57, 59, 60, 142
constant, 61
constructor, 64, 68, 136, 164
contradiction, 27

data reification, 1, 6
data type, *see* type
definedness
    of equality, 51, 63, 66, 247, 248
    of predicates, 40, 153
    of propositions, 33, 37, 151
    of quantified expressions, 50
    of relations, 153
definition, 18, 28, 81
    folding, *see* justification, by folding
    potential problems, 83, 92, 138, 169, 249
    recursive, 83, 137, 171–173
    subsidiary, 120
    unfolding, *see* justification, by unfolding
deMorgan laws
    predicate, 47
    propositional, 32
denoting term, 41, 51, 52, 65, 137
derived rule, *see* rule, derived
destructor, 135, 136, 148, 164
domain obligation, 184, 185, 236, 237
    example, 187
    for functions, 190

enumerated collection, 252, 253
enumerated type, *see* type
equality
    chains of, 54, 56, 141
    definedness of, *see* definedness, of equality
    of maps, 115
    of sequences, 136
    of sets, 93
    polymorphism of, 51

rewriting over, 56, 139, 141
explicit functions, 167–169

flatness, *see* type
function type, *see* type

generator, 72, 86, 133, 145
goals, 29

hypothesis, 11
    local, 15

implementation bias, 190
implicit functions, 170–171
    satisfaction of, 190
induction
    $\forall$-E/$\Rightarrow$-E-left "trick", 144
    $\Rightarrow$-E-left "trick", 79, 134, 143
    base case, 87
    hypothesis, 135
    rule, 72, 87, 134, 146
    rule for subtype, 84
    step, 87
induction scheme, 249, 251
inference rule, 9, 11
informal argument, 25, 26, 35, 53, 54, 56, 59, 139
initialisation condition, 166, 192
    adequacy, 183
instantiation, 11, 49, 174
invariant, 162, 165
    as subtype, 69, 163
    role in proofs, 178

justification, 12
    by *triv*, 27
    by folding, 29
    by sequent hypothesis, 35
    by unfolding, 29

knowns, 29

lemma, *see* rule
    abstraction of, 118
    extraction of, 54, 56, 60, 89, 103, 116–118, 125, 142
let expression, 256–258
    determinism of, 258, 259
LPF, 23, 33, 37, 40, 41, 51, 52

metavariable, 11, 67

natural deduction, 14
non-determinism, 175, 185

operation decomposition, 1
operation modelling, 7, 184

patterns, 254–256
polymorphic type definitions, 174
postcondition, 3, 170
precondition, 3, 169–170
predicate, 39
    definedness of, *see* definedness, of predicates
proof, 10, 12
    of symmetric rules, 27, 121
proof obligation, 4, satisfaction, satisfiability, well-formedness, *see* adequacy obligation, domain obligation, result obligation
    well-formedness of invariant, 154

quantifier
    definedness of, *see* definedness, of quantified expressions
    existential, 41, 42, 56, 59
    multiple, 48–50, 59
    unique existential, 56, 257
    universal, 41, 45
quote type, 264

read frame (role of), 177
reification, *see* data reification
result obligation, 184, 186, 236, 238
    example, 188
retrieve function, 7, 182–183
    adequacy, 183
    example, 187, 229
rule
    derived, 10, 25
    developing variants of, 93
    formation, 57, 64, 137, 138, 164, 165, 170, 174, 249
    formulation of, 34, 36, 151, 152
    naming conventions, 18
    selection of, 29

satisfaction obligation (for function), 190
satisfiability
    of implicit function definitions, 171, 234

of initial state, 167, 200, 205
of operations, 176, 213, 215, 217
of recursive functions, 172, 224
one-point version for functions, 171, 173
scope, 10
selector, 64, 65, 68, 164, 262
sequent, 15, 67, 70
strictness of function definitions, 168
subproof, 14
trivially true, 27
substitution
of equal values, 51, 65
of equivalent values, 158
subtype
induction rule for, 124
polymorphic, 123

theorem, *see* rule
theory, 10
token type, 263
turnstile, 14
type, 161
disjoint, 248
enumerated, 264
extension (by type union), 51, 61–63, 66, 69, 247
flatness, 246, 247
function, 246
inhabited, 50, 163
membership of, 40
typing assertion, 40, 41, 51

under-determinism, 173
under-specification, 173

validation condition, 5, 163, 177, 198, 200, 202, 206, 217, 219
validation conjecture, *see* validation condition
variable
bound, 41, 48
free, 40, 48
sequent, 67, 70
VDM, 1, 2, 23, 40, 245
VDM-SL, 1, 3, 19, 61, 65, 66, 69, 136, 146–148, 202, 245, 257, 258

well-formedness

of explicit functions, 168, 201, 203
of functions with preconditions, 169, 201
of initialisation, 167, 200, 205
of invariant, 163, 165, 200, 204, 205, 223
of postconditions, 170, 212, 234
of preconditions, 170, 201, 206, 212
of recursive functions , 224
of value definitions, 175
one-point version for functions, 168
proof, 154
witness value, 42

Index of Symbols

$\_$-set (set type)	85, 287	$\leq$	83, 285
$\_ \xrightarrow{m} \_$ (map type)	107, 302	μ	262
$\_ \xleftrightarrow{m} \_$ (bijective map type)	123, 305	$\mathbb{N}$	72, 284
$\_^*$ (sequence type)	133, 314	$\mathbb{N}_1$	82, 284
$\_^+$ (non-empty sequence type)	134, 315	$\neg$ (negation)	24, 268
[$\_$] (optional type)	66, 282	$\neq$	56, 277
$\ll \_ \mid \_ \gg$ (subtype)	67, 283	$\notin$	86, 289
{ }	86, 287	$\lor$ (disjunction)	24, 267
$\{\mapsto\}$ (empty map)	108, 302	† (map override)	119, 303
$\{\_\}$ (singleton set)	96, 289	+	75, 79, 284
$\{\_ \mapsto \_\}$ (singleton map)	305	▷ (range restriction)	114, 303
[ ]	133, 314	▷ (range subtraction)	114, 303
[$\_$] (singleton sequence)	137, 315	$\subset$	93, 288
$\forall$ (for all)	45, 91, 274, 289	$\subseteq$	92, 288
$\land$ (conjunction)	28, 268	$\times$	284
$\mathbb{B}$	149, 319	$\cup$	96, 288
$\circ$ (map composition)	129, 304	$\bigcup$ (distributed union)	97, 289
$\frown$ (sequence concatenation)	139, 315	⊌ (map merge)	120, 304
δ (delta)	33, 268	$\_ \mid \_$ (type union)	61, 281
$\_ \setminus \_$ (set difference)	96, 288	$\_ \times \_$ (product type)	63, 281
◁ (domain restriction)	113, 303	0	72, 284
◁ (domain subtraction)	112, 302	$\_ : \_$ (typing)	40
=	51, 277	$\_^{-1}$ (map inverse)	130, 304
= (on maps)	115, 303	$\vdash$ (turnstile)	14
= (on sets)	93, 288	*add*	86, 287
$\exists$ (exists)	41, 91, 273, 287	*addm*	108, 302
$\exists!$ (exists unique)	56, 91, 279, 289	*card*	95, 288
$\mathcal{F}$ (power set)	97, 289	*conc*	142, 315
>	82, 284	*cons*	133, 314
$\geq$	83, 284	*dom*	110, 302
$\Leftrightarrow$ (equivalence)	32, 268	*elems*	138, 315
$\Rightarrow$ (implication)	32, 268	*false*	32, 268
$\in$	86, 287	*fst*	64, 281
$\cap$	96, 288	*hd*	136, 314
$\bigcap$ (distributed intersection)	97, 289	if $\_$ then $\_$ else $\_$	57, 280
ι (iota)	57, 92, 279, 288	*inds*	145, 315
<	82, 285	*len*	137, 315

merge	130, 304	succ	72, 284
nil	66, 282	tl	136, 314
rng	111, 302	token	263
snd	64, 282	true	24, 267

Rule Index

{ }-form, **86**, 93, 96, 111, 205, 206, 246, 287
{ }-is-empty, **87**, 88, 90, 94, 116, **287**
{ }-is-subset, **93**, 206, **290**
{↦}-dom-disjoint, **305**
{↦}-form, **108**, 108, 205, 206, **302**
{↦}-form-bimap, 206, **305**
{↦}-is-1-1, **305**
{a}-comp, **290**
{a}-form, **96**, 98, 99, 119, 203, **290**
{$a \mapsto b$}-form, 214, **305**
[ ]-form, **134**, 135, 137, 142, 143, **314**
[ ]-form-queue, 235, **235**
[_]-⁀-cons, 146
[a]-≠-[ ], **316**
[a]-form, **137**, 146, **316**
∀-∀-comm, **49**, **274**
∀∀-E, **59**, **274**
∀∀-I, **59**, **274**
∀∀-subs, **274**
∀-∧-dist-contract, **274**
∀-∧-dist-expand, **274**
∀-δ-∨-inherit, **274**
∀-δ-I-¬, **274**
∀-⇔-E-left-δ, **274**
∀-⇔-E-right-δ, **274**
∀-⇔-subs, **274**
∀-⇔-subs-δ, **274**
∀-⇒-subs, **275**
∀-∨-dist-contract, **275**
∀-∨-I-left, **275**
∀-∨-I-right, **275**
∀ → ∀-set, **104**, **290**
∀ → ∃, **50**, **275**
∀ → ¬-∃-deM, **47**, **275**
∀-E, 46, **46**, 47, 48, 58, 59, 68, 144, **275**
∀-E-set, **91**, 214, 228, **290**
∀-fix, **48**, **275**
∀-form, **153**, **319**
∀-form-set, **153**, 154, 155, 204, **319**

∀-I, 45, **45**, 46, 48, 58, 59, 68, 103, 144, **275**
∀-I-set, **91**, 94, 95, 206, 213–216, 227, 228, **290**
∀-set → ∀, **104**, **290**
∀-subs, **46**, **275**
∧-∨-dist-contract, **268**
∧-∨-dist-expand, **268**
∧-ass-left, **269**
∧-ass-right, **269**
∧-comm, 31, **32**, **269**
∧-E-left, 28, **28**, 30–32, 188, 232, **269**
∧-E-right, 28, **28**, 29, 31, 32, 188, 232, 238, **269**
∧-form, **153**, 155, 204, 205, **319**
∧-form-sqt, **153**, 156, 157, 204, **319**
∧-I, 28, **28**, 30, 32, 45, 64, 65, 81, 188, 206, **269**
∧-subs-left, **269**
∧-subs-right, **269**
𝔹 → δ, **149**, 150–152, **319**
𝔹-eval, **150**, 150, **319**
○-defn-{↦}, **304**
○-defn-addm, **304**
○-form, **305**
⁀-ass, **316**
⁀-defn-[ ]-left, **139**, 140, 141, **315**
⁀-defn-[ ]-right, **139**, **316**
⁀-defn-cons-left, **139**, 141, **315**
⁀-form, **139**, 141–143, 146, **316**
δ-{↦}, **305**
δ-[ ]-I, **315**
δ-∀∀-I, **275**
δ-∀-inherit, **51**, **275**
δ-∀-inherit-set, **290**
δ-∧-inherit, **269**
δ-∧-inherit-sqt, **269**
δ-=-I, 34, **51**, 56, 57, **63**, 63, 81, 82, 215, 247, 263, **277**
δ-=-I-gen, **63**, **281**

δ-∃-inherit, 50, 82, 92, **273**
δ-∃-inherit-set, 92, **104**, **290**
δ->, 82, **285**
δ-⇔-inherit, **269**
δ-⇒-inherit, **269**
δ-⇒-inherit-sqt, **269**
δ-∈, 34, **90**, 94, 100, 153, **290**
δ-∈-dom-addm-I, **117**, **305**
δ-∈-dom-I, **305**
δ-∈-rng-I, **306**
δ-∩-empty, **290**
δ-<, **285**
δ-≤-≤, 103, **285**
δ-¬-inherit, **269**
δ-≠-I, **277**
δ-∨-I-left, 152, **269**
δ-∨-I-right, 152, **270**
δ-∨-inherit, **37**, **270**
δ-∨-inherit-sqt, 37, 37, **270**
δ-⊆, **291**
δ → 𝔹, **149**, 150, 152, 153, **319**
δ-compatible, **121**, **306**
δ-E, 34, **34**, 35, 36, 57, 144, 150–152, 215, **270**
δ-empty, **291**
δ-I, **34**, 34, 50, **270**
δ-I-¬, **34**, 34, 50, 152, **270**
δ-is-1-1, 125, **126**, **306**
δ-is-1-1-pred, **306**
◁-defn-{↦}, **113**, **303**
◁-defn-addm-∈, **113**, **303**
◁-defn-addm-∉, **113**, **303**
◁-form, **113**, **306**
◁-defn-{ }, **306**
◁-defn-{↦}, **112**, **302**
◁-defn-{a}-∉, **118**, **306**
◁-defn-addm-{a}-=, **306**
◁-defn-addm-{a}-≠, **118**, **306**
◁-defn-addm-∈, **113**, 117, **302**
◁-defn-addm-∉, **113**, 118, **303**
◁-form, **113**, 119, **306**
=-{ }-I, **94**, **291**
=-∨-≠, **277**
= → ⇔, **150**, **319**
=-cases, 88, 90, 215, 216, **278**
=-extend(a), 65, **65**, **278**
=-extend(b), **278**
=-form, 205, **319**

=-map-defn, **115**, **303**
=-self-I, **51**, 52, 65, 81, 83, 173, 258, **277**
=-seq-defn-cons, **136**, **315**
=-seq+-defn, **136**, **315**
=-set-defn, 93, **93**, 94, 247, **288**
=-set-E, **291**
=-set-I-⊆, **291**
=-set-I-sqt, **95**, 98, 99, **291**
=-subs-left(a), 53, **53**, 119, 141, 232, 238, **278**
=-subs-left(b), **51**, 53, 81, 122, 138, 140–142, 146, 206, 211, 214, 216, 227, 228, 235, 237, **277**
=-subs-right(a), **51**, 52, 55, 65, 150, 238, **277**
=-subs-right(b), 53, **53**, 55, 79, 225, 231, 235, **278**
=-symm(a), **52**, **278**
=-symm(b), **52**, **278**
=-trans(a), **53**, 210, **278**
=-trans(b), 141, **278**
=-trans(c), 122, **278**
=-trans-left(a), **278**
=-trans-left(b), **278**
=-trans-left(c), **278**
=-trans-right(a), **278**
=-trans-right(b), 55, **278**
=-trans-right(c), 122, **278**
=-type-inherit-left, 52, **52**, 55, 78, 111, 137, 138, 142, 143, 174, 203, 204, 225, 231, 250, **279**
=-type-inherit-right, **52**, 53, 66, **279**
∃∀-subs, 59, **275**
∃-∀ → ∀-∃, 49, **49**, **275**
∃-∧-dist-expand, 59, **276**
∃-∧-E-left, 59, **276**
∃-∧-E-right, 59, **276**
∃-∃-comm, 49, 50, **276**
∃∃-E, 49, 50, **276**
∃∃-I, 49, 50, **276**
∃∃-subs, 49, **276**
∃-⇔-subs, 59, **276**
∃-⇒-subs, 44, **276**
∃-∨-dist-contract, **276**
∃-∨-dist-expand, 59, **276**
∃ → ∃-set, **104**, **291**
∃ → ¬-∀-deM, 47, **47**, **276**
∃-E, **42**, 43, 44, 46, 48, 49, 58, 59, 232,

RULE INDEX

235, **273**
∃-E-set, **91**, 227, 228, **287**
∃-form, **319**
∃-form-set, **319**
∃-I, **42**, 43, 44, 46–50, 58, 59, 172, 205, 206, 232, 235, **273**
∃-I-1pt, 213–216, **276**
∃-I-set, **91**, **288**
∃-set → ∃, **104**, **291**
∃-split, **48**, 48, 50, **276**
∃-subs, **42**, 42, **276**
∃! ∀ → ∀ ∃, **279**
∃!-=-I, 208, 209, **279**
∃!-∨-dist-expand, **279**
∃! → ∃, **279**
∃!-E, **56**, **279**
∃!-E-set, **91**, **291**
∃!-form, **320**
∃!-form-set, **320**
∃!-I, **56**, **280**
∃!-I-set, **91**, 226–228, **291**
∃!-same, **57**, **280**
∃!-subs, **280**
>-irreflexive, **82**, **285**
>-total-order, **84**, **285**
>-trans, **82**, **285**
≥-0-I, **285**
≥-succ-I, **285**
⇔-¬-I, **37**, **270**
⇔ → =, **150**, 150, 151, **319**
⇔-comm, **270**
⇔-E-full, **270**
⇔-E-left, **270**
⇔-E-left-δ, **150**, **270**
⇔-E-left-¬, **270**
⇔-E-right, 95, **270**
⇔-E-right-δ, **150**, **270**
⇔-E-right-¬, **270**
⇔-form, **153**, **320**
⇔-I, **151**, **270**
⇔-I-∧, **270**
⇔-I-∧-¬, **271**
⇔-I-¬, **151**, **271**
⇔-self-I, 150, **271**
⇔-subs-left, **158**, **320**
⇔-subs-right, **158**, **320**
⇒-∧-left-E, **271**
⇒-¬-conseq, **271**

⇒-conseq, **271**
⇒-contrp, **37**, **271**
⇒-E-left, 33, **33**, 44, 80, 81, 84, 116, 117, 124, 125, 134, 135, 143, 144, 148, 232, **271**
⇒-E-right, **33**, 33, **271**
⇒-form, **153**, **320**
⇒-form-sqt, **153**, 158, **320**
⇒-I, 34, **34**, 81, 117, 124, 125, 144, 228, **271**
⇒-I-left-vac, **33**, 33, 35, 124, 125, 135, **271**
⇒-I-right-vac, **33**, 33, 35, 81, 117, 135, **271**
⇒-self-I, **271**
⇒-trans, **271**
∈-{a}-E, 98, 99, **291**
∈-{a}-I, **291**
∈-{a}-I-=, 98, 99, **291**
∈-∩-defn, **96**, 96
∈-∩-E, **291**
∈-∩-E-left, **291**
∈-∩-E-right, **292**
∈-∩-I, **292**
∈-⋂-defn, **97**, **289**
∈-∉-contr, 214, **292**
∈-∨-∉, 87, **87**, 89, **292**
∈-∪-defn, **96**, 96, **288**
∈-∪-E, 98, 99, **292**
∈-∪-I, **292**
∈-∪-I-left, 98, 99, **292**
∈-∪-I-right, 98, 99, **292**
∈-⋃-defn, **97**, **289**
∈-⋃-E, **292**
∈-⋃-I, **292**
∈-add-defn, 87, 89, **287**
∈-add-E, **89**, 99, **292**
∈-add-I, **292**
∈-add-I-elem, **89**, **292**
∈-add-I-elem-=, **89**, 89, 90, 99, **292**
∈-add-I-set, **89**, 89, 90, 99, **292**
∈-cases, **292**
∈-diff-defn, **96**, 96, **288**
∈-diff-E, **293**
∈-diff-E-left, **293**
∈-diff-E-right, **293**
∈-diff-I, **293**
∈-dom-addm-E, **117**, **306**

$\in$-dom-addm-E-$\notin$, **117**, **306**
$\in$-dom-addm-I-elem, **306**
$\in$-dom-addm-I-map, **306**
$\in$-dom-map-comp-I-$f(a)$, **131**, **307**
$\in$-elems-cons-E, **315**
$\in$-form, **153**, 157, **320**
$\in$-inds-E, **315**
$\in$-interval-defn, **103**, **293**
$\in$-*knownAircraft*-E, **227**, 227
$\in$-pow-defn, **97**, **289**
$\in$-rng-addm-I-elem, **307**
$\in$-rng-†-$\{a \mapsto b\}$-I-elem, **307**
$\in$-rng-addm-I-map, **307**
$\in$-rng-E, 130, **227**, **307**
$\in$-rng-I-$\exists$, **307**
$\in$-rng-I-at, 211, **227**, **307**
$\in$-rng-I-at-bimap, **307**
$\in$-set-comp-defn, 101, **101**, 105, **289**
$\in$-set-comp-E, **293**
$\in$-set-comp-I, **293**
$\in$-set-comp-I-$f(a)$, **293**
$\in$-those-defn, **100**, 101, 103, **105**, **293**
$\in$-those-E, **293**
$\in$-those-I, **293**
$\cap$-$\{a\}$-defn-$\in$, **294**
$\cap$-$\{a\}$-empty-E, **294**
$\cap$-$\cup$-dist-left, **294**
$\cap$-$\cup$-dist-right, **294**
$\cap$-$\cup$-empty-E-left, **294**
$\cap$-$\cup$-empty-E-right, **294**
$\cap$-$\cup$-left-empty-I, **294**
$\cap$-$\cup$-right-empty-I, **294**
$\cap$-add-I-$\in$, **294**
$\cap$-add-I-$\notin$, **294**
$\cap$-ass, **294**
$\cap$-comm, **294**
$\cap$-comp, **294**
$\cap$-defn-$\{\ \}$-left, **294**
$\cap$-defn-$\{\ \}$-right, **294**
$\cap$-form, **96**, 96, **288**
$\cap$-I-right-$\subseteq$, **294**
$\cap$-self, **295**
$\bigcap$-form, **97**, **289**
ι-defn, **280**
ι-form, **57**, **279**
ι-form-set, **92**, 226, **288**
ι-I, **57**, **279**
ι-I-set, **92**, **288**

$\triangleleft\vdash \neq$, **285**
$<$-form, **320**
$<$-irreflexive, **285**
$<$-total-order, **285**
$<$-trans, **285**
$\leq$ - $\leq$-defn, **83**, **284**
$\leq$-form, 204, **320**
$\leq$-succ-defn, **285**
N-cases, **286**
N-indn, 73, 76–81, **284**
N_1-supertype, **82**, **286**
N_1-I, **286**
N_1-indn, **84**, **286**
N_1-E, **82**, **286**
$\neg$-$\forall$ $\rightarrow$ $\exists$-deM, **47**, **277**
$\neg$-$\forall$-E, **277**
$\neg$-$\forall$-I, **277**
$\neg$-$\forall$-I-$\neg$, **47**, **277**
$\neg$-$\wedge$-E-deM, 32, **32**, **47**, **271**
$\neg$-$\wedge$-E-left, **271**
$\neg$-$\wedge$-E-right, **272**
$\neg$-$\wedge$-I-deM, **32**, 32, **272**
$\neg$-$\wedge$-I-left, **272**
$\neg$-$\wedge$-I-right, **272**
$\neg$-$\wedge$-I-sqt, **272**
$\neg$-$\exists$ $\rightarrow$ $\forall$-deM, **47**, **277**
$\neg$-$\exists$-E, **42**, 46, **273**
$\neg$-$\exists$-E-set, **91**, **288**
$\neg$-$\exists$-I, **42**, 45, 47, 50
$\neg$-$\exists$-I-set, **91**, **288**
$\neg$-$\exists$!-E, **280**
$\neg$-$\exists$!-I, 57, **280**
$\neg$-$\exists$!-I-vac, **280**
$\neg$-$\Rightarrow$-E, **272**
$\neg$-$\Rightarrow$-E-left, **272**
$\neg$-$\Rightarrow$-E-right, **272**
$\neg$-$\Rightarrow$-I, **272**
$\neg$-$\in$-dom-$\{\mapsto\}$-I, **116**, 117, **307**
$\neg$-$\in$-rng-$\{\mapsto\}$-I, 206, **307**
$\neg$-$<$-0, **286**
$\neg\neg$-E, 24, 24, 30–32, 46, 47, **268**
$\neg\neg$-I, **24**, 24, 30, 31, 45, **268**
$\neg$-$\neq$-self-I, 135, **279**
$\neg$-$\vee$-E-deM, 32, **272**
$\neg$-$\vee$-E-left, **25**, 25, 30, 31, **268**
$\neg$-$\vee$-E-right, 25, **25**, 30, 31, **268**
$\neg$-$\vee$-I, **25**, 25, 30, 31, 152, **268**
$\neg$-$\vee$-I-deM, 32, **272**

RULE INDEX

¬-add-⊆-I-elem, 295
¬-add-⊆-I-set, 295
¬-false-I, 151, 272
¬-form, **151**, 320
¬-*is-activated*-E, 210
≠-comm, 279
≠-form, 320
∉-{*a*}-I, 295
∉-∩-E, 295
∉-∩-I-left, 295
∉-∩-I-right, 295
∉-∪-E, 295
∉-∪-E-left, 295
∉-∪-E-right, 295
∉-∪-I, 295
∉-add-E, 295
∉-add-E-left, **89**, 295
∉-add-E-right, **89**, 295
∉-add-I, 89, **89**, 90, 295
∉-diff-E, 295
∉-diff-I-left, 218, 296
∉-diff-I-right, 296
∉-dom-◁-I-{*a*}, **118**, 119, 307
∉-dom-addm-E, 307
∉-dom-addm-E-left, 307
∉-dom-addm-E-right, 307
∉-dom-inv-I, **308**
∉-elems-[ ]-I, 316
∉-form, 320
∉-inds-[ ]-I, 316
∉-rng-addm-E, **308**
∉-rng-addm-E-left, **308**
∉-rng-addm-E-right, **308**
∉-rng-inv-I, **308**
∉-subset-I, 210, 214, **296**
∉-those-E, 296
∉-those-I, **296**
∨-∧-dist-contract, 272
∨-∧-dist-expand, 272
∨-ass-left, **37**, 63, 272
∨-ass-right, **37**, 63, 272
∨-comm, 26, 27, 28, 30, **273**
∨-E, 24, 24, 26, 27, 30, 31, 34, 36, 37, 42, 59, 62, 88, 90, 99, **267**
∨-E-left-¬, 26, **26**, 27, 28, 30, 31, 33, 273
∨-E-right-¬, 27, **27**, 27, 28, 30, 31, 33, 273

∨-form, 152, **152**, 320
∨-form-sqt, 152, **152**, 224, 320
∨-I-left, 24, **24**, 26, 30, 33, 34, 88–90, 151, **268**
∨-I-right, 24, **24**, 26, 30, 33, 34, 89, 90, 151, **268**
∨-subs-left, **273**
∨-subs-right, **273**
†-ass, **119**, 121, 122, **308**
†-comm, 122, **122**, **308**
†-defn-{↦}-left, **120**, 121, **308**
†-defn-{↦}-right, **119**, 121, **303**
†-defn-addm, **119**, **303**
†-form, 121, 122, 214, **308**
†-preserves-dom-⊆, 214, **308**
†-self, **119**, **308**
+ = 0-E, **79**, **286**
+-ass, **79**, **286**
+-comm, **79**, **286**
+-defn-0-left, 77, 78, **79**, 81, **284**
+-defn-0-left-rev, 141
+-defn-0-right, 78, 79, **286**
+-defn-succ-left, 77, 78, **79**, 79, 81, **284**
+-defn-succ-left-comm, 141, **286**
+-defn-succ-right, 78, 79, **286**
+-form, **76**, 76, 77, 81, 172, 174, 250, **286**
▷-{*a*}-not-empty-E, **308**
▷-defn-{↦}, **114**, **303**
▷-defn-{*a*}-∉, 210, **308**
▷-defn-addm-∈, **114**, **303**
▷-defn-addm-∉, **114**, **303**
▷-form, **114**, 203, **308**
▷-defn-{↦}, **114**, **303**
▷-defn-addm-∈, **114**, **303**
▷-defn-addm-∉, **114**, **303**
▷-form, **114**, **308**
⊂-defn, **93**, **288**
⊆-add-add-I, **296**
⊆-defn, 92, **92**, 93–95, **288**
⊆-dom-†-I, **309**
⊆-E, 204, 211, 214, 218, **296**
⊆-form, 204, **320**
⊆-I, **94**, 94, 95, **296**
⊆-self, **92**, **296**
⊆-trans, 204, **296**
×-ass, **286**
×-comm, **286**

×-defn-0-left, **284**
×-defn-succ-left, **284**
×-form, **287**
∪-∩-dist-left, **296**
∪-∩-dist-right, **296**
∪-add-left-I, **296**
∪-add-right-I, **296**
∪-ass, **297**
∪-comm, **98**, 98, **297**
∪-comp, **297**
∪-defn-{ }-left, **297**
∪-defn-{ }-left-rev, **297**
∪-defn-{ }-right, **297**
∪-defn-{ }-right-rev, **297**
∪-defn-those, **297**
∪-form, 96, **96**, 98, 99, **288**
∪-I-left-⊆, **297**
∪ of subsets is subset, **297**
∪-self, **297**
⋃-∪-dist, **297**
⋃-comp, **297**
⋃-defn-{ }, **104**, **297**
⋃-defn-$\{a\}$, **297**
⋃-defn-add, **297**
⋃-form, **97**, **289**
⊎-ass, **122**, 122, **309**
⊎-comm, **122**, **309**
⊎-defn, **121**, 122, **304**
⊎-defn-{↦}-left, 121, **121**, **309**
⊎-defn-{↦}-right, 121, **121**, **309**
⊎-form, **309**
|-ass-left, **62**, 62, 63, **281**
|-ass-right, **62**, 63, **281**
|-comm, **281**
|-E, 62, **62**, 63, **281**
|-I-left, **61**, 63, **281**
|-I-right, **61**, 63, 66
$0 < n(N_1)$, **287**
0-form, **72**, 73, 78, 79, 81, 137, 140, 141, **284**
Activate-lemma, **219**
add-⊆-E-left, **298**
add-⊆-E-right, **298**
add-⊆-I, **298**
add → ∪, **97**, 98, **298**
add-abs, **298**
add-add-form, **298**
add-comm, 118, **298**

add-comp, **298**
add-diff-⊆-I, **298**
AddFlight-dom-obl, **236**, 237, 238
AddFlight-dom-obl-simp, **238**
AddFlight-res-obl, **236**
AddFlight-res-obl-simp, **238**
add-form, **86**, 96, 98, 99, 111, **287**
add-reduction, **298**
addm-†-defn-∈, **309**
addm-†-defn-∉, **309**
addm-†-defn-compatible, **309**
addm-†-ident, **309**
addm → †, **309**
addm-comm, **109**, 118, **302**
addm-defn-◁-$\{a\}$-=, **118**, 119, 130, **309**
addm-extract, **309**
addm-form, **108**, 119, 125, **302**
addm-form-bimap, **309**
addm-overwrite, **109**, 117, **302**
aircraft-controller-unique, **202**
aircraft-in-unique-space, **202**
aircraft-in-unique-space$_1$, **226**, **226**
airspace-controller-unique, **202**
appl-defn-hd, **143**, 144, 145, **315**
appl-defn-tl, **143**, 144, 145, **315**
appl-form, 143, **143**, **316**
AssigMap-form-†, **239**
AssigMap-supertype, **227**
assigs$_1$-form-mk, 238
at-defn-†-$\{a ↦ b\}$-=, **216**, **309**
at-defn-†-$\{a ↦ b\}$-≠, **214**, **310**
at-defn-†-addm-=, **310**
at-defn-†-left, **310**
at-defn-†-right, **310**
at-defn-addm-=, **115**, **303**
at-defn-addm-≠, **115**, **303**
at-defn-map-comp, **127**, **304**
at-defn-map-comp-$f(a)$, **128**, **310**
at-defn-map-comp-left-set, **129**, **310**
at-form, **115**, 204, 209, 211, 214, **310**
at-form-bimap, 157, **310**
bimap-1-1, 208, **310**
bimap-1-1-¬, **310**
bimap-E, **123**, 124, 125, **310**
bimap-form, **123**, 125, **310**
bimap-indn, **124**, 148, **310**
bimap-supertype, **123**, 124, 125, 214, **311**
bimap-unique-rng-elem, **311**

RULE INDEX 359

buildQueue-defn$_0$, 234
buildQueue-defn, 236
buildQueue-form$_0$, 234
buildQueue-form, 234, 236
buildQueue-sat, 234
capacity-form, 205, 206
capacity-form-mk, 218, 232, 237
card=0-I, 210, 298
card≠0-E, 298
card-defn-{ }, 95, 95, 288
card-defn-∪, 298
card-defn-add, 95, 95, 95, 288
card-form, 95, 203, 298
Commission-sat, 213, 242
compatible-†-I-left, 121, 121, 122, 311
compatible-†-I-right, 121, 121, 122, 311
compatible-addm-E-left-∉, 311
compatible-addm-E-right, 311
compatible-comm, 120, 121, 311
compatible-defn, 120, 303
compatible-defn-{↦}-left, 120, 121, 311
compatible-defn-{↦}-right, 120, 121, 311
compatible-E, 120, 311
compatible-I, 120, 311
conc-defn-[ ], 143, 143, 316
conc-defn-cons, 143, 143, 316
conc-form, 142, 143, 316
condition-false, 58, 138, 142, 280
condition-true, 57, 172, 280
condition-true-ident, 137, 142, 280
cons-≠-[ ], 134, 138, 142, 316
cons → ⌒, 316
cons-form, 134, 141, 316
cons-form-queue, 235, 235
cons-form-seq+, 134, 314
cons-I, 136, 316
contradiction, 24, 27, 30, 31, 57, 130, 206, 268
control-form, 208, 210, 211
control-form-mk, 218, 232, 237
controllerOf-defn$_0$, 201
controllerOf-defn, 211
controllerOf-form, 202, 208
controllerOf-onduty, 202
controllerOf-wff, 211
Decommission-lemma, 217
diff-=-{ }-defn, 298
diff-∩-deM, 298

diff-∩-I, 299
diff-⊆-I, 299
diff-∪-deM, 299
diff-add-I-∈, 299
diff-add-I-∉, 299
diff-comp, 299
diff-defn-{ }-left, 299
diff-defn-{ }-right, 299
diff-form, 96, 97, 288
diff-I-⊆, 299
diff-self, 299
dom-{↦}-I, 210, 311
dom-◁-defn, 311
dom-≠-{ }-E, 311
dom-addm-∩-E-left, 312
dom-addm-∩-E-right, 312
dom-defn-{↦}, 110, 111, 116, 206, 302
dom-defn-†, 312
dom-defn-addm, 110, 110, 110, 111, 112, 302
dom-defn-addm-∈, 112, 312
dom-defn-inv, 131, 312
dom-defn-map-comp, 127, 304
dom-defn-map-comp-left-set, 129, 312
dom-*extrLoc*-defn, 230, 238, 239
dom-finite⇒rng-finite, 131, 312
dom-form, 110, 203, 204, 214, 218, 238, 312
dom-form-*AssigMap*, 226, 227, 238
dom-form-bimap, 155, 157, 204, 210, 211, 214, 218, 312
elems → those, 316
elems-defn-[ ], 235, 317
elems-defn-⌒, 139, 317
elems-defn-⌒-cons, 317
elems-defn-cons, 317
elems-defn-cons-{a}, 317
elems-defn-cons-queue, 235, 235
elems-form, 138, 317
elems-form-seq+, 157, 317
extrAss-*extrLoc*-inverse, 234, 234
extrAss-form, 233
extrLoc-†, 239, 239
extrLoc-defn$_0$, 229
extrLoc-form, 229, 229
false-contr, 273
false-E, 273
false-form, 151, 321

finite-set-image, **102**, **299**
fst-defn, **64**, **281**
fst-form, **64**, 65, 66, **281**
hd-defn-[a], **137**, **317**
hd-defn-cons, **136**, 142, 224, 225, **314**
hd-form, **136**, **317**
inds-defn-[ ], **317**
inds-form, **145**, **317**
inhabited⇒non-empty, **299**
init-ATC-form, **200**, 205
init-ATC-sat, **200**
init-ATC$_1$-adeq, **240**
initial-interval-form, **299**
initial-interval-1-form, **145**, **299**
interval-diff-defn, **299**
interval-finite, 103, **103**, **300**
interval-form, **103**, **300**
interval-empty, **299**
inv-AssigMap-form, **224**
inv-AssigMap-I, 227
inv-ATC-E-clause1, 214
inv-ATC-E-clause2, 214
inv-ATC-E-clause3, 214
inv-ATC-E-clause4, 214
inv-ATC-form, **200**
inv-ATC-I, **200**
inv-ATC-I-clause1, 211
inv-ATC-I-clause3, 210, 211
inv-ATC-I-mk-clause3, 218
inv-ATC-I-separate, 206, 214, 216
inv-ATC$_1$-I-mk-clause3, 238
inv-defn, **130**, **304**
inv-form, **131**, **312**
is-1-1-†-$\{a \mapsto b\}$-E-∉-rng, **312**
is-1-1-addm-E-∉-map, 125, **126**, **312**
is-1-1-addm-E-∉-rng, 125, **126**, 130, **313**
is-1-1-defn, **123**, **304**
is-1-1-E, **124**, **313**
is-1-1-I, **123**, **313**
is-activated-defn$_0$, **201**
is-activated-E, **207**, 208
is-activated-form, **201**
is-known-defn$_0$, **201**
is-known-E, 209, 211
is-known-form, **201**
ITE-form, **60**, **280**
ITE-form-sqt, **58**, 60, **280**
knownAircraft-†-lemma, **239**

len-defn-[ ], 140, 141, **317**
len-defn-[a], **317**
len-defn-⌢, 139, **139**, 141, **317**
len-defn-cons, 141, **317**
len-defn-seq+, **317**
len-form, **137**, 138, 141, 145, **318**
len-form-seq+, **318**
location-form, 209–211
location-form-mk, 218, 232, 237, 238
locOf-†-=, **239**
locOf-†-≠, **239**
locOf-form, **226**, 226
locOf-wff, **226**, 226
map-|-extend-dom-left, **313**
map-|-extend-dom-right, **313**
map-|-extend-rng-left, **313**
map-|-extend-rng-right, **313**
map-comp-defn-set, **128**, **305**
map-comp-form, **127**, **304**
map-comp-form-left, **313**
map-comp-form-left-set, **129**, **313**
map-comp-form-set-ident, **128**, **313**
map-comp-left-defn-*add*, **239**, **313**
map-indn, **109**, 111, 116, 117, 124, 125, **302**
merge-defn-$\{\mapsto\}$, **304**
merge-defn-add, **304**
merge-form, **314**
mk-ATC-defn, **200**, 231
mk-ATC-form, **199**, 206, 230
mk-ATC$_1$-form, 232
nil-form, **66**, **282**
no-double-assignment, **202**
non-empty-set-inhabited, **104**, **300**
nonRptng-defn$_0$, 224, **224**, 225
nonRptng-form, **224**, 225
nonRptng-wff, **224**
not activated ⇒ empty, **202**
numOfAircraft-defn$_0$, **200**, 203
numOfAircraft-defn, **203**, 204, 210
numOfAircraft-elm-defn, **230**, 238, 239
numOfAircraft-form, **200**, 203, 204, 210, 238
numOfAircraft-wff, **203**, 203, 204
onduty-defn, **200**
onduty-form, **200**, 205, 206, 211
onduty-form-mk, 232, 237
opt-|-extend-left, **282**

RULE INDEX 361

opt-|-extend-right, 69, 69, **282**
opt-E, **67**, **282**
opt-E-≠-nil, **67**, **282**
opt-I, **66**, **282**
pair-=-merge, **64**, **282**
pair-=-split, **64**, 64, **282**
pair-|-extend-left, **66**, **282**
pair-|-extend-right, **66**, **282**
pair-form, **64**, 66, **282**
pair-defn, **64**, 66, **281**
post-buildQueue-form, **234**
post-Commission-form, **212**
pow-comp, **300**
pow-form, **97**, **289**
pre-Commission-form, **212**
pre-controllerOf-form, **201**
pre-locOf-form, **226**
ResetCapacity-sat, **217**
$retr_1$-adeq, **229**, 231
$retr_1$-adeq-*assigs*, **231**, 232–234
$retr_1$-adeq-mk, **231**, 231
$retr_1$-defn$_0$, **229**, 231
$retr_1$-defn, 230, **230**
$retr_1$-defn-mk, **230**, 231, 232
$retr_1$-E-*capacity*, 237, **237**
$retr_1$-E-*control*, 237, **237**
$retr_1$-E-*location*, 237, **237**
$retr_1$-E-*onduty*, 237, **237**
$retr_1$-form, **229**
$retr_1$-wff, **230**, 230, 231
rng-defn, **314**
rng-defn-{↦}, **111**, 206, **302**
rng-defn-addm, **119**, **314**
rng-defn-addm-∈, 114, **114**, 116, 118, **314**
rng-defn-addm-∉, 111, **111**, 117–119, **302**
rng-defn-inv, **130**, **314**
rng-defn-map-comp, **129**, **314**
rng-*extrLoc*-lemma, **230**
rng-form, **112**, 204, 206, 210, 211, 214, 218, **314**
rng-form-*AssigMap*, **227**
rng-form-bimap, 155, 157, 204, 211, **314**
seq-⌢-indn, **146**, 146, **318**
seq-|-extend-left, **318**
seq-|-extend-right, **318**
seq-indn, **134**, 134, 135, 137–139, 142–144, 146–148, 172, 224, 225, **314**
seq-sep, **148**, 148, **318**

seq+-E, 135, **318**
seq+-hnf, **134**, 136, 147, **318**
seq+-I, **318**
seq+-indn, **148**, **318**
seq+-supertype, 135, **318**
sequent-E-basic, 68, **68**, **283**
sequent-E-basic-2, **70**, **283**
sequent-E-gen, 67, **68**, **283**
sequent-E-gen-2, **70**, 146, **283**
set-|-extend-left, **300**
set-|-extend-right, **300**
set-comp-defn-set, **101**, **289**
set-comp-form, **101**, 101, 105, **289**
set-comp-form-set-ident, **102**, **300**
set-comp-form-set-ident-global, **102**, **300**
set-comp-rewrite, **300**
set-image-form, **300**
set-indn, **87**, 87, 88, 90, 109, 235, **287**
snd-defn, **64**, **282**
snd-form, **64**, 65, 66, **282**
subtype-|-extend-left, **283**
subtype-|-extend-right, 69, **283**
subtype-E, 67, **67**, 68, 163, **283**
subtype-I, 67, **67**, 68, 163, **283**
subtype-subs, **67**, **283**
succ->-inherit, **84**, **287**
succ ≠ 0, **73**, 80, 81, **284**
succ-1-1, **75**, **284**
succ-1-1-≠, **287**
succ-form, **72**, 73, 78, 81, 138, 141, **284**
supertype, **67**, 67, 68, 163, **283**
those-=-form, **300**
those-∈-form, **300**
those-∨-form, **300**
those→{ }, **301**
those-form, **100**, 101, 103, **105**, **301**
those-form-∈-∉, **301**
those-form-rewrite, **301**
those-I, **301**
those-rewrite, **301**
those-weaken, **301**
tl-defn-[a], **137**, **318**
tl-defn-cons, **136**, 138, 142, 225, **314**
tl-form, **136**, **318**
true-form, **151**, **321**
true-I, **24**, 24, 30, 151, **267**
n=0 ⇔ n≤0, **287**

$n_2 < n_1 \vdash 0 < n_1$, **287**
$n < \text{succ}(n)$, **287**
$s_1 \setminus (s_1 \setminus s_2) = s_1 \cap s_2$, **302**
$s_1 \cap (s_1 \setminus s_2) = s_1 \setminus s_2$, **301**
$s_1 \cap (s_2 \setminus s_1) = \{\,\}$, **301**
$(s_1 \cap s_2) \subseteq s_2$, **301**
$(s_1 \cap s_2) \subseteq s_1$, **301**
$s_2 \subseteq (s_1 \cup s_2)$, **301**
$s_1 \subseteq (s_1 \cup s_2)$, **301**
$s_1 \cup (s_1 \setminus s_2) = s_1$, **302**
$s_1 \cup (s_2 \setminus s_1) = s_1 \cup s_2$, **302**